COLLEGE PHYSICS

MECHANICS, HEAT, AND SOUND

by

FRANCIS WESTON SEARS

Professor of Physics
Massachusetts Institute of Technology

and

MARK W. ZEMANSKY

Professor of Physics
College of the City of New York

Second Edition
with Supplementary Problems

ADDISON-WESLEY PUBLISHING COMPANY, INC.

CAMBRIDGE 42, MASS.

PREFACE

This volume is a textbook of College Physics based on Sears' three-volume work *Principles of Physics*. The material covered includes Mechanics, Heat, Sound, Electricity and Magnetism, Optics, and Atomic Physics. Those parts of Sears' original work that came within the scope of intermediate physics and which were therefore treated with the aid of calculus have been either removed or rewritten in simpler form. As a result, this text consists exclusively of material suitable for college students whose mathematical preparation goes no further than algebra and the elements of trigonometry. The total number of topics has also been reduced so that the complete text may be taught in two semesters.

The emphasis is on physical principles. Historical background and practical applications have been given a place of secondary importance.

Three systems of units are used: the English gravitational system because it is the one used in engineering work throughout the country; the cgs system because some familiarity with it is essential for any intelligent reading of the literature of physics; and the mks system because of its increasing use in electricity and magnetism, as well as because it seems destined eventually to supplant the cgs system.

The symbols and terminology, with few exceptions, are those recommended by the Committee on Letter Symbols and Abbreviations of the American Association of Physics Teachers as listed in the American Standard, ASA-Z10, published in 1947.

The main features of the first edition have been retained in the second. A completely new set of problems has replaced the old set and the following new material has been added to the body of the text: surface tension, kinetic theory of gases, convection coefficients, physics of music, Kirchhoff's laws, Ampere's law, simple algebraic derivations of mirror and lens formulas, interference of light with Lloyd's mirror and Pohl's mica plate, application of convergent polarized light to mineralogy, and optical activity.

The authors express their gratitude for the kind suggestions of their colleagues and friends: L. I. Bockstahler, M. V. Brown, C. D. Hodgman, M. Iona, Jr., M. S. Livingston, F. C. Rose, H. Semat, R. S. Shaw, J. D. Shea, F. W. Thiele, and I. Walerstein.

F. W. S.
M. W. Z.

Cambridge, 1952
New York, 1952

CONTENTS

CHAPTER 1

COMPOSITION AND RESOLUTION OF VECTORS

1-1 Force. Mechanics is the branch of physics and engineering which deals with the interrelations of force, matter, and motion. We shall begin with a study of forces. The term force, as used in mechanics, refers to what is known in everyday language as a *push* or a *pull*. We can exert a force on a body by muscular effort; a stretched spring exerts forces on the bodies to which its ends are attached; compressed air exerts a force on the walls of its container; a locomotive exerts a force on the train which it is drawing. In all of these instances the body exerting the force is in contact with the body on which the force is exerted, and forces of this sort are known as *contact* forces. There are also forces which act through empty space without contact, and are called *action-at-a-distance* forces. The force of gravitational attraction exerted on a body by the earth, and known as the *weight* of the body, is the most important of these for our present study. Electrical and magnetic forces are also action-at-a-distance forces, but we shall not be concerned with them for the present.

All forces fall into one or the other of these two classes, a fact that will be found useful later when deciding just what forces are acting on a given body. It is only necessary to observe what bodies are in contact with the one under consideration. The only forces on the body are then those exerted by the bodies in contact with it, together with the gravitational force or the weight of the body.

Those forces acting on a given body which are exerted by other bodies are referred to as *external* forces. Forces exerted on one part of a body by other parts of the same body are called *internal* forces.

1-2 Units and standards. The early Greek philosophers confined their activities largely to speculations about Nature, and to attempts to reconcile the observed behaviour of bodies with theological doctrines. What has been called the *scientific method* began to appear in the time of Galileo Galilei (1564–1642). Galileo's studies of the laws of freely falling bodies were made not in an attempt to explain *why* bodies fell toward the earth, but rather to determine *how far* they fell in a given time, and *how fast* they moved. Physics as it exists today has been called the science of measure-

1

ment, and the importance of quantitative knowledge and reasoning has been expressed by Lord Kelvin (1824–1907) as follows: "I often say that when you can measure what you are speaking about, and express it in numbers, you know something about it; but when you cannot express it in numbers, your knowledge is of a meagre and unsatisfactory kind; it may be the beginning of knowledge, but you have scarcely, in your thoughts, advanced to the stage of *Science*, whatever the matter may be."

The first step in the measurement of a physical quantity consists in choosing a *unit* of that quantity. As the result of international collaboration over a long period, practically all of the units used in physics are now the same throughout the world. The second step is an experiment that determines the ratio of the magnitude of the quantity to the magnitude of the unit. Thus, when we say that the length of a rod is 10 centimeters, we state that its length is ten times as great as the unit of length, the centimeter.

It is possible to simplify many of the equations of physics by the proper choice of units of physical quantities. Any set of units which is chosen so that these simplified equations can be used is called a *system* of units. We shall use three such systems in this book. They are, first, the *English gravitational* system; second, the meter-kilogram-second or *mks* system; and third, the centimeter-gram-second or *cgs* system. The units of these systems will be defined as the need for them arises.

Most of the fundamental units of physics are embodied in a physical object called a *standard*. One of the functions of the National Bureau of Standards in Washington, D. C., is to maintain in its vaults standards of various quantities with which commercial and technical measuring instruments can be compared for accuracy.

1-3 The pound. The unit of force which we shall use for the present is the English gravitational unit, the *pound*. Other units will be discussed in Chap. 5. This unit is embodied in a cylinder of platinum-iridium called the *standard pound*. The unit of force is defined as the weight of the standard pound. That is, it is a force equal to the force of gravitational attraction which the earth exerts on the standard pound. Since the earth's gravitational attraction for a given body varies slightly from one point to another on the earth's surface, it is further stipulated that the unit force shall equal the weight of the standard pound *at sea level and 45° latitude*.

In order that an unknown force can be compared with the force unit (and thereby measured) some measurable effect produced by a force must be used. One common effect of a force is to alter the dimensions or shape of a body on which the force is exerted; another is to alter the state of motion of the body. Both of these effects are used in the measurement of forces. In this chapter we shall consider only the former; the latter will be discussed in Chap. 5.

The instrument used to measure forces is the spring balance, which consists of a coil spring enclosed in a case for protection and carrying at one end a pointer that moves over a scale. A force exerted on the balance increases the length of the spring. The balance can be calibrated as follows: The standard pound is first suspended from the balance and the position of the pointer marked 1 lb. Any number of duplicates of the standard can then be prepared by suspending each of them in turn from the balance and removing or adding material until the index stands at 1 lb. Then, when two, three, or more of these are suspended simultaneously from the balance, the force stretching it is 2 lb, 3 lb, etc., and the corresponding positions of the pointer can be labelled 2 lb, 3 lb, etc. This procedure makes no assumptions about the elastic properties of the spring, except that the force exerted on it is always the same when its index stands at the same point. The calibrated balance can then be used to measure any unknown force.

1-4 Graphical representation of forces. Vectors. Suppose we are to slide a box along the floor by pulling it with a string or pushing it with a stick, as in Fig. 1-1. That is, we are to slide it by exerting a force on it. The point of view which we now adopt is that the motion of the box is caused not by the *objects* which push or pull on it, but by the *forces* which these exert. For concreteness assume the magnitude of the push or pull to be 10 lb. It is clear that simply to write "10 lb" on the diagram would not completely describe the force, since it would not indicate

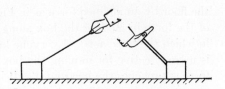

Fig. 1-1. The box is pulled by the string or pushed by the stick.

the direction in which the force was acting. One might write "10 lb, 30° above horizontal to the right," or "10 lb, 45° below horizontal to the right," but all of the above information may be conveyed more briefly if we adopt the convention of representing a force by an arrow. The length of the arrow, to some chosen scale, indicates the size or magnitude of the force, and the direction in which the arrow points indicates the direction of the force. Thus Fig. 1-2 (in which a scale of ⅛ in. = 1 lb has been chosen) is the force diagram corresponding to Fig. 1-1. (There are other forces acting on the box, but these are not shown in the figure.)

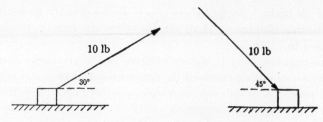

FIG. 1-2. The force diagram corresponding to Fig. 1-1.

Force is not the only physical quantity which requires the specification of direction as well as magnitude. For example, the velocity of a plane is not completely specified by stating that it is 300 miles per hour; we need to know the direction also. The concept of density, on the other hand, has no direction associated with it.

Quantities like force and velocity, which involve both magnitude and direction, are called *vector* quantities. Those like density, which involve magnitude only, are called *scalars*. Any vector quantity can be represented by an arrow, and this arrow is called a vector (or if a more specific statement is needed, a force vector or a velocity vector). We shall first consider force vectors only, but the ideas developed in dealing with them can be applied to any other vector quantity.

1-5 Components of a vector. When a box is pulled or pushed along the floor by an inclined force as in Fig. 1-1, it is clear that the effectiveness of the force in moving the box along the floor depends upon the direction in which the force acts. Everyone knows by experience that a given force is more effective for moving the box the more nearly the direction of the force approaches the horizontal. It is also clear that if the force is applied at an angle, as in Fig. 1-1, it is producing another effect in addition to moving the box ahead. That is, the pull of the string is in part tending to lift the box off the floor, and the push of the stick is in part forcing the box down against the floor. We are thus led to the idea of the *components* of a force, that is, the effective values of a force in directions other than that of the force itself.

The component of a force in any direction can be found by a simple graphical method. Suppose we wish to know how much force is available for sliding the box in Fig. 1-1 if the applied force is a pull of 10 lb directed 30° above the horizontal. Let the given force be represented by the vector *OA* in Fig. 1-3, in the proper direction and to some convenient scale. Line *OX* is the direction of the desired component. From point *A*, drop a perpendicular to *OX*, intersecting it at *B*. The vector *OB*, to the same scale as that used for the given vector, represents the component of OA in the direction OX. Measurements of the diagram show that if OA represents a force of 10 lb, then OB is about 8.7 lb. That is, the 10-lb force at an angle of 30° above the horizontal has an effective value of only about 8.7 lb in producing forward motion.

The component OB may also be computed as follows. Since OAB is a right triangle, it follows that

$$\cos 30° = \frac{OB}{OA},$$

$$OB = OA \cos 30°.$$

The lengths OB and OA, however, are proportional to the magnitudes of the forces they represent. Therefore the desired component OB, in pounds, equals the given force OA, in pounds, multiplied by the cosine of the angle between OA and OB. The magnitude of OB is therefore

$$OB \text{ (lb)} = OA \text{ (lb)} \times \cos 30°$$

$$= 10 \text{ lb} \quad \times .866$$

$$= 8.66 \text{ lb.}$$

This result agrees as well as could be expected with that obtained from measurements of the diagram. The superiority of the trigonometric method is evident, however, since it does not depend for accuracy on the careful construction and measurement of a scale diagram.

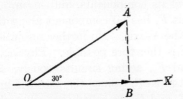

Fig. 1-3. Vector OB is the component of vector OA in the direction OX.

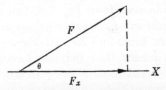

Fig. 1-4. $F_x = F \cos \theta$ is the X-component of F.

The line OX in Fig. 1-3 is called the X-axis, and the foregoing analysis may be generalized as follows. If a force F makes an angle θ with the X-axis (Fig. 1-4), its component F_x along the X-axis is

$$F_x = F \cos \theta. \tag{1-1}$$

It should be obvious that if the force F is at right angles to the X-axis, its component along that axis is zero (since $\cos 90° = 0$), and if the force lies along the axis, its component is equal to the force itself (since $\cos 0° = 1$).

The lifting component of an inclined force can be found as in Fig. 1-5. Line OY, called the Y-axis, is constructed in a vertical direction through O and a perpendicular dropped to this axis from the head of the arrow F. Evidently

$$F_y = F \cos \phi, \tag{1-2}$$

where ϕ is the angle between F and the Y-axis.

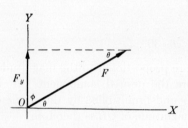

FIG. 1-5. $F_y = F \cos \phi = F \sin \theta$ is the Y-component of F.

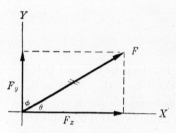

FIG. 1-6. The force F may be replaced by its rectangular components F_x and F_y.

It is also evident from Fig. 1-5 that

$$F_y = F \sin \theta. \tag{1-3}$$

If $F = 10$ lb and $\theta = 30°$, then $\phi = 60°$ and $\cos \phi = \sin \theta = 0.50$. Hence $F_y = 5$ lb.

Just as we may find the component of a given force in any direction, so may we find the component of any of its components, and so on. It will be seen from Fig. 1-6, however, that F_x has no component along the Y-axis and F_y has no component along the X-axis. No further resolution of the force into X- and Y-components is therefore possible. Physically this means that the two forces F_x and F_y, acting simultaneously, are equivalent in all respects to the original force F. Since the axes OX and OY are at right angles to one another, F_x and F_y are called the *rectangular components* of the force F. *Any force may be replaced by its rectangular components.* The fact that the force F has been replaced by its components F_x and F_y is indicated in Fig. 1-6 by crossing out lightly the vector F.

The process of finding the components of a vector is called the *resolution* of the vector, and one speaks of *resolving* a given vector into its rectangular components.

An experiment to show that a force may be replaced by its rectangular components is illustrated in Fig. 1-7. A small ring, to which are attached three cords, is placed on a pin set in a vertical board. Two of the cords pass over pulleys as shown. When weights of 8.66, 5, and 10 lb are

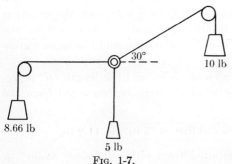

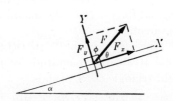

8.66 lb

5 lb

FIG. 1-7.

FIG. 1-8. F_x and F_y are the components of F, parallel and perpendicular to the surface of the plane.

suspended from the cords, with the cord carrying the 10-lb weight making an angle of 30° with the horizontal, it will be found that the pin can be removed and that the ring will remain at rest under the combined action of the pulls in the three cords. This shows that the 10-lb force, at an angle of 30° above the horizontal, is equivalent to a horizontal force of 8.66 lb to the right and a vertical force of 5 lb upward, since the ring can be held at rest by the application of two forces equal to these but oppositely directed.

It is frequently necessary to find the components of a force in other than horizontal and vertical directions. Thus in Fig. 1-8, where a block is being drawn up an inclined plane by the force F, it is desired to find the components of this force parallel and perpendicular to the surface of the plane. The X- and Y-axes are now drawn parallel and perpendicular to this surface, and the same procedure followed as before.

1-6 Composition of forces. When a number of forces are simultaneously applied at a point, it is found that the same effect can always be produced by a single force having the proper magnitude and direction. We wish to find this force, called the *resultant*, when the separate forces are known. The process is known as the *composition* of forces, and is evidently the converse problem to that of resolving a given force into components. Let us begin by considering some simple cases.

(1) Two forces at right angles. Suppose that two forces of 10 lb and 5 lb are applied simultaneously at the point O as in Fig. 1-9. To find the resultant force graphically, lay off the given forces OP and OQ to scale, and draw horizontal and vertical construction lines from P and Q,

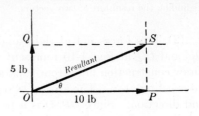

FIG. 1-9.

intersecting at S.   The arrow drawn from O to S represents the resultant of the given forces.   Its length, to the same scale as that used for the original forces, gives the magnitude of the resultant, and the angle θ gives its direction.

Since the length PS or OQ represents 5 lb, and the length OP represents 10 lb, the magnitude of the resultant may be computed from the right triangle OPS.   Thus

$$OS = \sqrt{\overline{OP}^2 + \overline{PS}^2} = \sqrt{(10 \text{ lb})^2 + (5 \text{ lb})^2} = 11.2 \text{ lb.}$$

The angle θ may also be computed from either its sine, cosine, or tangent.   Thus

$$\sin \theta = \frac{5}{11.2} = 0.447,$$

$$\cos \theta = \frac{10}{11.2} = 0.893,$$

$$\tan \theta = \frac{5}{10} = 0.500.$$

Using any one of these values we find from tables of natural functions

$$\theta = 26.5°.$$

We conclude, then, that a single force of 11.2 lb, at an angle of 26.5° above the horizontal, will produce the same effect as the two forces of 10 lb horizontally and 5 lb vertically.   Notice that the resultant is not the arithmetic sum of 5 lb and 10 lb.   That is, the two forces are not equivalent to a single force of 15 lb.

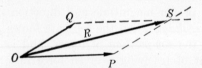

FIG. 1-10. Parallelogram method for finding the resultant of two vectors.

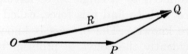

FIG. 1-11. Triangle method for finding the resultant of two vectors.

(2) Two forces not at right angles.   (a) Parallelogram method.   Let OP and OQ in Fig. 1-10 represent the forces whose resultant is desired. Draw construction lines from P parallel to OQ, and from Q parallel to OP, intersecting at S.   The arrow OS represents the resultant R in magnitude and direction.   Since $OPSQ$ is a parallelogram, this method is called the parallelogram method.   The magnitude and direction of the resultant may

be found by measurement or may be computed from the triangle OPS with the help of the sine and cosine laws.

NOTE. The diagonal QP is *not* the resultant of the given forces.

(b) Triangle method. Draw one force vector with its tail at the head of the other as in Fig. 1-11 (the construction may be started with either vector), and complete the triangle. The closing side of the triangle, OQ, represents the resultant. A comparison of Figs. 1-11 and 1-10 will show that the same resultant is obtained by either method.

FIG. 1-12.   Vector R is the resultant of vectors P and Q.

(3) Special case. Both forces in the same line. When both forces lie in the same straight line the triangle of Fig. 1-11 flattens out into a line also. To be able to see all of the force vectors, it is customary to displace them slightly as in Fig. 1-12. We then have Fig. 1-12(a) or 1-12(b), depending upon whether the two forces are in the same or opposite directions. Only in this case is the magnitude of the resultant equal to the sum (or difference) of the magnitudes of the components.

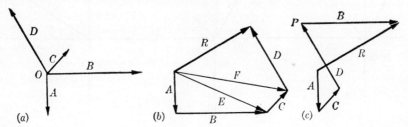

FIG. 1-13.   Polygon method.

(4) More than two forces. Polygon method. When more than two forces are to be combined, one may first find the resultant of any two, then combine this resultant with a third, and so on. The process is illustrated in Fig. 1-13, which shows the four forces A, B, C, and D acting simultaneously at the point O. In Fig. 1-13(b), forces A and B are first combined by the triangle method giving a resultant E; force E is then combined by the same process with C giving a resultant F; finally F and D are combined to obtain the resultant R. Evidently the vectors E and F need not have been drawn—one need only draw the given vectors in succession with the tail of each at the head of the one preceding it, and complete the polygon by a vector R from the tail of the first to the head

of the last vector. The order in which the vectors are drawn makes no difference, as shown in Fig. 1-13(c).

It has been assumed in the preceding discussion that all of the forces lie in the same plane. Such forces are called *co-planar*, and, except in a few instances, we shall consider only situations involving co-planar forces.

1-7 Composition of forces by rectangular resolution. While the polygon method is a satisfactory graphical one for finding the resultant of a number of forces, it is awkward for computation because one must work, in general, with oblique triangles. Therefore the usual method for finding the resultant of a number of forces is first to resolve all of the forces into their rectangular components along any convenient pair of axes; second, to find the algebraic sum of all of the X- and all of the Y-components; and third, combine these sums to obtain the final resultant. This process makes it possible to work with right triangles only, and is called the *method of rectangular resolution*. As an example, let us compute the resultant of the four forces in Fig. 1-14, which are the same as those in Fig. 1-13.

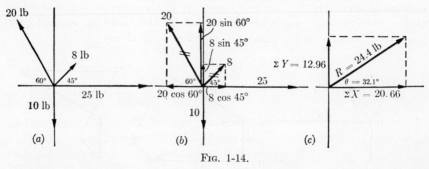

Fig. 1-14.

The forces are shown in Fig. 1-14(b) resolved into X- and Y-components. The 25-lb and the 10-lb forces are already along the axes and need not be resolved. It is customary to consider X-components which are directed toward the right as positive and those toward the left, negative. Similarly, Y-components in an upward direction are considered positive and those downward, negative. This convention of signs is not always adhered to, however. In general one chooses positive and negative directions so as to avoid minus signs if possible.

The X-component of the 8-lb force is $+8 \cos 45° = +5.66$ lb, and its Y-component is $+8 \sin 45° = +5.66$ lb. The X-component of the 20-lb force is $-20 \cos 60° = -10$ lb, its Y-component is $+20 \sin 60° = +17.3$ lb. The algebraic sum of the X-components is a force of $25 + 5.66 - 10 = +20.66$ lb toward the right. The algebraic sum of the Y-components is a force of $17.3 + 5.66 - 10 = +12.96$ lb upward. The resultant is equal to the square root of the sums of the squares of the resultant X- and Y-components (Fig. 1-14(c)). The angle which it makes with the X-axis can be found from its tangent. Thus

$$R = \sqrt{20.66^2 + 12.96^2} = 24.4 \text{ lb},$$

$$\tan \theta = \frac{12.96}{20.66} = 0.627,$$

$$\theta = 32.1°.$$

While three separate diagrams are shown in Fig. 1-14 for clarity, in practice one would carry out the entire construction in a single diagram.

The mathematical symbol for the algebraic sum of the X- or Y-components is ΣF_x or ΣF_y. (Σ is the Greek letter sigma or S, meaning "the sum of".) Hence one can write in general

$$R = \sqrt{(\Sigma F_x)^2 + (\Sigma F_y)^2},$$

$$\tan \theta = \frac{\Sigma F_y}{\Sigma F_x}.$$

1-8 Vector difference. The resultant of two vectors is also called their *vector sum*, and the process of finding the resultant is called *vector addition*. In many instances, as when computing accelerations or relative velocities, it is necessary to subtract one vector from another or to find their *vector difference*. This is done as follows: if A and B are the vectors, shown in Fig. 1-15(a), the vector difference $A - B$ can be written $A + (-B)$, that is, it is the vector *sum* of the vectors A and $-B$. The negative of a given vector has the same length as the given vector but points in the

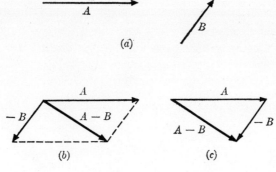

FIG. 1-15.

opposite direction.   Either the parallelogram method, Fig. 1-15(b), or the triangle method, Fig. 1-15(c), may then be employed to obtain the sum of A and $-B$.

Vector differences may also be found by the method of rectangular resolution.   Each vector is resolved into its X- and Y-components.   The difference between the X-components is the X-component of the desired vector difference; the difference between the Y-components is the Y-component of the vector difference.

Problems — Chapter 1

1-1. What is the basis for saying that force is a vector quantity?

1-2. A box is pushed along the floor as in Fig. 1-1 by a force of 40 lb making an angle of 30° with the horizontal. Using a scale of 1 in = 10 lb, find the horizontal and vertical components of the force by the graphical method. Check your results by calculating the components.

1-3. (a) How large a force F must be exerted on a block as in Fig. 1-8 in order that the component parallel to the plane shall be 16 lb? (b) How large will be the component F_y? Let $\alpha = 20°$, $\theta = 30°$, $\phi = 60°$. Solve graphically, letting 1 in = 8 lb.

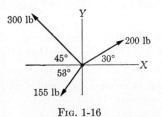

FIG. 1-16

1-4. The three forces shown in Fig. 1-16 act on a body located at the origin. (a) Find the X- and Y-components of each of the three forces. Use the graphical method and any convenient scale. (b) Use the method of rectangular resolution to find the resultant of the forces. (c) Find the magnitude and direction of a fourth force which must be added to make the resultant force zero. Indicate the fourth force by a diagram.

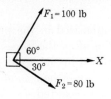

FIG. 1-17

1-5. Two men and a boy want to push a crate in the direction marked "X" in Fig. 1-17. The two men push with forces F_1 and F_2 whose magnitudes and directions are indicated in the figure. Find the magnitude and direction of the smallest force which the boy should exert.

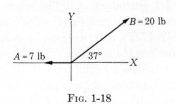

FIG. 1-18

1-6. (a) Find graphically the vector sum $A + B$ and the vector difference $A - B$ in Fig. 1-18. (b) Use the method of rectangular resolution to find the magnitude and direction of the resultant of vectors A and B.

1-7. Two forces, F_1 and F_2, act at a point. The magnitude of F_1 is 8 lb and its direction is 60° above the X-axis in the first quadrant. The magnitude of F_2 is 5 lb and its direction is 53° below the X-axis in the fourth quadrant. (a) What are the horizontal and vertical components of the resultant force? (b) What is the magnitude of the resultant? (c) Show in a diagram a graphical method for finding the magnitude and direction of the resultant. (d) What is the magnitude of the vector difference $F_1 - F_2$?

1-8. Two forces, F_1 and F_2, act upon a body in such a manner that the resultant force, R, has a magnitude equal to F_1 and makes an angle of 90° with F_1. Let $F_1 = R = 10$ lb. Find the magnitude and direction (relative to F_1) of the second force, F_2.

1-9. Find the resultant of the following set of forces by the method of rectangular resolution: 80 lb, vertically down; 100 lb, 53° above horizontal to the right; 60 lb, horizontal to the left. Check by the polygon method.

CHAPTER 2

STATICS

2-1 Introduction. The science of mechanics is based on three natural laws which were clearly recognized for the first time by Sir Isaac Newton (1642–1727) and were published in 1686 in his *Philosophiae Naturalis Principia Mathematica* ("The Mathematical Principles of Natural Science"). It should not be inferred, however, that the science of mechanics began with Newton. Many men had preceded him in this field, perhaps the most outstanding being Galileo who in his studies of accelerated motion had laid much of the groundwork for Newton's formulation of his three laws.

In this chapter we shall make use of only two of Newton's laws, the first and the third. Newton's second law will be discussed in Chap. 5.

2-2 Newton's first law. Newton's first law states that *when a body is at rest or moving with constant speed in a straight line, the* **resultant** *of* **all** *of the forces exerted* **on** *the body is zero.* The various girders, beams, columns, etc., which form the structure of a building or bridge, are bodies at rest. The forces exerted on them are their own weights, those exerted by other parts of the structure, and whatever loads the structure must carry. Since the resultant of all of the forces must be zero, if some of the forces are known the others may be computed. By successive application of Newton's first law to the various elements of a structure, the engineer can compute how much force each part must withstand and therefore how strong each girder, beam, or column must be.

In most instances the forces on a structural element are so distributed that the turning effect, or the *moment* of each force, must also be taken into account. We shall postpone this complication until the next chapter, and consider for the present only structures in which all of the forces intersect at a common point. We shall also limit the discussion to co-planar forces.

Notice particularly that three words are emphasized in the preceding statement of Newton's first law—"the *resultant* of *all* of the forces exerted *on* the body." Most of the difficulties encountered in the application of this law to specific problems are due to a failure to use the *resultant* force, or to include *all* of the forces, or to use the forces exerted *on* the body. Furthermore, since Newton's second law also involves the resultant of all

14

of the forces exerted on a body, it is extremely important that one should learn as early as possible how to recognize just what forces are exerted on a particular body.

When the resultant of all of the forces on a body is zero, the body is said to be in *equilibrium*. This will be the case if it is at rest or moving with constant speed in a straight line. Both of these cases are grouped under the common heading of problems in *statics*. From what has been said in the preceding chapter, the forces on a body in equilibrium must satisfy the following conditions:

$$\Sigma F_x = 0, \quad \Sigma F_y = 0. \tag{2-1}$$

These equations are sometimes called the "first condition of equilibrium."

A carefully drawn diagram, in which each force exerted on a body is represented by an arrow, is essential in the solution of problems of this sort. The standard procedure is as follows: First, make a neat sketch of the apparatus or structure. Second, choose some one body which is in equilibrium and in a separate sketch show all of the forces exerted on it. This is called "isolating" the chosen body. Write on the diagram, which should be sufficiently large to avoid crowding, the numerical values of all given forces, angles, and dimensions, and assign letters to all unknown quantities. When a structure is composed of several members, a separate force diagram must be constructed for each. Third, construct a set of rectangular axes and indicate on each force diagram the rectangular components of any inclined forces. Cross out lightly those forces which have been resolved. Fourth, obtain the necessary algebraic or trigonometric equations from the conditions that the algebraic sum of the X- and Y-components of the forces must be zero.

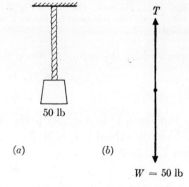

To begin with a simple example, consider the 50-lb block in Fig. 2-1 (a), hanging by a vertical cord. One contact force, the upward pull of the cord, acts on the block, and also one action-at-a-distance force, the downward gravitational pull of the earth or the weight of the block. Fig. 2-1(b) is the force diagram of the block, which itself is represented by the black dot. The force exerted

FIG. 2-1.   Forces on a hanging block.

on the block by the cord is lettered T; the gravitational force exerted on the block by the earth, or the weight of the block, is lettered W.

Then $\qquad\qquad\qquad\qquad \Sigma F_y = T - W,$

and since the block is in equilibrium and $\Sigma F_y = 0$,

$$T - W = 0 \quad \text{or} \quad T = W = 50 \text{ lb.}$$

That is, we find from Newton's first law that the cord pulls up on the block with a force equal to that with which the earth pulls down on the block.

2-3 Newton's third law. Newton's third law states that *whenever one body exerts a force on another, the second always exerts on the first a force which is equal in magnitude but oppositely directed.* These two forces are commonly referred to as an "action" and a "reaction," and the third law is often stated: "Action and reaction are equal and opposite."

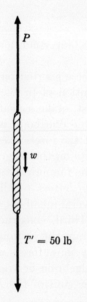

$T' = 50$ lb

Fig. 2-2. Forces on the cord in Fig. 2-1. Force T' is the reaction to force T in Fig. 2-1.

We shall illustrate the third law by a further consideration of the forces in Fig. 2-1. The force T in Fig. 2-1 is an upward force exerted *on the block* by the cord. The reaction to this force is an equal downward force exerted *on the cord* by the block and is represented by T' in Fig. 2-2, which is the force diagram of the cord. The other forces on the cord are its own weight w and the upward force P exerted on it at its upper end by the ceiling. Since the cord is also in equilibrium,

$$\Sigma F_y = P - w - T' = 0,$$
$$P = T' + w. \qquad\qquad (2\text{-}2)$$

But since T' in Fig. 2-2 is the reaction to T in Fig. 2-1, its magnitude, by Newton's third law, is 50 lb. Let the weight of the cord be 1 lb. Then from Eq. (2-2)

$$P = 51 \text{ lb}$$

and the ceiling pulls up on the cord with a force of 51 lb.

Finally, since the cord pulls down on the ceiling with a force equal to that with which the ceiling pulls up on the cord (third law), the downward force on the ceiling (P' in Fig. 2-3) is 51 lb.

If the weight of the cord is so small that it can be neglected, then from Eq. (2-2) $P = T' = 50$ lb, and since P and P' are equal, $P' = 50$ lb also. The downward pull on the ceiling (P') is then equal to the downward pull on the lower end of the cord (T'), and *a weightless cord may therefore be considered to transmit a force from one end to the other without change.*

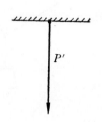

Fig. 2-3.   Force P' is the reaction to P in Fig. 2-2.

It should be noted carefully that although the forces T and W in Fig. 2-1 are equal and oppositely directed, one is *not* the reaction to the other. The reaction to the force T is, as we have seen, the force T' which the block exerts on the cord. What is the reaction to W? The force W is the force exerted on the block by the earth. The reaction to W must then be an equal but opposite force exerted on the earth by the block. That is, if the earth attracts the block with a force of 50 lb, the block attracts the earth with a force of 50 lb also.

A body subjected to pulls at its ends, as is the cord in Fig. 2-2, is said to be in *tension*. The force exerted by (or on) the cord at either end is called the tension in the cord. For the present we shall consider only weightless cords in which the tension is the same at both ends. For example, if the weight of the cord in Fig. 2-2 is zero, then $P = T' = 50$ lb, and the tension in the cord is 50 lb (*not* 100 lb).

2-4 Simple structures. Fig. 2-4(a) shows a 100-lb block hanging from a vertical cord which in turn is knotted to two cords making angles of 30° and 60° with the horizontal. The weights of the cords may be neglected. We wish to find the tension in each cord.

The tension in the vertical cord is evidently 100 lb. The inclined cords are not in contact with the block, and hence no information regarding the tensions in them can be obtained from a force diagram of the block. All three cords, however, exert forces on the knot which joins them. Hence the knot can be considered as a small body whose own weight is negligible and which is in equilibrium under the combined forces exerted by the three cords. In general, in any instance where a number of intersecting forces satisfy the condition of equilibrium, their *point of intersection* is treated as a small body in equilibrium.

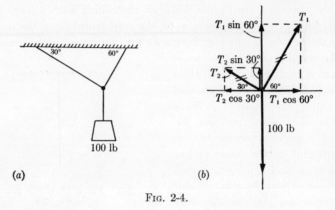

Fig. 2-4.

The force diagram of the knot is constructed in Fig. 2-4(b). Although the tensions T_1 and T_2 are not known in advance, an attempt should be made to draw them approximately to scale. We do know that their horizontal components are equal and opposite, so it is clear that T_1 must be larger than T_2. Do not make the mistake of drawing the vectors T_1 and T_2 equal in length to the cords which exert these forces. It can be seen that the larger force is exerted by the shorter cord.

From the conditions of equilibrium, we have

$$\Sigma F_x = T_1 \cos 60° - T_2 \cos 30° = 0,$$

$$\Sigma F_y = T_1 \sin 60° + T_2 \sin 30° - 100 = 0,$$

whence

$$T_1 = 86.6 \text{ lb}, \quad T_2 = 50 \text{ lb}.$$

Forces equal and opposite to T_1 and T_2 are exerted on the ceiling by the cords at their upper ends. These forces do not appear in the diagram since they are not forces exerted on the body for which the force diagram is drawn.

A common type of structure in which pushes, as well as pulls, are involved, is shown in Fig. 2-5(a.) The hanging body may be a street lamp or a sign. We wish to compute the tension in the supporting cable and the compression in the horizontal bar, called the *strut*, when the weight of the suspended body is known.

Three forces intersect at the outer end of the strut, and accordingly a force diagram, Fig. 2-5(b), is constructed for this point. The three forces are the downward pull of the vertical cable, the outward push of the strut, and the tension in the slanting cable. (The weights of the strut and cable are neglected.) When the force exerted by a body is a push in the direction of its length, as is the case with the weightless strut in Fig. 2-5, the body exerting it is said to be in *compression*. It is customary engineering practice to draw all force vectors with their tails at the origin. Hence vector C, representing the force exerted by the strut at its outer end, is shown as though it were a pull. For equilibrium, we must have

$$\Sigma F_x = C - T \cos 45° = 0,$$

$$\Sigma F_y = T \sin 45° - 80 = 0,$$

whence

$$T = 113 \text{ lb}, \quad C = 80 \text{ lb}.$$

From Newton's third law, it follows that the strut pushes on the wall to the left with a force which is equal and opposite to C, and the slanting cable pulls down and to the right on the wall with a force which is equal and opposite to T.

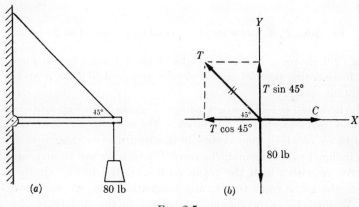

(a)   80 lb   (b)

Fɪɢ. 2-5.

2-5 Other examples of equilibrium. According to Newton's first law, the resultant force on a body is zero, both when the body is at rest and when it is moving in a straight line with constant speed. The examples in the preceding section dealt with bodies at rest. We now consider a few cases of linear motion with constant speed.

Before the time of Galileo and Newton, it was thought that in order to maintain such motion it was necessary that a force should continually be applied to the moving body, and indeed our experience seems to show that this is the case. For example, a steady push must be exerted on a book to move it at constant speed along a table top. However, if the surfaces of the book and table are made more and more smooth, that is, as friction is reduced, the force required to maintain the motion becomes

smaller and smaller.   The inference is that if friction could be eliminated
no force at all would be necessary to keep the book in motion, *once it had
been started.*   We shall postpone for the present the problem of finding the
forces while the body is being set in motion, as well as the consideration
of friction forces, and take up a number of examples of linear motion with
constant speed in the absence of friction.

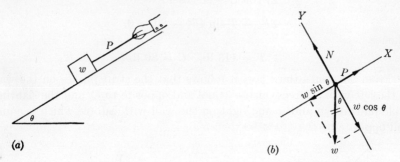

(a)   (b)

Fig. 2-6.   *P*, *N*, and *w* are the external forces exerted on the block.

Fig. 2-6 shows a block of weight *w* on a frictionless inclined plane.
What force acting parallel to the plane is required to draw it up the plane
at constant speed?

The first step is to construct a force diagram as in Fig. 2-6(b) showing
all of the forces exerted on the block.   These forces are, first, the weight
of the block *w* which acts vertically downward even though the block is
on an inclined plane; second, the force *P* which we are to find; and third,
the force *N* with which the plane pushes on the block.   If there is no
friction, the plane cannot exert any tangential force on the block, so the
force *N* must be perpendicular or *normal* to the surface of the plane.
Since *P* and *N* are at right angles, it will be simpler to choose *X*- and
Y-axes parallel and perpendicular to the surface of the plane.   Forces *N*
and *P* are then along the axes and need not be resolved.   The components
of *w* are *w* sin θ down the plane and *w* cos θ perpendicular to the plane.
Then for equilibrium,

$$\Sigma F_x = P - w \sin \theta = 0,$$

$$\Sigma F_y = N - w \cos \theta = 0.$$

Thus if the weight and the slope angle of the plane are known, the
desired force *P* can be found from the first equation and the push of the
plane from the second.   Notice that, since the sine of an angle is always
less than unity, the force *P* will always be smaller than the weight of the
body.   The ratio of the weight, which is the force that would be needed

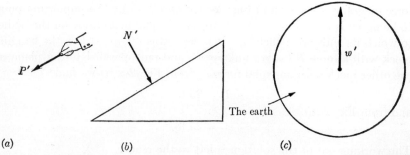

(a)   (b)   (c)

FIG. 2-7.   Forces P', N', and w' are the reactions to the forces P, N, and w in Fig. 2-6.

to lift the body vertically, to the force P is called the *mechanical advantage* of the inclined plane.

What are the reactions to the forces P, N, and w in Fig. 2-6? P is a force exerted on the block by the hand; the reaction to P is an equal and opposite force exerted on the hand by the block.   It is lettered P' in Fig. 2-7(a).   The force N is exerted on the block by the plane.   The reaction to N, lettered N' in Fig. 2-7(b), is equal and opposite to N, and is exerted on the plane by the block.   The force w is the gravitational force exerted on the block by the earth.   The reaction to w is an equal and opposite force exerted on the earth by the block.   It is lettered w' in Fig. 2-7(c) (obviously not to scale).

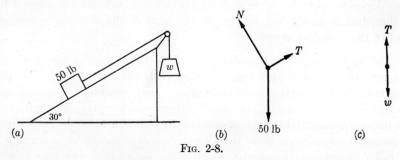

(a)   (b)   50 lb   (c)

FIG. 2-8.

Fig. 2-8 is a simple example of a case which is common in many types of moving machinery, the motion of two (or more) bodies connected together in some way.   In this case the two are connected by a flexible weightless cord passing over a frictionless pulley.   We wish to compute the weight of the hanging block which will just suffice to draw the 50-lb block up the plane with constant speed, once it has been set in motion.

In all problems such as this, which involve the motion of more than one body, it is essential to draw a force diagram for each body.   The **two** force diagrams are shown in Figs. 2-8(b) and 2-8(c). An important point to be noted is that the cord exerts forces of equal magnitude on the bodies to which its ends are attached. It pulls vertically upward on the hanging block with a force T (as yet unknown), and pulls parallel to the plane on the other block with an equal force. From Fig. 2-8(b) we find

$$T = 25 \text{ lb,}$$

and from Fig. 2-8(c)

$$w = 25 \text{ lb.}$$

The working out of the solution is left to the reader.

2-6 Friction. In the preceding section we discussed the motion of a body at constant speed when the friction forces were neglected. The next step will be to take friction into account, although the simple laws which will be given here can be expected to hold only approximately in an actual case.

Sliding friction means the force of opposition offered to the sliding of one surface over another. The force is due to the minute irregularities of one surface engaging in those of the other. In the case of metallic surfaces there may be an actual welding together of the "high spots" of the surfaces. The friction force between two surfaces depends on their nature, being smaller for hard smooth surfaces than for rough ones. The friction force also depends upon the force with which the two surfaces are pressed together, but is nearly independent of the area of the surfaces in contact and of their relative speed.

Rolling friction, the opposition offered to the rolling of one body on another, is in general very much smaller than sliding friction. For this reason the sliding friction force exerted on a shaft rotating in bearings can be reduced by installing ball or roller bearings, which replace sliding friction by rolling friction. However, the sliding friction of a well-lubricated shaft is already so small that there is no great gain in efficiency on mounting it in roller bearings. The chief reason for the use of such bearings in machinery is to reduce wear and to simplify lubrication problems.

Viscous friction. The motion of a body through a liquid or gas is opposed by a type of friction called viscous friction, which does not follow the same laws as sliding friction. The friction force, instead of being independent of the speed, is directly proportional to it, provided the speed is not too high. At higher speeds the force may increase with the square or some higher power of the speed. Viscous friction is discussed further in Chap. 14.

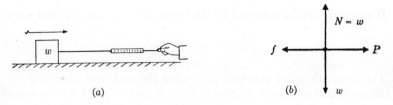

FIG. 2-9.

2-7 Coefficient of friction. Fig. 2-9 represents a block of weight w being pulled toward the right along a rough horizontal surface at constant speed by a force P. The normal force exerted by the surface on the block is lettered N. The direction of the friction force f, which always opposes the relative motion, is toward the left. (The forces N and f are actually the rectangular components of the force exerted on the block by the plane, but it is convenient to consider them as separate forces.) The friction force may be measured, indirectly, by attaching a spring balance to the block, as shown, and measuring the force P. Since the block moves at constant speed, the force P and the friction force are equal in magnitude. While the line of action of the friction force is actually along the lower face of the block, it is assumed here for simplicity that all forces intersect at the center of the block. We shall see in Chap. 3 how to treat the problem, taking into account the actual lines of action of the various forces.

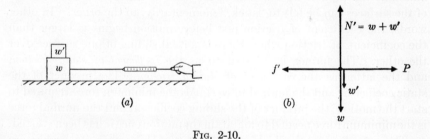

FIG. 2-10.

Suppose now that a second block of weight w' is placed on the first, as in Fig. 2-10(a), and the experiment repeated. The combined weight is now $w + w'$ and it is clear that the upward force N' will be larger than before, being now equal to $w + w'$. It is found by experiment that the friction force increases in the same proportion that the normal force increases. That is,

$$\frac{f'}{f} = \frac{N'}{N}, \quad \text{or} \quad \frac{f}{N} = \frac{f'}{N'} = \text{constant.}$$

If we represent the constant by the Greek letter μ (mu), we can write

$$\frac{f}{N} = \mu \quad \text{or} \quad f = \mu N. \tag{2-3}$$

The proportionality constant μ is called the *coefficient of sliding friction* or the *coefficient of kinetic friction*. Since f and N are both expressed in the same unit, μ is a pure number whose value is characteristic of the surfaces. Some typical coefficients of sliding friction are given in Table 2-1.

TABLE 2-1.—COEFFICIENTS OF SLIDING FRICTION

Materials	μ
Wood on wood, dry............................	.25–.50
Metals on metals, dry.........................	.15–1.4
Smooth surfaces, greased.....................	.05–.08

The direct proportion between the force of sliding friction and the normal force was first discovered by Charles Augustin Coulomb (1736–1806), who is more widely known for his experiments on the forces between electric charges.

If the block in Fig. 2-9 is initially at rest and the pull exerted by the spring balance is gradually increased from zero, it is found that a somewhat larger force is required to start the block in motion than is needed to maintain the motion at constant speed once it has been started. One of the surfaces can be felt to "stick," momentarily, to the other. In other words, the coefficient of friction just before motion begins is larger than the coefficient of friction when there is actual sliding of one surface over the other. The former is referred to as the *coefficient of static friction*, and the latter as the *coefficient of sliding friction*. The product of the static coefficient and the normal force equals the minimum force required to start the motion; the product of the sliding coefficient and the normal force is the minimum force needed to maintain the motion once it has been started.

The retarding force which stops an automobile when its brakes are applied is the friction force between the tires and the road, and the larger the coefficient of friction, the greater is the available force. Hence an automobile can be stopped in the shortest distance if the pressure on the brake pedal is such that the wheels are just on the point of "locking," without actually doing so. As long as the wheels do not actually slide, the coefficient of friction is the static coefficient. As soon as sliding starts the coefficient drops to the sliding coefficient, and the braking effect decreases.

As a numerical illustration, suppose that the block in Fig. 2-9 weighs

50 lb, the coefficient of static friction is 0.30, and the coefficient of sliding friction is 0.20.   The normal force N is equal in magnitude to the weight of the block and is therefore 50 lb.   If the block is initially at rest, the minimum force required to start it moving is equal and opposite to the force of static friction and is therefore $0.30 \times 50 = 15$ lb.   As soon as the block starts to slide, the coefficient of friction decreases to 0.20 and the force needed to maintain the block in motion at constant speed is $0.20 \times 50 = 10$ lb.

Let us now ask, how great is the friction force if the block is initially at rest and a horizontal force of 5 lb is exerted on it?   We have shown that a force of at least 15 lb is required to start the block moving, so it is clear that when the applied force is only 5 lb the block remains at rest. Since the block is in equilibrium, the friction force must be 5 lb also, in a direction opposite to that of the external force.   That is, if the block is at rest and any horizontal force less than 15 lb is exerted on it, it remains at rest and the friction force automatically adjusts itself to a value equal and opposite to the applied force.

It follows that the force of friction between two surfaces can be computed by the relation $f = \mu N$ *only when one surface is actually sliding over the other or is just on the point of sliding.*   In the former case the sliding coefficient applies, in the latter the static coefficient.   If neither of these conditions holds, the friction force adjusts itself to balance the applied force and may have any value from zero up to that given by the product of the static coefficient and the normal force.

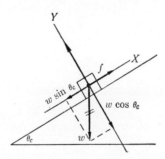

FIG. 2-11.   The critical angle θ_c is that at which the block slides down the plane at constant speed.

Example.   One end of a board upon which rests a block of weight w is raised until the angle of inclination is such that the block slides down the board at constant speed when it has once been set in motion (Fig. 2-11).   For a given coefficient of sliding friction what will be the angle of inclination?

The direction of the friction force is up the plane, opposite to the direction of motion. Let θ_c represent the critical angle at which the block just slides with constant speed. Take axes parallel and perpendicular to the surface of the plane and resolve the weight w into components. Then

$$\Sigma F_x = f - w \sin \theta_c = 0,$$
$$\Sigma F_y = N - w \cos \theta_c = 0,$$
$$f = \mu N.$$

From the simultaneous solution of these equations we find

$$\mu = \tan \theta_c.$$

This result provides a simple experimental method of measuring coefficients of sliding friction. The static coefficient may be measured in a similar way, by slowly increasing the angle of the plane until the block starts to slide. This angle is always steeper than that at which the block slides at constant speed.

———————

Problems — Chapter 2

2-1. A block rests on a horizontal surface. (a) What two forces act on it? (b) By what bodies are each of these forces exerted? (c) What are the reactions to these forces? (d) On what body is each reaction exerted, and by what body is each exerted?

2-2. A block is given a push along a table top, and slides off the edge of the table. (a) What force or forces are exerted on it while it is falling from the table to the floor? (b) What is the reaction to each force, that is, on what body and by what body is the reaction exerted? Neglect air resistance.

2-3. A block is at rest on an inclined plane. (a) Show in a diagram all of the forces acting on the block. (b) What is the reaction to each force?

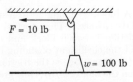

$F = 10$ lb

$w = 100$ lb

Fig. 2-12

2-4. A 10-lb force is applied horizontally to a string which runs over a pulley and is fastened to a 100-lb block resting on the floor, as shown in Fig. 2-12. (a) What is the direction and magnitude of the resultant force exerted by the string on the pulley? (b) What is the magnitude of the force which the 100-lb block exerts on the floor? (c) What is the magnitude of the force which the floor exerts on the 100-lb block? (d) What is the gravitational force on the 100-lb block?

2-5. Find the tension in each cord in Fig. 2-13 if the suspended weight is 200 lb.

2-6. Find the tension in the cable and the compression in the strut in Fig. 2-14. Let the weight of the suspended object in each case be 1000 lb. A weightless, pin-jointed, strut exerts a force along its length. Neglect the weight of the strut.

2-7. (a) In which of the parts of Fig. 2-15 can the tension T be computed, if the only quantities known are those explicitly given? (b) For each case in which insufficient information is given, state one additional quantity, a knowledge of which would permit solution.

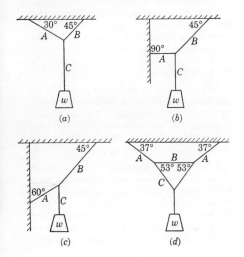

Fig. 2-13

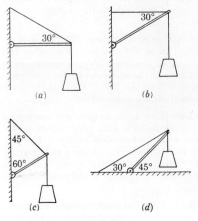

Fig. 2-14

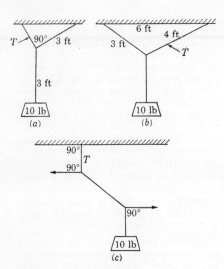

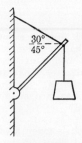

FIG. 2-15

FIG. 2-16

can withstand is 1000 lb and the maximum compression the strut can withstand is 2000 lb. The vertical rope is strong enough to carry any load required.

2-12. A small airplane weighing 3000 lb climbs steadily upward at a 30 degree angle. What is the propeller thrust and the lift? Assume that the lift is normal to the wings and that there is no drag due to air resistance.

2-13. A block weighing 20 lb rests on a horizontal surface. The coefficient of static friction between block and surface is 0.4 and the coefficient of sliding friction is 0.2. (a) How large is the friction force exerted on the block? (b) How great will the friction force be if a horizontal force of 5 lb is exerted on the block? (c) What is the minimum force which will start the block in motion? (d) What is the minimum force which will keep the block in motion once it has been started? (e) If the horizontal force is 10 lb, how great is the friction force?

2-14. A block is pulled to the right at constant velocity by a 10-lb force acting 30° above the horizontal. The coefficient of sliding friction between block and surface is 0.5. What is the weight of the block?

2-15. A block weighing 14 lb is placed on an inclined plane and connected to a 10-lb block by a cord passing over a small frictionless pulley as in Fig. 2-8. The coefficient of sliding friction between the block and the plane is 1/7. For what two values of θ will the system move with constant velocity?

Hint: $\cos \theta = \sqrt{1 - \sin^2\theta}$.

2-8. A horizontal boom 8 ft long is hinged to a vertical wall at one end, and a 500-lb body hangs from its outer end. The boom is supported by a guy wire from its outer end to a point on the wall directly above the boom. (a) If the tension in this wire is not to exceed 1000 lb, what is the minimum height above the boom at which it may be fastened to the wall? (b) By how many pounds would the tension be increased if the wire were fastened 1 ft below this point, the boom remaining horizontal? Neglect the weight of the boom.

2-9. One end of a rope 50 ft long is attached to an automobile. The other end is fastened to a tree. A man exerts a force of 100 lb at the midpoint of the rope, pulling it 2 ft to the side. What is the force exerted on the automobile?

2-10. Two 10-lb weights are suspended at opposite ends of a rope which passes over a light frictionless pulley. The pulley is attached to a chain which goes to the ceiling. (a) What is the tension in the rope? (b) What is the tension in the chain?

2-11. Find the largest weight which can be supported by the structure in Fig. 2-16 if the maximum tension the upper rope

Fig. 2-17

2-16. Block A, of weight w, slides down an inclined plane S of slope angle $37°$ at constant velocity while the plank B, also of weight w, rests on top of A. The plank is attached by a cord to the top of the plane (Fig. 2-17). (a) Draw a diagram of all the forces acting on block A. (b) If the coefficient of friction is the same between the surfaces A and B and between S and A, determine the coefficient of friction.

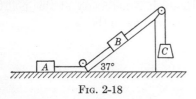

Fig. 2-18

2-17. Two blocks, A and B, are placed as in Fig. 2-18 and connected by ropes to block C. Both A and B weigh 20 lb and the coefficient of sliding friction between each block and the surface is 0.5. Block C descends with constant velocity. (a) Draw two separate force diagrams (not necessarily to scale) showing the forces acting on A and B. (b) Find the tension in the rope connecting blocks A and B. (c) What is the weight of block C?

Fig. 2-19

2-18. A flexible chain of weight w hangs between two hooks at the same height, as shown in Fig. 2-19. At each end the chain makes an angle θ with the horizontal. (a) What is the magnitude and direction of the force exerted by the chain on the hook at the left? (b) What is the tension in the chain at its lowest point?

CHAPTER 3

MOMENTS—CENTER OF GRAVITY

3-1 Introduction. Units and standards of length. It was pointed out in Chap. 2 that the forces on a structural element are often distributed in such a way that the turning effect of the force must be considered. For example, the weight w in Fig. 3-1, if acting alone, would cause the rod to rotate in a clockwise direction about the pivot at O, but its turning effect is counteracted by that of the tension in the cord AB. The turning effect of a force about a pivot is found to depend on the distance of the force from the pivot. Hence it is necessary at this point to define some of the common units of distance or length.

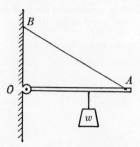

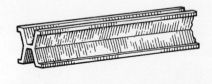

FIG. 3-1. The turning effect of the weight is counteracted by that of the cord AB.

FIG. 3-2. Portion of the standard meter bar.

The unit of length in the English gravitational system is the *foot*. This is the unit used in engineering in the United States and Great Britain. In scientific work throughout the world the unit of length is the *meter*, in the mks system, or the *centimeter* (= 1/100 meter) in the cgs system.

The *standard meter* is a bar of platinum-iridium of X-shaped cross section. The meter is defined as the distance between two fine transverse lines engraved on this bar, when the bar is at the temperature of melting ice. For many years the foot was defined as one-third of the distance between two lines on a similar one-yard standard, but to avoid the necessity of maintaining two standards of length when one is sufficient, the United States yard is now defined by the relation

$$1 \text{ yard} = \frac{3600}{3937} \text{ meter (exactly)}.$$

From this it follows that

$$1 \text{ foot} \ (= 1/3 \text{ yard}) = 0.3048006 \text{ meter}$$
$$= 30.48006 \text{ centimeters}.$$
$$1 \text{ inch} \ (= 1/12 \text{ foot}) = 2.5400 \text{ centimeters}.$$

A useful approximation, good to within 1%, is

$$1 \text{ foot} = 30 \text{ centimeters}.$$

It may be mentioned here that for the purpose of securing a standard of length which is as nearly permanent as anything can be, the length of the standard meter has been carefully compared with the wave length of one particular color of light emitted by cadmium vapor in an electric discharge. In one sense, then, the wave length of this light is the ultimate standard of length. The precise value found is

$$1 \text{ meter} = 1,553,164.13 \text{ wave lengths}.$$

3-2 Moment of a force. Torque.
Suppose that a rigid uniform rod is supported at its center on a frictionless knife edge as in Fig. 3-3, with a 4-lb weight suspended from a point 3 ft to the left of the knife edge.

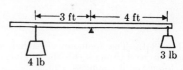

FIG. 3-3.

It is clear that this weight alone would cause the rod to rotate in a counterclockwise direction about the knife edge. Suppose we wish to balance the rotary effect of the 4-lb weight by hanging a 3-lb weight at some point to the right of the pivot. Everyone realizes that the 3-lb weight must be suspended at a greater distance from the pivot than the 4-lb weight, and trial would show that if it were hung at a distance of exactly 4 ft from the pivot, the rod would be in equilibrium. The rotary effect of a force about a pivot must then depend on something besides the magnitude of the force. Experiments such as the one described show that the effectiveness of a force in producing rotation about an axis is determined by the product of the force and the perpendicular distance from the axis to the line of action of the force.   This perpendicular distance is called the *lever arm* or the *moment arm* of the force.   Thus the moment arm of the 3-lb weight in Fig. 3-3 is 4 ft, and of the 4-lb weight it is 3 ft.

The product of a force and its moment arm is called the *moment* of the force, or the *torque* produced by the force.   We shall represent torque by the Greek letter τ (tau).   If forces are expressed in pounds and distances in feet, the unit of torque is one pound-foot.   One pound-foot is the torque produced by a force of one pound at a perpendicular distance of one foot from an axis.   Thus the torque due to the 3-lb force in Fig. 3-3 is $3 \times 4 = 12$ lb-ft clockwise, and that of the 4-lb force is 12 lb-ft counterclockwise. Other units occasionally used are the pound-inch, ounce-inch, etc.

While the units of force in the cgs and mks systems have not yet been defined, it may be stated here for completeness that the cgs unit of torque is one centimeter-dyne and the mks unit is one meter-newton.

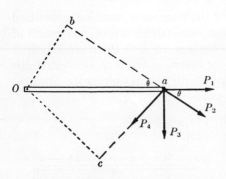

FIG. 3-4.   The moment of each force about an axis through O is the product of the force and its moment arm.

Fig. 3-4 shows a rod pivoted about an axis through O perpendicular to the plane of the diagram. Vectors P_1, P_2, etc., indicate various directions in which a force P might be exerted on the rod at point a.   It is evident from experience that the force will be most effective in producing rotation about the axis if its direction is that of P_3.   It will be less effective in the directions of P_2 and P_4, while if its direction is that of P_1, no rotation whatever will result, although the distance Oa is the same in all instances. Oa, however, is not the moment arm of all of the forces.   The moment arm is defined as *"the perpendicular distance from the axis to the line of action of the force."*   The line of action of a force is a line of indefinite length formed by extending the force vector in either direction, and the moment arm is the perpendicular distance from the axis to this line.

Thus in Fig. 3-4 the line of action of P_4 is shown extended to c, and the moment arm of P_4 is the distance Oc.   The line of action of P_2 is extended to point b, and Ob is the moment arm of P_2.   Since P_3 is at right angles to Oa, Oa is the moment arm of P_3.   The line of action of P_1 passes through O.   Hence the distance *from O to* the line of action is zero, and the moment of P_1 about O is zero.

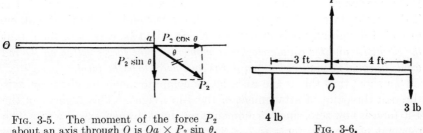

FIG. 3-5. The moment of the force P_2 about an axis through O is $Oa \times P_2 \sin \theta$.

FIG. 3-6.

Another point of view which may be adopted, and which is sometimes more convenient, is illustrated in Fig. 3-5. Force P_2 may be resolved into its rectangular components $P_2 \sin \theta$ and $P_2 \cos \theta$. Since the line of action of $P_2 \cos \theta$ passes through O, this component has no moment about O. The moment arm of the component $P_2 \sin \theta$ is the distance Oa. Hence the moment of the force P_2 about an axis through O is $P_2 \sin \theta \times Oa$. Comparison of Fig. 3-5 with the force P_2 of Fig. 3-4 will show that the same result is obtained whichever method may be used, since the distance Ob in Fig. 3-4 is equal to $Oa \sin \theta$.

3-3 Rotational equilibrium. When a number of co-planar forces act on a pivoted body, the resultant torque on the body is the algebraic sum of the torques due to the individual forces. In forming this algebraic sum, moments in one direction (say clockwise) are considered positive; those in the opposite direction, negative. If the resultant torque is zero we have the rotational analogue of Newton's first law; that is, if the body is already in rotation it continues to rotate uniformly; if at rest it remains at rest. In either case the body is in *rotational equilibrium.* Hence for complete equilibrium, including rotation, the following conditions must be satisfied

$$\Sigma F_x = 0, \quad \Sigma F_y = 0, \quad \Sigma \tau = 0. \qquad (3\text{-}1)$$

These equations constitute the two conditions of equilibrium.

The second equation may be used to compute the upward force exerted on the rod in Fig. 3-3 by the pivot. If this upward force is represented by P in Fig. 3-6, and if the weight of the rod is negligible, then

$$\Sigma F_y = 0$$

$$P - 4 - 3 = 0$$

$$P = 7 \text{ lb.}$$

In the particular arrangement shown in Figs. 3-3 and 3-6 it seemed most natural to compute moments about an axis through the pivot O.

But since the rod does not rotate, we could equally well have stated that it does not rotate about an axis through the left end, or the right end, or, in fact, through any point whatsoever.   It might be expected, then, that *the clockwise and the counterclockwise moments of the forces acting on the rod would be equal no matter what point was considered to be the pivot.*

To show that this is the case, let us compute moments about an axis through the point of attachment of the 4-lb weight.   The moment of the 4-lb force is now zero, since its moment arm about the new axis is zero.   The moment of the 7-lb force is $7 \times 3 = 21$ lb-ft counterclockwise, and the moment of the 3-lb force is $3 \times 7 = 21$ lb-ft clockwise.   The moments are thus equal and opposite if the axis is considered to pass through this point, and it can be shown that the same result will be obtained for any point whatever.   As an exercise, calculate the moments of the forces about an axis 4 ft to the left of point O, and show that the sum is zero.

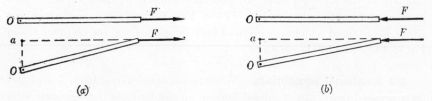

FIG. 3-7.   (*a*) Stable and (*b*) unstable equilibrium.

3-4 Stable and unstable equilibrium.   The upper diagram in Fig. 3-7(a) is a top view of a rod resting on a smooth horizontal surface and pivoted at one end O.   A force F is exerted on the other end of the rod as shown.   Fig. 3-7(b) is the same except that the force F is opposite in sense.   Whether the force acts toward the right or left, its moment about the pivot is zero and the rod is in equilibrium.   The two cases differ, however, in the following respect.   If the rod is given a small angular displacement as in the lower part of the figures, and the force F remains parallel to its original direction, a torque equal to $F \times Oa$ acts about the pivot.   It is evident from the diagrams that if the force is directed toward the right as in (a) the torque tends to return the rod to its initial position, while if the force is toward the left as in (b) the effect of the torque is to increase the displacement still further.   In the former case the equilibrium is said to be *stable*, in the latter case it is *unstable*, and we can say in general:

When a body is in rotational equilibrium, the equilibrium is stable if a small displacement gives rise to a restoring torque and unstable if a small displacement gives rise to a torque which tends to increase the displacement.

If the torque remains zero when the body is displaced, the equilibrium is *neutral*.

A circular cone resting on its base is in stable equilibrium; balanced on its apex it is in unstable equilibrium; resting on its side on a level surface it is in neutral equilibrium.

3-5 The resultant of a set of parallel forces. The resultant of two (or more) forces is defined as the single force which, if acting alone, will produce the same effect as the simultaneous action of its components. The method of finding the resultant of a number of *intersecting* forces has been explained in Chap. 1. However, if the forces are parallel their lines of action do not intersect and these methods cannot be used.

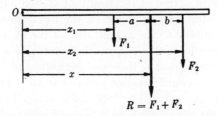

Fig. 3-8.   Force R is the resultant of the parallel forces F_1 and F_2.

Let Fig. 3-8 represent a rod pivoted at O and acted upon by the parallel forces F_1 and F_2, at distances x_1 and x_2 from an axis through O. We wish to find the resultant of F_1 and F_2. Since both forces are in the same direction, the *magnitude* of their resultant R must equal their algebraic sum.

$$R = F_1 + F_2.$$

The effect of F_1 and F_2, in this instance, is to produce rotation about O, and since the resultant must produce the same effect as its components, the *line of action* of the resultant must be in such a position that the moment of the resultant about O is equal to the algebraic sum of the moments of the components. That is, the line of action of the resultant R must be at such a distance x from the axis that

$$Rx = F_1x_1 + F_2x_2$$

or, since $R = F_1 + F_2$,

$$(F_1 + F_2)x = F_1x_1 + F_2x_2,$$

$$x = \frac{F_1x_1 + F_2x_2}{F_1 + F_2}. \tag{3-2}$$

The expression for the position of the line of action of R can be put in a somewhat different form.   Referring to Fig. 3-8 we have

$$R(x_1 + a) = (F_1 + F_2)\,(x_1 + a) = F_1x_1 + F_2(x_1 + a + b).$$

Expanding and cancelling, we find that

$$F_1a = F_2b, \quad \text{or}$$

$$\frac{a}{b} = \frac{F_2}{F_1}. \tag{3-3}$$

That is, the line of action of the resultant of two parallel forces in the same sense, divides the distance between the forces into two parts which are inversely proportional to the magnitudes of the forces.

Since the distance from the axis, x_1, does not appear in Eq. (3-3), the line of action of the resultant is the same regardless of the point at which the rod is pivoted, or even if it is not pivoted at all.   That is, if the pivot were removed from the rod in Fig. 3-8, the combined effect of F_1 and F_2 would be to cause the rod as a whole to move down, and at the same time to rotate in a clockwise direction.   The single force R at the position x would be found to produce exactly the same effect

This process can evidently be extended to include any number of parallel forces.   The general expressions for the magnitude of the resultant and the position of its line of action become

$$R = \Sigma F, \tag{3-4}$$

$$x = \frac{\Sigma Fx}{\Sigma F}, \tag{3-5}$$

where ΣF is the algebraic sum of the forces, and ΣFx is the algebraic sum of the moments.   The position of the line of action of the resultant does not depend on the position of the axis, which may be taken through any convenient point.   When applying these equations, whatever convention of signs is adopted for the F's and x's must be used consistently.   The algebraic sign of each Fx product is determined by the signs of its factors.

Example. Find the magnitude and line of action of the resultant of the three forces in Fig. 3-9.

Let us first take the axis through point O, and consider forces positive if upward and distances positive if to the right of O. Then

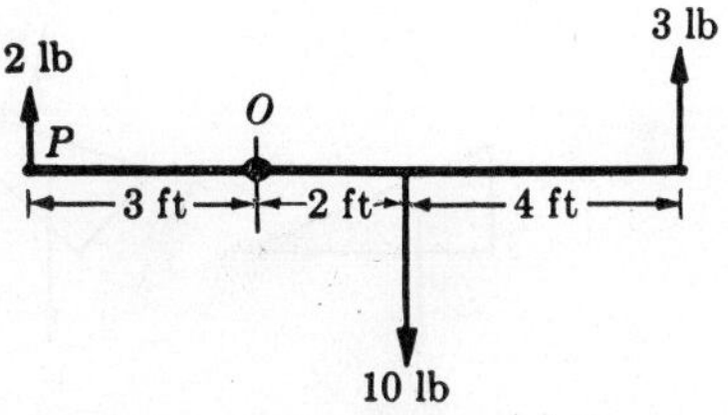

$$R = \Sigma F = +2 - 10 + 3 = -5 \text{ lb},$$

Fig. 3-9.

$$x = \frac{\Sigma Fx}{\Sigma F} = \frac{(+2) \times (-3) + (-10) \times (+2) + (+3) \times (+6)}{+2 - 10 + 3}$$

$$= \frac{-8}{-5} = +1.6 \text{ ft}$$

and the three forces are equivalent to a downward force of 5 lb whose line of action is 1.6 ft to the right of O.

If the axis is taken through point P,

$$x = \frac{(+2) \times (0) + (-10) \times (+5) + (+3) \times (+9)}{+2 - 10 + 3}$$

$$= +4.6 \text{ ft}$$

and the line of action is 4.6 ft to the right of P, which is the same as 1.6 ft to the right of O.

3-6 Center of gravity. The weight of a body is defined as the force of gravitational attraction exerted on the body by the earth. This gravitational pull, however, is not merely one force exerted on the body as a whole. Each small element of the body is attracted by the earth, and the force which is called the weight of the body is in reality the resultant of all of these small parallel forces. Its magnitude, and the position of its line of action, may be calculated by the methods explained in the preceding section.

The direction of the gravitational force on each element of a body is vertically down, so the direction of the resultant is vertically down also, regardless of the orientation of the body. The line of action of the resultant will, however, occupy a different position relative to the body as the orientation of the body is altered. (See Fig. 3-10.)

It is found that however a body may be oriented there is always a common point through which all of these lines of action pass. This point is called the *center of gravity* of the body, and its position is shown in Fig. 3-10(d), in which the lines of action of the weight in the three previous orientations are indicated. The body's weight may therefore be treated

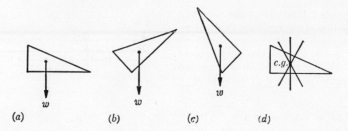

FIG. 3-10. The line of action of the weight passes through the center of gravity.

as a single force whose point of application is the center of gravity, although actually the "point of application" has no significance.   All one can say is that the line of action of the weight passes through the center of gravity.

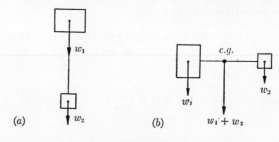

FIG. 3-11.

The center of gravity of any number of bodies whose own centers of gravity are known is located as follows.   The center of gravity of any *two* bodies must lie on the line joining their centers of gravity.   This follows at once from the fact that if the bodies are placed with their centers in a vertical line as in Fig. 3-11(a), both of their weights lie along this line and hence the resultant lies on this line also.   The exact position of the common center of gravity on this line may be found by placing the bodies with the line of centers horizontal as in Fig. 3-11(b), when the line of action of their combined weights is simply that of the resultant of two parallel forces.   From Eq. (3-3) we may then say that the center of gravity of two bodies lies in the line joining their centers of gravity, and divides the distance between the centers into two parts which are inversely proportional to the two weights.   The two bodies may be replaced by a single body whose center of gravity is at this point and whose weight equals the sum of the weights of the two bodies.   This fictitious body may then be combined with a third, and so on.

Example. Find the position of the center of gravity of the three weights in Fig. 3-12.

The center of gravity of the two 4-lb weights is at point a, halfway between them. That is, they may be replaced by a single 8-lb weight at point a. When this is combined with the 16-lb weight, the center of gravity is found to be at a point 1 ft below the 16-lb weight, and the group is equivalent to a single 24-lb weight at this point.

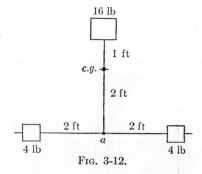

FIG. 3-12.

A more general method is to construct a pair of X- and Y-axes, specify the position of the center of gravity of each weight by its X- and Y-coordinates, and imagine the pull of gravity to be first parallel to the Y-axis and then parallel to the X-axis. In the former case the X-coordinate of the line of action of the combined weight, and therefore the X-coordinate of the center of gravity, is

$$\bar{x} = \frac{w_1 x_1 + w_2 x_2 + \ldots}{w_1 + w_2 + \ldots} = \frac{\Sigma w x}{\Sigma w}, \tag{3-6}$$

where $\bar{x}$ is the X-coordinate of the center of gravity, and x_1, x_2, etc., are the X-coordinates of the separate weights. Similarly the Y-coordinate of the center of gravity is

$$\bar{y} = \frac{\Sigma w y}{\Sigma w}. \tag{3-7}$$

Example.   Find the position of the center of gravity of the three weights in Fig. 3-12 by the general method explained above.

Construct a convenient set of rectangular axes as in Fig. 3-13.

$$w_1 = \ 4 \text{ lb}, \quad x_1 = 0, \qquad y_1 = 0,$$

$$w_2 = \ 4 \text{ lb}, \quad x_2 = 4 \text{ ft}, \quad y_2 = 0,$$

$$w_3 = 16 \text{ lb}, \quad x_3 = 2 \text{ ft}, \quad y_3 = 3 \text{ ft},$$

$$\bar{x} = \frac{\Sigma w x}{\Sigma w} = \frac{(4 \times 0) + (4 \times 4) + (16 \times 2)}{4 + 4 + 16} = 2 \text{ ft},$$

$$\bar{y} = \frac{\Sigma w y}{\Sigma w} = \frac{(4 \times 0) + (4 \times 0) + (16 \times 3)}{4 + 4 + 16} = 2 \text{ ft},$$

which checks the previous answer.

To calculate the center of gravity of a flat body of any shape, it is necessary to make use of the calculus. From the physical standpoint the important thing to remember is that the weight of a body is the resultant of an infinite number of infinitesimal forces, and that its line of action passes through the center of gravity in all orientations.

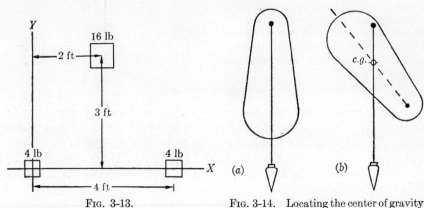

FIG. 3-13.   FIG. 3-14.   Locating the center of gravity
                                           of a flat object.

The position of the center of gravity of a body of complex shape is best found by experiment, based on the fact that a pivoted body is in stable equilibrium only when its center of gravity is vertically below the pivot. By pivoting a body successively from two points, two lines may be located at whose point of intersection the center of gravity must lie. Fig. 3-14 illustrates this method as applied to an irregularly shaped flat plate

---

Examples. (1) Compute the tension in the supporting cable in Fig. 3-15, if the strut weighs 40 lb and its center of gravity is at its center. Compute also the force exerted on the strut at its point of attachment to the wall.

NOTE. The arrangement is the same as that of Fig. 2-5 on page 19 except that the weight of the strut is now to be taken into account.

Isolate the strut and show all of the forces exerted on it, as in Fig. 3-15(b). The force at the wall is unknown in magnitude and direction. Instead of working with an unknown force at an unknown angle it is simpler to treat the horizontal and vertical *components* as unknowns, and combine them later to find their resultant. These components are lettered H and V in Fig. 3-15 (b). Resolve the tension T into components as shown. Then from the conditions of equilibrium,

$$\Sigma F_y = T \sin 45° + V - 40 - 80 = 0,$$

$$\Sigma F_x = H - T \cos 45° = 0,$$

$$\Sigma \tau = (80 \times 8) + (40 \times 4) - (T \sin 45° \times 8) = 0,$$

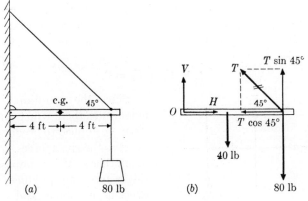

FIG. 3-15.

where the moments are computed about an axis through point O. Solution of these simultaneous equations gives $T = 141$ lb, $V = 20$ lb, $H = 100$ lb.

(2) In Chap. 2 a number of examples were discussed in which a body was dragged along a rough surface and where, for simplicity, all of the forces exerted on the body were assumed to intersect at its center. We are now in a position to take into account the actual lines of action of the forces in such cases. Fig. 3-16 shows a table which is being pulled to the right at constant speed by a horizontal force P. The center of gravity of the table is midway between front and rear legs. N_1 and N_2 are the upward forces at the front and rear legs, and μN_1 and μN_2 are the friction forces. The coefficient of friction is 0.40.

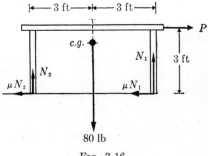

FIG. 3-16.

We wish to find the forces P, N_1, and N_2.

From the conditions of equilibrium,

$$\Sigma F_x = P - \mu N_1 - \mu N_2 = 0,$$

$$\Sigma F_y = N_1 + N_2 - 80 = 0,$$

$$\Sigma \tau = (P \times 3) + (N_2 \times 6) - (80 \times 3) = 0,$$

where the moments are computed about an axis through the point of contact between the front legs and the floor. From these simultaneous equations, we find

$$N_1 = 56 \text{ lb}, \quad N_2 = 24 \text{ lb}, \quad P = 32 \text{ lb}.$$

3-7 Couples. An interesting and important case involving parallel forces occurs when a body is acted on by two forces which are equal in magnitude but opposite in direction (or sense) and whose lines of action do not coincide. Such a pair of forces is called a *couple* (Fig. 3-17). If we set out to find the resultant of these parallel forces by the methods used in Sec. 3-3 we find

$$R = F_1 - F_2 = 0.$$

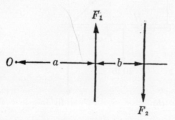

FIG. 3-17. The equal and oppositely directed forces F_1 and F_2 constitute a couple.

Since the resultant is of zero magnitude, there is no point at which it can be applied to produce the same effect as the given forces. Looked at in another way, it is impossible for a single force to produce the same effect as a couple, and conversely, there is no single force which will balance a couple. *The sole effect of a couple is to produce rotation*, and a couple can be balanced only by another couple which is equal and opposite.

The moment of a couple is found as follows. If moments are taken about an axis through O and perpendicular to the plane of the diagram (Fig. 3-17), we find

$$\Sigma\tau_o = F_2 \times (a + b) - F_1 \times a$$
$$= F_2a + F_2b - F_1a.$$

But since F_1 and F_2 are equal in magnitude,

$$\Sigma\tau_o = F_2b = F_1b.$$

That is, the resultant torque produced by a couple is equal to the product of *either* of the forces constituting the couple and the perpendicular distance between their lines of action. This product is called the moment of the couple. Furthermore, since the distance a does not appear in the expression for the moment, it follows that the moment of a couple is the same about *all* axes perpendicular to the plane of the forces constituting the couple.

A common example of a couple is afforded by the forces acting on a compass needle in the earth's magnetic field. The north and south poles are urged in opposite directions

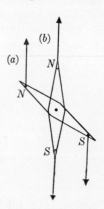

FIG. 3-18.

with equal forces. Since the resultant *force* on the needle is zero there is no tendency for it to move north or south as a whole. If it is originally in position (*a*) in Fig. 3-18, the effect of the couple is to rotate it clockwise to position (*b*). In this position the moment of the couple becomes zero and the north-south direction is therefore the position of stable equilibrium.

Problems — Chapter 3

3-1. Give an example to show that the following statement is false: Any two forces acting on a body can be combined into a single resultant force that would have the same effect.

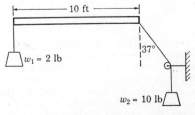

FIG. 3-20

3-3. A single force is to be applied to the bar in Fig. 3-20, to maintain it in equilibrium in the position shown. The weight of the bar can be neglected. (a) What are the X- and Y-components of the required force? (b) What is the tangent of the angle which the force must make with the bar? (c) What is the magnitude of the required force? (d) Where should the force be applied?

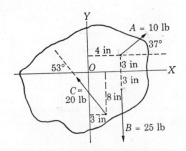

FIG. 3-19

3-2. (a) Find the X- and Y-components of forces A, B, and C in Fig. 3-19. (b) Find the sum of the X-components and the sum of the Y-components of all the forces. (c) What is the resultant force on the body (give both magnitude and direction)? (d) What is the resultant torque about an axis through point O, perpendicular to the plane of the diagram? Is the torque clockwise or counterclockwise?

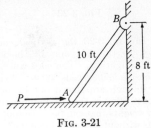

FIG. 3-21

3-4. End A of the bar AB in Fig. 3-21 rests on a frictionless horizontal surface, while end B is hinged. A horizontal force P of 12 lb is exerted on end A. Neglect the weight of the bar. (a) What are the horizontal and vertical components of the force exerted by the bar on the hinge at B? (b) Show in a sketch all of the forces acting on the bar.

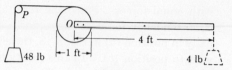

Fig. 3-24

3-7. A circular disk 1 ft in diameter, pivoted about a horizontal axis through its center O, has a cord wrapped around its rim. The cord passes over a frictionless pulley P and is attached to a body of weight 48 lb. A uniform rod 4 ft long is fastened to the disk with one end at the center of the disk. The apparatus is in equilibrium, with the rod horizontal as shown in Fig. 3-24. (a) What is the weight of the rod? (b) What is the new equilibrium direction of the rod when a second body weighing 4 lb is suspended from the outer end of the rod as shown by the dotted line?

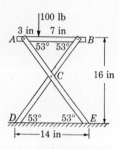

Fig. 3-22

3-5. A weightless camp stool pivoted at points A, B, and C rests on a frictionless floor, as in Fig. 3-22. A vertical force of 100 lb is exerted on the member AB. (a) Calculate the forces exerted by the floor on the stool at D and E. (b) Calculate the vertical components of the forces exerted on member AB by the legs. (c) Calculate and show in a diagram the horizontal and vertical components of all the forces acting on leg AE.

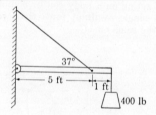

Fig. 3-25

3-8. Find the tension in the cable and the force exerted on the strut by the wall in Fig. 3-25.

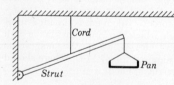

Fig. 3-23

3-6. In Fig. 3-23 the vertical cord is attached to the midpoint of the strut, which is weightless. The cord will break if the tension in it exceeds 500 lb. Weights of 100 lb each are placed one by one in the pan. What is the maximum number of such weights that can be safely put into the pan without the cord breaking?

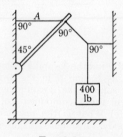

Fig. 3-26

3-9. Find the tension in cord A in Fig. 3-26. The boom is uniform and weighs 400 lb.

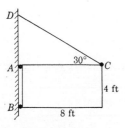

Fig. 3-27

3-10. A gate 8 ft long and 4 ft high weighs 80 lb. Its center of gravity is at its center, and it is hinged at *A* and *B*. To relieve the strain on the top hinge a wire *CD* is connected, as shown in Fig. 3-27. The tension in *CD* is increased until the horizontal force at hinge *A* is zero. (a) What is the tension in the wire *CD*? (b) What is the magnitude of the horizontal component of force at hinge *B*? (c) What is the combined vertical force exerted by hinges *A* and *B*?

3-11. A uniform oak plank is 20 ft long, and weighs 250 lb. The plank has one end on the ground and rests on a smooth cylindrical fence rail 5 ft above the ground at a distance of 12 ft measured horizontally from the end on the ground. A 200-lb weight hangs from the upper end of the plank. (a) What must be the magnitude of the force exerted on the plank by the rail? (b) Calculate the components of the force exerted on the plank by the ground.

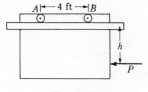

Fig. 3-28

3-12. A garage door is mounted on an overhead rail as in Fig. 3-28. The wheels at *A* and *B* have rusted so that they do not roll, but slide along the track. The coefficient of sliding friction is 0.5. The distance between the wheels is 4 ft. and

each is 1 ft in from the vertical sides of the door. The door is symmetrical and weighs 160 lb. It is pushed to the left at constant velocity by a horizontal force *P*. (a) If the distance *h* is 3 ft, what is the vertical component of the force exerted on each wheel by the track? (b) Find the maximum value *h* can have without causing one wheel to leave the track.

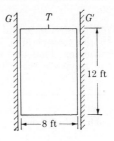

Fig. 3-29

3-13. A freight elevator weighing 2000 lb and having dimensions of 8 × 8 × 12 ft hangs from a cable with a small clearance between vertical frictionless guides, *G* and *G'*, as shown in Fig. 3-29. A load of 1200 lb is placed in the elevator with its center of gravity 2 ft to the left of the center of the floor. The elevator is then moved upward at constant velocity. (a) Show in a diagram the location and direction of the forces exerted by the guides on the elevator. (b) Compute the magnitude of these forces.

3-14. A uniform ladder 35 ft long rests against a vertical wall with its lower end 21 ft from the wall. The ladder weighs 80 lb. The coefficient of friction between the foot of the ladder and the ground is 0.4. A man weighing 150 lb starts up the ladder. How far up the ladder can he climb before the ladder starts to slip?

3-15. A roller 2 ft in diameter weighs 100 lb. What is the horizontal force necessary to pull the roller over a brick 2 inches high?

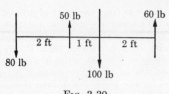

Fig. 3-30

3-16. Find the magnitude and line of action of the resultant of the four forces in Fig. 3-30.

3-17. Weights of 3, 6, 9, and 12 lb are fastened to the corners of a light wire frame 2 ft square. Find the position of the center of gravity of the weights.

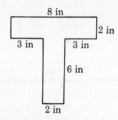

Fig. 3-31

3-18. Find the position of the center of gravity of the T-shaped plate in Fig. 3-31.

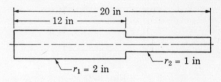

Fig. 3-32

3-19. A machine part, shown in cross section in Fig. 3-32, consists of two homogeneous, solid, coaxial cylinders. Where is its center of gravity?

3-20. A uniform ladder 20 ft long weighing 80 lb, leans against a vertical frictionless wall with its lower end 12 ft from the wall. (a) Compute the magnitude and direction of the resultant force exerted on the lower end of the ladder. (b) In a carefully drawn diagram to scale show all of the forces acting on the ladder.

CHAPTER 4

RECTILINEAR MOTION

4-1 Motion. At the beginning of Chap. 1 it was stated that mechanics is concerned with the relations of force, matter, and motion. The preceding chapters have dealt with forces and we are now ready to discuss the mathematical methods of describing motion. This branch of mechanics is called *kinematics*.

Motion may be defined as a continuous change in position. We shall restrict the discussion in this chapter to motion along a straight line, or *rectilinear* motion. In order to specify the position of a body moving along a line, some fixed reference point on the line is chosen as the *origin*. The distance from the origin to the body is called the *coordinate* of the body. The coordinate is usually considered positive if the body is at the right of the origin, negative if it is at the left.

Suppose that a body, which at some one instant is at point a on the line OX in Fig. 4-1, is found at a later instant at point b. The origin is at O, the coordinate of point a is x_0, and the coordinate of point b is x.

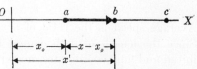

Fig. 4-1. The vector from a to b is the displacement.

The *displacement* of the body is defined as the vector drawn from a to b; its magnitude is evidently $x - x_0$. The displacement is the same whatever motion the body may have performed. For example, if the body moves from a to c and back to b, its displacement is still defined as the vector from a to b. That is, the displacement is always the vector from the initial point to the end point.

The total space moved over by the body, or the sum of the segments ac and cb, is called the *length of path*. Length of path is considered a scalar, not a vector.

4-2 Average velocity and average speed. The *average velocity* of a moving body is defined as the ratio of its displacement to the time interval in which the displacement occurred.

$$\text{Average velocity (a vector)} = \frac{\text{displacement (a vector)}}{\text{elapsed time (a scalar)}}.$$

47

Average velocity is a vector, since the ratio of a vector to a scalar is itself a vector, and its direction is the same as that of the displacement.

Let t_0 be the time at which the body is at point a, Fig. 4-1, and let t be the time at which it passes point b. The elapsed time is $t - t_0$ and the magnitude of the average velocity is therefore

$$\bar{v} = \frac{x - x_0}{t - t_0}. \tag{4-1}$$

(A bar over the symbol for a quantity signifies an average value.)

If the final position of the body is at the right of its initial position, the displacement $x - x_0$ is positive. If the final position is at the left of the initial position, the displacement is negative. The elapsed time $t - t_0$ is positive always. Hence the algebraic sign of the average velocity is the same as that of the displacement, and a positive average velocity indicates a displacement toward the right and vice versa.

The *average speed* of a moving body is defined as the ratio of length of path to elapsed time.

$$\text{Average speed (a scalar)} = \frac{\text{length of path (a scalar)}}{\text{elapsed time (a scalar)}}.$$

Average speed is the ratio of a scalar to a scalar and is itself a scalar. Since the length of path cannot be expressed as the difference between initial and final coordinates, no expression like Eq. (4-1) can be written for average speed. Except in special cases the displacement and length of path of a moving body are not numerically equal. Therefore the average speed and average velocity of a moving body will, in general, differ numerically. However, velocity and speed are both the ratio of a length to a time and both are therefore expressed in terms of the same unit.

All systems of units employ the same unit of time, the *second*. One second (strictly speaking, one "mean solar second") is defined as 1/86,400 of a mean solar day. A mean solar day is the mean or average time for the earth to make one rotation on its axis relative to the sun. The figure 86,400 comes from dividing the day into 24 hours and the hour into 3600 seconds. $24 \times 3600 = 86,400$. There is no physical standard of time corresponding to the standards of length or force, except insofar as the earth and sun may be considered to constitute the standard.

The unit of velocity (or speed) in the English system is one foot per second, abbreviated ft/sec. The corresponding unit in the mks system is one meter per second (m/sec) and in the cgs system it is one centimeter per second (cm/sec). Many other units, such as the mile per hour, are in common use.

Eq. (4-1) may be cleared of fractions and written

$$(x - x_0) = \bar{v}\,(t - t_0) \tag{4-2}$$

or in words, displacement equals the product of average velocity and elapsed time.

It is often useful to solve Eq. (4-2) for the coordinate x.

$$x = x_0 + \bar{v}\,(t - t_0). \tag{4-3}$$

If time is counted from the instant when the body is at point a, then $t_0 = 0$ and Eq. (4-3) becomes

$$x = x_0 + \bar{v}t. \tag{4-4}$$

If point a is at the origin then $x_0 = 0$ and Eq. (4-4) simplifies further to

$$x = \bar{v}t. \tag{4-5}$$

Example. A runner on a straight track passes a point 50 ft from the starting line at the instant when a stop watch reads $12\frac{3}{5}$ sec, and passes a second point 158 ft from the starting line when the same watch reads $16\frac{1}{5}$ sec. What was his average velocity in ft/sec?

Take the origin at the starting line. Then $x_0 = 50$ ft, $x = 158$ ft, $t_0 = 12.6$ sec, $t = 16.2$ sec. Hence

$$\bar{v} = \frac{158 - 50}{16.2 - 12.6} = \frac{108}{3.6} = 30 \text{ ft/sec.}$$

4-3 Instantaneous velocity. The velocity of a moving body at some one instant of time, or at some one point of its path, is called its *instantaneous velocity*. Instantaneous velocity is a concept that requires careful definition. Velocity is the ratio of a displacement to a time interval. An instant of time, however, has no duration and consequently a body can undergo no displacement precisely at an instant. This logical difficulty is avoided as follows.

The lettered points in Fig. 4-2 represent successive positions of a body moving toward the right along the X-axis. Consider the average velocity of the body first over the displacement ae, then over the

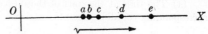

FIG. 4-2.   Instantaneous velocity is the limiting ratio of displacement to elapsed time.

successively shorter displacements ad, ac, and ab. The shorter the displacement the more nearly will the average velocity over this displacement equal the instantaneous velocity at point *a*.   *The instantaneous velocity at a point* may therefore be defined as *the average velocity over an extremely small displacement which includes the point.*

Notice that although the displacement is extremely small the time interval by which it must be divided to obtain the instantaneous velocity is small also.   The quotient is not necessarily a small quantity.

In the notation of calculus the displacement *ab* is written Δx and the corresponding time interval Δt.   The average velocity is then

$$\bar{v} = \Delta x / \Delta t.$$

The limiting value of the average velocity, when Δx and Δt are infinitesimally small, is the instantaneous velocity *v*.   Hence

$$v = \lim_{\Delta t \to 0} \frac{\Delta x}{\Delta t}. \tag{4-6}$$

Eq. (4-6) may be considered the definition of instantaneous velocity.

When the change in a quantity is divided by the time interval during which the change occurred, the quotient is called the *time rate of change*, or simply the *rate of change of the quantity*.   Average velocity is therefore the *average rate of change of position* and instantaneous velocity is the *instantaneous rate of change of position*.

Since Δt is necessarily a positive quantity, it follows that *v* has the same algebraic sign as Δx.   Hence a positive velocity indicates motion toward the right and vice versa, if we use the usual convention of signs.

Example.   The coordinate of a body moving along the *X*-axis is given by

$$x = 10t^2,$$

where *x* is in cm and *t* in sec.   Compute the average velocity of the body over the time interval from: (a) 2 to 2.1 sec; (b) 2 to 2.001 sec; (c) 2 to 2.00001 sec; (d) What is its instantaneous velocity exactly at 2 sec?

(a) The time at the start of the interval under consideration, or t_0, is 2 sec.   The corresponding coordinate, x_0, is

$$x_0 = 10 \times 2^2 = 40 \text{ cm.}$$

At the end of the first interval $t = 2.1$ sec and

$$x = 10 \times (2.1)^2 = 44.1 \text{ cm.}$$

Hence

$$\bar{v} = \frac{44.1 - 40}{2.1 - 2} = \frac{4.1}{.1} = 41 \text{ cm /sec.}$$

(b) When $t = 2.001$ sec,

$$x = 10 \times (2.001)^2 = 40.04001 \text{ cm},$$

$$v = \frac{40.04001 - 40}{2.001 - 2} = \frac{.04001}{.001} = 40.01 \text{ cm/sec.}$$

(c) When $t = 2.00001$ sec,

$$x = 10 \times (2.00001)^2 = 40.000400001 \text{ cm},$$

$$\bar{v} = \frac{40.000400001 - 40}{2.00001 - 2} = \frac{.000400001}{.00001} = 40.0001 \text{ cm/sec.}$$

(d) In general, when $t = 2 + \Delta t$,

$$x = 10 \times (2 + \Delta t)^2 = 10 \times [4 + 4\Delta t + (\Delta t)^2]$$

$$= 40 + 40\Delta t + 10 \, (\Delta t)^2$$

$$\bar{v} = \frac{[40 + 40\Delta t + 10 \, (\Delta t)^2] - 40}{(2 + \Delta t) - 2}$$

$$= \frac{40\Delta t + 10 \, (\Delta t)^2}{\Delta t}$$

$$= 40 + 10\Delta t.$$

The instantaneous velocity is defined as the limiting value of the average velocity when Δt is so small as to be practically zero. But when Δt is very small, the term $10\Delta t$ is negligible in comparison with 40, so that the instantaneous velocity is 40 cm/sec.

This example shows how the average velocity becomes more and more nearly equal to the instantaneous velocity as the time interval is made smaller and smaller.

4-4 Uniform motion. The simplest type of motion that a body can undergo is one in which the body covers equal distances along a straight line in equal time intervals. This is known as *uniform rectilinear motion*, and is characterized by the fact that the velocity is constant at all times. Hence the average velocity and the instantaneous velocity are the same, and

$$v = \bar{v} = \frac{x - x_0}{t - t_0}.$$

If time is counted from the instant when the body is at the origin, then $t_0 = 0$ and $x_0 = 0$, whence

$$\boxed{v = \frac{x}{t}.} \qquad \left(\begin{matrix}\text{Uniform rectilinear} \\ \text{motion only}\end{matrix}\right) \quad (4\text{-}7)$$

4-5 Average acceleration.   Except in certain special cases the velocity of a moving body changes continuously as the motion proceeds.   When this is the case the body is said to move with *accelerated motion,* or to have an *acceleration.*

Fig. 4-3 again represents a body moving to the right along the X-axis. Suppose that by the methods explained in the preceding section we have

found its instantaneous velocity at point a to have the value v_0, represented by the vector v_0 in Fig. 4-3. Similarly the instantaneous velocity at point b has been found to be v. The *average acceleration* during the interval while the body moves from

Fig. 4-3.   Average acceleration is the ratio of change in velocity to elapsed time.

a to b is defined as the *ratio of the change in velocity to the elapsed time.*

$$\text{Average acceleration (a vector)} = \frac{\text{change in velocity (a vector)}}{\text{elapsed time (a scalar)}},$$

$$\bar{a} = \frac{v - v_0}{t - t_0}, \tag{4-8}$$

where t_0 and t are the times corresponding to the velocities v_0 and v.   Since v and v_0 are vectors, the quantity $(v - v_0)$ is a *vector difference* and must be found by the methods explained in Sec. 1-8.   However, since in rectilinear motion both vectors lie in the same straight line, the magnitude of the vector difference in this special case equals the difference between the magnitudes of the vectors.   The more general case, in which v and v_0 are not in the same direction, will be considered in Chap. 9.

In the English system of units, where the unit of velocity is the ft/sec and the unit of time the second, the unit of acceleration is one foot per second, per second, abbreviated ft/sec^2.   In the mks and cgs systems the units of acceleration are respectively one meter per second, per second (m/sec^2) and one centimeter per second, per second (cm/sec^2).

In accordance with the usual convention of sign, if $v - v_0$ is a positive quantity the acceleration is positive also and directed toward the right. When the absolute magnitude of the velocity of a body decreases, that is, when the body is slowing down, it is said to have a *deceleration* or to be *decelerated.*

Example.   The instantaneous velocity of an automobile is 10 ft/sec, 3 sec after it starts, and increases to 40 ft/sec at 6 sec after the start.   Find the average acceleration.

$t_0 = 3$ sec, $v_0 = 10$ ft/sec, $t = 6$ sec, $v = 40$ ft/sec. The change in velocity is $40 - 10 = 30$ ft/sec and the elapsed time is $6 - 3 = 3$ sec. Hence

$$\bar{a} = \frac{30}{3} = 10 \text{ ft/sec}^2.$$

4-6 Instantaneous acceleration.   The instantaneous acceleration of a body, that is, its acceleration at some one instant of time or at some one point of its path, is defined in the same way as instantaneous velocity. Let the points a and b in Fig. 4-3 be taken closer and closer together. The smaller the distance between them, the more nearly will the average acceleration over this distance equal the instantaneous acceleration at point a.   We accordingly define the *instantaneous acceleration* at a point as the *average acceleration over an extremely small displacement which includes the point.*

Let Δv represent the change in velocity during a time interval Δt.   The average acceleration during this time is then

$$\bar{a} = \Delta v / \Delta t.$$

The limiting value of the average acceleration, when Δt and Δv are infinitesimally small, is the instantaneous acceleration a.   Hence

$$a = \lim_{\Delta t \to 0} \frac{\Delta v}{\Delta t} \cdot \qquad (4\text{-}9)$$

Since acceleration is a change in velocity divided by the time interval during which the change takes place, average acceleration is the *average rate of change of velocity* and instantaneous acceleration is the *instantaneous rate of change of velocity.*   Instantaneous acceleration plays an important part in the laws of mechanics.   Average acceleration is less frequently used.   Hence from now on when the term "acceleration" is used we shall understand it to mean "instantaneous acceleration" unless otherwise specified.

The definition of acceleration just given applies to motion along a path of any shape, straight or curved.   When a body moves in a curved path the *direction* of its velocity changes, and this change in direction also gives rise to an acceleration, as will be explained in Chap. 9.

4-7 Rectilinear motion with constant acceleration.   The simplest kind of accelerated motion is one in which the acceleration is constant, that is, the velocity changes at the same rate throughout the motion.   The *velocity*, of course, is not constant in accelerated motion, and to state that the acceleration is constant simply means that the velocity increases (or decreases) by the same amount in each unit of time.

Now the average value of a quantity that does not change is simply the constant value of the quantity. Hence in motion with constant acceleration the average acceleration $\bar{a}$ can be replaced by the constant acceleration a and Eq. (4-7) becomes

$$a = \frac{v - v_0}{t - t_0}.$$ (4-10)

If Eq. (4-10) is solved for v we obtain

$$v = v_0 + a\ (t - t_0).$$ (4-11)

This equation can be interpreted as follows: the quantity a is the rate of change of velocity or the change per unit time. The quantity $(t - t_0)$ is the duration of the time interval in which we are interested. The product of (change in velocity per unit time) and (duration of time interval), or the product $a(t - t_0)$, is simply the total change in velocity. When this is added to the initial velocity, v_0, the sum is the velocity at the end of the interval.

If we start counting time from the instant when the velocity is v_0, then $t_0 = 0$ and

$$\boxed{v = v_0 + at\,.}$$ (4-12)

Having found an expression for the velocity of the body at any time, we next derive an expression for its coordinate at any time. We have shown in Eq. (4-5) that the displacement of a body moving along the X-axis is

$$x = \bar{v}t,$$ (4-5)

where $\bar{v}$ is the average velocity.

If the velocity of a body increases at a constant rate, i.e., if its acceleration is constant, its average velocity during any time interval equals one-half the sum of the velocities at the beginning and at the end of the interval. That is,

$$\bar{v} = \frac{v_0 + v}{2}.$$ (4-13)

Note carefully that Eq. (4-13) is *not* true, in general, except when the acceleration is constant. Substituting Eq. (4-13) in Eq. (4-5), we get

$$x = \frac{v_0 + v}{2} \times t. \qquad (4\text{-}14)$$

Eqs. (4-12) and (4-14) are the fundamental equations applicable to linear motion with constant acceleration. By combining them, we may obtain two more very useful equations. Thus, substituting for v in Eq. (4-14) the value of v given by Eq. (4-12), we have

$$x = \frac{v_0 + v_0 + at}{2} \times t$$

or

$$x = v_0 t + \tfrac{1}{2} a t^2. \qquad (4\text{-}15)$$

Also, substituting for t in Eq. (4-14) the value of t given by Eq. (4-12), we have

$$x = \frac{v_0 + v}{2} \times \frac{v - v_0}{a}$$

$$= \frac{v^2 - v_0^2}{2a},$$

or finally

$$v^2 = v_0^2 + 2ax. \qquad (4\text{-}16)$$

Eqs. (4-12), (4-14), (4-15), and (4-16), which have been boxed in to show their importance, are the usual forms of the equations of motion with constant acceleration. They are special cases where x_0 and t_0 are both zero.

4-8 Freely-falling bodies.   The most common example of motion with (nearly) constant acceleration is that of a body falling toward the earth. In the absence of air resistance it is found that all bodies, regardless of their size or weight, fall with the same acceleration at the same point on the earth's surface, and if the distance covered is not too great the acceleration remains constant throughout the fall.   The effect of air resistance and the decrease in acceleration with altitude will be neglected. This idealized motion is spoken of as "free fall," although the term includes rising as well as falling.

The acceleration of a freely-falling body is called the acceleration due to gravity, or the acceleration of gravity, and is denoted by the letter g.

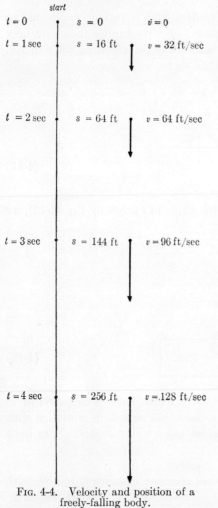

start

$t = 0$ — $s = 0$ — $\dot{v} = 0$

$t = 1\,\text{sec}$ — $s = 16\,\text{ft}$ — $v = 32\,\text{ft/sec}$

$t = 2\,\text{sec}$ — $s = 64\,\text{ft}$ — $v = 64\,\text{ft/sec}$

$t = 3\,\text{sec}$ — $s = 144\,\text{ft}$ — $v = 96\,\text{ft/sec}$

$t = 4\,\text{sec}$ — $s = 256\,\text{ft}$ — $v = 128\,\text{ft/sec}$

Fig. 4-4. Velocity and position of a freely-falling body.

At or near the earth's surface it is approximately $32\,\text{ft/sec}^2$, $9.8\,\text{m/sec}^2$, or $980\,\text{cm/sec}^2$. More precise values, and small variations with latitude and elevation, will be considered later.

Note. The quantity "g" is sometimes referred to simply as "gravity," or as "the force of gravity," both of which are incorrect. "Gravity" is a phenomenon, and the "force of gravity" means the force with which the earth attracts a body, otherwise known as the weight of the body. The letter "g" represents the *acceleration* caused by the force resulting from the phenomenon of gravity.

It is customary, when using Eqs. (4-12), (4-14), (4-15), and (4-16) in an analysis of the motion of a freely-falling body, to replace a by g and to consider the motion as taking place along the Y-axis. Thus these equations become

$$v = v_0 + gt,$$

$$y = \frac{v_0 + v}{2} \times t,$$

$$y = v_0 t + \tfrac{1}{2} gt^2,$$

$$v^2 = v_0^2 + 2gy.$$

Fig. 4-4 shows the velocities and positions of a freely-falling body released from rest ($v_0 = 0$) for the first few seconds of its fall. The positive direction has been chosen downward to avoid negative signs.

Example.   To illustrate the application of the equations of motion with constant acceleration, the following example will be analyzed in detail.   A ball is thrown (nearly) vertically upward from the cornice of a building, leaving the thrower's hand with a velocity of 48 ft/sec and just missing the cornice on the way down.   (Fig. 4-5.)   Find the maximum height reached, the time to reach the highest point, and the position and velocity of the ball 2 sec and 5 sec after leaving the thrower's hand.   Neglect air resistance.

In elementary courses in physics, a problem such as this is usually solved by first finding the maximum height reached and then assuming the ball to be dropped from that point.   This procedure is necessary because the equations of motion taught in such courses do not include the initial velocity but are written simply

$$v = gt,$$

$$h = \tfrac{1}{2}gt^2,$$

$$v^2 = 2gh.$$

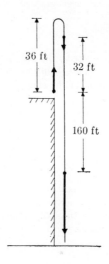

Our equations, which include the initial velocity, are more general and avoid the necessity of breaking up the problem into two parts.   However, it is important that proper attention be paid to the algebraic signs of displacements, velocities, and accelerations.   Let us take the origin at the point where the ball leaves the thrower's hand, and the upward direction as positive.   Then the initial velocity, being upward, is positive, and

$$v_0 = + 48 \text{ ft/sec.}$$

Fig. 4-5.

The acceleration, however, is downward, even though the velocity at the start is in an upward direction.   Hence

$$g = - 32 \text{ ft/sec}^2.$$

To find the maximum height reached, we can make use of the fact that the velocity at that point is zero.   Then from $v = v_0 + gt$ one may find the time to reach the highest point, and from $v^2 = v_0^2 + 2gy$ one may find its position.   Substituting the given data, we obtain

$$0 = 48 + (-32)\, t,$$

$$t = 1.5 \text{ sec,}$$

$$0^2 = (48)^2 + 2\,(-32)\, y,$$

$$y = +36 \text{ ft.}$$

So the ball rises 36 ft above the origin and reaches the highest point in 1.5 sec.

The height can also be found from $y = v_0 t + \frac{1}{2} g t^2$, using for t the computed value of 1.5 sec.

$$y = 48 \times 1.5 + \frac{1}{2} (-32) (1.5)^2$$
$$= +36 \text{ ft}.$$

We next compute the position and velocity 2 sec after the ball is thrown.

$$y = 48 \times 2 + \frac{1}{2} (-32) (2)^2$$
$$= +32 \text{ ft};$$
$$v = 48 + (-32) (2)$$
$$= -16 \text{ ft/sec}.$$

In other words, the ball is 32 ft above its starting point, and is moving down (v is negative) with a velocity of 16 ft/sec.

At 5 sec after the start,

$$y = (48 \times 5) + \frac{1}{2} (-32) (5)^2$$
$$= -160 \text{ ft};$$
$$v = 48 + (-32) (5)$$
$$= -112 \text{ ft/sec}.$$

That is, the ball is now 160 ft below the starting point (y is negative) and is moving down with a velocity of 112 ft/sec. Notice that y does not represent the total space moved over by the ball, or its length of path, but only its distance from the origin or its displacement.

Fig. 4-6 is a "multiflash" photograph of a freely-falling golf ball. This photograph was taken with the aid of the ultra-high-speed stroboscopic light source developed by Dr. Harold E. Edgerton of the Massachusetts Institute of Technology. By means of this source a series of intense flashes of light can be produced. The interval between successive flashes is controllable at will, and the duration of each flash is so short (a few millionths of a second) that there is no blur in the image of even a rapidly moving body. The camera shutter is left open during the entire motion, and as each flash occurs the position of the ball at that instant is recorded on the photographic film.

Included in the photograph are a clock and a scale. The clock hand rotates continuously, requiring two seconds to make one complete revolution. The small divisions around its circumference correspond to 1/100 sec each. Since the position of the clock hand is photographed at each flash, the time interval between flashes is automatically recorded. The divisions on the scale are 1 cm apart.

The equally spaced light flashes subdivide the motion into equal time intervals Δt. The corresponding displacements, Δx, can be read from the photograph, using the centimeter scale. The average velocity between each pair of flashes, $\Delta x / \Delta t$, can therefore be calculated, and since the time interval Δt can be made very small (of the order of a few hundredths of a second), these average velocities are a good approximation to instantaneous velocities. Since the time intervals are all equal, the velocity of the ball between any two flashes is directly proportional to the separation of its corresponding images in the photograph. If the velocity were constant, the images would be equally spaced. The increasing separation of the images during the fall shows that the velocity is continually increasing or the motion is accelerated. By comparing two successive displacements of the ball, the *change* in velocity in the corresponding time interval can be found. Careful measurements, preferably on an enlarged print, show that this change in velocity is the same in each time interval. In other words, the motion is one of *constant* acceleration.

4-9 Velocity components. Relative velocity. Velocity is a vector quantity involving both magnitude and direction. A velocity may therefore be resolved into components, or a number of velocity components combined into a resultant.

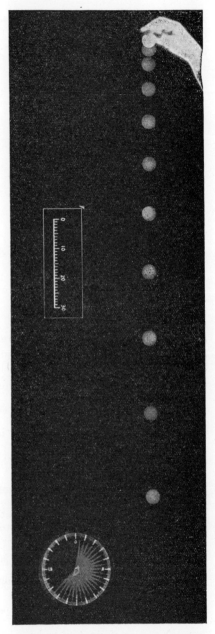

Fig. 4-6. Multiflash photograph (retouched) of a freely-falling golf ball.

As an example of the former process, suppose that a ship is steaming 30° E of N at 20 mi/hr in still water. Its velocity may be represented by the arrow in Fig. 4-7, and one finds by the usual method that its velocity component toward the east is 10 mi/hr, while toward the north it is 17.3 mi/hr.

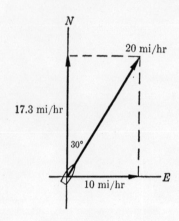

FIG. 4-7. Resolution of a velocity vector into components.

Velocity, like position, can only be specified relative to some reference frame or set of axes; the axes themselves may or may not be in motion. Ordinarily, velocities are specified relative to axes fixed with respect to the earth and considered to be "at rest," although of course they partake of the motion of the earth through space. In what follows, the expression "the velocity of a body" is understood to mean its velocity relative to the earth.

The velocity of one body relative to another when the second is in motion (relative to the earth) *is the vector difference between the velocities of the bodies* (relative to the earth). Specifically, if the bodies are designated by A and B, and their velocities (relative to the earth) by v_A and v_B, the velocity of A relative to B is

$$v_{AB} = v_A - v_B \text{ (vector difference)} \qquad (4\text{-}17)$$

and the velocity of B relative to A is

$$v_{BA} = v_B - v_A \text{ (vector difference).}$$

Example. Automobile A, traveling at 30 mi/hr on a straight level road, is ahead of automobile B traveling in the same direction at 20 mi/hr. What is the velocity of A relative to B and the velocity of B relative to A?

Since both vectors are in the same straight line, the magnitude of their vector difference equals their arithmetic difference. The velocity of A relative to B is

$$v_{AB} = v_A - v_B = 30 - 20 = +10 \text{ mi/hr}$$

and the operator of car B sees car A pulling away from him at the rate of 10 mi/hr.

The velocity of B relative to A is

$$v_{BA} = v_B - v_A = 20 - 30 = -10 \text{ mi/hr}$$

and the operator of car A (if he looks back) sees car B dropping behind him (v_{BA} is negative) at 10 mi/hr.

Eq. (4-17) may be written

$$v_A = v_B + v_{AB} \text{ (vector sum)}.$$

That is, the velocity of body A (relative to the earth) is the vector sum of the velocity of B (relative to the earth) and the velocity of A relative to B. In general, then, when one body is in motion relative to a second, *the velocity of the first is the vector sum of the velocity of the second and the velocity of the first relative to the second.*

Examples. (1) The compass of a plane indicates that it is headed due north, and its airspeed indicator shows that it is moving through the air at 120 mi/hr. If there is a wind of 50 mi/hr blowing from west to east, what is the velocity of the plane relative to the earth?

The velocity of the air is 50 mi/hr, due east. The velocity of the plane *relative to the air* is 120 mi/hr, due north. The velocity of the plane is the vector sum of these velocities, and from the construction in Fig. 4-8 it is 130 mi/hr, 22.5° E of N. The two velocities of 120 mi/hr and 50 mi/hr can be considered the components of the actual velocity of the plane.

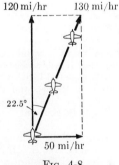

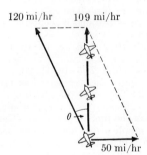

FIG. 4-8.   FIG. 4-9.

(2) In what direction should the pilot of the plane set his course in order to travel due north? What will then be his velocity relative to the earth?

The course set by the pilot is the direction in which the plane would actually travel in still air. It is thus in the direction of the velocity of the plane relative to the air. The resultant velocity must be due north. These velocities are related as in Fig. 4-9, from which we find the angle θ to be 24.5° W of N, and the resultant velocity to be 109 mi/hr, due north.

Problems — Chapter 4

4-1. The 2-mile record on an indoor track is 8 min, 51 sec. To what average velocity does this correspond in (a) mi/sec? (b) mi/hr? (c) cm/sec? (d) ft/sec?

4-2. A body moves along a straight line, its distance from the origin at any instant being given by the equation $x = 8t - 3t^2$, where x is in centimeters and t is in seconds. (a) Find the average velocity of the body in the interval from $t = 0$ to $t = 1$ sec, and in the interval from $t = 0$ to $t = 4$ sec. (b) Find the expression for the average velocity in the interval from t to $t + \Delta t$. (c) What is the limiting value of this expression as Δt approaches zero? (d) Find the time or times at which the body is at rest. (e) Find the expression for the acceleration at any time.

4-3. An automobile is provided with a speedometer calibrated to read ft/sec rather than mi/hr. The following series of speedometer readings was obtained during a start.

Time (sec) 0 2 4 6 8 10 12 14 16
Velocity
(ft/sec) 0 0 2 5 10 15 20 22 22

(a) Compute the average acceleration during each 2-sec interval. Is the acceleration constant? Is it constant during any part of the time? (b) Make a velocity-time graph of the data above, using scales of 1 in = 2 sec horizontally, and 1 in = 5 ft/sec vertically. Draw a smooth curve through the plotted points. What distance is represented by 1 sq in? What is the displacement in the first 8 sec? In the entire 16 sec? What is the acceleration when $t = 8$ sec? When $t = 13$ sec? When $t = 15$ sec?

4-4. The graph in Fig. 4-10 shows the velocity of a body plotted as a function of time.
(a) What is the instantaneous acceleration at $t = 3$ sec?
(b) What is the instantaneous acceleration at $t = 7$ sec?
(c) What is the instantaneous acceleration at $t = 11$ sec?

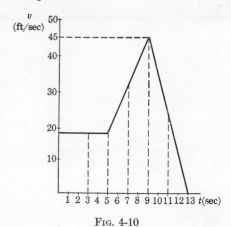

Fig. 4-10

(d) How far does the body go in the first 5 sec?
(e) How far does the body go in the first 9 sec?
(f) How far does the body go in the first 13 sec?

4-5. The makers of a certain automobile advertise that it will accelerate from 15 to 50 mi/hr in high in 13 sec. Compute the acceleration in ft/sec², and the distance the car travels in this time, assuming the acceleration to be constant.

4-6. An airplane taking off from a landing field has a run of 1200 ft. If it starts from rest, moves with constant acceleration, and makes the run in 30 sec, with what velocity in ft/sec did it take off?

4-7. A subway train starts from rest at a station and accelerates at a rate of 4 ft/sec² for 10 sec. It then runs at constant speed for 30 sec, and decelerates at 8 ft/sec² until it stops at the next station. Find the *total* distance covered.

4-8. A sled starts from rest at the top of a hill and slides down with a constant acceleration. The sled is 140 ft from the top of the hill 2 sec after passing a point which is 92 ft from the top. Four seconds after passing the 92-ft point it is 198 ft from the top, and 6 seconds after passing the point it is 266 ft from the top.

(a) What is the average velocity of the sled during each of the 2-second intervals after passing the 92-ft point?

(b) What is the acceleration of the sled?

(c) What was the velocity of the sled when it passed the 92-ft point?

(d) How long did it take to go from the top to the 92-ft point?

(e) How far did the sled go during the first second after passing the 92-ft point?

(f) How long does it take the sled to go from the 92-ft point to the midpoint between the 92-ft mark and the 140-ft one?

(g) What is the velocity of the sled as it passes the midpoint in part (f)?

4-9. The speed of an automobile going north is reduced from 45 to 30 mi/hr in a distance of 264 ft. Find

(a) the magnitude and direction of the acceleration.

(b) the time of application of the brakes,

(c) the distance in which the car can be brought to rest from 30 mi/hr, assuming the acceleration of part (a).

4-10. An automobile and a truck start from rest at the same instant, with the automobile initially at some distance behind the truck. The truck has a constant acceleration of 4 ft/sec², and the automobile an acceleration of 6 ft/sec². The automobile overtakes the truck after the truck has moved 150 ft. (a) How long does it take the auto to overtake the truck? (b) How far was the auto behind the truck initially? (c) What is the velocity of each when they are abreast?

4-11. A juggler performs in a room whose ceiling is 9 ft above the level of his hands. He throws a ball vertically upward so that it just reaches the ceiling. (a) With what initial velocity does he throw the ball? (b) How many seconds are required for the ball to reach the ceiling?

He throws a second ball upward with the same initial velocity, at the instant that the first ball is at the ceiling. (c) How long after the second ball is thrown do the two balls pass each other?

(d) When the balls pass each other, how far are they above the juggler's hands?

4-12. An object is thrown vertically upward. It has a speed of 32 ft/sec when it has reached one-half its maximum height. (a) How high does it rise? (b) What is its velocity and acceleration 1 sec after it is thrown? (c) 3 sec after? (d) What is the average velocity during the first half-sec?

4-13. A student determined to test the law of gravity for himself walks off a skyscraper 900 ft high, stop-watch in hand, and starts his free fall (zero initial velocity). Five seconds later, Superman arrives at the scene and dives off the roof to save the student. (a) What must Superman's initial velocity be in order that he catch the student just before the ground is reached? (b) What must be the height of the skyscraper so that even Superman can't save him? (Assume that Superman's acceleration is that of any freely falling body.)

4-14. A ball is thrown nearly vertically upward from a point near the cornice of a tall building. It just misses the cornice on the way down, and passes a point 160 ft below its starting point 5 sec after it leaves the thrower's hand. (a) What was the initial velocity of the ball? (b) How high did it rise above its starting point? (c) What was the magnitude of its velocity as it passed a point 64 ft below the starting point?

4-15. A ball is thrown vertically upward from the ground and a student gazing out of the window sees it moving upward past him at 16 ft/sec. The window is 32 ft above the ground. (a) How high does the ball go above the ground? (b) How long does it take to go from a height of 32 ft to its highest point? (c) Find its velocity and acceleration ½ sec after it left the ground, and 2 sec after it left the ground.

4-16. A ball is thrown vertically upward from the ground with a velocity of 80 ft/sec. (a) How long will it take to rise to its highest point? (b) How high does the ball rise? (c) How long after projection will the ball have a velocity of 16 ft/sec upward? of 16 ft/sec downward? (d) Calculate the acceleration of the ball from the data and results in part (c). (e) When is the displacement of the ball zero? (f) When is the magnitude of the ball's velocity equal to half of its velocity of projection? (g) When is the magnitude of the ball's displacement equal to half of the greatest height to which it rises? (h) What is the magnitude and direction of the acceleration while the ball is moving upward? while moving downward? when at the highest point?

4-17. The distance of a body from a point A is given by the equation $x = 20t + 8t^2 - t^3$, where x is in feet and t in seconds. (a) Write the equation in modified form so as to give the distance x_1 between the body and a point B, 10 ft in the negative direction from A. (b) Write another equation which gives the distance x_2 from the body to a moving point C. At $t = 0$, the point C is at the same position as point A. Point C has a velocity of $+10$ ft/sec.

4-18. Two piers A and B are located on a river, one mile apart. Two men must make round trips from pier A to pier B and return. One man is to row a boat at a velocity of 4 mi/hr relative to the water, and the other man is to walk on the shore at a velocity of 4 mi/hr. The velocity of the river is 2 mi/hr in the direction from A to B. How long does it take each man to make the round trip?

4-19. A ball rolling on an inclined plane moves with a constant acceleration. One ball is released from rest at the top of an inclined plane 18 m long and reaches the bottom 3 sec later. At the same instant that the first ball is released a second ball is projected upward along the plane from its bottom with a certain initial velocity. The second ball is to travel part way up the plane, stop, and return to the bottom so that it arrives simultaneously with the first ball. (a) Find the acceleration. (b) What must be the initial velocity of the second ball? (c) How far up the plane will it travel?

4-20. When a train has a speed of 10 mi/hr eastward, raindrops which are falling vertically with respect to the earth make traces on the windows of the train which are inclined 30° to the vertical. (a) What is the horizontal component of a drop's velocity with respect to the earth? with respect to the train? (b) What is the velocity of the raindrop with respect to the earth? with respect to the train?

4-21. An airplane pilot wishes to fly due north. A wind of 60 mi/hr is blowing toward the west. If the flying speed of the plane (its speed in still air) is 180 mi/hr, in what direction should the pilot set his course? What is the speed of the plane over the ground? Illustrate with a vector diagram.

4-22. An airplane pilot sets a compass course due west and maintains an air speed of 120 mi/hr. After flying for one-half hour he finds himself over a town which is 75 mi west and 20 mi south of his starting point. (a) Find the wind velocity, in magnitude and direction (b) If the wind velocity were 60 mi/hr due south, in what direction should the pilot set his course in order to travel due west? Take the same air speed of 120 mi/hr.

CHAPTER 5

NEWTON'S SECOND LAW

5-1 Introduction. In the preceding chapters we have discussed separately the concepts of force and acceleration. We have made use, in statics, of Newton's first law, which states that when the resultant force on a body is zero, the acceleration of the body is also zero. The next logical step is to ask how a body behaves when the resultant force on it is *not* zero. The answer to this question is contained in Newton's second law, which states, in part, that when the resultant force is not zero, the body moves with accelerated motion. The acceleration, with a given force, depends on a property of the body known as its mass, and before proceeding with the discussion of the second law, we devote the next section to the concept of mass.

This part of mechanics, which includes both the study of motion and the forces that bring about the motion, is called *dynamics*. In its broadest sense, dynamics includes nearly the whole of mechanics. Statics treats of special cases in which the acceleration is zero, and kinematics deals with motion only.

5-2 Mass. The term mass, as used in mechanics, refers to that property of matter which in everyday language is described by the word *inertia*. We know from experience that an object at rest will never start to move of itself—a push or pull must be exerted on it by some other body. In more technical language, an external force is required to accelerate the body, and we say the force is needed because the body has inertia.

It is also a familiar fact that a force is required to slow down or stop a body which is already in motion, and that a sidewise force must be exerted on a moving body to deviate it from a straight line. In these instances also, we say the force is necessary because the body possesses inertia.

It will be seen that the processes above (i.e., speeding up, slowing down, or changing direction) involve a change in either the magnitude or the direction of the velocity of the body. In other words, in every case the body is accelerated. We may therefore say: inertia is that property of matter because of which a force must be exerted on a body in order to accelerate it.

To assign a numerical value to the inertia of any given body, we choose as a standard some one body whose inertia is arbitrarily taken as unity, and state the inertia of all other bodies in terms of this standard. The inertia of a body, when stated in this quantitative way, is called its *mass*. *Mass is a quantitative measure of inertia.*

FIG. 5-1. Kilogram No. 20, the national standard of mass.

The mass of a body is an invariant property of the body, independent of its velocity[1], acceleration, position on the earth's surface or height above the earth's surface. In the latter two respects it differs from the weight of the body, which varies with position and elevation.

The standard of mass in both the mks and cgs systems is a platinum-iridium cylinder called the *standard kilogram.* The original standard is kept in Sèvres, France, and one or more accurate duplicates are possessed by most other countries. They are not all identical in mass with the original standard, but this is not of importance, since their masses relative to the standard are accurately known.

The unit of mass in the mks system is the mass of the standard kilogram. The unit of mass in the cgs system is 1/1000 as great as the mass of the standard kilogram and is called one gram.

There is no mass standard in the English gravitational system of units. That is, government laboratories do not preserve in their vaults a certain piece of matter whose mass is equal to the unit mass. The English system is based on standards of *force*, length, and time, and the unit of mass is defined in terms of these standards, as will be explained shortly.

The pound of force was defined on page 2 as the force of the earth's gravitational attraction at sea level and 45° latitude on a specified body called the standard pound. To avoid the unnecessary duplication in maintaining two such standard bodies, the standard kilogram and the standard pound, the latter is now *defined* in terms of the standard kilogram by the relation that its mass shall equal 0.4535924277 kilograms.

---

[1] Except that at very high velocities, approaching the velocity of light, relativity effects result in an appreciable increase in mass.

5-3 Newton's second law. The observations described at the beginning of the preceding section point to a connection between force, mass, and acceleration. To obtain the quantitative relation between them, consider the following series of (idealized) experiments.

(1) A block of any arbitrary mass is placed on a level, frictionless surface and accelerated along the surface by a horizontal force exerted on it by a spring balance. For concreteness, suppose the balance has been calibrated in pounds as described on page 3. With the calibrated balance we can exert forces of 1, 2, 3, etc., lb on the block, and measure with a scale and stop watch the corresponding accelerations. The results of this series of experiments will show that with a constant mass, the acceleration is directly proportional to the accelerating force and is in the same direction as the force.

$$a \propto F \text{ (when } m \text{ is constant)}. \qquad (5-1)$$

(2) For the second series of experiments, we may start with our standard kilogram and prepare a number of duplicates of it, testing them for equality of mass by observing that all accelerate at the same rate when acted on by the same force. Combinations of these will give us masses of 2 kgm, 3 kgm, etc.

Now let us apply in successive experiments the same force (any force will do) to masses of 1 kgm, 2 kgm, 3 kgm, etc., and measure the accelerations. This series of experiments leads to the result that with a constant force, the acceleration is inversely proportional to the mass.

$$a \propto \frac{1}{m} \text{ (when } F \text{ is constant)}. \quad (5-2)$$

The results of both series of experiments may now be expressed by the single relation

$$a \propto \frac{F}{m} . \qquad (5-3)$$

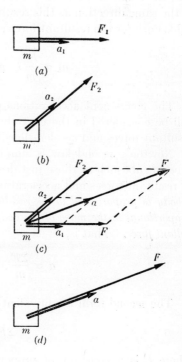

FIG. 5-2. The acceleration of a body is proportional to the resultant force exerted on the body and is in the direction of the resultant force.

This obviously reduces to Eq. (5-1) or Eq. (5-2) when m **or** F is constant.

(3) Let us next experiment with more than one force acting on the body. Suppose we have found that the force F_1, acting alone, produces an acceleration a_1 in the same direction as F_1 as in Fig. 5-2 (a). Similarly, force F_2 produces an acceleration a_2 as in Fig. 5-2 (b). If we now apply forces F_1 and F_2 simultaneously as in Fig. 5-2 (c), we find that the observed acceleration a is the same as the vector sum of the accelerations a_1 and a_2, and furthermore that the same acceleration results if instead of applying F_1 and F_2 simultaneously, we apply a single force F equal to the vector sum of F_1 and F_2 as in Fig. 5-2 (d).

These experiments show, first, that when a number of forces are exerted on a body at the same time, each force acts independently of the others and produces the same acceleration as if it alone were present, and, second, that the resultant acceleration is proportional to the resultant force and is in the same direction as this resultant. Hence, the proportion, Eq. (5-3), holds both for the resultant force and for each of its components. That is,

$$a_1 \propto \frac{F_1}{m}, \quad a_2 \propto \frac{F_2}{m}, \quad a \propto \frac{F}{m}.$$

The component accelerations produced by the components of a force will be considered in the next chapter. For the moment we shall discuss resultant forces and accelerations only.

Newton's second law is simply a formal statement of the results of experiments such as those just described. If we restrict it for the present to resultant forces and accelerations, it may be stated: *The acceleration of a body is proportional to the resultant force exerted on the body, is inversely proportional to the mass of the body, and is in the same direction as the resultant force.* That is,

$$a \propto \frac{\Sigma F}{m}, \quad \text{or} \quad \Sigma F \propto ma.$$

The second form is equivalent to

$$\Sigma F = kma, \tag{5-4}$$

where k is a constant of proportionality. The magnitude of the proportionality constant will depend on the units in which force, mass, and acceleration are expressed. For example, it is found by experiment that a resultant force of one pound imparts an acceleration of 14.6 ft/sec^2 to a mass of one kilogram.   Then if these units are used

$$k = \frac{\Sigma F}{ma} = \frac{1 \text{ lb}}{1 \text{ kgm} \times 14.6 \text{ ft/sec}^2} = 0.0685 \frac{\text{lb-sec}^2}{\text{kgm-ft}}.$$

It is obviously inconvenient to have to remember all of the values of "k" that would be required to take care of all possible combinations of units, but since the value of "k" is determined solely by the units chosen for F, m, and a, why not use a combination that will give "k" some simple, easily remembered value?   The simplest choice, of course, is to make $k = 1$, and the so-called *systems* of mechanical units are all set up with this end in view.   It may well happen, as indeed it does, that some of the required units are unfamiliar ones but the advantage of making $k=1$ outweighs the disadvantage of defining new units.

If we use a system of units in which $k = 1$, Eq. (5-4) reduces to

$$\Sigma F = ma. \qquad\qquad (5\text{-}5)$$

This equation is usually considered to be the mathematical formulation of Newton's second law.   It is probably the most important equation in mechanics.   Note carefully that it is a *vector* equation; that is, the resultant acceleration a is in the same direction as the resultant force ΣF. The *algebraic* relation $\Sigma F = ma$ alone is not a complete statement of the law.

We can see from Eq. (5-5) the physical conditions that must be fulfilled for motion with constant acceleration; namely, if a is constant, then F must be constant also.   In other words, motion with constant acceleration is motion under the action of a constant force.   If the force varies, the acceleration varies in direct proportion, since the mass m is constant.

It is also evident from Eq. (5-5) that if the resultant force on a body is zero, the acceleration of the body is zero and its velocity is constant. Hence, if the body is in motion, it continues to move with no change in the magnitude or direction of its velocity; if at rest, it remains at rest (its velocity is then constant and equal to zero).   But these are evidently the conditions to which Newton's *first* law applies, and we see that the first law is merely a special case of the second when ΣF and a are both zero. There are thus only two independent laws of Newton, the second and the third.

5-4 Systems of units. If we adopt $\Sigma F = ma$ as the expression of Newton's second law, it follows that when $m = 1$ unit of mass and $a = 1$ unit of acceleration, then $\Sigma F = 1$ unit of force. In other words, the units of force, mass, and acceleration must be so chosen that *unit force imparts unit acceleration to unit mass.* Obviously we are not at liberty to choose all three units arbitrarily. We may, however, choose any two of them and use Eq. (5-5) to fix the magnitude of the third.

In the meter-kilogram-second system of units, the kilogram fixes the unit of mass, and the meter and second together fix the unit of acceleration. The unit of force in this system must then be of such magnitude that it imparts an acceleration of one meter per second, per second, to a mass of one kilogram. This force is called *one newton.*

A newton is that force which imparts to a mass of one kilogram an acceleration of one meter per second, per second.

The newton is equal to a force of 0.224 lb.

In the centimeter-gram-second system, the unit of mass is the gram, and the unit of acceleration is the centimeter per second, per second. The unit force in this system must be of such magnitude that it imparts an acceleration of one centimeter per second, per second, to a mass of one gram. This force is called *one dyne.*

A dyne is that force which imparts to a mass of one gram an acceleration of one centimeter per second, per second.

Since 1 kgm = 1000 gm and 1 meter = 100 cm, it follows that 1 newton = 100,000 dynes = 10^5 dynes. One dyne is a force of 2.24×10^{-6} lb.

We have already defined the English gravitational unit of force, the pound; and of acceleration, the foot per second, per second. As in the other systems, we wish to have unit force impart unit acceleration to unit mass. The unit mass in this system must then be of such magnitude that when acted on by a force of one pound, its acceleration is one foot per second, per second. This mass is called *one slug.*

A slug is that mass to which a force of one pound imparts an acceleration of one foot per second, per second.

The slug is equal to 14.6 kilograms.

The newton, dyne, and slug are called *derived* units, as distinguished from the *fundamental* units, the pound force and the kilogram mass.

As a summary, then, when Newton's second law is written in the form $\Sigma F = ma$ (with $k = 1$), the following combinations of units may be used:

$$\Sigma F \text{ (in newtons)} = m \text{ (in kgm)} \quad \times a \text{ (in m/sec}^2),$$
$$\Sigma F \text{ (in dynes)} \quad = m \text{ (in grams)} \times a \text{ (in cm/sec}^2),$$
$$\Sigma F \text{ (in pounds)} \quad = m \text{ (in slugs)} \times a \text{ (in ft/sec}^2).$$

5-5 Weight and mass. Every body in the universe exerts a force of gravitational attraction on every other body. The earth attracts the book and pencil lying on your desk; each of these attracts the other; the earth attracts the moon; the sun attracts the earth and the other planets of the solar system as well as the most distant stars; and each of these bodies pulls back on each of the others which attract it, with an equal and opposite force. This phenomenon of universal gravitational attraction will be considered in more detail in Sec. 5-9. At present we are concerned with one aspect of it only, namely, the force of gravitational attraction between the earth and bodies on or near its surface. *The force of gravitational attraction which the earth exerts on a body is called the* **weight** *of the body.*

Thus the statement that a man weighs 160 lb is equivalent to stating that he is attracted by the earth with a force of 160 lb. Since the weight of a body is a force, it must be expressed in force units, that is, in *pounds* in the English system, and in *newtons* or *dynes* in the mks or cgs systems.

The mass of a body, although it is not the same thing as the body's weight, is directly proportional to the weight. To show this, let us apply Newton's second law to any freely-falling body of mass m. The resultant force on the body is its weight w, its acceleration is g, and the equation $\Sigma F = ma$ becomes $w = mg$. In other words, the weight of a body, when expressed in terms of the force unit of any system, is numerically equal to the mass of the body, in the mass unit of that system, multiplied by the corresponding value of the acceleration of gravity.

$$w = mg, \quad m = \frac{w}{g}. \tag{5-7}$$

The reader undoubtedly knows that the force of gravitational attraction between two bodies decreases as the distance between them increases. Therefore, the weight of a body, or the force of gravitational attraction between the body and the earth, is not an invariant property of the body but diminishes as the elevation of the body is increased, because of the increased distance to the earth's center. Since the mass of a body is an invariant property of the body, entirely independent of its position, it follows from Eq. (5-7) that the acceleration of gravity varies in direct proportion to the variation in a body's weight.   That is, the reason that g is smaller at high altitudes than at low is that a body weighs less at high altitudes and therefore accelerates more slowly in free fall.

Examples: (1) The acceleration of gravity at St. Michael, Alaska, is 32.221 ft/sec^2. At Panama, in the Canal Zone, it is 32.094 ft/sec^2.   What is the weight in pounds, at each of these points, of a body whose mass is exactly 3 slugs?
Ans.: 96.663 lb; 96.282 lb.

(2) What is the mass, in slugs, of a man whose weight is 160 lb at a point where $g = 32.0$ ft/sec^2?   What would be his weight at a point where $g = 32.2$ ft/sec^2?
Ans.: 5 slugs, 161 lb.

(3) Compute your own mass in slugs.   Take $g = 32.2$ ft/sec^2.

(4) What is the mass of a body which, hanging at rest from a cord, produces a tension of 10^6 dynes in the cord?   What is the weight of the body, in cgs and mks units?   Let $g = 980$ cm/sec^2.
Ans.: 1020 gm, 10^6 dynes, 10 newtons.

(5) 454 grams weigh one pound.   Compute your own mass in kilograms and your own weight in newtons.

(6) What is the mass, in grams, of a body which weighs exactly one dyne at a point where $g = 980$ cm/sec^2?   What is the mass, in kilograms, of a body which weighs exactly one newton at this point?   What is the mass, in slugs, of a body whose weight is one pound at a point where $g = 32$ ft/sec^2?
Ans.: 1/980 gm (about 1 milligram); 1/9.8 kgm (about one-tenth of a kilogram or 100 gm); $\frac{1}{32}$ slug.

(Unless otherwise stated, the value of g in the following examples will be taken as 32 ft/sec^2, 9.8 m/sec^2 or 980 cm/sec^2.)

(7) What resultant force is necessary to accelerate a block weighing 48 lb at the rate of 6 ft/sec^2?
It is first necessary to find the mass of the block in slugs.   Since one slug weighs 32 lb, a body weighing 48 lb has a mass of 1.5 slugs.   Then from Newton's second law

$$\Sigma F = ma = 1.5 \times 6 = 9 \text{ lb.}$$

(8) What resultant force is necessary to accelerate a block whose mass is 48 gm at the rate of 6 cm/sec²?

Since the mass of the block is given directly,

$$\Sigma F = ma = 48 \times 6 = 288 \text{ dynes.}$$

(9) A 10-kgm block rests on a horizontal surface. What constant horizontal force is required to give it a velocity of 4 m/sec in 2 sec, starting from rest, if the friction force between block and surface is constant and equal to 5 newtons?

Since the forces are constant, the block moves with constant acceleration, and since the velocity increases from zero to 4 m/sec in 2 sec, the acceleration is

$$a = \frac{v - v_0}{t} = \frac{4}{2} = 2 \text{ m/sec}^2.$$

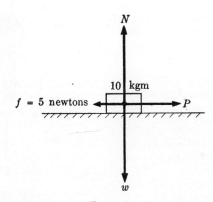

Fig. 5-3.

Let *P*, Fig. 5-3, represent the required horizontal force. The *resultant* force ΣF exerted on the block is then

$$\Sigma F = P - f = P - 5.$$

Finally, since resultant force equals mass times acceleration,

$$\Sigma F = ma$$

$$P - 5 = 10 \times 2 = 20 \text{ newtons}$$

$$P = 20 + 5 = 25 \text{ newtons.}$$

(10) An elevator weighing 8 tons is given an upward acceleration of 4 ft/sec². Find the tension in the supporting cable.

Let T, Fig. 5-4, represent the tension in pounds. The resultant force F acting on the elevator is $T - w = T - 16,000$ lb. The mass of the elevator is 500 slugs. Hence,

$$\Sigma F = ma$$
$$T - 16,000 = 500 \times 4$$
$$T = 18,000 \text{ lb or 9 tons.}$$

(11) With what force will the elevator push upward on a 160-lb passenger, while the elevator is accelerating at the above rate?

The passenger is represented schematically in Fig. 5-5. The forces on him are the upward push P of the elevator floor, and his weight of 160 lb acting down. The resultant force is therefore $P - w = P - 160$ lb. Hence,

$$\Sigma F = ma$$
$$P - 160 = 5 \times 4$$
$$P = 180 \text{ lb.}$$

According to Newton's third law the passenger exerts an equal and opposite force on the elevator floor. Hence, while the elevator is accelerating upward at 4 ft/sec², a 160-lb passenger presses down on the floor with a force of 180 lb.

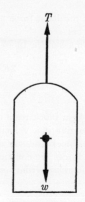

Fig. 5-4. The resultant force is $T\text{-}w$.

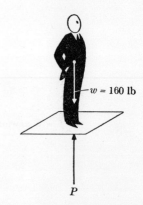

$w = 160$ lb

P

Fig. 5-5. The resultant force is $P\text{-}w$.

(12) The driver of an automobile, traveling at 30 mi/hr on a level road, applies the brakes and comes to rest in a distance of 100 ft. If the weight of car and load is 1600 lb, and the acceleration is constant, find the friction force between tires and road.

The mass of the automobile is 50 slugs. Its acceleration may be found from

$$v^2 = v_0{}^2 + 2ax$$
$$0 = (44)^2 + 2a\,(100)$$
$$a = -9.68 \text{ ft/sec}^2.$$

The magnitude of the braking force P is therefore

$$P = ma = 50 \times (-9.68) = -484 \text{ lb.}$$

The minus sign means that the force is toward the left if the car was originally moving toward the right.

(13) With what acceleration will a block slide down a frictionless plane, inclined at an angle θ with the horizontal?

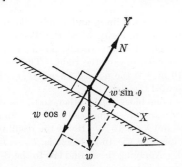

FIG. 5-6. N and w are the forces exerted on the block. The resultant force is $w \sin \theta$.

The forces acting on the block are its weight and the normal force exerted by the plane. (Fig. 5-6.) Neither the weight nor the mass of the block is given as part of the data. Hence a letter must be used to represent one or the other. Let the weight be called w. Take axes parallel and perpendicular to the surface of the plane and resolve w into its components. Since the block remains on the plane, the Y-components are in equilibrium and $N = w \cos \theta$. The only remaining force is then $w \sin \theta$, which is therefore the resultant force exerted on the block. In terms of its weight w, the mass of the block is $m = w/g$. Hence,

$$\Sigma F = ma$$
$$w \sin \theta = \frac{w}{g} a$$
$$a = g \sin \theta.$$

Since the weight does not appear in the final result, it follows that any block, regardless of its weight, will slide down a frictionless inclined plane of slope angle θ with an acceleration $g \sin \theta$.

The following examples illustrate situations in which more than one body is involved. A similar example has been considered earlier (see page 21). It will be emphasized again that in such instances it is necessary to consider each part of the system separately, and to show in separate force diagrams *all* of the forces exerted *on* that part of the system under consideration. This procedure is spoken of as *isolating* one part of the system at a time. The complete group of forces acting *on* the isolated part of the system is called a *set of forces*. It is extremely important to understand this process of isolating a part of a system, and to be able to recognize the set of forces acting on it.

(14) A 16-lb and an 8-lb block (Fig. 5-7) on a horizontal frictionless surface, are connected by cord A and are pulled along the surface with a uniform acceleration of 4 ft/sec² by a second cord B. Show in a diagram the set of forces acting on each body and find the tension in each cord.

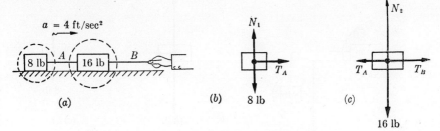

FIG. 5-7.

Each body is to be isolated as indicated by the dotted lines, and a force diagram drawn for each. Let T_A and T_B represent the tensions in cords A and B. The set of forces acting on the 8-lb block consists of (a) its weight of 8 lb, vertically down; (b) the normal push of the surface on it, N_1; (c) the tension T_A toward the right. The set of forces on the 16-lb block are (a) its weight of 16 lb; (b) the normal force N_2; (c) the tension T_A toward the left; (d) the tension T_B toward the right.

Cord A simply serves to transmit a force from one block to the other, so the forces labelled T_A constitute an action-and-reaction pair and are numerically equal. Since neither block has a vertical acceleration, $N_1 = 8$ lb and $N_2 = 16$ lb. Hence the resultant force on the 8-lb block is T_A, and the resultant force on the 16-lb block is $T_B - T_A$. The acceleration of each block is 4 ft/sec² (given). Applying the second law to the 8-lb block, we have

$$T_A = \frac{8}{32} \times 4. \tag{5-8}$$

Applying the second law to the 16-lb block gives

$$T_B - T_A = \frac{16}{32} \times 4. \tag{5-9}$$

Hence

$$T_A = 1 \text{ lb}, \; T_B = 3 \text{ lb}.$$

Notice carefully that although the hand exerts a pull of 3 lb on the system through cord B, this pull is *not* transmitted as a 3-lb force to the 8-lb block. It is cord A which pulls on the 8-lb block, and the tension in cord A is only one pound.

If the tension in cord B only is desired, the two blocks may be considered together. Their combined mass is $\frac{3}{4}$ slug, and the resultant force exerted *on the combination* is simply the tension in cord B. Therefore

$$T_B = \tfrac{3}{4} \times 4 = 3 \text{ lb.} \tag{5-10}$$

If Eqs. (5-8) and (5-9) are added, one obtains

$$T_B = \left(\frac{8}{32} + \frac{16}{32} \right) \times 4 = 3 \text{ lb,}$$

which is the same as Eq. (5-10). That is, the algebraic equation obtained by adding the equations for the isolated parts of a system will always be the same as that secured by considering the system as a whole.

(15) Suppose the 8-lb block hangs vertically as in Fig. 5-8. Neglect all friction forces and the inertia of the pulley. Find the acceleration and the tension in the cord.

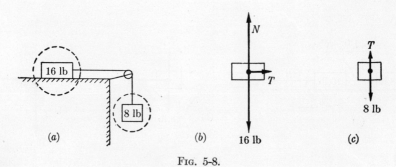

Fig. 5-8.

Isolate as indicated by the dotted lines. The only effect of the pulley is to change the direction of the cord, which pulls with the same force, T, on each block. The resultant force on the block on the table is T lb. The resultant force on the hanging block is $8 - T$ lb. Hence,

$$T = \frac{16}{32} \times a, \quad 8 - T = \frac{8}{32} \times a,$$

and

$$a = 10\tfrac{2}{3} \text{ ft/sec}^2, \quad T = 5\tfrac{1}{3} \text{ lb}.$$

Notice carefully that although the earth pulls on the hanging block with a force of 8 lb, this force is not transmitted to the 16-lb block. The force on the latter is the tension in the connecting cord, and this must be less than 8 lb; otherwise the 8-lb block would not accelerate downward.

5-6 D'Alembert's principle. Newton's second law,

$$\Sigma F = ma,$$

can be written

$$\Sigma F - ma = 0. \tag{5-11}$$

It was pointed out by D'Alembert that this form of the equation could be interpreted as follows: Suppose that in addition to the actual forces exerted on a body there was also exerted a *fictitious* force, equal in magnitude but opposite in sense, to the product ma; in other words, a fictitious force $-ma$. This force is sometimes called an "inertial force" or an "inertial reaction." Then, since ΣF represents the resultant of the *actual* external forces, $\Sigma F - ma$ represents the resultant of *all* the forces including the fictitious force $-ma$. Eq. (5-11) then states that the resultant force on the body is zero. Hence the problem reduces to an equilibrium problem and can be treated by the methods of statics. That is, every body, whether accelerated or not, can be considered in equilibrium under the combined effect of the actual forces exerted on it, together with a fictitious force equal in magnitude to ma but oppositely directed. This is D'Alembert's principle.

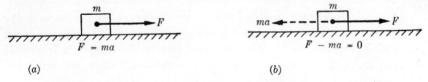

Fig. 5-9. (a), the Newtonian viewpoint; (b), the D'Alembert viewpoint.

The Newtonian and the D'Alembert points of view are illustrated in Fig. 5-9, which represents a body of mass m, pulled to the right on a level, frictionless surface by an external force F. The Newtonian viewpoint, in Fig. 5-9 (a), is that the resultant force is the force F, and this resultant force equals the product of mass and acceleration. The D'Alembert viewpoint, in Fig. 5-9 (b), is that the resultant force is $F - ma$ and is equal to zero.

Note that if D'Alembert's principle is used, one must abandon or modify the usual statement of Newton's second law. That is, it is not true that the resultant force (in the D'Alembert sense) equals the product of mass and acceleration, since the resultant force (in the D'Alembert sense) is always zero, even when a body is accelerated.

Considered merely as a technique for solving problems, there is little to choose between the viewpoints of Newton and D'Alembert, since both lead to the same algebraic equations, but for the purpose of understanding the principles of dynamics, the Newtonian method is much to be preferred and we shall make no use of fictitious D'Alembert forces in this book.

It should be stated for completeness that there is, in fact, more to D'Alembert's principle than the mere addition of a fictitious force, $- ma$, to the actual set of forces on a body. If the observer's reference system moves with the same acceleration as the body, the body has no acceleration relative to the observer. The observer (who knows about Newton's second law) therefore reasons that since the acceleration of the body (as far as he can tell) is zero, the resultant force on the body must be zero. He accordingly concludes that in addition to the "real" forces whose resultant is F, another force, $- ma$, is acting on the body to preserve equilibrium. For further analysis of the equations of motion in accelerated systems, the reader is referred to a more advanced text on Mechanics.

5-7 Density. The density of a homogeneous material is defined as its mass per unit volume. Densities are therefore expressed in grams per cubic centimeter, kilograms per cubic meter, or slugs per cubic foot. We shall represent density by the greek letter ρ (rho).

$$\rho = \frac{m}{V}, \quad m = \rho V. \qquad (5\text{-}12)$$

In engineering work in this country, and in everyday life as well, the term density is used for the *weight* per unit volume, the common unit being the pound per cubic foot. This quantity may be distinguished from that defined above by calling it the "weight-density." For example, the weight-density of water is 62.5 lb per cubic foot; its density is $\dfrac{62.5}{32.2} = 1.94$ slugs per cubic foot.

The *specific gravity* of a material is the ratio of its density to that of water and is therefore a pure number. The specific gravity of lead, for example, is 11.3 in any system of units. The density of lead, in English

TABLE II.—DENSITIES

Material	Density (gm/cm³)
Aluminum.........	2.7
Brass..............	8.6
Copper.............	8.9
Gold...............	19.3
Ice................	0.92
Iron...............	7.8
Lead...............	11.3
Platinum...........	21.4
Silver.............	10.5
Steel..............	7.8
Mercury...........	13.6
Ethyl alcohol.......	0.81
Benzene...........	0.90
Glycerin...........	1.26
Water.............	1.00

units, is $11.3 \times 1.94 = 21.9$ slugs/ft³ and its "weight-density" is $21.9 \times 32.2 = 706$ lb/ft³. In cgs units the density of water[1] is 1 gm/cm³ and the density of lead is 11.3 gm/cm³. In mks units the density of water is 1000 kgm/m³ and the density of lead is 11,300 kgm/m³.

"Specific gravity" is an exceedingly poor term since it has nothing to do with gravity. "Relative density" would describe the concept more precisely.

5-8 The equal-arm analytical balance. The equal-arm analytical balance is a common laboratory instrument for measuring masses with a high degree of precision. Although the process of using a balance is spoken of as "weighing," and the standard masses used with the balance are called a "set of weights," it is actually mass and not weight which the balance measures.

The essential feature of the equal-arm analytical balance is a light, rigid beam on which are firmly mounted three equally spaced agate knife-edges, parallel to one another and perpendicular to the length of the beam. The central knife-edge rests on a polished plane agate plate, supported from the floor of the balance case. The scale pans are hung from two similar plates resting on the knife-edges at the ends of the beam. A vertical pointer, fastened to the beam, swings in front of a scale.

The knife-edges act as practically frictionless pivots. Since the scale pans can swing freely about their supporting knife-edges, the center of

---

[1] Small variations with temperature are neglected here.

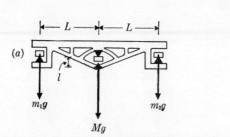
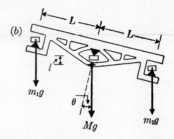

FIG. 5-10. The equal-arm analytical balance.

gravity of pan and weights will always be directly below the knife-edges. The center of gravity of the beam is directly below the central knife-edge when the beam is horizontal. The beam is, therefore, a body in equilibrium under the action of a number of parallel forces.

In using the balance, a body of unknown mass, say m_1, is placed in the left pan, and known masses m_2 are placed in the right. Suppose m_2 is slightly larger than m_1. The forces acting on the balance beam are shown in Fig. 5-10 (a). Mg is the weight of the beam. Since this force has no moment about the central knife-edge, the resultant torque on the beam is

$$(m_2 g) L - (m_1 g) L = (m_2 - m_1) gL$$

in a clockwise direction. This unbalanced torque causes the beam to deflect clockwise as in Fig. 5-10 (b). As it does so, the deflecting torque decreases, becoming

$$(m_2 - m_1) gL \cos \theta,$$

while at the same time the restoring torque $Mgl \sin \theta$ comes into play. A position of equilibrium will eventually be reached, in which these two torques become equal. If θ is the equilibrium angle, then from $\Sigma \tau = 0$,

$$Mgl \sin \theta = (m_2 - m_1) gL \cos \theta,$$

$$\sin \theta / \cos \theta = \tan \theta = \frac{m_2 - m_1}{M} \frac{L}{l}. \tag{5-13}$$

Hence, if the standard mass m_2 is adjusted until $\theta = 0$, it follows that $m_2 = m_1$, and the unknown mass is equal to the standard mass.

The most sensitive balance is one which deflects through the largest angle θ for a given difference between m_1 and m_2. But if θ is to be large, then from Eq. (5-13), L should be large and M and l should be small. In other words, by using a long light beam, with its center of gravity only a short distance below the central pivot, the sensitivity of the balance may be made as large as desired. Unfortunately, the same conditions which make for great sensitivity also make the balance extremely slow in taking up its final position. Hence a compromise must be struck between sensitivity and time of swing. A good balance will measure to a tenth of a milligram, and a really excellent instrument to a hundredth or a thousandth of a milligram.

If the lengths of the balance arms are not exactly equal, the mass needed to balance an unknown mass will depend upon which scale pan is used for the known and which for the unknown. Corrections for this error may be made by balancing with the unknown first on one side and then on the other. The true mass is then the geometric mean, or the square root of the product, of the standard masses required for balance.

In work of the highest precision, correction must be made for the buoyancy of the air if the density of the unknown mass differs from that of the standard masses. This correction will be explained in a later chapter.

5-9 Newton's law of universal gravitation. Throughout our study of mechanics we have been continually encountering forces due to gravitational attraction between the earth and bodies on its surface, forces which are called the weights of the bodies. We now wish to study this phenomenon of gravitation in somewhat more detail.

The law of universal gravitation was discovered by Sir Isaac Newton, and was first announced by him in the year 1686. It may be stated:

Every particle of matter in the universe attracts every other particle with a force which is directly proportional to the product of the masses of the particles and inversely proportional to the square of the distance between them.

$$F \propto \frac{mm'}{r^2}.$$

The proportion above may be converted to an equation on multiplication by a constant G which is called the gravitational constant.

$$F = G\frac{mm'}{r^2}. \tag{5-14}$$

There seems to be no certain evidence that Newton was led to deduce this law from speculations concerning the fall of an apple to the earth. His first published calculations to justify its correctness had to do with the motion of the moon around the earth.

The numerical value of the constant G depends on the units in which force, mass, and distance are expressed. Its magnitude can be found experimentally by measuring the force of gravitational attraction between two bodies of known masses m and m', at a known separation.   For bodies of moderate size the force is extremely small, but it can be measured without too much difficulty by the Cavendish balance, adapted for this purpose by Sir Henry Cavendish in the year 1798 from a similar balance invented by Coulomb for studying forces of electrical attraction and repulsion.

The Cavendish balance consists of two small spheres of mass m (Fig. 5-11), usually of gold or platinum, mounted at opposite ends of a light horizontal rod which is supported at its center by a fine vertical fibre such as a quartz thread.   A small mirror fastened to the fibre reflects a beam of light onto a scale.   To use the balance, two large spheres of mass M, usually of lead, are brought up to the positions shown.   The forces of gravitational attraction between the large and small spheres result in a couple which twists the fibre and mirror through a small angle, thereby moving the light beam along the scale.

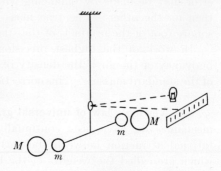

FIG. 5-11.   Principle of the Cavendish balance.

By using an extremely fine fibre, the deflection of the light beam may be made sufficiently large so that the gravitational forces can be measured quite accurately.   The numerical value of the gravitational constant, as measured in this way, is found to be

$$G = 6.670 \times 10^{-8} \text{ dyne-cm}^2/\text{gm}^2$$

or

$$6.670 \times 10^{-11} \text{ newton-m}^2/\text{kgm}^2.$$

Example: Compute the force of gravitational attraction between the large and small spheres of a Cavendish balance, if $m = 1$ gm, $M = 500$ gm, $r = 5$ cm.   (Two spheres attract one another as if the mass of each were concentrated at its center.)

$$F = \frac{6.67 \times 10^{-8} \times 1 \times 500}{(5)^2} = 1.33 \times 10^{-6} \text{ dynes}$$

or about one-millionth of a dyne!

5-10 The mass of the earth.   Since the constant G in Eq. (5-14) can be found from measurements in the laboratory, the mass of the earth may be computed.   From measurements on freely-falling bodies, we know that the earth attracts a one-gram mass at its surface with a force of (about) 980 dynes.   The distance between the centers of the masses is the radius of the earth, 6380 km or 6.38×10^8 cm.   Therefore,

$$980 = \frac{6.67 \times 10^{-8} \times 1 \times M}{(6.38 \times 10^8)^2}$$

where M is the mass of the earth.   Hence

$$M = 5.98 \times 10^{27} \text{ grams.}$$

The volume of the earth is

$$V = \frac{4}{3} \pi R^3 = 1.09 \times 10^{27} \text{ cm}^3.$$

The average density of the earth is

$$\rho = \frac{M}{V} = \frac{5.98 \times 10^{27} \text{ gm}}{1.09 \times 10^{27} \text{ cm}^3}$$

$$= 5.5 \frac{\text{gm}}{\text{cm}^3}.$$

This is considerably larger than the average density of the material near the earth's surface, so that the interior of the earth must be of much higher density.

5-11 Variations in "g."   The acceleration of gravity, g, is the acceleration imparted to a body by its own weight.   Its weight, however, can be written

$$w = G \frac{mM}{R^2},$$

where m is the mass of the body, M is the mass of the earth, and R is the distance to the earth's center.   Then since $w = mg$,

$$mg = G \frac{mM}{R^2}$$

$$g = \frac{GM}{R^2}. \tag{5-15}$$

Since G and M are constants, the acceleration of gravity should decrease with increasing distance from the center of the earth. In other words, it should be smaller at high altitudes. This is illustrated by the data in the following table:

Station	Elevation, meters	g, cm/sec²	g, ft/sec²
Cambridge, Mass..........	14	980.398	32.1652
Worcester, Mass...........	170	980.324	32.1628
Denver, Col..............	1638	979.609	32.1393

The earth is not a perfect sphere but an oblate spheroid, slightly flattened at the poles. Hence the distance from sea level to the earth's center decreases slightly as one proceeds north or south from the equator, and g at sea level should increase with increasing north or south latitude. Some data illustrating this are given in the following table:

Station	Latitude	g, cm/sec²	g, ft/sec²
Canal Zone...............	9° 00′	978.243	32.0944
Jamaica..................	17° 58′	978.591	32.1059
Bermuda.................	32° 21′	979.806	32.1548
Cambridge...............	42° 23′	980.398	32.1652
Standard Station...........	**45°**	**980.665**	**32.1740**
Greenland................	70° 27′	982.534	32.2353

Local deposits of ore, oil, or other substances whose density is greater or less than the average density of the earth, will cause local variations in g for points at the same latitude and elevation. Conversely, from a knowledge of such variations, conclusions can be drawn as to the presence of deposits of ore or oil beneath the earth's surface. Hence the precise measurement of g is one of the methods of geophysical prospecting. Such measurements are made with a pendulum of special construction.

Because of the decrease of g with altitude, it is only approximately correct to state that a body falls toward the earth with constant acceleration. Actually, the acceleration continually increases as the body approaches the earth, air resistance being neglected. For most purposes, however, this variation is negligible.

Problems — Chapter 5

(For problem work, use the approximate values of $g = 32$ ft/sec² = 9.8 m/sec² = 980 cm/sec². A force diagram should be constructed for each problem.)

5-1. (a) What resultant horizontal force is required to accelerate a 1600-lb automobile on a level road at 8 ft/sec²? (b) A 1600-gm block rests on a horizontal frictionless surface. What horizontal force is needed to accelerate it at 8 cm/sec²? (c) A 1600-kgm block rests on a horizontal frictionless surface. What horizontal force is needed to accelerate it at 8 m/sec²?

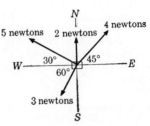

Fig. 5-12

5-2. The Springfield rifle bullet weighs 150 grains (7000 grains = 1 lb), its muzzle velocity is 2700 ft/sec, and the length of the rifle barrel is 30 in. Compute the resultant force accelerating the bullet, assuming it to be constant.

5-3. A body of mass 15 kgm rests on a frictionless horizontal plane and is acted on by a horizontal force of 30 newtons. (a) What acceleration is produced? (b) How far will the body travel in 10 sec? (c) What will be its velocity at the end of 10 sec?

5-4. A body of mass 50 gm is at rest at the origin, $x = 0$, on a horizontal frictionless surface. At time $t = 0$ a force of 10 dynes is applied to the body parallel to the X-axis, and 5 sec later this force is removed. (a) What are the position and velocity of the body at $t = 5$ sec? (b) If the same force (10 dynes) is again applied at $t = 15$ sec, what are the position and velocity of the body at $t = 20$ sec?

5-5. If action and reaction are always equal and opposite, why don't they always cancel one another and leave no net force for accelerating a body?

5-6. Fig. 5-12 is a top view of a block whose mass is 5 kgm, resting on a horizontal frictionless surface and acted on by four horizontal forces. Find the magnitude and direction of the acceleration of the block.

5-7. The mass of a certain object is 10 gm. (a) What would its mass be if taken to the planet Mars? (b) Is the expression $F = ma$ valid on Mars? (c) Newton's second law is sometimes written in the form $F = Wa/g$ instead of $F = ma$. Would this expression be valid on Mars? (d) If a Martian scientist hangs this 10-gm mass on a spring balance calibrated correctly on the earth, would the spring balance read 10 gm? (e) How do you reconcile this with your answer to (a)?

5-8. A block weighing 10 lb is held up by a string which can be moved up or down. What conclusions can you draw regarding magnitude and direction of the acceleration and velocity of the upper end of the string, when the tension in the string is (a) 5 lb, (b) 10 lb, (c) 15 lb?

5-9. A body hangs from a spring balance supported from the roof of an elevator. (a) If the elevator has an upward acceleration of 4 ft/sec² and the balance reads 45 lb, what is the true weight of the body? (b) Under what circumstances will the balance read 35 lb? (c) What will the balance read if the elevator cable breaks?

5-10. A body starting from rest is pulled along a horizontal frictionless surface by a constant force for 10 sec. At the end of this time the velocity is 10 cm/sec.

For the next 10-sec interval the force is zero. At the end of this interval a force of one-half the original force, and in the opposite direction, is applied until the body comes to rest. (a) Make a graph of velocity vs time. (b) Give the time when the body comes to rest. (c) How far did the body move in the first 10-sec interval? (d) What is the total distance traveled by the body? (Note: All these questions can be answered by reference to the graph.)

5-11. A transport plane is to take off from a level landing field with two gliders in tow, one behind the other. Each glider weighs 2400 lb, and the friction force or drag on each may be assumed constant and equal to 400 lb. The tension in the towrope between the transport plane and the first glider is not to exceed 2000 lb. (a) If a velocity of 100 ft/sec is required for the take-off, how long a runway is needed? (b) What is the tension in the towrope between the two gliders, while the planes are accelerating for the take-off?

5-12. If the coefficient of friction between tires and road is 0.5, what is the shortest distance in which an automobile can be stopped when traveling at 60 mi/hr?

5-13. A locomotive weighing 100 tons is to pull a train of n cars on a level track. Each car weighs 10 tons. The coefficient of friction between the wheels and the track is 0.2. If the train is to be capable of an acceleration of 0.65 ft/sec^2 without slipping, how many cars can the locomotive haul? Neglect all friction except that between the wheels and the track.

5-14. An 80-lb packing case is on the floor of a truck. The coefficient of static friction is 0.25. Calculate all the forces acting on the packing case and show them in a force diagram for each of the following cases: (a) The truck is at rest. (b) The truck is traveling in a straight line with a constant velocity. (c) The truck is accelerating at 6 ft/sec^2.

5-15. A block of mass 2.5 slugs rests on a horizontal surface. The coefficient of static friction between the block and the surface is 0.3 and the coefficient of sliding friction is 0.25. The block is acted upon by a variable horizontal force P. This force is initially zero and increases with time at the constant rate of 2 lb/sec. (a) When will the block start to move? (b) What is its acceleration 8 sec after it starts to move?

5-16. A 200-gm body starts from rest and slides down a smooth inclined plane. If it travels 120 cm during the third second, what is the angle of inclination of the plane?

5-17. A balloon is descending with a constant acceleration a, less than the acceleration of gravity g. The weight of the balloon, with its basket and contents, is w. What weight, W, of ballast should be released so that the balloon will begin to be accelerated upward with constant acceleration a? Neglect air resistance.

5-18. A 64-lb block is pushed up a 37° inclined plane by a horizontal force of 100 lb. The coefficient of sliding friction is 0.25. Find (a) the acceleration, (b) the velocity of the block after it has moved a distance of 20 ft along the plane, (c) the normal force exerted by the plane.

5-19. A block rests on an inclined plane which makes an angle θ with the horizontal. The coefficient of sliding friction is 0.5 and the coefficient of static friction is 0.75. (a) As the angle θ is increased, find the minimum angle at which the block starts to slip. (b) At this angle, find the acceleration once the block has begun to move. (c) How long a time is required for the block to slip 20 ft along the inclined plane?

5-20. (a) What constant horizontal force is required to drag a 16-lb block along a horizontal surface with an acceleration of 4 ft/sec^2, if the coefficient of sliding friction between block and surface is 0.5? (b)

What weight, hanging from a cord attached to the 16-lb block and passing over a pulley, will produce this acceleration?

5-21. A block weighing 8 lb resting on a horizontal surface is connected by a cord passing over a light frictionless pulley to a hanging block weighing 8 lb. The coefficient of friction between the block and the horizontal surface is 0.5. Find (a) the tension in the cord and (b) the acceleration of each block.

5-22. A block having a mass of 2 kgm is projected up a long 30° incline with an initial velocity of 22 m/sec. The coefficient of friction between the block and the plane is 0.3. (a) Find the friction force acting on the block as it moves up the plane. (b) How long does the block move up the plane? (c) How far does the block move up the plane? (d) How long does it take the block to slide down from its position in part (c) to the bottom? (e) With what velocity does it arrive at the bottom? (f) If the mass of the block had been 5 kgm instead of 2 kgm, would the answers in the preceding parts be changed?

5-23. An elevator which weighs 4000 lb has two cables attached to it. One cable goes over a frictionless pulley to a 2400-lb counterweight which hangs freely; the other cable goes to the hoisting motor. Because of friction between the elevator and its guides, the tension in the hoisting cable must be 2000 lb to lift the elevator at a constant speed. (a) What is the friction force on the elevator? (b) What tension in the hoisting cable will allow the elevator to descend with constant speed? (c) What is the tension in the counterweight cable when the elevator is being lifted at constant speed? When it is being lowered at constant speed? (d) What tension in the hoisting cable will raise the elevator with an acceleration of 4 ft/sec²? (e) If the elevator is moving upward at a constant speed, what would the tension in the hoisting cable have to become to slow down the elevator at a rate of 4 ft/sec²? (f) If the elevator is moving

downward, what is the tension in the hoisting cable if the elevator is decelerating 4 ft/sec²? (g) If the hoisting cable broke what would be the acceleration of the elevator? (h) What is the tension in the counterweight cable in parts (d), (e), (f), and (g)?

5-24. A 30-lb block on a level frictionless surface is attached by a cord passing over a small pulley to a hanging block originally at rest 4 ft above the floor. The hanging block strikes the floor in 2 seconds. (a) Find the weight of the hanging block. (b) Find the tension in the string while both blocks were in motion.

5-25. A block is projected up along a 37° inclined plane by a spring gun. Its initial velocity is 128 ft/sec. The coefficient of sliding friction between block and plane is 0.25. The block weighs 100 lb. In how many seconds will the block reach its highest position?

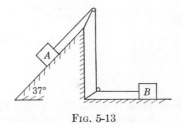

Fɪɢ. 5-13

5-26. Two blocks, each having mass 20 kgm, rest on frictionless surfaces as shown in Fig. 5-13. Assuming the pulleys to be light and frictionless, compute: (a) the time required for block *A* to move 1 m down the plane, starting from rest, (b) the tension in the cord connecting the blocks.

5-27. A block of mass 200 gm rests on the top of a block of mass 800 gm. The combination is dragged along a level surface at constant velocity by a hanging block of mass 200 gm as in Fig. 5-14 (a). (a) The first 200-gm block is removed from the 800-gm block and attached to the hanging block, as in Fig. 5-14 (b). What is now the acceleration of the sys-

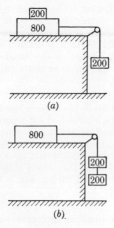

(a)

(b).

FIG. 5-14

tem? (b) What is the tension in the cord attached to the 800-gm block in part (b) of the figure?

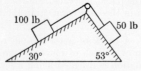

FIG. 5-15

5-28. Block A in Fig. 5-15 weighs 3 lb and block B weighs 30 lb. The coefficient of friction between B and the horizontal surface is 0.1. (a) What is the weight of block C if the acceleration of B is 6 ft/sec² toward the right? (b) What is the tension in each cord when B has the acceleration stated above?

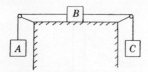

FIG. 5-16

5-29. Two blocks connected by a cord passing over a small frictionless pulley rest on frictionless planes as shown in Fig. 5-16. (a) Which way will the system move?

(b) What is the acceleration of the blocks?
(c) What is the tension in the cord?

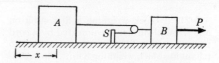

FIG. 5-17

5-30. Two blocks are connected as shown in Fig. 5-17. A string is fastened to block A, passes over the weightless pulley on block B, and is fastened to a support S. Block A weighs 16 lb, block B weighs 4 lb. The blocks, pulled by a force P, slide along a frictionless surface. The displacement of block A is found to be $x = 2t^3$, where x is in feet and t in seconds. (a) What is the acceleration of block A when $t = 5$ sec? (b) What is the tension T in the string at this moment? (c) What is the force P at this moment?

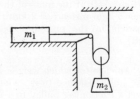

FIG. 5-18

5-31. In terms of m_1, m_2, and g, find the accelerations of both blocks in Fig. 5-18. Neglect all friction and the masses of the pulleys.

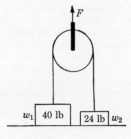

FIG. 5-19

5-32. The weights w_1 and w_2 in Fig. 5-19 are initially at rest on the floor. They are connected by a weightless string passing over a weightless and frictionless pulley. An upward force F is applied to the pulley. Find the accelerations a_1 of w_1 and a_2 of w_2 when F is (a) 24 lb, (b) 40 lb, (c) 72 lb, (d) 90 lb, (e) 120 lb.

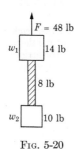

F = 48 lb

w_1 14 lb

8 lb

w_2 10 lb

Fig. 5-20

5-33. The two blocks in Fig. 5-20 are connected by a heavy uniform rope which weighs 8 lb. An upward force of 48 lb is applied as shown. (a) What is the acceleration of the system? (b) What is the tension at the top of the 8-lb rope? (c) What is the tension at the midpoint of the rope?

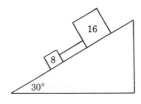

16

8

30°

Fig. 5-21

5-34. Two blocks, weighing 8 and 16 lb respectively, are connected by a string and slide down a 30° inclined plane, as in Fig. 5-21. The coefficient of friction between the 8-lb block and the plane is 0.25 and between the 16-lb block and the plane it is 0.5. (a) Calculate the acceleration of each block. (b) Calculate the tension in the string.

5-35. Weights of 10 lb and 6 lb hang 4 ft above the floor from the ends of a cord passing over a frictionless pulley. Both weights start from rest. (a) How long a time is required for the 10-lb weight to reach the floor? (b) How much higher will the 6-lb weight rise, after the 10-lb weight strikes the floor?

5-36. A man who weighs 160 lb stands on a platform which weighs 80 lb. He pulls a rope which is fastened to the platform and runs over a pulley on the ceiling. With what force does he have to pull in order to give himself and the platform an upward acceleration of 2 ft/sec²?

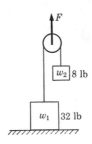

4 ft

6 ft

Fig. 5-22

5-37. A flexible rope 10 ft long, weighing $\frac{1}{2}$ lb per foot, passes over a small frictionless pulley. It is released from rest with 4 ft of the rope hanging from one side and 6 ft from the other side of the pulley, as in Fig. 5-22. (a) What is the initial acceleration of the rope? (b) What is the acceleration of the rope when a length x hangs from the right-hand side of the pulley?

F

w_2 8 lb

w_1 32 lb

Fig. 5-23

5-38. Weights w_1 and w_2 are connected by a weightless string passing over a weightless and frictionless pulley, as shown in Fig. 5-23. (a) What is the maximum upward force F which can be applied to the pulley without causing w_1 to leave the floor? (b) What is the acceleration of w_2 when this maximum force F is applied to the pulley?

5-39. In an experiment using the Cavendish balance to measure the gravitational constant G, it is found that a sphere of mass 4 gm attracts another sphere of mass 800 gm with a force of 13×10^{-6} dyne, when the distance between the centers of the spheres is 4 cm. The acceleration of gravity at the earth's surface is 980 cm/sec², and the radius of the earth is

6400 km. Compute the mass of the earth from these data.

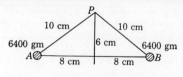

FIG. 5-24

5-40. Two spheres, each of mass 6400 gm, are fixed at points A and B (Fig. 5-24). (a) Find the magnitude and direction of the initial acceleration of a sphere of mass 10 gm, if released from rest at point P and acted on only by forces of gravitational attraction of the spheres at A and B.

CHAPTER 6

MOTION OF A PROJECTILE

6-1 Projectiles. In this chapter we shall discuss the motion of a projectile, such as a baseball or golf ball, a bomb released from a plane, a rifle bullet, or the shell of a gun. The path followed by a projectile is called its *trajectory*. The trajectory is affected to a large extent by air resistance, which makes an exact analysis of the motion extremely complex. In fact, the subject of exterior ballistics, which is the term applied to the calculation of the trajectories of bullets or shells, is a science in itself. We shall, however, neglect the (important) effects of air resistance and assume that the motion takes place in empty space.

The motion of a projectile is most readily analyzed with the aid of Newton's second law expressed in component form. As we saw in the preceding chapter, each component of the force exerted on a body can be considered to produce its own component of acceleration. Then if F_x and F_y are the X- and Y-components of a force F exerted on a body of mass m, the X-component of the force equals the product of the mass and the X-component of acceleration, and the Y-component of the force equals the product of the mass and the Y-component of acceleration.

$$F_x = ma_x, \quad F_y = ma_y. \tag{6-1}$$

The force F is often the resultant of a number of applied forces. Hence Eq. (6-1) can be written

$$\Sigma F_x = ma_x, \quad \Sigma F_y = ma_y. \tag{6-2}$$

If the mass is in equilibrium, a_x and a_y are both zero. Hence, for equilibrium,

$$\Sigma F_x = 0, \quad \Sigma F_y = 0.$$

That is, Eq. (6-2) includes the first condition of equilibrium as a special case.

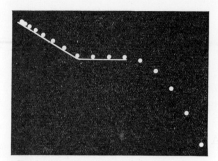

Fig. 6-1.   Constant acceleration down the incline, constant velocity on the level track, and a combination of constant velocity and constant acceleration after leaving the track.

6-2 Motion of a body projected horizontally. Fig. 6-1 is a multiflash photograph of a ball which rolls down an inclined track, then along a horizontal track, and finally leaves the track and moves as a projectile. After leaving the track, the only force on the ball is its weight. Hence

$$\Sigma F_x = \quad 0 = ma_x, \qquad (6\text{-}3)$$

$$\Sigma F_y = mg = ma_y. \qquad (6\text{-}4)$$

Since the horizontal force component is zero, there is no horizontal acceleration and the horizontal velocity component remains constant and equal to the velocity on the level portion of the track. This is proved by the fact that the *horizontal* spacing of the images remains the same throughout the trajectory. On the other hand, since there is a resultant vertical force, there will be a vertical acceleration in the direction of this force. The *vertical* spacing of the images therefore increases along the trajectory.

The vertical acceleration is found from Eq. (6-4); namely, $a_y = g$. That is, the vertical acceleration is the same as that of a body falling in a vertical line and is quite unaffected by the fact that the body has at the same time a horizontal velocity component. The forward velocity of the body does not "support" it in flight.

An interesting demonstration of this fact is afforded by the experiment shown in Fig. 6-2. One ball is projected horizontally from a spring gun at the upper left of the picture. As it leaves the muzzle of the gun, it operates a small tripswitch which opens the circuit of an electromagnet and releases a second ball at the upper right. It will be seen that both balls fall at precisely

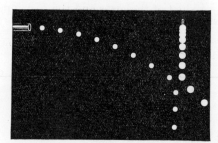

Fig. 6-2.   The vertical acceleration is the same for both bodies.

the same rate, and that when the first reaches the line of motion of the second, a collision takes place in mid-air.

Fig. 6-3 is a drawing corresponding to a portion of the trajectory of Fig. 6-1. *X*- and *Y*-axes have been constructed with origin at the point

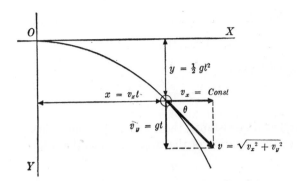

Fig. 6-3. Trajectory of a body projected horizontally.

where the ball leaves the track and begins its flight as a projectile. Let $t_0 = 0$ at the origin, and t the time when the ball is in the position shown. The velocity of the ball can be found by computing separately its horizontal and vertical components and combining them by the usual methods for vector addition. The horizontal velocity component is denoted in Fig. 6-3 by v_x. We have seen that the horizontal acceleration is zero and that the horizontal velocity component, v_x, remains constant throughout the motion. Since the vertical acceleration is g (taking the downward direction as positive), the vertical velocity component at time t is

$$v_y = gt$$

(the *initial vertical* velocity is zero).

The magnitude of the velocity is therefore

$$v = \sqrt{v_x{}^2 + v_y{}^2}.$$

and its direction can be found from

$$\tan \theta = v_y/v_x.$$

The velocity vector, v, is tangent to the trajectory, and its direction at any instant is the direction in which the projectile is moving at that instant. The horizontal *displacement* at time t is

$$x = v_x t$$

and the vertical displacement is

$$y = \tfrac{1}{2} gt^2.$$

The equation of the trajectory may be found by eliminating t from the two preceding equations. From the first we have $t^2 = \dfrac{x^2}{v_x{}^2}$, and introducing this in the second gives

$$y = \left(\tfrac{1}{2}\,\frac{g}{v_x{}^2}\right)x^2.$$

Since g and v_x are constants, the expression in parentheses is a constant, say k. Hence the equation of the trajectory has the form

$$y = kx^2,$$

which will be recognized as the equation of a parabola.

Example: The ball in Fig. 6-3 leaves the track with a velocity v_x of 8 ft/sec. Find its position and velocity after $\frac{1}{4}$ sec.

The horizontal displacement is

$$x = v_x t = 8 \times \tfrac{1}{4} = 2 \text{ ft,}$$

and the vertical displacement is

$$y = \tfrac{1}{2}\,gt^2 = \tfrac{1}{2} \times 32 \times (\tfrac{1}{4})^2 = 1 \text{ ft.}$$

The ball is therefore two feet out from its starting point and one foot down.

The horizontal velocity component is

$$v_x = \text{constant} = 8 \text{ ft/sec,}$$

and the vertical component at this instant is

$$v_y = gt = 32 \times \tfrac{1}{4} = 8 \text{ ft/sec.}$$

The resultant velocity is therefore

$$v = \sqrt{v_x{}^2 + v_y{}^2} = \sqrt{(8)^2 + (8)^2} = 8\sqrt{2} \text{ ft/sec,}$$

and since

$$\tan \theta = \frac{v_y}{v_x} = \frac{8}{8} = 1,$$

the direction of the velocity is 45° below the horizontal.

6-3 Body projected at an angle. In the most general case of projectile motion the body is given an initial velocity at some angle θ above (or below) the horizontal. Such a trajectory is shown in the multiflash photograph of Fig. 6-4, to which have been added X- and Y-axes and velocity vectors. Let v_0 represent the initial velocity

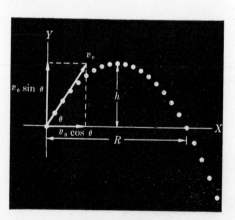

FIG. 6-4. Trajectory of a body projected at an angle with the horizontal.

(called the muzzle velocity if the projectile is a bullet or shell).   Its horizontal and vertical components are

$$v_{0x} = v_0 \cos \theta, \quad v_{0y} = v_0 \sin \theta.$$

(The upward direction is considered positive.)

As in Fig. 6-2, the horizontal velocity component remains constant throughout the motion.   The vertical part of the motion is one of constant downward acceleration, and is the same as that of a body projected vertically upward with an initial velocity $v_0 \sin \theta$.   At a time t after the start, the horizontal velocity is

$$v_x = v_{0x} = v_0 \cos \theta = \text{constant} \tag{6-5}$$

and the vertical velocity

$$v_y = v_{0y} - gt = v_0 \sin \theta - gt. \tag{6-6}$$

The horizontal displacement is

$$x = v_{0x}t = (v_0 \cos \theta) \, t \tag{6-7}$$

and the vertical displacement

$$y = v_{0y}t - \tfrac{1}{2} gt^2 = (v_0 \sin \theta) \, t - \tfrac{1}{2} gt^2. \tag{6-8}$$

The maximum height, h, is reached at a time when the vertical velocity component has decreased to zero.   Setting $v_y = 0$ in Eq. (6-6), we find for this time

$$t = \frac{v_0 \sin \theta}{g}.$$

Hence from Eq. (6-8) the maximum height is

$$h = \frac{v_0^2 \sin^2 \theta}{2g}. \tag{6-9}$$

The time for the body to return to its initial elevation is found from Eq. (6-8) by setting $y = 0$.   This gives

$$t = \frac{2v_0 \sin \theta}{g}. \tag{6-10}$$

Notice that this is just twice the time to reach the highest point.

The horizontal displacement when the ball returns to its initial elevation is called the *horizontal range*.   Introducing the time to reach this point in Eq. (6-7), we find

$$R = \frac{2v_0^2 \sin \theta \cos \theta}{g}. \tag{6-11}$$

Since $2 \sin \theta \cos \theta = \sin 2\theta$, Eq. (6-11) may be written

$$R = \frac{v_0{}^2 \sin 2\theta}{g}. \tag{6-12}$$

The horizontal range is thus proportional to the square of the initial velocity for a given angle of elevation. Since the maximum value of $\sin 2\theta$ is unity, the maximum horizontal range R_{max} is $v_0{}^2/g$. But if $\sin 2\theta = 1$, $2\theta = 90°$ and $\theta = 45°$. Hence the maximum horizontal range, in the absence of air resistance, is attained with an angle of elevation of $45°$.

From the standpoint of gunnery, what one usually wishes to know is what the angle of elevation should be for a given muzzle velocity v_0 in order to hit a target whose position is known. If target and gun are at the same elevation and the target is at a distance R, Eq. (6-12) may be solved for θ.

$$\theta = \tfrac{1}{2} \sin^{-1}\left(\frac{Rg}{v_0{}^2}\right) = \tfrac{1}{2} \sin^{-1}\left(\frac{R}{R_{max}}\right).$$

Provided R is less than the maximum range, this equation has two solutions for values of θ between $0°$ and $90°$. Thus if $R = 800$ ft, $g = 32$ ft/sec^2, and $v_0 = 200$ ft/sec,

$$2\theta = \sin^{-1}\left(\frac{800 \times 32}{200^2}\right) = \sin^{-1}(0.64)$$

$$= 40°, \quad \text{or} \quad 180° - 40° = 140°.$$

$$\theta = 20° \quad \text{or} \quad 70°.$$

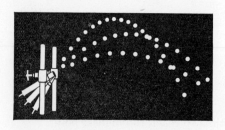

FIG. 6-5. An angle of elevation of $45°$ gives the maximum horizontal range.

Either of these angles gives the same range. Of course the time of flight and the maximum height reached are both greater for the high angle trajectory.

Fig. 6-5 is a photograph of three trajectories, taken on the same film, of a ball projected from a spring gun with angles of elevation of $30°$, $45°$ and $60°$. It will be seen that the horizontal ranges are (very nearly) the same for the $30°$ and $60°$ elevations, and that both are less than the range when the angle is $45°$. (The spring gun does not impart exactly the same initial velocity to the ball as the angle of elevation is altered.)

If the angle of "elevation" is below the horizontal, as for instance in the motion of a ball after rolling off a sloping roof, or the trajectory of a bomb released by a dive bomber, exactly the same principles apply.   The horizontal velocity component remains constant and equal to $v_0 \cos \theta$. The vertical motion is the same as that of a body projected *downward* with an initial velocity $v_0 \sin \theta$.   Minus signs can be avoided by taking the downward direction as positive.

————————

Example: A projectile is fired with a muzzle velocity of 1200 ft/sec at an angle of elevation of 15° above the horizontal as in Fig. 6-6.   At what height will it strike a vertical cliff distant 15,000 ft horizontally from the gun?   Find the magnitude and direction of its velocity when it strikes.   Neglect air resistance.

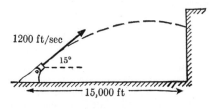

Fig. 6-6.

The horizontal component of velocity is
$$1200 \times \cos 15° = 1200 \times .966 = 1160 \text{ ft/sec}.$$

The time to travel a horizontal distance of 15,000 ft is
$$\frac{15,000}{1160} = 12.9 \text{ sec}.$$

The initial vertical component of velocity is
$$1200 \times \sin 15° = 1200 \times .259 = 311 \text{ ft/sec}.$$

The vertical height 12.9 sec after firing is
$$311 \times 12.9 - \tfrac{1}{2} \times 32 \times (12.9)^2 = 1360 \text{ ft}$$

and hence this is the height at which it strikes the cliff.
The vertical component of velocity is
$$311 - 32 \times 12.9 = -102 \text{ ft/sec}.$$

The resultant velocity is
$$\sqrt{1160^2 + 102^2} = 1160 \text{ ft/sec}.$$

The angle below the horizontal is
$$\tan^{-1} \frac{102}{1160} = \tan^{-1} .088 = 5 \text{ degrees}.$$

Problems — Chapter 6

6-1. A golf ball is driven horizontally from a point which is 96 ft above a level fairway. If it strikes the ground at a point distant 150 yd *horizontally* from the start, what was its initial velocity?

6-2. A block weighing 8 lb rests on a frictionless horizontal table top 4 ft high. The block is initially 6 ft from the edge of the table. A horizontal force P pushes it from rest to the edge of the table top, at which point P is removed. If the block leaves the table with a velocity of 12 ft/sec, find (a) the force P, (b) the horizontal distance from the table at which the block strikes the floor, (c) the horizontal and vertical components of its velocity when it reaches the floor.

6-3. A level flight bomber, flying at 300 ft/sec, releases a bomb at an elevation of 6400 ft. (a) How long before the bomb strikes the earth? (b) How far does it travel horizontally? (c) Find the horizontal and vertical components of its velocity when it strikes.

6-4. A block passes a point 10 ft from the edge of a table with a velocity of 12 ft/sec. It slides off the edge of the table, which is 4 ft high, and strikes the floor 4 ft from the edge of the table. What was the coefficient of sliding friction between block and table?

6-5. A bombing plane in level flight releases three bombs at intervals of 2 sec. Compute the vertical distance between the first and second, and between the second and third, (a) at the instant the third is released, (b) after the first bomb has fallen 900 ft. Neglect air resistance.

6-6. A tennis ball is thrown by a student standing on the north side of the street to a student standing on the south side with a velocity whose horizontal component is 88 ft/sec with respect to the street. In what direction must the tennis ball be thrown with respect to the earth

so that it appears to go straight across the street when seen by a boy on a truck moving eastward with a velocity of 44 ft/sec?

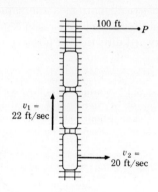

FIG. 6-7

6-7. A train is traveling at a constant velocity $v_1 = 22$ ft/sec across a bridge over a river. A man inside one of the cars throws a stone horizontally out of a window in a direction perpendicular to the direction of motion of the train. The initial velocity of the stone in this direction is $v_2 = 20$ ft/sec. The stone hits the water at the point P, 100 ft in a horizontal direction from the bridge. (See Fig. 6-7.) (a) Where is the car window from which the stone was thrown when the stone hits the water? (Neglect air friction.) (b) How far below the car window is the surface of the water?

6-8. A projectile is fired with an initial velocity of 80 ft/sec at an angle of 53° above the horizontal. Calculate: (a) the *horizontal* distance moved from the starting point three seconds after it is fired; (b) the *vertical* distance above the starting point at the same time; (c) the horizontal and vertical *components* of its velocity at this time.

6-9. A trench mortar fires a projectile at an angle of 53° above the horizontal with a muzzle velocity of 200 ft/sec. A tank is advancing directly toward the mortar on level ground at a speed of 10 ft/sec. What should be the distance from mortar to tank at the instant the mortar is fired in order to score a hit? Neglect air resistance.

6-10. The horizontal component of the displacement of a body when it is at P, a point on its trajectory, is 350 ft. The origin of coordinates is at the point of projection. As the body passes the point P its velocity is 100 ft/sec at an angle of 37 degrees below the horizontal. (a) What is the magnitude and direction of the velocity of projection? (b) What is the vertical component of the displacement of the body when it is at point P? (c) Using the velocity of projection from (a), the time of flight and the acceleration due to gravity, find *graphically* the magnitude and direction of the velocity of the body at P. (d) Using the velocity of projection from (a), the time of flight and the acceleration due to gravity, find *graphically* the magnitude and the direction of the displacement of the body at P. (e) Draw the line which represents the distance traveled or length of path from the point of projection to P. How would you determine the distance traveled?

6-11. A player kicks a ball at an angle of 37° with the horizontal and with an initial velocity of 48 ft/sec. A second player standing at a distance of 100 ft from the first in the direction of the kick starts running to meet the ball at the instant it is kicked. How fast must he run in order to catch the ball before it hits the ground?

6-12. A baseball leaves the bat at a height of 4 ft above the ground, traveling at an angle of 45° with the horizontal, and with a velocity such that the horizontal range would be 400 ft. At a distance of 360 ft from home plate is a fence 30 ft high. Will the ball be a home run?

6-13. A ball A is projected from O with an initial velocity $v_0 = 700$ cm/sec in a direction 37° above the horizontal. A

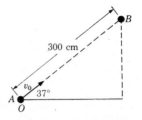

Fig. 6-8

ball B 300 cm from O on a line 37° above the horizontal is released from rest at the instant A starts. (a) How far will B have fallen when it is hit by A? (b) In what direction is A moving when it hits B? (Fig. 6-8.)

6-14. A projectile shot at an angle of 60° above the horizontal strikes a building 80 ft away at a point 48 ft above the point of projection. (a) Find the velocity of projection. (b) Find the magnitude and direction of the velocity of the projectile when it strikes the building.

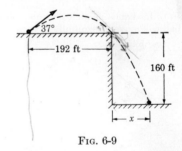

Fig. 6-9

6-15. A ball is thrown, as shown in Fig. 6-9, with an initial velocity v_0 at an angle of 37° above the horizontal, from a point 192 ft from the edge of a vertical cliff 160 ft high. The ball just misses the edge of the cliff. (a) Find the initial velocity v_0. (b) Find the distance x beyond the foot of the cliff where the ball strikes the ground.

6-16. A bomber is making a horizontal bombing run on a destroyer from an altitude of 25,600 ft. The magnitude of the velocity of the bomber is 300 mi/hr. (a) How much time is available for the destroyer to change its course after the bombs are released? Neglect air resistance. (b) If the bomber is to be shot down before its bombs can reach the ship, what is the maximum angle that the line of sight from ship to bomber can make with the horizontal? Draw a diagram, showing distances approximately to scale.

6-17. A bomber, diving at an angle of 53° with the vertical, releases a bomb at an altitude of 2400 ft. The bomb is observed to strike the ground 5 sec after its release. (a) What was the velocity of the bomber, in ft/sec? (b) How far did the bomb travel horizontally during its flight? (c) What were the horizontal and vertical components of its velocity just before striking? Air resistance may be neglected.

6-18. A man is riding on a flat car traveling with a constant velocity of 30 ft/sec (Fig. 6-10). He wishes to throw a ball through a stationary hoop 16 ft above the height of his hands in such a manner that the ball will move horizontally as it passes

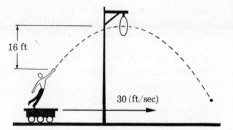

16 ft

30 (ft/sec)

FIG. 6-10

through the hoop. He throws the ball with a velocity of 40 ft/sec with respect to himself. (a) What must be the vertical component of the initial velocity of the ball? (b) How many seconds after he releases the ball will it pass through the hoop? (c) At what horizontal distance in front of the hoop must he release the ball?

6-19. A 15-lb stone is dropped from a cliff in a high wind. The wind exerts a steady horizontal 10-lb force on the stone as it falls. Is the path of the stone a straight line, a parabola, or some more complicated path? Explain.

CHAPTER 7

WORK AND ENERGY

7-1 Work. In everyday life, the word *work* is applied to any form of activity that requires the exertion of muscular or mental effort. In physics, however, the term is used in a very restricted sense. Fig. 7-1 represents a body moving in a horizontal direction which we shall take as the X-axis. A constant force F, at an angle θ with the direction of motion, is exerted by some outside agent on the body. *The work W done by this agent, while the body undergoes a displacement x, is defined as the product of the displacement and the component of the force in the direction of the displacement.* Thus

$$W = (F \cos \theta) \cdot x. \qquad (7\text{-}1)$$

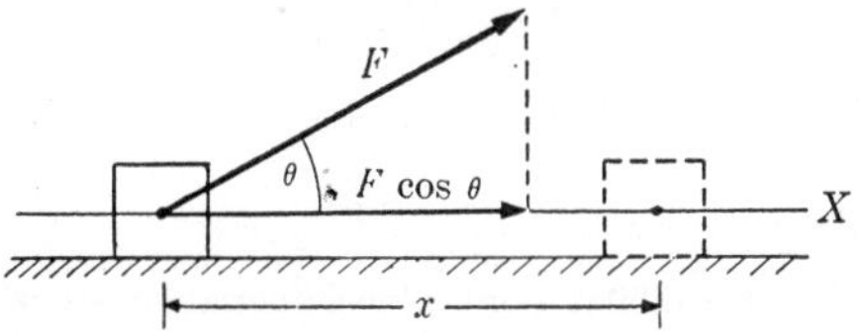

FIG. 7-1. The work done by the force F in a displacement x is $(F \cos \theta) \cdot x$.

The concept of work is so important that it will bear further discussion. Work is done only when a force is exerted on a body while the body at the same time moves in such a way that the force has a component in the direction of motion. Thus work is done when a weight is lifted, or a spring is stretched, or a gas is compressed in a cylinder. On the other hand, although it would be considered "hard work" to hold a heavy weight stationary at arm's length, no work would be done in the technical sense, since there is no motion. Even if one were to walk along a horizontal floor carrying the weight, no work would be done, since the (vertical) force has no component in the direction of the (horizontal) motion.

A locomotive does work while pulling a moving train, but if the brakes of the train should become locked so as to prevent motion, then no work would be done no matter how great a force the locomotive were to exert. The expanding gas in the cylinders of an automobile engine does work in pushing against the moving pistons, but if the motion of the pistons were to be prevented in some way, no work would be done by the gas in the cylinders no matter how great its pressure.

In the English system, the unit of force is the pound and the unit of distance is the foot. The unit of work in this system is therefore *one*

101

foot-pound. (The order of terms is interchanged to distinguish this unit from the unit of torque, the pound-foot.) *One foot-pound* may be defined as *the work done when a constant force of one pound is exerted on a body which moves a distance of one foot in the same direction as the force.*

In the mks system, where forces are expressed in newtons and distances in meters, the unit of work is the *newton-meter.* The reader can supply the definition of a newton-meter from the definition above of a foot-pound. In the cgs system the unit of work is the *dyne-centimeter.* One dyne-centimeter is called *one erg;* one newton-meter is called *one joule.* There is no corresponding single term for one foot-pound.

Since 1 meter = 100 cm and 1 newton = 10^5 dynes, it follows that 1 newton-meter = 10^7 dyne-centimeters, or

$$1 \text{ joule} = 10^7 \text{ ergs.}$$

Also, from the relations between the newton and pound, and the meter and foot,

$$1 \text{ joule} = 0.7376 \text{ foot-pounds,}$$
$$1 \text{ foot-pound} = 1.356 \text{ joules.}$$

Examples. (1) A box weighing 100 lb is pushed 20 ft along a level floor at constant velocity by a horizontal force. The coefficient of sliding friction between box and floor is 0.30. How many foot-pounds of work are done?

The force required to maintain the motion of the box is 30 lb. Since the distance moved in the direction of the force is 20 ft, the work done is 600 foot-pounds.

(2) How much work would be required to drag the same box 20 ft along the floor by a rope attached to the box, making an angle of 30° with the horizontal?

The force is not in the same direction as the motion. The first step is to find from

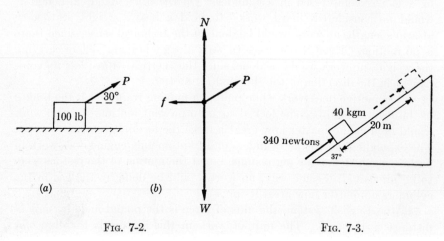

(*a*)   (*b*)

Fig. 7-2.   Fig. 7-3.

a force diagram as in Fig. 7-2(b) how large a force P is required.   This turns out to be 29.4 lbs.   Hence

$$W = (P \cos \theta) \cdot x$$
$$= 29.4 \times .866 \times 20$$
$$= 512 \text{ foot-pounds.}$$

(3) A constant force of 340 newtons parallel to the sloping surface of a 37° inclined plane pushes a 40 kgm block a distance of 20 meters up the sloping surface.   (Fig. 7-3.) How much work is done by the force?

The force is constant and in the same direction as the displacement.   Hence,

$$W = 340 \times 20 = 6800 \text{ newton-meters}$$
$$= 6800 \text{ joules.}$$

7-2 Kinetic energy.   Consider an unbalanced constant horizontal force F imparting a constant acceleration a to the body of mass m, shown in Fig. 7-4, which moves on a *frictionless* surface.   Suppose the speed of the body increases from v_1 to v_2 during the displacement x.   The work done is

$$W = Fx.$$

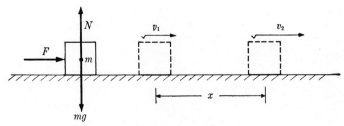

FIG. 7-4.   Under the action of a constant horizontal force, a mass undergoes an increase of speed from v_1 to v_2.

But $F = ma$, and $v_2{}^2 = v_1{}^2 + 2ax$.   Hence

$$W = ma \frac{v_2{}^2 - v_1{}^2}{2a},$$

and

$$W = \tfrac{1}{2}mv_2{}^2 - \tfrac{1}{2}mv_1{}^2.$$

Notice that neither F nor x appears in this expression for the work done. F could have been large and x small or the reverse might have been true. Only the mass of the body and its original and final speeds enter into the expression.   No work was done in lifting the body; no work was done against friction; no work was done in compressing a spring; the only work that was done by the outside agency responsible for exerting the force was to increase the quantity $\frac{1}{2}mv^2$ from the original value $\frac{1}{2}mv_1^2$ to the final value $\frac{1}{2}mv_2^2$. We define the *kinetic energy* K of a body to be one-half the product of the mass and the square of the speed. Thus

$$K = \tfrac{1}{2}mv^2. \tag{7-2}$$

When, therefore, a body is caused to move along a horizontal frictionless surface, and no work is done except to increase the speed of the body, the work done is equal to the change in kinetic energy.

Examples. (1) Find the kinetic energy of a body whose mass is 100 gm at a moment when the speed is 20 cm/sec.

$$K = \tfrac{1}{2}mv^2$$

$$= \frac{1}{2} \times 100 \text{ gm} \times 400 \,\frac{\text{cm}^2}{\text{sec}^2}$$

$$= 50 \times 400 \,\frac{\text{gm-cm}}{\text{sec}^2} \cdot \text{cm}$$

$$= 20{,}000 \text{ dyne-cm}$$

$$= 20{,}000 \text{ ergs.}$$

(2) Find the kinetic energy of a 2-kgm mass moving with a speed of 4 m/sec.

$$K = \frac{1}{2} \times 2 \text{ kgm} \times 16 \,\frac{\text{m}^2}{\text{sec}^2}$$

$$= 16 \,\frac{\text{kgm-m}}{\text{sec}^2} \cdot \text{m}$$

$$= 16 \text{ newton-meters}$$

$$= 16 \text{ joules.}$$

(3) Find the kinetic energy of a 128-lb body moving with a speed of 11 ft/sec, remembering that $m = w/g$.

$$K = \frac{1}{2} \times \frac{128 \text{ lb}}{32 \text{ ft/sec}^2} \times 121 \,\frac{\text{ft}^2}{\text{sec}^2}$$

$$= 242 \text{ ft-lb.}$$

7-3 Gravitational potential energy. Suppose a body of mass m (or of weight $w = mg$) is lifted vertically with uniform motion from a point where its center of gravity is at a distance y_1 above an arbitrarily chosen plane (*the reference level*) to a height y_2. Suppose there is no friction.

The force necessary to lift the body is constant, equal in magnitude to the weight mg, and directed vertically upward. Therefore the work is

$$W = mg(y_2 - y_1)$$

or

$$W = mgy_2 - mgy_1 = wy_2 - wy_1.$$

Now suppose the body starts at the same place but is moved an extremely small distance Δy vertically upward, then is given a very small horizontal displacement, then a small vertical displacement $\Delta y'$, then horizontal, and so on, until it has been transferred along a zigzag path to any point at a height y_2 above the reference level. No work is done in the small horizontal steps, since the force necessary to effect this transfer is always vertically upward, and hence the total work is the sum of the work done in the vertical displacements only. Thus

$$W = mg(\Delta y + \Delta y' + \cdots).$$

But

$$(\Delta y + \Delta y' + \cdots) = y_2 - y_1.$$

Therefore

$$W = mgy_2 - mgy_1 = wy_2 - wy_1.$$

By making the zigzag steps as small as we please, we may cause the body to go from *any* point at a height y_1 above the reference level to *any other* point at a height y_2, along a path which is any desired approximation to a smooth curve. The net work done will always be $mgy_2 - mgy_1$, and in this expression *the nature of the path connecting the two points does not enter*, provided there is no friction. The only effect of the outside agency responsible for exerting the force was to increase the quantity mgy from its original value mgy_1 to the final value mgy_2. We define the *gravitational potential energy* V_G of a body to be the product of the weight and the height of its center of gravity above an arbitrarily chosen reference level. Thus

$$\boxed{V_G = mgy = wy.} \tag{7-3}$$

When, therefore, a body is caused to move with uniform motion along any frictionless path from one point to another, and no work is done except to raise the level of the center of gravity of the body, the work done is equal to the change in gravitational potential energy.

7-4 Absolute values of potential and kinetic energy. The definition of gravitational potential energy, mgy, implies that the potential energy is zero when $y = 0$, that is, when the body is at the reference level. To be specific, suppose this level to be the top of the laboratory table. If the reference level had been taken at some lower elevation such as the floor, the potential energy would not be zero at the table top. If it had been taken at the ceiling, the potential energy at the table top would be negative. It will be seen that the gravitational potential energy of a body at any point depends on the arbitrary choice of a reference level and hence is indeterminate to that extent. The indeterminacy is not of importance, however, since in any practical case one is concerned only with differences in potential energy, which are independent of the reference level. It is usually most convenient to choose this level at or below the lowest point in any specific problem, which avoids the appearance of negative energies.

Another aspect of potential energy should be pointed out here. When a man picks up a weight from the floor and raises it above his head, he has in effect inserted his body between the weight and the earth and pushed the weight one way with his hands, and the earth the other way with his feet. The general principle involved is obscured in this common example by the disparity in mass between the earth and the body lifted—the displacement of the earth is so much smaller than that of the body. Imagine an Atlas standing on one small planetoid and "lifting" another of the same size as the first. We may then ask, "To which body has potential energy been given?" If the bodies are of equal size, each will move an equal distance from its original position, and the process is better described as "separating" the bodies rather than "lifting" one of them. It is evident in this imaginary example that the potential energy should not be assigned to either body singly but rather that it represents a joint property of the *system*. The potential energy of the two planetoids is greater when they are separated than when they are close together.

The same is evidently true whatever the ratio of masses of the bodies, and therefore it applies to our original example of a man lifting a weight. The potential energy is not a property of the weight alone but a joint property of the system weight + earth. Although this aspect of potential energy must be kept in mind, we shall nevertheless, for convenience, continue to speak of "the potential energy of a raised weight" as if it were associated with the weight alone.

Considerations similar to those above apply to kinetic energy also. We say that an object at rest in the laboratory has no kinetic energy, since its velocity is zero. But although it has no velocity relative to the earth, it partakes in the motion of the earth about its axis, the revolution of the earth about the sun, and the motion of the whole solar system through space.

7-5 Potential energy of a stretched spring. Gravitational potential energy is only one of many forms of potential energy. Another type commonly encountered is the potential energy of an elastic body which has been distorted in some way. The subject of elasticity will be discussed more fully in a later chapter. For the present it will suffice to state that when most solid bodies are distorted, the force needed to produce the distortion increases in direct proportion to the distortion, provided the latter is not too great. This property of matter was one of the first to be studied quantitatively and the statement above was published by Robert Hooke in 1678. It is known as Hooke's law.

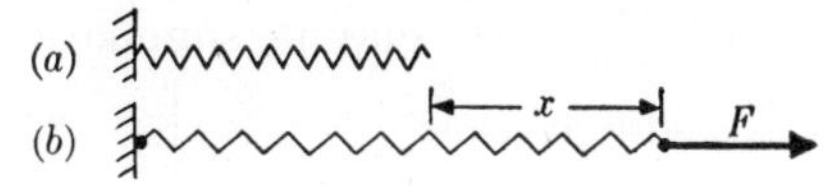

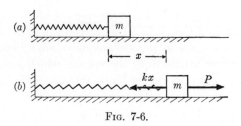

(a)

(b) $\longleftarrow x \longrightarrow$ F

FIG. 7-5.

To be specific, let us consider a coil spring subjected to a stretching force. Fig. 7-5(a) represents an unstretched spring. In Fig. 7-5(b) the spring has been stretched a distance x above its normal or no-load length. The force required to hold it in this position is F. Hooke's law, in mathematical form, states that

$$F \propto x \quad \text{or} \quad F = kx, \tag{7-4}$$

where k is a constant of proportionality called the *force constant* or the *stiffness coefficient* of the spring. The force constant may be defined as the ratio of the force to the extension it produces above the no-load length, or the force per unit elongation. It is expressed in pounds/foot, newtons/meter, or dynes/centimeter.

(a) m

$\longleftarrow x \longrightarrow$

(b) kx m P

FIG. 7-6.

In Fig. 7-6(a), a block of mass m on a horizontal frictionless surface is connected to a fixed point by a spring. The spring is assumed to have its natural unstretched length and the force exerted by it on the block is zero. Suppose now an exceedingly small force toward the right is applied on the block by some outside agency, thereby imparting to the block a very small acceleration to the right, causing the block to move very slowly. As soon as the block moves slightly to the right the spring becomes slightly stretched and exerts a small elastic force to the left. If the applied force is not increased, the block will stop and no further stretch of the spring will take place.

Imagine, however, the applied force to increase continuously in such a way that its value is always a trifle larger than the elastic force but not large enough to provide an appreciable acceleration to the block. Let the applied force increase in this way until the spring is stretched an amount x, at which point the force has the value $P = kx$, as in Fig. 7-6(b). The features of this process may be summarized as follows:

1. The process is exceedingly slow.

2. The applied force and the elastic force of the spring are at all times during the motion very nearly equal in magnitude and opposite in direction; that is, the block is practically in equilibrium at all times.

3. The applied force varies continuously, proportional to the amount of stretch, from an initial value zero to a final value kx.

4. The block never acquires appreciable kinetic energy.

5. There is no change in gravitational potential energy.

Work, however, has been done by the outside agency responsible for the applied force. Since this force has varied linearly from zero to the value kx, its average value is $kx/2$ and the work done may be computed by multiplying the average force by the displacement x. Thus

$$W = \tfrac{1}{2}kx \times x = \tfrac{1}{2}kx^2.$$

Since this work has not succeeded in supplying the block with either kinetic energy or gravitational potential energy, and since no work was done against friction, some part of the system must have been supplied with energy. We therefore attribute to the spring, which has been stretched an amount x, *elastic potential energy* V_E of amount $\tfrac{1}{2}kx^2$. Thus

$$V_E \left\{ \begin{matrix} \text{Elastic potential energy} \\ \text{of a stretched spring} \end{matrix} \right\} = \tfrac{1}{2}kx^2. \qquad (7\text{-}5)$$

Example: A force of 5 lb is found to stretch a screen door spring 6 in. What is the potential energy of the spring when opening the door stretches it 18 inches?

Since a 5-lb force stretches the spring 6 inches the force constant k, or the ratio of force to extension, is

$$k = \frac{5}{\frac{1}{2}} = 10 \text{ lb/ft.}$$

Hence
$$V_E = \tfrac{1}{2} \times 10 \times (1.5)^2 = 11.3 \text{ ft-lb.}$$

7-6 The principle of conservation of energy. Fig. 7-7 represents a body of mass m which is being drawn up a rough inclined plane of slope angle ϕ by a *constant* force P applied from the outside. The force P may be imagined to be the pull of a string drawn by one's hand, or by a motor or an engine. The body passes a point at elevation y_1 with velocity v_1, and passes a second point at elevation y_2 with velocity v_2.

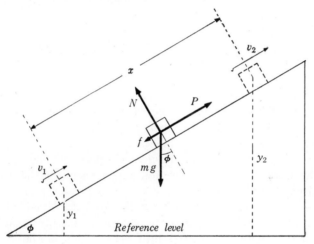

Fig. 7-7. The work done by the force P (applied from the outside) equals the increase in kinetic energy plus the increase in gravitational potential energy, plus the energy transformed into heat (work done against friction).

Taking the positive X-direction up the plane, and calling the acceleration in this direction a, we have from Newton's second law

$$\Sigma F_x = ma,$$

or

$$P - mg \sin \phi - f = ma.$$

Since all the terms on the left are constant, it follows that a is constant, and therefore

$$v_2{}^2 = v_1{}^2 + 2ax,$$

or

$$a = \frac{v_2{}^2 - v_1{}^2}{2x}.$$

Substituting this value of a in Newton's second law, we get

$$P - mg \sin \phi - f = m\,\frac{v_2{}^2 - v_1{}^2}{2x}.$$

After multiplying through by x, the equation becomes

$$Px = \tfrac{1}{2}mv_2{}^2 - \tfrac{1}{2}mv_1{}^2 + mgx \sin \phi + fx.$$

But, from Fig. 7-6,

$$x \sin \phi = y_2 - y_1.$$

Hence

$$Px = \tfrac{1}{2}mv_2{}^2 - \tfrac{1}{2}mv_1{}^2 + mgy_2 - mgy_1 + fx. \qquad (7\text{-}6)$$

Each term in Eq. (7-6) has a simple interpretation:

Px is the work done by the outside agent responsible for exerting the applied force, and is therefore the energy supplied from the outside.

$\tfrac{1}{2}mv_2{}^2 - \tfrac{1}{2}mv_1{}^2$ is the change in kinetic energy.

$mgy_2 - mgy_1$ is the change in gravitational potential energy.

fx is the work done against friction and is therefore the energy converted or transformed into heat.

Eq. (7-6) states that the energy supplied from the outside is equal to the change in kinetic energy plus the change in gravitational potential energy plus the energy converted into heat. This is the *principle of conservation of energy* and is seen to be a consequence of Newton's second law. If the body had been connected to a spring which was stretched as the body moved, two more terms would have appeared in the right-hand member of Eq. (7-6), representing the change in elastic potential energy.

If we let K_1 and K_2 represent the initial and final kinetic energies, respectively, V_1 and V_2 the initial and final potential energies (both gravitational and elastic) respectively, and W_f the work done against friction, then the principle of conservation of energy may be written

$$\begin{Bmatrix} \text{Work done or energy} \\ \text{supplied from the outside} \end{Bmatrix} = (K_2 - K_1) + (V_2 - V_1) + W_f. \qquad (7\text{-}7)$$

Examples.   (1) A body slides from rest without friction down a track consisting of one quadrant of a circle of radius R (Fig. 7-8).   Find the velocity at the bottom.

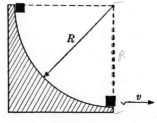

There is no energy supplied from without.

The change in kinetic energy is $\frac{1}{2}mv^2 - 0$.

The change in gravitational potential energy is $0 - mgR$.

No energy has been converted into heat.

Hence

$$0 = \tfrac{1}{2}mv^2 - mgR$$

or

$$v^2 = 2gR.$$

Fig. 7-8.

The velocity is seen to be that which would be acquired in free fall through a vertical height R.

(2) A 10-lb block is projected up a 37° inclined plane, with a velocity at the foot of the plane of 32 ft/sec.   It is observed to ascend a distance of 20 ft along the sloping surface of the plane, stop, and slide back to the bottom.   (a) Compute the friction force f acting on the block.   (b) Find the velocity of the block when it returns to the foot of the plane.

Consider first the upward motion only:

There is no energy supplied from without.

The change in kinetic energy is $0 - \dfrac{1}{2} \times \dfrac{10}{32} \times (32)^2$ ft-lb.

The change in gravitational potential energy is $10 \times 20 \sin 37° - 0$ ft-lb.
The energy converted into heat is $20f$ ft-lb.

Hence

$$0 = -\frac{1}{2} \times \frac{10}{32} \times (32)^2 + 10 \times 20 \sin 37° + 20f$$

or

$$20f = 160 - 120$$

and

$$f = 2 \text{ lb.}$$

Consider next the downward motion:

The change in kinetic energy is $\dfrac{1}{2} \times \dfrac{10}{32} \times v^2 - 0$ ft-lb.

The change in gravitational potential energy is $0 - 10 \times 20 \sin 37°$ ft-lb.
The energy converted into heat is 40 ft-lb.

Hence

$$0 = \frac{1}{2} \times \frac{10}{32} \times v^2 - 10 \times 20 \sin 37° + 40$$

or

$$v^2 = \frac{64}{10} \times 80 = 512$$

and

$$v = 23 \text{ ft/sec.}$$

7-7 Conservative and dissipative forces.   Work must be done by some outside agent to lift a body vertically at constant velocity; we have shown that this work is equal to the increase in gravitational potential energy of the body.   Work must also be done by an outside device to slide a body at constant velocity along a rough horizontal surface; in this case the potential energy of the body does not change and the work done is converted to heat.   Why is it that although external work must be done in both cases, we have an increase in potential energy in the first example and not in the second?   The distinction becomes evident when we consider the process of returning the body to its initial position.

We may say that in the first instance work was done against the gravitational pull of the earth, while in the second instance work was done against the force of friction.   If the weight is lowered at constant velocity to its original position, the gravitational force remains constant in magnitude and direction.   The descending weight can therefore be made to do work (it could, for example, raise a second equal weight connected to it by a string passing over a pulley) and since the force and distance are the same in both ascent and descent, the work obtainable equals that originally expended.   In other words, the work is *recoverable*, or in still other words, the net work done in a round trip is zero.

Contrast this with the behaviour of the friction force.   When we slide the body on the rough surface back to its original position, the friction force reverses and instead of recovering the work done in the first displacement we must again do work on the return trip.   The net work done in a round trip is not zero.

This difference between gravitational forces and friction forces is the criterion that determines whether or not there is an increase in potential energy when work is done.   If the work can be recovered there is an increase in potential energy; if the work can not be recovered there is no increase.   Forces such as those of gravity or the force exerted by a spring, where the work is recoverable, are called *conservative* forces.   Forces like those of sliding friction are called *nonconservative* or *dissipative* forces. Only when all the forces are conservative is the mechanical energy of a system conserved, and only when work is done against a conservative force is there an increase in potential energy.

It may be objected that since the heat developed when friction is present is equivalent to the energy dissipated, this heat might be used to operate a heat engine whose output could be used to raise a weight.   This question will be answered more fully in a later chapter in connection with the second law of thermodynamics.   For the present we shall simply state that while part of the heat can be converted back to mechanical work, it is never possible to recover all of it.

7-8 Power. The time element is not involved in the definition of work. The same amount of work is done in raising a given weight through a given height whether the work is done in one second, or one hour, or one year. In many instances, however, it is necessary to consider the *rate* at which work is done as well as the total amount of work accomplished. The rate at which work is done by a working agent is called the *power* developed by that agent.

If a quantity of work W is done in a time interval t the average power $\bar{P}$ is defined as

$$\text{Average power} = \frac{\text{work done}}{\text{time interval}},$$

$$\bar{P} = \frac{W}{t}.$$

If the rate of doing work is not uniform, the power at any instant is the ratio of the work done to the time interval, when both are extremely small.

$$\text{Instantaneous power } P = \frac{\Delta W}{\Delta t}. \tag{7-8}$$

In the English system, where work is expressed in foot-pounds and time in seconds, the unit of power is one foot-pound per second. Since this unit is inconveniently small, a larger unit called the horsepower (hp) is in common use. 1 hp = 550 ft-lb/sec = 33,000 ft-lb/min. That is, a 1 hp motor, running at full load, is doing 33,000 ft-lb of work every minute it runs.

The mks unit of power is one joule per second, which is called one *watt*. This is also an inconveniently small unit, and power is more commonly expressed in *kilowatts* or kw (1 kw = 1000 watts = 1000 joules/sec), or *megawatts* (1 megawatt = 1000 kw = 1,000,000 watts).

The cgs power unit is one erg per second. No single term is assigned to this unit.

A common misconception is that there is something inherently *electrical* about a watt or a kilowatt. This is not the case. It is true that electrical power is usually expressed in watts or kilowatts, but the power consumption of an incandescent lamp could equally well be expressed in horse-power, or an automobile engine rated in kilowatts.

From the relations between the newton, pound, meter, and foot, it is easy to show that 1 hp = 746 watts = 0.746 kw, or about ¾ of a kilowatt. This is a useful figure to remember.

Having defined two units of power, the horsepower and the kilowatt, we may use these in turn to define two new units of work, the *horsepower-hour* and the *kilowatt-hour* (kwh).

One horsepower-hour is the work done in one hour by an agent working at the constant rate of one horsepower.

Since such an agent does 33,000 ft-lb of work each minute, the work done in one hour is 60 × 33,000 = 1,980,000 ft-lb.

$$1 \text{ horsepower-hour} = 1.98 \times 10^6 \text{ foot-pounds.}$$

One kilowatt-hour is the work done in one hour by an agent working at the constant rate of one kilowatt.

Since such an agent does 1000 joules of work each second, the work done in one hour is 3600 × 1000 = 3,600,000 joules.

$$1 \text{ kilowatt-hour} = 3.6 \times 10^6 \text{ joules.}$$

Notice carefully that the horsepower-hour and the kilowatt-hour are units of *work*, not power.

One aspect of work or energy which may be pointed out here is that although it is an abstract physical quantity, it nevertheless has a monetary value. A pound of force or a foot-per-second of velocity are not things which are bought and sold as such, but a foot-pound or a kilowatt-hour of energy are quantities offered for sale at a definite market rate. In the form of electrical energy, a kilowatt-hour can be purchased at a price varying from a few tenths of a cent to a few cents, depending on the locality and the quantity purchased. In the form of heat, 778 ft-lb (one Btu) costs about a thousandth of a cent.

7-9 Power and velocity. Suppose a constant force F is exerted on a body, while the body undergoes a displacement x in the direction of the force. The work done is

$$W = Fx$$

and the average power developed is

$$\bar{P} = \frac{W}{t} = F\frac{x}{t}.$$ (7-9)

But $\frac{x}{t}$ is the average velocity, $\bar{v}$. Hence

$$\bar{P} = F\bar{v}.$$

If the time interval is made extremely short Eq. (7-9) reduces to

$$P = F\frac{\Delta x}{\Delta t}$$

or

$$\boxed{P = Fv,}$$ (7-10)

where P and v are instantaneous values.

Example: A locomotive traveling at 50 ft/sec exerts a draw-bar pull of 20,000 lb. What horsepower does it develop?

$$P = Fv$$
$$= 20,000 \times 50 = 1,000,000 \text{ ft-lb/sec}$$
$$= \frac{1,000,000}{550} = 1820 \text{ hp.}$$

7-10 Simple machines. A machine is a force-multiplying device. Its purpose is not to convert one form of energy into another, but merely to exert a force on an object which is different from (usually larger than) the force which is applied on the machine from the outside. Simple machines such as an inclined plane, a screw jack, a lever, a crank and axle, or a pulley system, shown in Fig. 7-9, play an important rôle in everyday life. Any one of these machines may be symbolized by the diagram of Fig. 7-10, where a weight w is imagined to be lifted a height y by the application of a force F acting through a distance s.

The force multiplication factor of a machine is expressed by the ratio w/F, known as the actual mechanical advantage R_A. Thus

$$R_A = \frac{w}{F}.$$

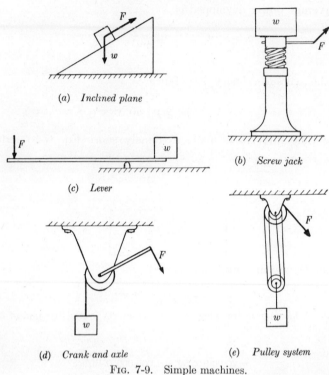

(a)   Inclined plane

(b)   Screw jack

(c)   Lever

(d)   Crank and axle   (e)   Pulley system

Fig. 7-9.   Simple machines.

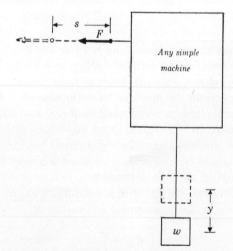

Fig. 7-10.   Schematic diagram of a machine.   The applied force F acts through a
distance s, and the weight w is lifted a height y.

The work input to the machine (supplied by the external agent responsible for the applied force F) is Fs, whereas the work output of the machine is wy.   From the principle of conservation of energy,

$$Fs = wy + W_f,$$

where W_f is the work done against friction in the machine.   The ideal mechanical advantage R_I which the machine would have if there were no friction may be calculated from this equation by setting $W_f = 0$ and solving for w/F, whence

$$R_I = \frac{s}{y}.$$

The efficiency E of the machine is defined as the work output divided by the work input, or

$$E = \frac{wy}{Fs} = \frac{w/F}{s/y},$$

or

$$\boxed{E = \frac{R_A}{R_I}.}\qquad (7\text{-}11)$$

The ideal mechanical advantage of a machine may usually be calculated from simple geometrical considerations.   Assuming s to be, say, one foot, it is a simple matter to calculate the corresponding value of y, whence $R_I = s/y$.   If, therefore, w and F are measured, the efficiency of the machine may be computed from Eq. (7-11).

7-11 Work done when a variable force is exerted.   The work done in stretching a spring, discussed in Sec. 7-5, is one example of a common situation in which work is done by an agent exerting a force which is not constant.   Unless the force varies in some simple way, it is not easy to find its average value and hence the methods used in Sec. 7-5 for finding the work done can not always be applied.

However, the work can always be computed graphically as follows. In Fig. 7-11(a) the curved line is the graph of a force which varies in some arbitrary way with the distance s.   Let the distance be subdivided into short segments Δs_1, Δs_2, etc., and approximate the varying force by a force that remains constant at the value F_1 over the distance Δs_1, then increases to the constant value F_2 over the distance Δs_2, etc., as indicated by the zigzag line.   The work that would be done by the agent exerting the

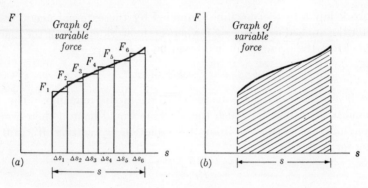

FIG. 7-11. The work done by an agent exerting a variable force equals the shaded area in part (b).

constant force F_1 in the displacement Δs_1 would be $F_1 \times \Delta s_1$; the work done in the displacement Δs_2 would be $F_2 \times \Delta s_2$; etc. The total work W done would be

$$W = F_1 \times \Delta s_1 + F_2 \times \Delta s_2 + \cdots$$

But the products $F_1 \times \Delta s_1$, $F_2 \times \Delta s_2$, etc., are the *areas* of the various vertical strips, and the total work is evidently equal to the total area of these strips. As the subdivisions are made smaller and smaller, the total area of these strips becomes more and more nearly equal to the shaded area between the smooth curve and the horizontal axis, and vertical lines at the ends of the displacement s as in Fig. 7-11(b).

Hence if a graph is constructed of any variable force, the work done can be determined by computing (or measuring) the area between the curve and the distance axis.

Example: Use the graphical method described above to find the work done in stretching a spring.

The force required to stretch a spring is directly proportional to the stretch and is shown by the straight line in Fig. 7-12. The work done is equal to the shaded triangular area. The area of a triangle equals one-half the product of base and altitude. The base of the triangle is x, its altitude is kx, and its area is

Area $= \frac{1}{2} \times x \times kx = \frac{1}{2}kx^2 =$ work,

which is the same as the answer obtained in Sec. 7-5 using the average force.

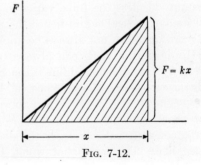

FIG. 7-12.

7-12 Mass and energy. While the mass of a body can ordinarily be considered constant, there is ample experimental evidence that actually it is a function of the velocity of the body, increasing with increasing velocity according to the relation

$$m = \frac{m_0}{\sqrt{1 - (v^2/c^2)}},$$

where m_0 is the "rest mass" of the body, c is the velocity of light, and v the velocity of the body.

This equation was predicted by Lorentz and Einstein on theoretical grounds based on relativity considerations and it has been directly verified by experiments on rapidly moving electrons and ions. The increase in mass is not appreciable until the velocity approaches that of light and therefore it ordinarily escapes detection.

When one calculates the work done in setting a body in motion and takes into account the variation of mass with velocity, the expression for the work, which is equal to the kinetic energy, is

$$K = mc^2 - m_0c^2 = (m - m_0)c^2. \tag{7-12}$$

That is, the kinetic energy equals the increase in mass over the rest mass, multiplied by the square of the velocity of light. This is the famous Einstein relation between mass and energy. The kinetic energy is in ergs if m is in grams and c is in cm/sec. When the velocity is small compared with the velocity of light, the expression above reduces to the familiar form $\frac{1}{2} mv^2$.

We shall illustrate the general form of the kinetic energy equation by an example taken from the field of nuclear physics. When the nucleus of a lithium atom is struck by a rapidly moving proton (the nucleus of a hydrogen atom), a momentary union of the two nuclei takes place, after which the compound nucleus breaks up into two alpha particles. (Alpha particles are the nuclei of helium atoms.) The alpha particles recoil in almost opposite directions and move initially with very high velocities. Their combined kinetic energy is much greater than the kinetic energy of the original proton. The source of this kinetic energy is the so-called "binding energy" of the nuclear particles. That is, the potential energy of the assemblage of protons and neutrons that makes up the unstable composite nucleus is larger than the potential energy when the same number of particles are combined in the form of two helium nuclei. A crude analogy is that of two masses forced apart by a compressed spring, but tied together by a cord. If the cord is cut, the potential energy of the spring is transformed into kinetic energy of the recoiling masses.

The rest mass of a proton is 1.6715×10^{-24} gm. The rest mass of a lithium nucleus is 11.6399×10^{-24} gm, and that of an alpha particle is 6.6404×10^{-24} gm. Although the proton is moving when it collides with the lithium nucleus, its velocity is not great and we may assume its mass equal to its rest mass. Hence the mass of the original system is

$$(1.6715 + 11.6399) \times 10^{-24} = 13.3114 \times 10^{-24} \text{ gm.}$$

The rest mass of the two alpha particles is

$$2 \times 6.6404 \times 10^{-24} = 13.2808 \times 10^{-24} \text{ gm.}$$

The alpha particles must therefore be traveling with such velocity that their (combined) masses are increased from 13.2808×10^{-24} gm to 13.3114×10^{-24} gm. Then from Eq. (7-16) their (combined) kinetic energy is

$$K = (13.3114 - 13.2808) \times 10^{-24} \times (3 \times 10^{10})^2$$

$$= 2.75 \times 10^{-5} \text{ erg.}$$

Let us compare this with the energy released in a typical chemical reaction. When 2 moles of hydrogen combine with one mole of oxygen to form 2 moles of water in the reaction

$$2H_2 + O_2 = 2H_2O,$$

116,000 calories are released. This energy is shared among the H_2O molecules, of which there are $2 \times 6.02 \times 10^{23} = 12 \times 10^{23}$ molecules. (One mole of any substance contains 6.02×10^{23} molecules.) Since 1 calorie $= 4.2$ joules $= 4.2 \times 10^7$ ergs, 1.16×10^5 cal $= 4.87 \times 10^{12}$ ergs, and the energy per molecule is

$$\frac{4.87 \times 10^{12}}{12 \times 10^{23}} = 4 \times 10^{-12} \text{ erg.}$$

The energy released in the nuclear reaction above is roughly 10 million times as great.

The computation of the energy released in the nuclear reaction is verified by observing the distance the alpha particles travel in air at atmospheric pressure before being brought to rest by collisions with other molecules. This distance is found to be 8.31 cm. (One way of making such measurements is with the help of a cloud chamber, illustrated in Fig.

49-5.)   A series of independent experiments is then performed in which the range of alpha particles of known energy is measured.   These experiments show that in order to travel 8.31 cm, an alpha particle must have an initial kinetic energy of 1.38×10^{-5} erg.   The energy of the two alphas together is therefore

$$2 \times 1.38 \times 10^{-5} = 2.76 \times 10^{-5} \text{ erg.}$$

This is in excellent agreement with the energy computed from the excess mass.

Problems — Chapter 7

7-1. The locomotive of a freight train exerts a constant force of 6 tons on the train while drawing it at 50 mi/hr on a level track. How many foot-pounds of work are done by the locomotive in a distance of 1 mi?

7-2. An 80-lb block is pushed a distance of 20 ft along a level floor at constant speed by a force at an angle of 30° below the horizontal. The coefficient of friction between block and floor is 0.25. How many foot-pounds of work are done?

7-3. The force in pounds required to stretch a certain spring a distance of x ft beyond its unstretched length is given by $F = 10x$. (a) What force will stretch the spring 6 in? 1 ft? 2 ft? (b) How much work is required to stretch the spring 6 in? 1 ft? 2 ft?

7-4. A block is pushed 4 ft along a horizontal surface by a horizontal force of 10 lb. The opposing force of friction is 2 lb. (a) How much work is done by the agent exerting the 10-lb force? (b) How much energy is converted into heat?

7-5. (a) Compute the kinetic energy of an 1800-lb automobile traveling at 30 mi/hr. (b) How many times as great is the kinetic energy if the velocity is doubled?

7-6. Compute the kinetic energy, in ergs and in joules, of a 2-gm rifle bullet traveling at 500 m/sec.

7-7. What is the potential energy of a 1600-lb elevator at the top of the Empire State building, 1248 ft above street level? Assume the potential energy at street level to be zero.

7-8. What is the increase in potential energy of a 1-kgm body when lifted from the floor to a table 1 meter high?

Fig. 7-13

7-9. A meter stick whose mass is 300 gm is pivoted at one end as in Fig. 7-13 and displaced through an angle of 60°. What is the increase in its potential energy?

7-10. The scale of a certain spring balance reads from zero to 400 lb and is 8 in long. (a) What is the potential energy of the spring when it is stretched 8 in? 4 in? (b) When a 50-lb weight hangs from the spring?

7-11. A block weighing 16 lb is pushed 20 ft along a horizontal frictionless surface by a horizontal force of 8 lb. The block starts from rest. (a) How much work is done? What becomes of this work? (b) Check your answer by computing the acceleration of the block, its final velocity, and its kinetic energy.

7-12. In the preceding problem, suppose the block had an initial velocity of 10 ft/sec, other quantities remaining the same. (a) How much work is done? (b) Check by computing the final velocity and the increase in kinetic energy.

7-13. A 16-lb block is lifted vertically at a constant velocity of 10 ft/sec through a height of 20 ft. How great a force is required? How much work is done? What becomes of this work?

7-14. A 25-lb block is pushed 100 ft up the sloping surface of a plane inclined at an angle of 37° to the horizontal by a constant force F of 32.5 lb acting parallel to the plane. The coefficient of friction between the block and plane is 0.25. (a) How much work is done by the agent exerting the force F? (b) Compute the increase in kinetic energy of the block. (c) Compute the increase in potential energy of the block. (d) Compute the work done against friction. What becomes of this work? (e) What can you say about the sum of b, c, and d?

7-15. A man whose mass is 70 kgm walks up to the third floor of a building. This is a vertical height of 12 meters above the street level. (a) How many joules of work has he done? (b) By how much has he increased his potential energy? (c) If he climbs the stairs in 20 sec, how many watts has he expended?

7-16. A pump is required to lift 200 gallons of water per minute from a well 20 ft deep and eject it with a speed of 30 ft/sec. How much work is done per minute in lifting the water? How much in giving it kinetic energy? What horsepower engine is needed?

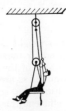

FIG. 7-14

7-17. A man weighing 150 lb sits on a platform suspended from a movable pulley and raises himself by a rope passing over a fixed pulley. (Fig. 7-14.) Assuming no friction losses, find: (a) The force he must exert. (b) The increase in his energy when he raises himself 2 ft. Answer part (b) by calculating his increase in potential energy, and also by computing the product of the force on the rope and the length of rope passing through his hands.

7-18. A 4800-lb elevator starts from rest and is pulled upward with a constant acceleration of 10 ft/sec². (a) Find the tension in the supporting cable. (b) What is the velocity of the elevator after it has risen 45 ft? (c) Find the kinetic energy of the elevator 3 sec after it starts. (d) How much is its potential energy increased in the first 3 sec? (e) What horsepower is required when the elevator is traveling 22 ft/sec?

7-19. A barrel weighing 250 lb is suspended by a rope 30 ft long. What horizontal force is necessary to hold the barrel sideways 5 ft from the vertical? How much work is done in moving it to this position?

7-20. How much work will be done in lifting a 50-lb weight to a height of 25 ft assuming that 25 percent of the *total* work done is used in overcoming friction?

7-21. The spring of a spring-gun has a stiffness coefficient of 3 lb per inch. It is compressed 2 inches and a ball weighing 0.02 lb is placed in the barrel against the compressed spring. (a) Compute the maximum velocity with which the ball leaves the gun when released. (b) Determine the maximum velocity if a resisting force of 2.25 lb acts on the ball.

7-22. A block weighing 2 lb is forced against a horizontal spring of negligible mass, compressing the spring an amount $x_1 = 6$ inches. Upon releasing the block, it moves on a horizontal table top a distance $x_2 = 2$ ft before coming to rest. The spring constant k is 8 lb/ft. (Fig. 7-15.) What is the coefficient of friction, μ, between the block and the table?

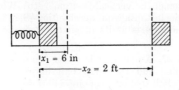

FIG. 7-15

7-23. A 2-kgm block is dropped from a height of 40 cm onto a spring whose force constant, k, is 1960 newtons/meter. Find the maximum distance the spring will be compressed.

7-24. A 16-lb projectile is fired from a gun with a muzzle velocity of 800 ft/sec at an angle of elevation of 45°. The angle is then increased to 90° and a similar projectile is fired with the same muzzle velocity. (a) Find the maximum heights attained by the projectiles. (b) Show that the total energy at the top of the trajectory is the same in the two cases. (c) Using the energy principle, find the height attained by a similar projectile if fired at an elevation angle of 30°.

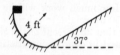

FIG. 7-16

7-25. The track shown in Fig. 7-16 consists of a frictionless quarter-circle of radius 4 ft, smoothly joined to a rough inclined plane of angle 37°. A block is released from rest at the top of the quarter-circle. The coefficient of friction between the block and the inclined plane is 0.3. What fraction of the kinetic energy which the block possesses at the bottom of the track is dissipated by friction as the block slides up the plane?

7-26. A small sphere of mass m is fastened to a weightless string of length 2 ft to form a pendulum. The pendulum is swinging so as to make a maximum angle of 60° with the vertical. (a) What is the velocity of the sphere when it passes through the vertical position? (b) What is the instantaneous acceleration when the pendulum is at its maximum deflection?

7-27. A man stands at the top of a 37° incline and throws a ball horizontally. The ball strikes at a point 240 ft down the incline. (a) If the ball had been thrown with the same initial speed but at an angle of 37° above a horizontal surface, how far would it have traveled before striking? (Neglect air resistance.) (b) If the ball weighs 0.5 lb and is in the thrower's hand for $\frac{1}{8}$ sec, what is the average horsepower developed while the ball is being thrown?

7-28. An automobile weighing 2000 lb has a maximum speed of 100 ft/sec on a horizontal road when the engine is developing full power of 50 horsepower. What is its maximum speed if the road rises 1 ft in 20 ft? Assume all friction forces to be constant.

7-29. A string is attached to the upper side of a 350-gm block of wood placed on an inclined plane. When the string is parallel to the plane, a tension of 260,000 dynes in the string will pull the block up the plane at a constant speed. When the tension in the string is 150,000 dynes, the block moves down the plane with constant speed. (a) What is the force of friction between the block and the plane? (b) What is the actual mechanical advantage of the inclined plane? (c) What is the ideal mechanical advantage of the inclined plane? (d) What is the efficiency of the inclined plane?

7-30. An 800-lb weight is to be raised with uniform speed by means of a screw jack. The lever arm of the screw jack is 18 inches long and there are 4 threads to the inch. (a) Find the least force required if the efficiency is 20 percent. (b) What is the actual mechanical advantage? (c) What is the ideal mechanical advantage?

7-31. A screw jack moves upward $\frac{1}{4}$ in when turned through one revolution, that is, the pitch is $\frac{1}{4}$ in. What load could be lifted if a force of 20 lb is applied at the end of a bar 2 ft long, if friction is neglected?

7-32. A force of 6 lb is required to raise a weight of 30 lb by means of a pulley system. If the weight is raised 1 ft while the applied force acts through a distance of 8 ft, find (a) the ideal mechanical advantage, (b) the actual mechanical advantage, and (c) the efficiency.

7-33. Prove that the ideal mechanical advantage of the inclined plane shown in Fig. 7-9 (a) is equal to the length of the plane divided by its height.

7-34. Prove that the ideal mechanical advantage of the lever shown in Fig. 7-9 (c) is the distance from the fulcrum to the point of application of F divided by the distance from the fulcrum to the point of application of the load.

7-35. Prove that the ideal mechanical advantage of the crank and axle shown in Fig. 7-9 (d) is equal to the length of the crank divided by the radius of the wheel.

7-36. A body moves a distance of 10 ft under the action of a force which has the constant value of 5.5 lb for the first 6 ft and then decreases to a value of 2 lb as

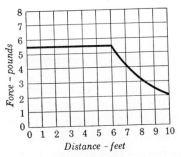

Distance - feet

Fig. 7-17

shown by the graph in Fig. 7-17. (a) How much work is done in the first 6 ft of the motion? (b) How much work is done in the last 4 ft?

7-37. An atomic bomb containing 20 kgm of plutonium explodes. The rest mass of the products of the explosion is less than the original rest mass by one ten-thousandth of the original rest mass. (a) How much energy is released in the explosion? (b) If the explosion takes place in one microsecond, what is the average power developed by the bomb? (c) How much water could the released energy lift to a height of one mile?

CHAPTER 8

IMPULSE AND MOMENTUM

8-1 Impulse and momentum. In the preceding chapter it was shown how the concepts of work and energy are developed from Newton's laws of motion. We shall next see how two similar concepts, those of *impulse* and *momentum*, also arise from Newton's laws. The most common use of these concepts is in connection with problems in impact.

Fig. 8-1 represents two bodies that approach one another on a smooth horizontal surface, collide, and then recede from one another. Quantities relating to the first body are unprimed, those relating to the second are primed. The subscript 0 refers to values before the collision, and symbols without subscripts refer to values after the collision.

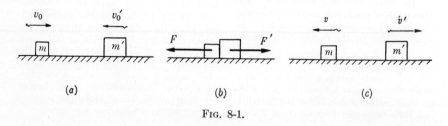

Fig. 8-1.

Since the plane is horizontal and frictionless, the only forces of interest are those which either body exerts on the other during the time the two are in contact. These forces are designated by F and F' in Fig. 8-1(b). From Newton's third law, F and F' are equal in magnitude and oppositely directed. That is, $F = -F'$. The forces F and F' will both vary during the collision. Of course, both are zero before contact. Both are small at the first instant of contact, then both increase to a maximum, and both decrease and become zero when the bodies separate. A force that varies with the time in this manner is called an *impulsive force* and is plotted on a force-time diagram in Fig. 8-2(a) where the impulsive force is seen to start at time t_0, rise to a large maximum and end at time t. Suppose the total time interval $t - t_0$ is subdivided into any number of parts $\Delta t_1, \Delta t_2, \ldots$ and rectangles are drawn as in Fig. 8-2(b) whose jagged outline approximates the smooth curve. Clearly, the larger the number of subdivisions the more closely will the smooth curve be approximated and the more closely will the sum of the areas of the rectangles approach the area under the smooth curve.

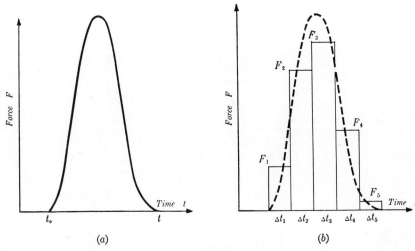

$$\text{Fig. 8-2.}$$

Let us therefore replace the continuously varying impulsive force by a force which remains constant at the value F_1 during the time interval Δt_1, then jumps instantaneously to the value F_2, maintaining this value for a time Δt_2, and so on. If the velocity of the body of mass m is originally v_0, and changes to the value v_1 at the end of the first time interval, we have, from Newton's second law

$$F_1 = m \frac{v_1 - v_0}{\Delta t_1}$$

or

$$F_1 \Delta t_1 = mv_1 - mv_0;$$

and similarly for the other time intervals

$$F_2 \Delta t_2 = mv_2 - mv_1$$
$$F_3 \Delta t_3 = mv_3 - mv_2$$
$$F_4 \Delta t_4 = mv_4 - mv_3$$
$$F_5 \Delta t_5 = mv - mv_4$$

where v is the velocity at the end of the last time interval. Adding these equations, we notice that all terms in the right-hand member cancel except mv_0 and mv. Hence

$$\Sigma F \Delta t = mv - mv_0. \tag{8-1}$$

If we now imagine the total time interval $t - t_0$ subdivided into a larger number of steps, the left-hand member of Eq. (8-1) becomes the area under the smooth curve, while the right-hand member remains un-affected.   We have, therefore, the *rigorous* result that

$$\left\{ \begin{array}{c} \text{Area under} \\ \text{the } F\text{-}t \text{ curve} \end{array} \right\} = mv - mv_0. \tag{8-2}$$

Similarly,

$$\left\{ \begin{array}{c} \text{Area under} \\ \text{the } F'\text{-}t \text{ curve} \end{array} \right\} = m'v' - m'v_0'. \tag{8-3}$$

It is useful to give names to the terms in Eqs. (8-2) and (8-3).   The product of the mass and velocity of a body is called its *momentum*.

$$\boxed{\text{Momentum} = mv.}$$

The area under the F-t curve is called the *impulse* of the force and is represented by J.   Thus

$$\boxed{\text{Impulse of a force} = J = \left\{ \begin{array}{c} \text{Area under} \\ \text{the } F\text{-}t \text{ curve} \end{array} \right\}.}$$

Eq. (8-2) or (8-3) may therefore be stated verbally as follows: *The change in momentum of either body equals the impulse of the force exerted on the body.*

If in a special case the force is constant, the area is merely $F(t - t_0)$ and

$$\text{Impulse of a constant force} = J = F(t - t_0). \tag{8-4}$$

The unit of impulse is one pound-second in the English system, one newton-second in the mks system, and one dyne-second in the cgs system. The units of momentum in the three systems are one slug-ft/sec, one kgm-m/sec and one gm-cm/sec.   The unit of impulse in any system is equivalent to the corresponding unit of momentum, as is easily seen, for example, by recalling from Newton's second law that

$$F = m \quad \times \quad a,$$

$$1 \text{ lb} = 1 \text{ slug} \times 1 \frac{\text{ft}}{\text{sec}^2}.$$

Hence

$$1 \text{ lb-sec} = 1 \frac{\text{slug-ft}}{\text{sec}}.$$

Momentum and impulse, unlike energy and work, are vector quantities. The momentum vector of a moving body is in the same direction as its velocity; the direction of an impulse vector is the same as that of the force producing the impulse.

Examples. (1) A golf ball weighs $1\frac{2}{3}$ oz. If its velocity immediately after being driven is 225 ft/sec, what was the impulse of the blow?

Since the ball is initially at rest, its change in momentum is equal to its final momentum, or

$$mv - mv_0 = \frac{1.67}{16 \times 32} \times 225 = 0.734 \text{ slug-ft/sec.}$$

Hence, since impulse and change in momentum are numerically equal, the impulse of the blow is $J = 0.734$ lb-sec.

Note that the *force* of the blow cannot be computed from the data above. Any *force* such that the area under the F–t curve = .734 lb-sec, or any constant force acting for a time interval of such length that the product $F\ (t - t_0) = 0.734$ lb-sec, would result in the same velocity. Only if the time of duration of the blow is known, can the force, assuming it to be constant, be computed. An analysis of golf strokes carried out by Dr. Edgerton of M.I.T. with the aid of the high speed stroboscope, shows that a golf ball remains in contact with the club face for about half a thousandth of a second (0.0005 sec). Let us assume the force constant during this time.

Then

$$J = F(t - t_0),$$

$$F = \frac{J}{t - t_0} = \frac{0.734}{.0005} = 1470 \text{ lb.}$$

The figure above gives the *time average* force whether it is constant or not.

(2) A ball weighing $\frac{1}{4}$ lb is thrown horizontally against a vertical wall. Its velocity before striking is 64 ft/sec and it rebounds with a velocity of 48 ft/sec. The time of contact with the wall is 0.05 sec. Compute the momentum of the ball before and after the collision and the force exerted on it by the wall. Assume the force constant.

$$\text{Momentum before collision} = mv_0 = \frac{\frac{1}{4}}{32} \times 64 = 0.5 \text{ slug-ft/sec.}$$

$$\text{Momentum after collision} = mv = \frac{\frac{1}{4}}{32} \times (-48) = -0.375 \text{ slug-ft/sec.}$$

(Consider the initial direction of motion positive.)

The change in momentum is $mv - mv_0 = -.375 - .500 = -.875$ slug-ft/sec. Hence the impulse of the force on the ball is $J = -.875$ lb-sec, and if the time is .05 sec and the force is constant,

$$F = \frac{J}{t - t_0} = \frac{-.875}{.05} = -17.5 \text{ lb}.$$

The minus sign means that the direction of the force on the ball is opposite to its initial velocity.

8-2 Conservation of momentum.   Let us return to a consideration of Eqs. (8-2) and (8-3)

$$mv - mv_0 = \text{impulse of } F, \quad m'v' - m'v_0' = \text{impulse of } F'.$$

We know from Newton's third law that, at every instant,

$$F = -F'.$$

Hence

$$\text{Impulse of } F = - \text{ impulse of } F',$$

and therefore

$$mv - mv_0 = - (m'v' - m'v_0')$$

or

$$\boxed{mv_0 + m'v_0' = mv + m'v'.} \tag{8-5}$$

The left side of Eq. (8-5) is the total momentum of the system before the collision, the right side is the total momentum after the collision.   We have therefore derived the extremely important result that *the total momentum of the colliding bodies is unaltered by the collision*.   This fact is called the *principle of conservation of momentum*.   It is one of the most important principles in mechanics.

Notice that detailed knowledge of how the forces F and F' vary is unnecessary.   The impulses of the forces are necessarily equal in magnitude and opposite in direction and hence they produce equal and opposite changes in momentum.   The net change in momentum is therefore zero.

A more general statement of the principle of conservation of momentum, which does not restrict it to a collision between two bodies, is as follows:

The total momentum of a system can only be changed by external forces acting on the system.   The internal forces, being equal and opposite and acting for equal times, produce equal and opposite changes in momentum which cancel one another.   Hence, *the total momentum of an isolated system is constant in magnitude and direction.*

Example: The Springfield rifle weighs 9.69 lb and fires a bullet weighing 150 grains (1 lb = 7000 grains) at a muzzle velocity of 2700 ft/sec. Compute the recoil velocity of the rifle if freely suspended.

The momentum of rifle and bullet before firing is zero. Hence, after firing, the forward momentum of the bullet is numerically equal to the backward momentum of the rifle. The mass of the rifle is $\frac{9.69}{32}$ slugs and that of the bullet is $\frac{150}{7000 \times 32}$ slugs.

Then

$$\frac{150}{7000 \times 32} \times 2700 = \frac{9.69}{32} \times v,$$

$$v = 5.9 \text{ ft/sec.}$$

(The forward momentum of the burnt gases, which is quite appreciable, has been neglected.)

It is important to note that the kinetic energies of the bullet and rifle are *not* equal. The explanation is evident when one considers that a body acquires kinetic energy when work is done on it, the work being the product of the force and the distance moved. While the gases are propelling the bullet forward and the rifle backward, although the force on each is the same, the distance moved by the bullet is relatively large (the length of the barrel) while the distance moved by the slowly recoiling rifle is much less. Hence the work done on the bullet is much greater than the work done on the rifle and its kinetic energy is correspondingly greater. Momentum, however, being equal to the product of force and *time*, is the same for both bullet and rifle.

Referring to the example of the Springfield, we find

$$K_{\text{bullet}} = \tfrac{1}{2}mv^2 = \frac{1}{2}\left(\frac{150}{7000 \times 32}\right)\left(2700\right)^2 = 2{,}440 \text{ ft-lb.}$$

$$K_{\text{rifle}} = \tfrac{1}{2}MV^2 = \frac{1}{2}\left(\frac{9.69}{32}\right)\left(5.9\right)^2 = 5.25 \text{ ft-lb.}$$

8-3 Elastic and inelastic collisions. Coefficient of restitution. Although the momentum remains constant when two (or more) bodies collide, the same is not necessarily true of the kinetic energy. If the kinetic energy *does* remain constant the collision is called *perfectly elastic*. At the opposite extreme from a perfectly elastic collision is one in which the colliding bodies stick together as would two lumps of putty and both move with the same velocity after the collision. In this case the collision is *perfectly inelastic*. Depending on the properties of the colliding bodies, all intermediate cases between perfectly elastic and perfectly inelastic collisions are possible. Collisions between bodies of finite size such as two billiard balls are never completely elastic and the only instances of perfectly elastic collisions known are those between atoms, molecules, and electrons. Even these may not be perfectly elastic if the kinetic energies of the particles are sufficiently great.

If a collision between two bodies is perfectly elastic, the equations

$$(\tfrac{1}{2}mv_0^2 + \tfrac{1}{2}m'v_0'^2) = (\tfrac{1}{2}mv^2 + \tfrac{1}{2}m'v'^2) \text{ (Conservation of energy)}$$

and

$$(mv_0 + m'v_0') = (mv + m'v') \text{ (Conservation of momentum)}$$

must both be satisfied. (The primes and subscripts have the same significance as in Fig. 8-1.) These may be written

$$m(v_0^2 - v^2) = m'(v'^2 - v_0'^2),$$

$$m(v_0 - v) = m'(v' - v_0').$$

When the first is divided by the second, we obtain

$$v_0 + v = v' + v_0'$$

or finally,

$$v_0 - v_0' = -(v - v').$$

But $v_0 - v_0'$ is the relative velocity before the collision and $v - v'$ is the relative velocity after the collision. Hence, in a perfectly elastic collision the relative velocity is reversed in direction but unaltered in magnitude.

The degree to which a pair of colliding bodies approach perfect elasticity is expressed by their *coefficient of restitution, e,* which is defined as the negative ratio of the relative velocity after collision to the relative velocity before collision.

$$e = -\frac{v - v'}{v_0 - v_0'}. \tag{8-6}$$

From what has just been shown, the coefficient of restitution is unity if the colliding bodies are perfectly elastic, and is zero if the bodies are perfectly inelastic. These are the two extremes and, in general, the coefficient of restitution has some value between zero and unity.

When a ball is dropped onto and rebounds from a fixed plate it has, in effect, collided with the earth. The mass of the earth is so large its velocity is practically unaltered by the collision. Hence in this special case,

$$e = -\frac{v}{v_0}.$$

The relative velocity before the collision is simply the velocity acquired in falling from a height h_0 or $\sqrt{2gh_0}$. If, after colliding, the ball rises to a height h, the relative velocity after the collision is $-\sqrt{2gh}$ (the downward direction is considered positive). Hence the coefficient of restitution is

Fig. 8-3.

$$e = -\frac{-\sqrt{2gh}}{\sqrt{2gh_0}} = \sqrt{\frac{h}{h_0}}$$

and a simple way of measuring it is to measure these two heights. The value obtained represents a joint property of the ball and the surface.

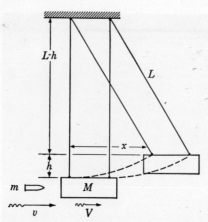

FIG. 8-4. The ballistic pendulum.

Fig. 8-3 is a multiflash photograph of a golf ball dropping onto and rebounding from an iron plate. The heights h_0 and h can be measured from the photograph and the velocities before and after colliding can be found from the spacing of the images before and after impact.

8-4 The ballistic pendulum. Another example of the principle of conservation of momentum is afforded by the ballistic pendulum, used to measure the velocity of a rifle bullet and illustrated in Fig. 8-4. A wooden block of mass M hangs vertically by a cord. A bullet of mass m, whose velocity v is to be measured, is fired horizontally into the block and remains embedded in it. After the bullet has come to rest in the block, both block and bullet have the common velocity V. From the principle of conservation of momentum

$$mv = (M + m)V.$$

The block now swings until its center of gravity has risen through a vertical height h such that the potential energy at the top of the swing is equal to the kinetic energy at the bottom. That is,

$$(M + m)gh = \tfrac{1}{2}(M + m)V^2, \quad \text{or}$$

$$V^2 = 2gh.$$

The vertical rise h is usually small and is best obtained indirectly by measuring the horizontal displacement x. It will be seen from Fig. 8-4 that if L is the length of the pendulum,

$$(L - h)^2 + x^2 = L^2, \quad \text{or}$$

$$h = \frac{h^2 + x^2}{2L}.$$

If h is small compared with x, then h^2 may be negelected and $h = x^2/2L$.

In practice, the mass of the bullet is usually negligible compared to that of the pendulum. Then

$$mv = MV, \quad V = \sqrt{2gh} = x\sqrt{g/L}$$

$$v = \frac{Mx}{m}\sqrt{g/L}. \qquad\qquad (8\text{-}7)$$

Example: A bullet of mass 20 gm is fired into a ballistic pendulum of mass 5 kgm. The center of gravity of the pendulum rises 10 cm after being struck. Find the initial velocity of the bullet.

The potential energy of the pendulum at the top of its swing was

$$Mgh = 5 \times 9.8 \times .10 = 4.9 \text{ joules}.$$

This is equal to the kinetic energy at the bottom of the swing and the velocity at this point was therefore

$$V = 1.4 \text{ m/sec}.$$

Hence the momentum of the pendulum at the start of its swing was

$$MV = 5 \times 1.4 = 7.0 \text{ kgm-m/sec}.$$

This is equal to the original momentum of the bullet, mv. Therefore

$$mv = 7.0 = .02v,$$

$$v = 350 \text{ m/sec} = 1150 \text{ ft/sec}.$$

It must be emphasized that this is an inelastic collision and the kinetic energy of the bullet before the collision is not equal to the kinetic energy of the pendulum after the collision. The latter, computed above, is 4.9 joules. The kinetic energy of the bullet was

$$\tfrac{1}{2}mv^2 = \frac{1}{2} \times .02 \times (350)^2$$

$$= 1220 \text{ joules}.$$

Hence only about one-half of one percent of the kinetic energy of the bullet is transferred to the pendulum.

8-5 Newton's second law.

Newton himself did not state his second law in the form in which we have used it. A free translation (Newton's "Principia" was written in Latin) is as follows:

"Change of motion is proportional to the applied force, and takes place in the direction of the force. . . . Quantity of motion is proportional to mass and velocity conjointly."

From Newton's definition of "motion," or "quantity of motion," it is evident that he used this term for the concept we now call momentum.

It is also clear from his writings that the term "change" meant "rate of change" and that the "applied force" referred to the resultant force. Hence in current terminology Newton's statement is:

"Rate of change of momentum is proportional to the resultant force and is in the direction of this force."

In mathematical language this becomes

$$\frac{\Delta(mv)}{\Delta t} \propto F,$$

or

$$F = k\frac{\Delta(mv)}{\Delta t}.$$

If the mass m is constant, this reduces to

$$F = km\frac{\Delta v}{\Delta t} = kma,$$

which is the form we have used, with k made equal to unity by proper choice of units.

We have pointed out in Sec. 7-12 that while the mass of a body can ordinarily be considered constant, it increases with increasing velocity according to the relation

$$m = \frac{m_0}{\sqrt{1 - (v^2/c^2)}},$$

where m_0 is the "rest mass" of the body, c is the velocity of light, and v the velocity of the body. However, if the mass cannot be considered constant, we cannot set $F = ma$ and the original form of Newton's law must be used.

It is a striking example of Newton's genius, that although he could scarcely have previsioned the theory of relativity, he appreciated the fact that momentum is an entity more fundamental than mass.

8-6 The principles of jet propulsion. The flight of a rocket, driven upward by the jet of rapidly moving gas ejected from its tail, is a sight familiar to everyone. Recent applications of the principles of jet propulsion to projectiles and airplanes indicate the increasing importance of this type of motive power. We shall consider briefly the physical principles involved.

A jet propulsion motor, in principle, is merely a combustion chamber in which solid or liquid fuel is burned, and which has an opening or jet to direct the gaseous products of combustion in the desired direction. For concreteness, let us consider the flight of a rocket. The momentum of the rocket is initially zero. When its charge of fuel is ignited, the stream of exhaust gases acquires a momentum in the downward direction, and since momentum is conserved, the rocket acquires an equal and oppositely directed momentum. From the viewpoint of the forces involved, the gas in the combustion chamber pushes downward on the gases in the jet, and upward on the body of the rocket.

We must consider more than the beginning of the motion, however. At the start of its flight, while the rocket is moving slowly, the rocket motor is a very inefficient device. Practically all of the *energy* developed at this stage is used to give kinetic energy to the rapidly moving exhaust gases and very little energy is acquired by the rocket itself. But as the rocket gains velocity the exhaust gases, which are expelled with a certain velocity *relative to the rocket,* move more and more slowly relative to the earth. When the rocket has acquired a velocity relative to the earth, equal to the velocity with which the exhaust gases are expelled from it, these gases as they leave the rocket (or better, as the rocket leaves them) are at rest relative to the earth and their kinetic energy is therefore zero. Hence at this velocity all of the energy developed by the fuel is imparted to the rocket. The energy which a rocket carries in its charge of fuel can therefore be utilized much more effectively if the rocket is initially given a "boost" by some auxiliary means.

It should be noted that a rocket does not depend on the atmosphere for its propulsion, but would actually perform better in the absence of an atmosphere because of lessened air resistance. A helicopter is able to rise vertically only because its propeller sets a stream of air into downward motion. The downward force on the air is equal to the rate of change of downward momentum of the air stream, and the equal and opposite reaction to this force supports the helicopter. The rocket motor, on the other hand, pushes down on its own products of combustion and does not depend on the presence of an external atmosphere.

It can readily be seen why jet propulsion is eminently suitable for stratosphere flight at high velocity. In the stratosphere, where the density of the air is small, it is difficult for a conventional propeller to get a "bite" of the air so as to produce rearward momentum, but this is no handicap to a jet propulsion motor since it reacts on its own exhaust. Furthermore, the efficiency of jet propulsion is a maximum when the forward velocity of the motor is sufficiently great so that it equals the (relative) velocity of ejection of the exhaust gases.

Problems — Chapter 8

8-1. (a) What is the momentum of a 10-ton truck whose velocity is 30 mi/hr? At what velocity will a 5-ton truck have (b) the same momentum? (c) the same kinetic energy?

8-2. A block of mass 100 gm, initially at rest on a horizontal frictionless surface, is acted on by a horizontal force $F = 10^4 + 3 \times 10^3 t$, where F is in dynes and t is in seconds. There is no friction. (a) Plot a force-time diagram for values of t from $t = 0$ to $t = 5$ sec. (b) What is the impulse during the first five seconds? (c) What is the velocity of the block when $t = 5$ sec? (d) Use the principle of conservation of energy to calculate the work done by the force in the first 5 sec.

8-3. A bullet having a mass of 0.05 kgm, moving with a velocity of 400 m/sec, penetrates a distance of 0.1 m in a wooden block firmly attached to the earth. Assume the decelerating force constant. Compute (a) the deceleration of the bullet, (b) the decelerating force, (c) the time of deceleration, (d) the impulse of the collision. Compare the answer to part (d) with the initial momentum of the bullet.

8-4. A rocket burns 50 gm of fuel per second, ejecting it as a gas with a velocity of 500,000 cm/sec. (a) What force does this gas exert on the rocket? Give the result in dynes and newtons. (b) Would the rocket operate in free space? (c) If it would operate in free space, how would you steer it? Could you brake it?

8-5. On a frictionless table, a 3-kgm block moving 4 m/sec to the right collides with an 8-kgm block moving 1.5 m/sec to the left. (a) If the two blocks stick together what is the final velocity? (b) If the two blocks make a perfectly elastic head-on collision, what are their final velocities? (c) How much mechanical energy is converted into heat in the collision of part (a)?

8-6. (a) Two blocks of mass 300 gm and 200 gm are moving toward one another along a horizontal frictionless surface with velocities of 50 cm/sec and 100 cm/sec, respectively. Find the velocity of the center of gravity of the system. (b) If the blocks collide and stick together, find their final velocity. (c) Find the kinetic energy of the system before the collision, with respect to an origin moving with the center of gravity. (d) Find the loss of kinetic energy during the collision.

8-7. A 160-lb man standing on skates on ice throws a 6-oz ball horizontally with a speed of 80 ft/sec. (a) With what speed and in what direction will the man begin to move? (b) If the man throws 4 such balls every 3 sec, what is the average force acting on him? (c) What acceleration does the man have in (b), assuming that the ice is frictionless and that the decrease in mass due to throwing the balls is negligible?

8-8. A 4000-lb automobile going eastward on Chestnut Street at 40 mi/hr collides with a truck weighing 4 tons which is going southward across Chestnut Street at 15 mi/hr. If they become coupled on collision, what is the magnitude and direction of their velocity immediately after colliding?

8-9. When a bullet of mass 10 gm strikes a ballistic pendulum of mass 2 kgm, the center of gravity of the pendulum is observed to rise a vertical distance of 10 cm. The bullet remains embedded in the pendulum. Calculate the velocity of the bullet.

8-10. A bullet weighing 0.01 lb is shot through a 2-lb wooden block suspended on a string 5 ft long. The block is observed to swing through an angle of 5°. Find the speed of the bullet as it emerges from the block, if its initial speed is 1000 ft/sec.

8-11. A bullet of mass 2 gm, traveling in a horizontal direction with a velocity of 500 m/sec, is fired into a wooden block of mass 1 kgm, initially at rest on a level surface. The bullet passes through the block and emerges with its velocity reduced to 100 m/sec. The block slides a distance of 20 cm along the surface from its initial position. (a) What was the coefficient of sliding friction between block and surface? (b) What was the decrease in kinetic energy of the bullet? (c) What was the kinetic energy of the block, at the instant after the bullet passed through it?

8-12. A body initially at rest on a level frictionless surface is acted on by a constant horizontal force for 8 sec. During this time 480 ergs of work are done on the body by the force and the body acquires 120 gm-cm/sec of momentum. Find (a) the mass of the body, (b) its speed at the end of the 8-sec interval, (c) the distance moved during the 8 sec, (d) the force.

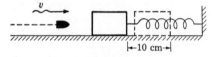

FIG. 8-5

8-13. A rifle bullet of mass 10 gm strikes and embeds itself in a block of mass 990 gm which rests on a horizontal frictionless surface and is attached to a coil spring as shown in Fig. 8-5. The impact compresses the spring 10 cm. Calibration of the spring shows that a force of 100,000 dynes is required to compress the spring 1 cm. (a) Find the maximum potential energy of the spring. (b) Find the velocity of the block just after the impact. (c) What was the initial velocity of the bullet?

8-14. A body of mass 600 gm is initially at rest. It is struck by a second body of mass 400 gm initially moving with a velocity of 125 cm/sec toward the right along the X-axis. After the collision the 400-gm body has a velocity of 100 cm/sec

at an angle of 37° above the X-axis in the first quadrant. Both bodies move on a horizontal frictionless plane. (a) What is the magnitude and direction of the velocity of the 600-gm body after the collision? (b) What is the loss of kinetic energy during the collision?

8-15. A railroad handcar is moving along straight frictionless tracks. In each of the following cases the car initially has a total weight (car and contents) of 500 lb and is traveling with a velocity of 10 ft/sec. Find the final velocity of the car in each of the three following cases. (a) A 50-lb weight is thrown sideways out of the car with a velocity of 8 ft/sec relative to the car. (b) A 50-lb weight is thrown backwards out of the car with a velocity of 10 ft/sec relative to the car. (c) A 50-lb weight is thrown into the car with a velocity of 12 ft/sec relative to the ground and opposite in direction to the velocity of the car.

8-16. An open-topped freight car weighing 10 tons is coasting without friction along a level track. It is raining very hard, with the rain falling vertically down. The car is originally empty and moving with a velocity of 2 ft/sec. (a) What is the velocity of the car after it has traveled long enough to collect one ton of rain water? (b) What would be its velocity if it had a small vertical drain pipe in the floor which allowed the one ton of water to leak out of the bottom as fast as it came in?

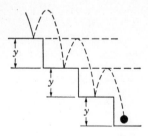

FIG. 8-6

8-17. A 1-lb rubber ball bounces down a flight of stairs, each time rising to the height y of the step above, as shown in Fig. 8-6. (a) Find the coefficient of restitution. (b) If the height of each step, y, is 1 ft, what is the maximum kinetic energy of the ball?

8-18. A ball is dropped from rest onto a fixed horizontal surface and rebounds to a height which is 64% of its original height. (a) What is the coefficient of restitution? (b) With what vertical velocity must the ball strike the surface to rebound to a height of 25 ft?

CHAPTER 9

CIRCULAR MOTION

9-1 Introduction. The concepts of velocity and acceleration were introduced in Chap. 4 in connection with linear motion. However, one has only to glance at some piece of machinery such as a lathe or an automobile engine to realize that rotational motion is of much more common occurrence than is motion in a straight line. The concepts of linear displacement, and average and instantaneous linear velocity and acceleration, have their exact counterparts in rotational motion.

We shall begin this part of the subject by discussing motion of rotation about a fixed axis, for example, the motion of a grinding wheel or the flywheel of a stationary engine. The center line of the shaft on which the wheel is mounted is called the *axis*. All points on the axis remain stationary during the motion, while other points in the body move in circles concentric with the axis and in planes perpendicular to it. Hence such motion is called *circular motion*.

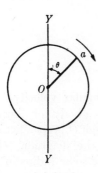

FIG. 9-1.

The position of every point in a body rotating in this way is evidently completely specified if the angular position of any radius of the body is known, relative to some fixed direction. That is, if the rotating body is represented by the circle of Fig. 9-1, and Oa is a radius fixed in the body, the angle θ which Oa makes with the Y-axis is sufficient to determine the position of every point in the body. If the radius Oa is vertical at the start of the motion, and the body rotates in a clockwise direction, the angle θ increases continually as the motion proceeds. It will be seen that the angle θ, in circular motion, corresponds to the coordinate x in rectilinear motion. Angles measured in one direction from the fixed axis are considered positive, those in the opposite direction, negative. It is found convenient to express angles in radians rather than in degrees.

One radian is the angle subtended at the center of a circle by an arc of length equal to the radius of the circle. (Fig. 9-2(a).) Since the radius is contained 2π times

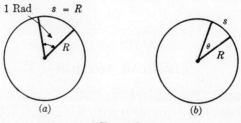

FIG. 9-2.

$(2\pi = 6.28\ldots)$ in the circumference, there are 2π or $6.28\ldots$ radians in one complete revolution or $360°$.   Hence

$$1 \text{ radian} = \frac{360}{2\pi} = 57.3\ldots \text{ degrees.}$$

$$
\begin{aligned}
360° &= 2\pi \text{ radians} = 6.28\ldots \text{ radians}\\
180° &= \pi \quad\quad\text{``} \quad = 3.14\ldots \quad\text{``}\\
90° &= \pi/2 \quad\text{``} \quad = 1.57\ldots \quad\text{``}\\
60° &= \pi/3 \quad\text{``} \quad = 1.05\ldots \quad\text{``}
\end{aligned}
$$

and so on.

In general (Fig. 9-2(b), if θ represents any arbitrary angle subtended by an arc of length s on the circumference of a circle of radius R, then θ (in radians) is equal to the length of the arc s divided by the radius R.

$$\theta = \frac{s}{R}, \quad s = R\theta.$$

An angle in radians, being defined as the ratio of a length to a length, is a pure number.

9-2 Angular velocity. Fig. 9-3 represents a body rotating about an axis through O perpendicular to the plane of the diagram. Oa is the position of some radius in the body at time t_0 and Ob is the position of the same radius at a later time t. The angular coordinates of the radius, measured from the vertical reference line, are θ_0 and θ. The *angular displacement* of the radius (which is the same for all radii) is $\theta - \theta_0$ or $\Delta\theta$. The *average angular*

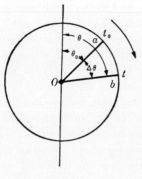

FIG. 9-3.

velocity, represented by $\bar{\omega}$ (omega), is defined as *the ratio of the angular displacement to the elapsed time.*

$$\text{Average angular velocity} = \frac{\text{angular displacement}}{\text{elapsed time}}$$

$$\bar{\omega} = \frac{\theta - \theta_0}{t - t_0} = \frac{\Delta\theta}{\Delta t}.$$

Angular velocity is expressed in radians per second.

Instantaneous angular velocity, ω, is the limiting ratio of angular displacement to elapsed time when both are extremely small, or, it is *the instantaneous rate of change of angular displacement.*

$$\omega = \lim_{\Delta t \to 0} \frac{\Delta\theta}{\Delta t}.$$

Although the equations of angular motion take a somewhat simpler form when angular velocities are expressed in rad/sec, it is more common engineering practice to express them in revolutions per second (rps) or revolutions per minute (rpm). Since there are 2π radians in one complete revolution the number of rad/sec equals 2π times the number of rps and $2\pi/60$ times the number of rpm.

There are two common methods for measuring angular velocity. In the first, a revolution counter is held against the end of a rotating shaft and the number of revolutions in a measured time interval is noted. The angular displacement and the time interval are thus measured directly and their ratio gives the average angular velocity. The second method employs a tachometer (see page 157) which reads instantaneous angular velocity directly, although most tachometers are calibrated to read rpm rather than rad/sec. The common automobile speedometer is a tachometer whose readings are proportional to the instantaneous angular velocity of the drive shaft to which it is connected. Since the linear velocity of the car is proportional to the angular velocity of the drive shaft, the tachometer can be calibrated to read miles per hour rather than rpm or rad/sec.

When a body rotates with *constant* angular velocity its instantaneous angular velocity is equal to its average angular velocity, whatever the duration of the time interval. This sort of motion is well illustrated by the armature of a synchronous motor or the hands of a Telechron clock. If the angular velocity is constant we may write

$$\omega = \frac{\theta - \theta_0}{t - t_0},$$

where ω is the constant angular velocity and the time interval may be of any length. Then

$$\theta - \theta_0 = \omega(t - t_0)$$

and if t_0 and θ_0 are both zero

$$\theta = \omega t. \qquad (9\text{-}1)$$

Eq. (9-1) is exactly analogous to the equation

$$x = vt$$

for a body moving with constant linear velocity.

9-3 Angular acceleration. While a rotating body is speeding up or slowing down, that is, while its angular velocity is changing, it is said to have an angular acceleration. Let ω_0 represent its instantaneous angular velocity at a time t_0, and ω its angular velocity at a later time t. The *average angular acceleration*, represented by $\bar{\alpha}$ (alpha), is defined as *the ratio of the change in angular velocity to the elapsed time.*

$$\text{Average angular acceleration} = \frac{\text{change in angular velocity}}{\text{elapsed time}}$$

$$\bar{\alpha} = \frac{\omega - \omega_0}{t - t_0} = \frac{\Delta\omega}{\Delta t}.$$

If the angular velocity is in radians per second and the time in seconds, the angular acceleration will be in radians per second, per second, or rad/sec^2.

Instantaneous angular acceleration, α, is the ratio of the change in angular velocity to the elapsed time during an extremely short time interval, or, it is *the instantaneous rate of change of angular velocity.*

$$\alpha = \lim_{\Delta t \to 0} \frac{\Delta\omega}{\Delta t}. \qquad (9\text{-}2)$$

Example: The following set of readings of the tachometer of an airplane engine were taken at two-second intervals:

Time (sec)	0	2	4	6	8	10	12	14	16	18
Angular velocity (rpm)	1000	1000	1500	2000	2500	3000	3500	3800	4000	4000

Compute the average angular acceleration, in rad/sec^2, during each two-second interval. Was the angular acceleration constant during the entire time? During any part of the time?

In the interval between 0 and 2 sec there was no change in angular velocity. Hence the angular acceleration was zero during this interval. In the interval from 2 to 4 sec the angular velocity increased from 1000 to 1500 rpm, or from 105 to 157 rad/sec. The increase in angular velocity was therefore $157 - 105 = 52$ rad/sec, and since the time interval was 2 sec the average angular acceleration was $52/2 = 26$ rad/sec^2.

The remainder of the example is left as an exercise.

9-4 Constant angular acceleration. When the angular velocity of a body changes by equal amounts in equal intervals of time, the angular acceleration is constant. Under these circumstances the average and instantaneous angular accelerations are equal, whatever the duration of the time interval. One may therefore write

$$\alpha = \frac{\omega - \omega_0}{t - t_0}$$

or

$$\omega = \omega_0 + \alpha(t - t_0), \tag{9-3}$$

where α is the constant instantaneous angular acceleration.

If $t_0 = 0$,

$$\boxed{\omega = \omega_0 + \alpha t.} \tag{9-4}$$

Eq. (9-4) has precisely the same form as Eq. (4-12) on page 54 for linear motion with constant acceleration and may be interpreted in the same way.

The angular displacement of a rotating body, or the angle turned through by the body, corresponds to the linear displacement of a body moving along a straight line. The expression for the angular displacement can be found with the help of the average angular velocity. If the angular acceleration is constant, the angular velocity increases at a uniform rate and its average value during any time interval equals half the sum of its values at the beginning and end of the interval. That is,

$$\bar{\omega} = \frac{\omega_0 + \omega}{2}. \tag{9-5}$$

If $\theta_0 = 0$ when $t_0 = 0$, $\theta = \bar{\omega}t$ and hence

$$\boxed{\theta = \frac{\omega_0 + \omega}{2} \cdot t.} \tag{9-6}$$

Eqs. (9-4) and (9-6) are the fundamental equations applicable to rotation with constant angular acceleration. By combining them we may obtain two more very useful equations. Thus, substituting for ω in Eq. (9-6) the value of ω given by Eq. (9-4), we have

$$\theta = \frac{\omega_0 + \omega_0 + \alpha t}{2} \cdot t$$

or

$$\boxed{\theta = \omega_0 t + \tfrac{1}{2}\alpha t^2,} \qquad (9\text{-}7)$$

which corresponds to Eq. (4-15) on page 55.

Also, substituting for t in Eq. (9-6) the value of t given by Eq. (9-4), we have

$$\theta = \frac{\omega_0 + \omega}{2} \cdot \frac{\omega - \omega_0}{\alpha}$$

$$= \frac{\omega^2 - \omega_0^2}{2\alpha},$$

or finally

$$\boxed{\omega^2 = \omega_0^2 + 2\alpha\theta,} \qquad (9\text{-}8)$$

which corresponds to Eq. (4-16) on page 55. The following table will serve to emphasize the similarity between the equations for motion with constant linear acceleration and those for motion with constant angular acceleration.

Motion with constant linear acceleration	Motion with constant angular acceleration
$a = \text{const.}$	$\alpha = \text{const.}$
$v = v_0 + at$	$\omega = \omega_0 + \alpha t$
$x = v_0 t + \tfrac{1}{2}at^2$	$\theta = \omega_0 t + \tfrac{1}{2}\alpha t^2$
$x = \dfrac{v_0 + v}{2} t$	$\theta = \dfrac{\omega_0 + \omega}{2} t$
$v^2 = v_0^2 + 2ax$	$\omega^2 = \omega_0^2 + 2\alpha\theta$

9-5 Angular velocity and acceleration as vectors. The vector nature of a quantity like force or linear velocity is obvious, and it seems natural to represent such quantities by arrows. It is also true, although not as obvious, that angular velocity and angular acceleration are also vectors and, like force and linear velocity, can be represented by arrows. The vector representing an angular velocity (or acceleration) is drawn along

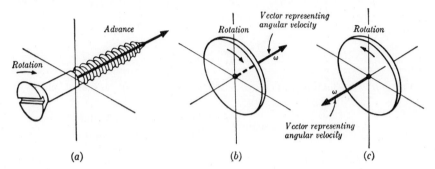

Fig. 9-4. Angular velocity may be represented by a vector along the axis.

the axis of rotation. Its length, to some chosen scale, represents the magnitude of the angular velocity (or acceleration). Imagine now the axis to be a screw with a right-hand thread. The sense of the vector, by convention, is that in which the screw would advance when turned in the direction of the angular velocity (or acceleration). (See Fig. 9-4.) Any quantity associated with an axis can be represented in this way by a vector, and we shall make use of such vectors later in connection with gyroscopic motion.

9-6 Tangential velocity. The angular displacement, angular velocity, and angular acceleration of a rotating body are characteristic of the body as a whole. We wish to consider next the displacement, velocity, and acceleration of some specified point in a rotating body. Every point in a body rotating about a fixed axis moves in a circle with center on the axis. The circle in Fig. 9-5(a) represents the path of such a point. The *displacement* of the point as it moves from p to q is defined as the vector drawn from p to q. The *length of path* is the length of the arc s. It will be seen that these definitions are generalizations of the corresponding definitions on page 47 for a body in linear motion.

The *average velocity* of the point is defined as the ratio of its displacement to the length of the time interval between p and q. Its *average speed* is the ratio of length of path to the time interval.

$$\text{Average velocity (a vector)} = \frac{\text{displacement (a vector)}}{\text{elapsed time (a scalar)}}.$$

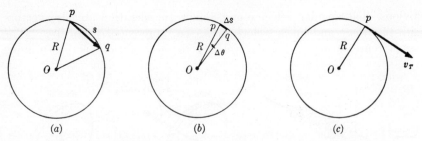

(a)   (b)   (c)

Fig. 9-5.   The limiting ratio of Δs to Δt is the instantaneous tangential velocity

$$\text{Average speed (a scalar)} = \frac{\text{length of path (a scalar)}}{\text{elapsed time (a scalar)}}.$$

The direction of the average velocity vector is the same as that of the displacement.   Since the lengths of the arc s and the chord pq are different, the average velocity and the average speed, in Fig. 9-5(a), are not numerically equal.

The *instantaneous velocity* of the point, at p, is defined as its average velocity over an extremely short displacement which includes p.   The *instantaneous speed* is the average speed over a short displacement.   However, if the displacement is extremely small as in Fig. 9-5(b), the lengths of the vector pq and the arc Δs become practically equal.   The instantaneous velocity and the instantaneous speed are therefore numerically equal.   In other words, the *magnitude* of the instantaneous velocity is equal to the instantaneous speed.

The direction of an extremely short displacement at point p is the same as the direction of the circle at p, that is, the displacement is in the direction of the tangent at p and is perpendicular to the radius Op.   The instantaneous velocity at p is therefore tangent to the circle at p and it is often called the tangential velocity and written v_T.   It is represented by the vector v_T in Fig. 9-5(c).

An important and useful relation connects the angular velocity of a rotating body and the tangential velocity of any point in the body.   The angle $\Delta\theta$, in Fig. 9-5(b), is given by

$$\Delta\theta = \frac{\Delta s}{R}.$$

When both sides are divided by Δt we get

$$\frac{\Delta\theta}{\Delta t} = \frac{1}{R}\frac{\Delta s}{\Delta t}$$

and in the limit, when $\Delta t \to 0$,

$$\lim_{\Delta t \to 0} \frac{\Delta \theta}{\Delta t} = \frac{1}{R} \lim_{\Delta t \to 0} \frac{\Delta s}{\Delta t}.$$

But $\displaystyle\lim_{\Delta t \to 0} \frac{\Delta \theta}{\Delta t}$ is the instantaneous angular velocity ω, and $\displaystyle\lim_{\Delta t \to 0} \frac{\Delta s}{\Delta t}$ is the magnitude of the tangential velocity v_T. Hence

$$\omega = \frac{v_T}{R}, \quad v_T = R\omega. \tag{9-9}$$

The tangential velocity of any point in a rotating body is therefore equal to the product of the angular velocity of the body and the distance of the point from the axis.

If ω, in Eq. (9-9), is in rad/sec, v_T will be in ft/sec when R is expressed in feet, m/sec when R is in meters, and cm/sec when R is in centimeters.

Example: An airplane motor and propeller are set up in a test block. The propeller blades are each 6 ft long. (a) When the propeller is rotating at 1200 rpm compute the tangential velocity of the blade tips. (b) What is the tangential velocity of a point on the blade, halfway between axis and tip?

(a) $\omega = 1200 \text{ rpm} = 1200 \times \dfrac{2\pi}{60} = 40\pi \text{ rad/sec,}$

$$v_T = R\omega = 6 \times 40\pi = 240\pi = 755 \text{ ft/sec}$$
$$= 514 \text{ mi/hr.}$$

(b) $v_T = 3 \times 40\pi = 120\pi = 378 \text{ ft/sec}$
$$= 257 \text{ mi/hr.}$$

9-7 Acceleration of a point in circular motion. The general definition of acceleration is the rate of change of velocity. Velocity, however, is a vector quantity, involving magnitude and direction. The velocity of a moving point will therefore change if either the magnitude or the direction of its velocity changes. Of course, both may change simultaneously. Hence a moving point may have an acceleration arising either from a change in the magnitude or in the direction of its velocity, or both.

The circle in Fig. 9-6(a) represents the path of a point in a body rotating about a fixed axis through O. Let ω_0 be the angular velocity of the body when the point is at p. The corresponding tangential velocity is $v_0 = R\omega_0$. We shall assume that the rotating body has an angular acceleration. Then when the point under consideration reaches q, the angular

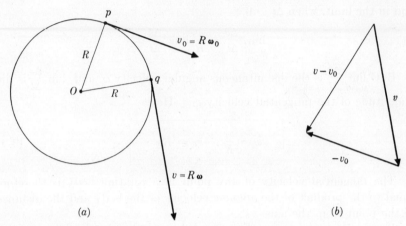

FIG. 9-6. The vector $v - v_0$ is the vector change in velocity.

velocity will have increased to a larger value ω and the tangential velocity
to a value $v = R\omega$. (The subscript T is omitted from the tangential
velocity for simplicity.)

The *average acceleration* between points p and q is defined as the change
in velocity divided by the time interval between p and q. The change in
velocity must now be considered as a *vector* change, or the *vector difference*
between v and v_0. This vector difference, which is itself a vector, may be
found by either of the methods for subtracting vectors explained in Sec.
1-8. In Fig. 9-6(b), the vectors v and v_0 have been kept parallel to their
directions in Fig. 9-6(a), and the change in velocity or the vector difference $v - v_0$ has been found by the triangle method. The average acceleration is

$$\text{Average acceleration (a vector)} = \frac{\text{change in velocity (a vector)}}{\text{elapsed time (a scalar)}},$$

$$\bar{a} = \frac{v - v_0 \ (\text{vector difference})}{t - t_0},$$

where t_0 and t are the times at points p and q. The direction of the average acceleration is the same as that of the vector $v - v_0$. The *instantaneous
acceleration* may be found by letting points p and q in Fig. 9-6(a) approach
more and more closely.

Case I. *Angular velocity is constant.* (*Point describes uniform circular
motion.*) Let p and q in Fig. 9-7(a) represent two positions of the

point very close together.   The velocity at p is represented by the vector
v_0, and at q by the vector v.   Notice carefully that although the magnitude of the velocity is constant (the vectors v_0 and v are of the same
length), there has nevertheless been a change in velocity because of the
change in the direction of motion.   This change in velocity, $v - v_0$ or Δv,
is shown in Fig. 9-7(b).

The instantaneous acceleration at point p is the limiting ratio of the
vector change in velocity to the elapsed time.

$$a = \lim_{\Delta t \to 0} \frac{\Delta v}{\Delta t}.$$

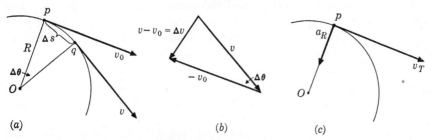

FIG. 9-7.   Tangential velocity and radial acceleration.

To calculate the magnitude of this acceleration, we first note, from Fig.
9-7(a), that $\Delta\theta = \Delta s/R$, whereas from Fig. 9-7(b), $\Delta\theta$ is almost equal to
$\Delta v/v$, since $\Delta\theta$ is exceedingly small.   Hence

$$\frac{\Delta v}{v} = \frac{\Delta s}{R} \quad \text{(approx.)}$$

and

$$\Delta v = \frac{v}{R} \Delta s. \quad \text{(approx.)}$$

When both sides of this equation are divided by the time interval Δt, we
obtain

$$\frac{\Delta v}{\Delta t} = \frac{v}{R} \frac{\Delta s}{\Delta t}. \quad \text{(approx.)}$$

When $\Delta t \to 0$, the following exact equation results:

$$\lim_{\Delta t \to 0} \frac{\Delta v}{\Delta t} = \frac{v}{R} \lim_{\Delta t \to 0} \frac{\Delta s}{\Delta t}.$$

The limiting value of the ratio on the left is recognized as the instantaneous
acceleration, while that on the right is the speed v.   Hence

$$a = \frac{v^2}{R}.$$

(9-10)

The direction of the acceleration, as has been pointed out, is the same as that of the change in velocity Δv. As the angle $\Delta\theta$ becomes smaller, the vectors v_0 and v come more and more nearly into coincidence and the angle between their direction and that of the vector Δv approaches a right angle. In the limit, the vector Δv is exactly at right angles to v. Hence the instantaneous acceleration is at right angles to the tangential velocity and is directed inward toward the center, or along the radius. For this reason it is often called a *radial* or a *centripetal* acceleration and written a_R. The instantaneous tangential velocity and radial acceleration, at the instant the point is at p, are shown in Fig. 9-7(c).

Note that although the vector Δv becomes vanishingly small in the limiting case, the time interval by which it must be divided to obtain the instantaneous acceleration becomes small also. The quotient, a_R, is not necessarily a small quantity.

Finally, from Eq. (9-10) and the relation $v_T = R\omega$, we may write two equivalent expressions for the radial acceleration:

$$a_R = \frac{v_T^2}{R} = R\omega^2.$$

(9-11)

Case II. *Angular velocity variable.* Consider next the more general case, illustrated in Fig. 9-8, in which the rotating body has an angular acceleration α. Then the magnitude of the angular velocity is not constant and the vector v is longer than the vector v_0 as well as being in a different direction. The change in velocity, found by the usual method, is the vector Δv in Fig. 9-8(b). This vector may be resolved into the components Δv_R and Δv_T. The component Δv_R corresponds exactly to the vector Δv in Fig. 9-7(b). The component Δv_T is equal to the difference in *length* between the vectors v and v_0. That is, this component represents the change in velocity brought about by a change in the *magnitude* of the tangential velocity, while the component Δv_R is the change arising from a change in *direction*.

In the limit, as $\Delta\theta \to 0$, the directions of v and v_0 come more nearly into coincidence. The vector Δv_T in the limit, coincides with the direction of either and therefore lies along the tangent, whence the subscript T. The

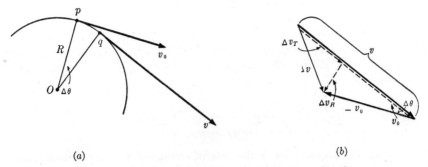

(a)   (b)

FIG. 9-8.   Radial and tangential components of acceleration.

vectors Δv_T and Δv_R may be considered as *rectangular* components of Δv, resolved along the tangent and the radius instead of parallel to the X- and Y-axes.

The limiting ratio of the vector Δv_T to the elapsed time is the *instantaneous tangential acceleration*. It is conveniently expressed as follows: Let ω_0 and ω represent the initial and final angular velocities in Fig. 9-8(a), corresponding to the positions p and q. The lengths of the vectors v_0 and v are then $v_0 = R\omega_0$ and $v = R\omega$. Since Δv_T is the difference in length of these vectors,

$$\Delta v_T = R\omega - R\omega_0 = R(\omega - \omega_0) = R\Delta\omega.$$

When the first and last terms are divided by Δt we obtain, in the limit,

$$\lim_{\Delta t \to 0} \frac{\Delta v_T}{\Delta t} = R \lim_{\Delta t \to 0} \frac{\Delta \omega}{\Delta t}.$$

The term on the left is, by definition, the tangential acceleration, and $\lim_{\Delta t \to 0} \frac{\Delta \omega}{\Delta t}$ is the instantaneous angular acceleration α. Hence

$$a_T = R\alpha. \qquad (9\text{-}12)$$

Like radial acceleration, tangential acceleration is expressed in ft/sec², m/sec², or cm/sec².

The expressions for the radial and tangential components of the acceleration of a point in circular motion may now be combined to obtain the resultant acceleration a.

$$a = \sqrt{a_R{}^2 + a_T{}^2} = \sqrt{(R\omega^2)^2 + R^2\alpha^2}.$$

Summary

(1) When a point moves in a circle, its length of path s, its tangential velocity v_T, and its tangential acceleration a_T are related to its angular displacement θ, its angular velocity ω, and its angular acceleration α by the equations

$$s = R\theta$$
$$v_T = R\omega$$
$$a_T = R\alpha.$$

(2) Radial acceleration is the rate of change of velocity arising from a change in direction of this velocity. Its direction is radially inward toward the center and it is related to the angular and tangential velocities by

$$a_R = \frac{v_T{}^2}{R} = R\omega^2.$$

(3) Tangential acceleration is the rate of change of velocity arising from a change in the magnitude of this velocity. It is related to the angular acceleration by

$$a_T = R\alpha.$$

Example: A disk of radius 10 cm starts from rest and accelerates about a horizontal axis through its center with a constant angular acceleration of 2 rad/sec². A point p on the rim of the disk is located vertically above the center at the start. At the end of 1 sec find (a) the position of the point, (b) its radial acceleration, (c) its tangential acceleration, (d) its resultant acceleration.

(a) $\quad \theta = \omega_0 t + \frac{1}{2}\alpha t^2 = \frac{1}{2} \times 2 \times 1^2 = 1$ rad.

Hence the point is located as in Fig. 9-9.

(b) $a_R = R\omega^2$

$\quad \omega^2 = \omega_0{}^2 + 2\alpha\theta = 2 \times 2 \times 1 = 4 \left(\dfrac{\text{rad}}{\text{sec}}\right)^2$

$\quad a_R = 10 \times 4 = 40$ cm/sec².

(c) $a_T = R\alpha = 10 \times 2 = 20$ cm/sec².

(d) $\quad a = \sqrt{a_R{}^2 + a_T{}^2} = \sqrt{40^2 + 20^2} = 45.7$ cm/sec².

$\quad \tan \phi = \dfrac{a_T}{a_R} = \dfrac{20}{40} = 0.5, \quad \phi = 26.5°.$

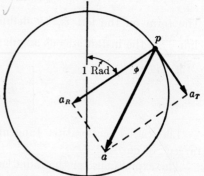

FIG. 9-9.

FIG. 9-10. Multiflash photograph showing the relation between tangential and angular acceleration.

The relation between the linear and angular aspects of circular motion is illustrated in the multiflash photograph of Fig. 9-10. A cord is wrapped around the outside of a circular disk whose horizontal axis is supported in ball bearings. A weight hangs from the end of the cord. One radius is marked on the disk and is horizontal at the start of the motion. When the disk is released, the weight moves down with constant linear acceleration and the disk rotates counterclockwise with constant angular acceleration.

The angle between any two successive positions of the radius, divided by the flash interval, equals the average angular velocity during that interval. Evidently the angles become progressively larger as the motion proceeds, showing that the angular velocity is increasing. Careful measurements show the increases to be equal between each consecutive pair of flashes, or, in other words, the angular acceleration is constant.

The distance moved by the descending weight during any time interval is the same as the circumferential distance moved by any point on the rim of the disk in the same interval. The velocity and acceleration of the weight are therefore numerically equal to the tangential velocity and acceleration of a point on the rim of the disk. It is evident that the weight moves with increasing velocity and careful measurements show the rate of increase to be constant.

Since the angular displacement, velocity, and acceleration can be found from measurements on the disk, and tangential displacement, velocity, and acceleration from measurements on the falling weight, and the radius of the disk can be measured, the relations $s = R\theta$, $v_T = R\omega$, and $a_T = R\alpha$ can all be verified.

9-8 Centripetal and centrifugal forces. Everyone has at some time or other performed the experiment of tying a stone or weight to a cord, and whirling the stone in a circle. While the stone is revolving it can be felt to pull outward on one's hand, and conversely the hand must exert an inward pull on the stone.

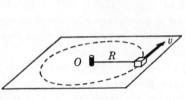

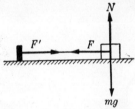

FIG. 9-11.

FIG. 9-12. Force F is the centripetal force. Force F', the reaction to F, is the centrifugal force.

To reduce the problem to its essential terms let us imagine a pin O set into a horizontal frictionless table top as in Fig. 9-11. A small body of mass m is attached to the pin by a cord of length R, and set revolving about it with an angular velocity ω, a tangential velocity v_T and a radial acceleration $a_R = v_T{}^2/R = \omega^2 R$. According to Newton's second law, a force must be exerted on the body to produce this radial acceleration, and the direction of this force must be the same as the direction of the acceleration or toward the center of the circle. It is therefore called a central or *centripetal* force. (The term "centripetal" means literally "seeking a center.") Since

$$F = ma \quad \text{and} \quad a = v_T{}^2/R = \omega^2 R,$$

the magnitude of the centripetal force is

$$F = mv_T{}^2/R = m\omega^2 R. \tag{9-13}$$

This inward force is provided by the cord, which is evidently in tension and which therefore exerts an outward force, equal and opposite to the centripetal force, on the pin at the center. This outward force is called a *centrifugal* force. (The term "centrifugal" means literally "fleeing a center.") The force diagram of the system is given in Fig. 9-12, where F and F' are the equal and opposite forces exerted by the cord on the bodies to which its ends are attached. Force F is the centripetal, force F'

the centrifugal force.   Centripetal and centrifugal forces always constitute
an action-and-reaction pair, the former being the resultant inward force
on the revolving body and the latter the reaction to this force.

Unfortunately, there exists much confusion of thought with respect to
centrifugal forces.   A current notion is that centrifugal force is an outward
force exerted *on a revolving body*, causing it to "fly out from the center."
There is also the impression that centripetal and centrifugal forces are in
some way different from pushes and pulls exerted by sticks and strings,
and that they constitute a third class of forces in addition to contact and
action-at-a-distance forces.   This is not the case.   Centripetal forces, like
other forces, are pushes or pulls exerted on some material body by some
other material body, and their designation as "centripetal" refers only to
the effect they produce (a change in direction) and not to something
inherently different in their nature.

9-9 The banking of curves.   Fig. 9-13 is a front view of the truck of
a railway car of mass m approaching the reader with velocity v, and rounding a curve of radius R whose center is at the right of the diagram.   In
order to maintain the motion in a curved path, it is necessary that a centripetal force, equal to mv^2/R, shall be exerted on the truck.   The direction
of this force is toward the center of the circle, or, in this case, toward
the right.   The centripetal force is provided by the outer rail pushing
toward the right against the flange of the outer wheel, and is represented
by P in Fig. 9-13.   The other forces exerted on the truck are its weight,
mg, and the upward push of the rails, N.   For simplicity these forces are

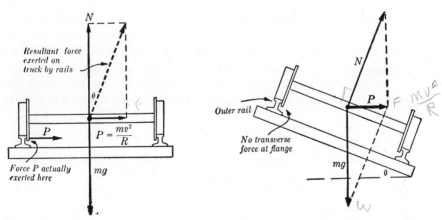

FIG. 9-13.   Forces on a railway truck   FIG. 9-14.   Forces when the track is
rounding a curve on an unbanked track.   banked.

shown as if they all acted at the center of gravity. The resultant force exerted on the truck by the rails is shown by the dotted vector.

If, now, the rails, instead of being level, are "banked" as in Fig. 9-14, so as to be perpendicular to the direction of the force which they must exert on the truck, this force becomes a normal force, and the pressure of the rails against the wheel flanges need no longer be relied on to keep the truck moving in a circle. The *vertical component* of the normal force now supports the weight of the truck, and its *horizontal component* provides the centripetal force. The resultant of the entire set of forces is the same in both Figs. 9-13 and 9-14, namely, the centripetal force *P*.

The banking angle θ which the roadbed makes with the horizontal is equal to the angle θ in Fig. 9-13. Hence

$$\tan \theta = \frac{mv^2/R}{mg} = \frac{v^2}{Rg} \cdot \tag{9-14}$$

It can be seen from this equation that the tangent of the angle of banking is proportional to the square of the velocity and inversely proportional to the radius of the curve. For a given radius no one angle is correct for all velocities. Hence in the design of highways and railroads, curves are banked for the average velocity of the traffic over them, and will be somewhat too steep for velocities lower than the average and vice versa.

The same considerations determine the correct banking angle of a plane when making a turn. The angle should be such that the resultant of the lift and the centripetal force is perpendicular to the wing surfaces. (Fig. 9-15.)

9-10 The conical pendulum. Fig. 9-16 represents a small body of mass m revolving in a horizontal circle at constant angular velocity ω at the end of a light cord of length L. We shall ignore the interval during which the motion was being started and consider only the state of affairs after the mass has been set in motion. If θ is the constant angle which the cord makes with the vertical, the radius R of the circle in which it is moving is

$$R = L \sin \theta.$$

As the body swings around its path, the cord sweeps over the surface of a cone. Hence the device is called a *conical pendulum.*

The forces exerted on the body when in the position shown are its weight, mg, the tension T in the cord, and nothing else. There is a great temptation to add an outward "centrifugal" force to the diagram, but, as we have seen, it does not belong in the set of forces acting on the body.

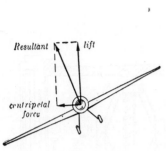

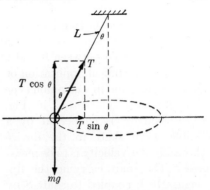

FIG. 9-15.   FIG. 9-16.   The conical pendulum.

We know furthermore that the acceleration of the body is directed toward the center of the horizontal circle in which it is moving. Hence we choose axes in this direction and at right angles to it, and resolve the tension T into components as shown. The resultant Y-force is $T \cos \theta - mg$ and the resultant X-force is $T \sin \theta$. Then from the second law

$$\Sigma F_y = T \cos \theta - mg = ma_y,$$

$$\Sigma F_x = T \sin \theta = ma_x.$$

But $a_y = 0$, since the elevation of the body does not change, and $a_x = v^2/R = \omega^2 R$. Therefore

$$T \cos \theta = mg, \tag{9-15}$$

$$T \sin \theta = m\omega^2 R.$$

Since $R = L \sin \theta$,

$$T \sin \theta = m\omega^2 L \sin \theta,$$

$$T = m\omega^2 L.$$

When this value of T is inserted in Eq. (9-15) we obtain

$$m\omega^2 L \cos \theta = mg,$$

$$\cos \theta = \frac{g}{\omega^2 L} \cdot \tag{9-16}$$

That is, this relation must hold between the angular velocity, the length of the supporting cord, and the angle θ. Hence for a given angular velocity and a cord of given length, there is a definite angle θ which the cord must make with the vertical. This equation explains why the ball revolves in a circle of larger radius as its angular velocity is increased. If ω increases, $\cos \theta$ must decrease and the angle θ must increase, since the cosine of an angle between 0 and 90° decreases as the angle increases.

A useful technical application of this effect is found in a common type of tachometer, illustrated in Fig. 9-17. Shaft S is connected by a flexible drive shaft to the device whose angular velocity is to be measured. The shaft carrying the flyweights W is coupled to shaft S by a gear and pinion. The flyweights are connected by a linkage mechanism to collars F and C. Collar F is fixed to the shaft but collar C is free to move up or down. The collars are forced apart by the coil spring.

When the shaft S rotates, the flyweights move out, compressing the coil spring until a position is reached where the force exerted by

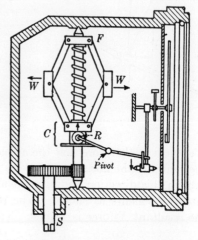

Fig. 9-17. A common type of tachometer. (*Courtesy of Pioneer Instrument Company.*)

the spring through the linkage provides the requisite centripetal force. The motion of collar C is transmitted by the roller R and a system of levers and gears to the pointer on the dial of the instrument.

9-11 Motion in a vertical circle. Fig. 9-18 represents a small body attached to a cord of length R and whirling in a vertical circle about a fixed point O to which the other end of the cord is attached. The motion, while circular, is not one of constant angular velocity, since the body accelerates on the way down and decelerates on the way up.

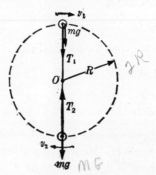

Fig. 9-18. Motion in a vertical circle.

Let v_1 represent the velocity of the body as it passes the highest point. The forces acting on it at this point are its weight mg and the tension T_1 in the cord, both acting downward. The resultant force is $T_1 + mg$, and therefore at this point

$$T_1 + mg = \frac{mv_1^2}{R},$$

or

$$T_1 = \frac{mv_1^2}{R} - mg. \tag{9-17}$$

Since by definition the centripetal force is the resultant inward force on a body in circular motion, the centripetal force in this instance is provided partly by the body's weight and partly by the tension in the cord.

Similarly, at the lowest point of the circle

$$T_2 - mg = \frac{mv_2^2}{R},$$

or

$$T_2 = \frac{mv_2^2}{R} + mg, \tag{9-18}$$

where T_2 and v_2 represent the tension and the velocity at this point, and the upward direction has been taken as positive.

With motion of this sort, it is a familiar fact that there is a certain critical velocity below which the cord becomes slack at the highest point. To find this velocity, set $T_1 = 0$ in Eq. (9-17).

$$0 = \frac{mv_1^2}{R} - mg,$$

$$v_1 = \sqrt{gR}. \tag{9-19}$$

The corresponding velocity at the lowest point may be found from energy considerations. The decrease in potential energy between top and bottom is $2mgR$, and this must equal the increase in kinetic energy. Hence

$$2mgR = \tfrac{1}{2}mv_2^2 - \tfrac{1}{2}mv_1^2$$
$$= \tfrac{1}{2}mv_2^2 - \tfrac{1}{2}mgR,$$
$$v_2 = \sqrt{5gR}.$$

That is, the body must have at least this velocity at the bottom of the circle if it is to get over the top without having the string slacken.

The multiflash photographs of Fig. 9-19 illustrate another case of motion in a vertical circle; a small ball "looping-the-loop" on the inside of a vertical circular track. The inward normal force exerted on the ball by the track takes the place of the tension T in Fig. 9-18.

Fig. 9-19.   Multiflash photographs of a ball looping-the-loop in a vertical circle.

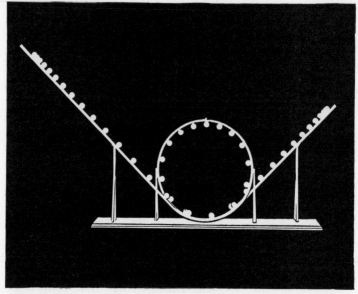

Fig. 9-19(a).

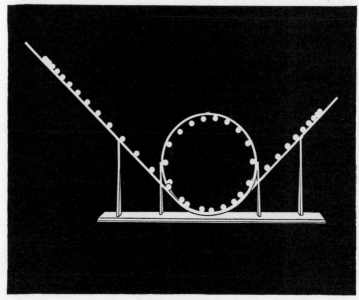

Fig. 9-19(b).

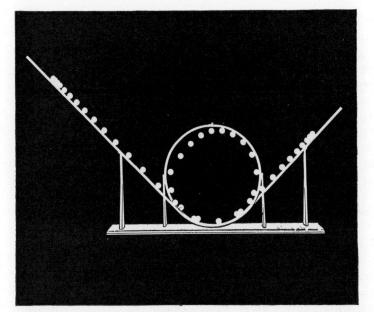

Fig. 9-19(c).

Fig. 9-19(d).

In Fig. 9-19(a) the ball is released from such an elevation that its velocity at the top of the track is greater than the critical velocity, $\sqrt{gR}$. In Fig. 9-19(b) the ball starts from a lower elevation and reaches the top of the circle with a velocity such that its own weight is larger than the requisite centripetal force. In other words, the track would have to pull outward to maintain the circular motion. Since this is impossible, the ball leaves the track and moves for a short distance in a parabola. This parabola soon intersects the circle, however, and the remainder of the trip is completed successfully.

In Fig. 9-19(c) the start is made from a still lower elevation, the ball leaves the track sooner, and the parabolic path is clearly evident. In Fig. 9-19(d), while the ball eventually returns to the track, the collision is so nearly at right angles that it bounces a few times and finally rolls off.

9-12 The centrifuge. A centrifuge is a device for whirling an object with a high angular velocity. The consequent large radial acceleration is equivalent to increasing the value of g, and such processes as sedimentation, which would otherwise take place only slowly, can be greatly accelerated in this way. Very high speed centrifuges, called ultracentrifuges, have been operated at angular velocities as high as 180,000 rpm, and small experimental units have been driven as fast as 1,300,000 rpm.

Problems — Chapter 9

9-1. (a) What angle in radians is subtended by an arc 6 ft in length, on the circumference of a circle whose radius is 4 ft? (b) What angle in radians is subtended by an arc of length 78.54 cm on the circumference of a circle of diameter 100 cm? What is this angle in degrees? (c) The angle between two radii of a circle is 0.60 radian. What length of arc is intercepted on the circumference of a circle of radius 200 cm? of radius 200 ft?

9-2. Compute the angular velocity, in rad/sec, of the crankshaft of an automobile engine rotating at 4800 rpm.

9-3. (a) A cylinder 6 inches in diameter rotates in a lathe at 750 rpm. What is the tangential velocity of the surface of the cylinder? (b) The proper tangential velocity for machining cast iron is about 2 ft/sec. At how many rpm should a piece of stock 2 inches in diameter be rotated in a lathe?

9-4. An electric motor running at 1800 rpm has on its shaft three pulleys, of diameters 2, 4 and 6 in respectively. Find the linear velocity of the surface of each pulley, in ft/sec. The pulleys may be connected by a belt to a similar set on a countershaft; the 2 in to the 6 in, the 4 in to the 4 in, and the 6 in to the 2 in. Find the three possible angular velocities of the countershaft, in rpm.

9-5. A wheel 2.4 ft in diameter starts from rest and accelerates uniformly to an angular velocity of 100 rad/sec in 20 sec. Find the angular acceleration and the angle turned through.

9-6. The angular velocity of a flywheel decreases uniformly from 1000 rpm to 400 rpm in 5 sec. Find the angular acceleration and the number of revolutions made by the wheel in the 5-sec interval. How many more seconds are required for the wheel to come to rest?

9-7. A flywheel requires 3 sec to rotate through 234 radians. Its angular velocity at the end of this time is 108 rad/sec. Find its constant angular acceleration.

9-8. A flywheel whose angular acceleration is constant and equal to 2 rad/sec^2, rotates through an angle of 100 radians in 5 sec. How long had it been in motion at the beginning of the 5-sec interval if it started from rest?

9-9. (a) Distinguish clearly between tangential and radial acceleration. (b) A flywheel rotates with constant angular velocity. Does a point on its rim have a tangential acceleration? a radial acceleration? (c) A flywheel is rotating with constant angular acceleration. Does a point on its rim have a tangential acceleration? a radial acceleration? Are these accelerations constant in magnitude?

9-10. At time $t = 0$ a body is moving East at 10 cm/sec. At time $t = 2$ sec it is moving 25° North of East at 14 cm/sec. Find graphically its change in velocity during this time and its average acceleration.

9-11. A wheel 30 inches in diameter is rotating about a fixed axis with an initial angular velocity of 2 revolutions per sec. The acceleration is 3 rev/sec^2. (a) Compute the angular velocity after 6 sec. (b) Through what angle has the wheel turned in this time interval? (c) What is the tangential velocity of a point on the rim of the wheel at $t = 6$ sec? (d) What is the resultant acceleration of a point on the rim of the wheel at $t = 6$ sec?

9-12. A wheel having a diameter of 1 ft starts from rest and accelerates uniformly to an angular velocity of 900 rpm in 5 sec. (a) Find the position at the end of 1 sec of a point originally at the top of the wheel. (b) Compute and show in a diagram the magnitude and direction of the acceleration at the end of 1 sec.

9-13. A small sphere of mass m is fastened to a weightless string of length 2 ft to form a pendulum. The pendulum is swinging so as to make a maximum angle of 60° with the vertical. Compute and show in a diagram the magnitude and direction of the resultant acceleration of the sphere when the string makes an angle of (a) 60° and (b) 37° with the vertical.

9-14. A stone of mass 1 kgm is attached to a string 1 m long, of breaking strength 500 newtons, and is whirled in a horizontal circle. With what speed will the stone fly off if the angular velocity is just great enough so that the string breaks?

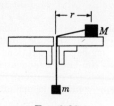

FIG. 9-20

9-15. A block of mass M rests on a turntable which is rotating at constant angular velocity ω. A smooth cord runs from the block through a hole in the center of the table down to a hanging block of mass m. The coefficient of friction between the first block and the turntable is μ. (See Fig. 9-20.) Find the largest and smallest values of the radius r for which the first block will remain at rest relative to the turntable.

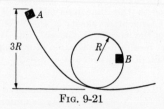

FIG. 9-21

9-16. A small body of mass m slides without friction around the loop-the-loop apparatus shown in Fig. 9-21. It starts from rest at point A at a height $3R$ above the bottom of the loop. When it reaches

point B at the end of a horizontal diameter of the loop, compute (a) its radial acceleration, (b) its tangential acceleration, (c) its resultant acceleration. Show these accelerations in a diagram, approximately to scale.

9-17. A car moves in a curve of radius of curvature R. The wheel base of the car is b, and the height of the center of gravity from the ground is h. With what velocity must the car move in order that the vertical force on the inside wheels is reduced to zero?

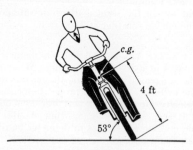

FIG. 9-22

9-18. A boy riding a bicycle at 12 ft/sec rounds a curve and finds he must incline his bicycle at an angle of 53° with the horizontal in order to keep from tipping over. The combined weight of the boy and bicycle is 180 lb and the combined center of gravity is as shown in Fig. 9-22. (a) Draw a diagram showing all of the forces acting on the bicycle and rider. (b) Calculate the radius of the curve. (c) Calculate the friction force between the road and bicycle tire.

9-19. An airplane is flying at 120 mi/hr, in a horizontal circle of radius 5000 ft. (a) What is the banking angle, θ, of the plane? (b) What is the magnitude and direction of the resultant force on the airplane? (c) What is the magnitude of the aerodynamic force on the wing?

9-20. A motorcycle velodrome is 40 ft in diameter, and the coefficient of friction between tires and boards is 0.4. (a) Draw a diagram of the forces acting on the motorcycle when it is moving in a horizontal circle around the vertical wall of the velodrome. (b) Compute the minimum speed of the motorcycle. (c) If the motorcycle and rider weigh 320 lb, find the vertical and horizontal forces acting on the track at this speed.

Fɪɢ. 9-23

9-21. A two-ton coaster rolls on a track as shown in Fig. 9-23. It starts at *S* with zero velocity, rolls down to *A* (100 ft below *S*) where the radius of curvature is 50 ft, and then up to *B* (50 ft below *S*) where the radius of curvature is again 50 ft. (a) What force is exerted on the track as the roller coasts by point *A*? (b) By point *B*? (c) Is the track adequately designed? (It is built to take a force of 20 tons.)

9-22. A small sphere is placed in a grooved vertical circular track of radius 30 cm. When the track is spinning about a vertical axis with a constant angular velocity of 7 rad/sec, the sphere takes a position given by the angle θ as shown in Fig. 9-24. (a) Draw a diagram showing

the direction and magnitude of all the forces acting on the sphere. (b) Find the angle θ.

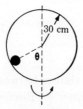

Fɪɢ. 9-24

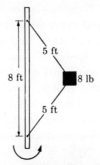

Fɪɢ. 9-25

9-23. The 8-lb block in Fig. 9-25 is attached to a vertical rod by means of two strings. When the system rotates about the axis of the rod with an angular velocity of 4 rad/sec the strings are extended as shown in the diagram. What is the tension in (a) the upper string, (b) the lower string?

CHAPTER 10

ROTATION

10-1 Relation between torque and angular acceleration. In the preceding chapter we discussed motion of rotation about a fixed axis without inquiring into the "causes" of the motion. If we go back to fundamental principles, the motion of each particle of matter in a rotating body is determined by Newton's second law. That is, the resultant force exerted on a particle is at every instant equal to the product of the mass of the particle and its acceleration, and is in the same direction as the acceleration. It turns out, however, that simplification is possible if instead of working with the accelerations of the individual particles of a rotating body we consider the *angular acceleration* of the body, which is the same for all particles, and instead of dealing with the forces on the particles we consider the *resultant torque* on the body as a whole. That is, we look for a relation between resultant torque and angular acceleration which will correspond to Newton's second law connecting resultant force with linear acceleration.

To start the discussion, let us consider the simple case of a single particle of mass m moving in a circular path of radius r about the point O, as shown in Fig. 10-1. At the moment under consideration the particle has a linear acceleration a in the direction of the resultant force F. Resolving F and a into radial and tangential components, we have, along the tangential axis,

$$F_t = ma_t,$$

and multiplying through by r,

$$F_t r = mra_t.$$

But $F_t r$ is the torque of F about O and $a_t = r\alpha$. Therefore

$$\boxed{\tau = mr^2\alpha} \quad \text{(for a single particle).}$$

$$(10-1)$$

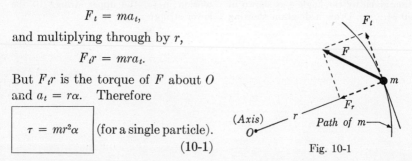

Fig. 10-1

Consider next the case of two particles of masses m_1 and m_2, moving in circular paths with radii r_1 and r_2 about a point O, shown in Fig. 10-2. Acting on particle 1 is an external force F_1 exerted by an outside agent.

An external force F_2 acts on particle 2 also. But these are not the only forces acting on the particles. The particles exert forces on each other either by gravity or by electrical attraction. Whatever its origin, the force exerted by either particle on the other is called an *internal force*. As shown in Fig. 10-2, an internal force F_{12} is exerted on particle 1 by particle 2, and similarly an internal force F_{21} is exerted on particle 2 by particle 1. These forces act along the line joining the two particles and, by Newton's third law,

$$F_{12} = -F_{21}.$$

Applying Newton's second law to particle 1, we get, *along the tangential axis*,

$$(F_1)_t + (F_{12})_t = m_1(a_1)_t,$$

and multiplying through by r_1,

$$(F_1)_t r_1 + (F_{12})_t r_1 = m_1 r_1 (a_1)_t.$$

But $(F_1)_t r_1$ is the torque of F_1 about O, and $(F_{12})_t r_1$ is the torque of F_{12} about O. Also, $(a_1)_t = r_1 \alpha$. Hence

$$\tau_1 + \tau_{12} = m_1 r_1^2 \alpha. \tag{10-2}$$

If the two particles are rigidly connected, the internal forces are of such a character that both particles have the same angular acceleration. When a "rigid body" executes rotation about a fixed axis, all particles in the body have the same angular acceleration. We may therefore write, in a similar manner, for particle 2,

$$\tau_2 + \tau_{21} = m_2 r_2^2 \alpha. \tag{10-3}$$

Adding the equations for the two particles, we get

$$\tau_1 + \tau_2 + \tau_{12} + \tau_{21}$$
$$= (m_1 r_1^2 + m_2 r_2^2)\alpha. \tag{10-4}$$

It is clear, however, from Fig. 10-2 that

$$\tau_{12} = F_{12}h,$$

and

$$\tau_{21} = F_{21}h.$$

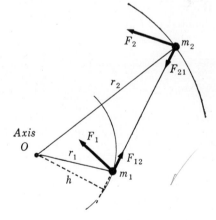

Fig. 10-2.

Since $F_{12} = -F_{21}$, we therefore get that

$$\tau_{12} + \tau_{21} = 0. \tag{10-5}$$

That is, *the sum of the torques of the internal forces about the axis is zero.* Equation (10-4) therefore becomes

$$\tau_1 + \tau_2 = (m_1 r_1^2 + m_2 r_2^2)\alpha$$

or

$$\Sigma\tau \begin{pmatrix} \text{of the external} \\ \text{forces only} \end{pmatrix} = (m_1 r_1^2 + m_2 r_2^2)\alpha. \tag{10-6}$$

If there were three particles, two internal forces would act on particle 1, producing torques about the axis equal to τ_{12} and τ_{13}. The torques of the internal forces on particles 2 and 3 would be, respectively, τ_{21}, τ_{23}, and τ_{31}, τ_{32}. When these are added, we would get

$$(\tau_{12} + \tau_{21}) + (\tau_{23} + \tau_{32}) + (\tau_{13} + \tau_{31}) = 0,$$

since each parenthesis would vanish, and this is evidently true for any number of particles such as those making up a rigid body. Hence when external forces act on a rigid body pivoted about a fixed axis, the sum of the torques of the external forces is equal to

$$\underset{\text{external}}{\Sigma\tau} = (m_1 r_1^2 + m_2 r_2^2 + \cdots)\alpha. \tag{10-7}$$

The quantity in parentheses plays a fundamental role in rotation. It obviously depends not only on the total mass of the body but also upon the way in which this mass is distributed about the axis. This quantity, denoted by I and defined by the equation

$$\begin{aligned} I &= m_1 r_1^2 + m_2 r_2^2 + \cdots \\ &= \Sigma m r^2, \end{aligned} \tag{10-8}$$

is called the *moment of inertia*. The fundamental equation for the rotation of a rigid body, expressed by Eq. (10-7), may therefore be written

$$\Sigma\tau = I\alpha, \tag{10-9}$$

which is the rotational analog of $\Sigma F = ma$.

It is evident from its definition that moment of inertia is expressed in slug-ft² in the English system, kgm-m² in the mks system, and gm-cm² in the cgs system.

Example: A rope is wrapped around the surface of a flywheel 2 ft in radius and a 10-lb weight hangs from the rope (Fig. 10-3). The wheel is free to rotate about a horizontal axis through its center. Compute its angular acceleration and the tension in the rope if the moment of inertia of the wheel is 1.5 slug-ft².

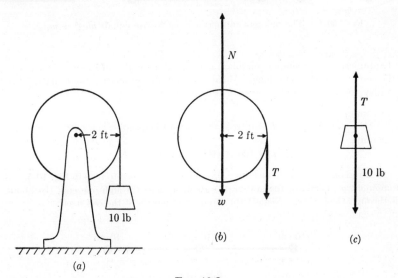

FIG. 10-3.

Isolate the flywheel, as in Fig. 10-3(b). Taking moments about the axis,

$$\Sigma \tau = I\alpha,$$
$$2T = 1.5\alpha.$$

Isolating the 10-lb weight, as in Fig. 10-3(c),

$$\Sigma F = ma,$$
$$10 - T = \frac{10}{32} a.$$

Also, since the linear acceleration of the weight equals the tangential acceleration of the surface of the flywheel,

$$a = R\alpha = 2\alpha.$$

Simultaneous solution of these equations gives

$$a = 18.9 \text{ ft/sec}^2,$$
$$\alpha = 9.4 \text{ rad/sec}^2,$$
$$T = 7.1 \text{ lb}.$$

10-2 Moment of inertia and radius of gyration. The moment of inertia of a small particle depends only on its mass and its radial distance from the axis, not on its angular position. Thus each of the arrangements in Fig. 10-4 has the same moment of inertia, $m_1r_1^2 + m_2r_2^2$.

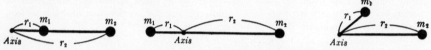

FIG. 10-4. The moment of inertia in each case equals $m_1r_1^2 + m_2r_2^2$.

Examples. (1) A simple pendulum consists of a small lead sphere of mass 100 gm at the end of a cord 1 meter long. What is its moment of inertia about an axis through the upper end of the cord, perpendicular to its length?

In mks units,

$$I = 0.10 \times (1)^2 = 0.10 \text{ kgm-m}^2.$$

In cgs units,

$$I = 100 \times (100)^2 = 10^6 \text{ gm-cm}^2.$$

(2) A rod one meter long has three 10-gm blocks clamped to it as in Fig. 10-5. Find the moment of inertia of the system (a) about an axis through one end, (b) about an axis through the center. Neglect the moment of inertia of the rod itself.

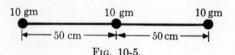

FIG. 10-5.

(a) If the axis passes through one end,

$$I = \Sigma mr^2 = 10 \times (0)^2 + 10 \times (50)^2 + 10 \times (100)^2$$
$$= 125,000 \text{ gm-cm}^2.$$

(b) If the axis passes through the center,

$$I = \Sigma mr^2 = 10 \times (50)^2 + 10 \times (0)^2 + 10 \times (50)^2$$
$$= 50,000 \text{ gm-cm}^2.$$

This example illustrates an extremely important fact, namely, that the moment of inertia of a body, unlike its mass, is not a unique property of the body but depends on the location of the axis about which the moment of inertia is computed. Thus in this example, the moment of inertia of the system about an axis through one end is $2\frac{1}{2}$ times as great as its moment of inertia about an axis through the center.

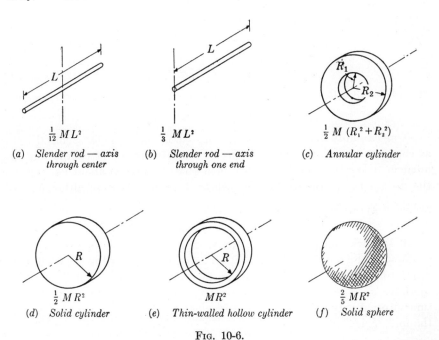

(a) *Slender rod — axis through center* $\frac{1}{12} M L^2$

(b) *Slender rod — axis through one end* $\frac{1}{3} M L^2$

(c) *Annular cylinder* $\frac{1}{2} M (R_1^2 + R_2^2)$

(d) *Solid cylinder* $\frac{1}{2} M R^2$

(e) *Thin-walled hollow cylinder* $M R^2$

(f) *Solid sphere* $\frac{2}{5} M R^2$

Fig. 10-6.

For a body which is not composed of discrete point masses but is a continuous distribution of matter, the summation expressed in the definition of moment of inertia, $I = \Sigma mr^2$, must be evaluated by the methods of calculus. The moments of inertia of a few simple but important bodies are listed in Fig. 10-6 for convenience.

Whatever the shape of a body, it is always possible to find a radial distance from any given axis at which the mass of the body could be concentrated without altering the moment of inertia of the body about that axis. This distance is called the *radius of gyration* of the body about the given axis, and is represented by k.

If the mass M of the body actually were concentrated at this distance, the moment of inertia would be that of a particle of mass M at a distance k from an axis, or Mk^2. Since this equals the actual moment of inertia, I, then

$$Mk^2 = I,$$

$$k = \sqrt{\frac{I}{M}} \cdot \qquad (10\text{-}10)$$

Equation (10-10) may be considered the definition of radius of gyration.

Example: What is the radius of gyration of a slender rod of mass M and length L about an axis perpendicular to its length and passing through the center?

The moment of inertia about an axis through the center is $I_0 = \frac{1}{12}ML^2$. Hence

$$k_0 = \sqrt{\frac{\frac{1}{12}ML^2}{M}} = \frac{L}{2\sqrt{3}} = 0.289L.$$

The radius of gyration, like the moment of inertia, depends on the location of the axis.

Note carefully that, in general, the mass of a body can *not* be considered as concentrated at its center of gravity for the purpose of computing its moment of inertia. For example, when a rod is pivoted about its center, the distance from the axis to the center of gravity is zero, although the radius of gyration is $\dfrac{L}{2\sqrt{3}}$.

10-3 Work and power in rotational motion. Suppose a force F acts as shown in Fig. 10-7 at the rim of a pivoted wheel of radius R, while the wheel rotates through a small angle $\Delta\theta$. If this angle is small enough, the force may be regarded as constant during the correspondingly small time interval. By definition, the work done by the outside agent exerting the force F is

$$\Delta W = F\Delta s.$$

But $\Delta s = R\Delta\theta$, so that

$$\Delta W = FR\Delta\theta.$$

But FR is the torque, τ, due to the force F, so we have finally

$$\boxed{\Delta W = \tau\Delta\theta.} \qquad (10\text{-}11)$$

If the torque is constant while the angle changes by a finite amount from θ_1 to θ_2,

$$W = \tau(\theta_2 - \theta_1).$$

That is, the work done by a constant torque equals the product of the torque and the angular displacement.

If τ is expressed in pound-feet, the work is in foot-pounds. If τ is in meter-newtons the work is in joules, and if τ is in centimeter-dynes the work is in ergs.

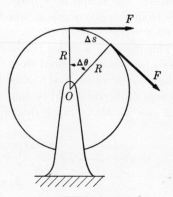

FIG. 10-7.

When both sides of Eq. (10-11) are divided by the small time interval Δt, we obtain

$$\frac{\Delta W}{\Delta t} = \tau \frac{\Delta \theta}{\Delta t}.$$

But $\dfrac{\Delta W}{\Delta t}$ is the rate of doing work or the power, and $\dfrac{\Delta \theta}{\Delta t}$ is the angular velocity. Hence

$$P = \tau\omega. \qquad\qquad (10\text{-}12)$$

That is, the instantaneous power developed by an agent exerting a torque equals the product of the torque and the instantaneous angular velocity.

Example: The drive shaft of an automobile rotates at 3600 rpm and transmits 80 hp from the engine to the rear wheels. Compute the torque developed by the engine.

$$\omega = 3600 \times \frac{2\pi}{60} = 120\pi \text{ rad/sec,} \quad \omega$$

$$80 \text{ hp} = 44{,}000 \text{ ft-lb/sec,}$$

$$550$$

$$\tau = \frac{P}{\omega} = \frac{44{,}000}{120\pi} = 117 \text{ lb-ft.}$$

10-4 Kinetic energy of rotation. Consider again the pivoted wheel shown in Fig. 10-7. In the absence of friction or air resistance, the only torque about the axis O is that exerted by the outside agent responsible for the force F. We have seen that this torque τ is equal to

$$\tau = I\alpha.$$

In a short time interval during which the body rotates through a small angle $\Delta\theta$, the torque may be regarded as constant, and therefore the angular acceleration is constant. Multiplying both sides by $\Delta\theta$, we get

$$\tau\Delta\theta = I\alpha\Delta\theta. \qquad\qquad (10\text{-}13)$$

If the original angular velocity of the body was ω_0, then, after rotation through an angle $\Delta\theta$, the final angular velocity ω is given by Eq. (9-8). Namely,

$$\omega^2 = \omega_0{}^2 + 2\alpha\Delta\theta,$$

or

$$\alpha\Delta\theta = \tfrac{1}{2}\omega^2 - \tfrac{1}{2}\omega_0{}^2.$$

Also, $\tau\Delta\theta$ is the work W supplied from the outside.   Therefore, Eq. (10-13) may be written

$$W = \tfrac{1}{2}I\omega^2 - \tfrac{1}{2}I\omega_0^2, \qquad (10\text{-}14)$$

which shows that the effect of the work delivered to the body from the outside is to change the quantity $\tfrac{1}{2}I\omega^2$ from its original value $\tfrac{1}{2}I\omega_0^2$ to its final value $\tfrac{1}{2}I\omega^2$.   There has been no change of potential energy and, in the absence of friction, no energy has been converted into heat.   In accordance with the ideas developed in Chapter 7, we denote the quantity $\tfrac{1}{2}I\omega^2$ as the kinetic energy of rotation, thus

$$K = \tfrac{1}{2}I\omega^2. \qquad (10\text{-}15)$$

If, in addition to the applied torque τ, there is also a frictional torque τ_f in the opposite direction, Eq. (10-13) is changed to

$$(\tau - \tau_f)\Delta\theta = I\alpha\Delta\theta,$$

and Eq. (10-14) becomes

$$W = \tfrac{1}{2}I\omega^2 - \tfrac{1}{2}I\omega_0^2 + W_f,$$

where $W_f = \tau_f\Delta\theta$ is the work done against friction, or the energy converted into heat.   In the case of a composite system consisting of bodies that undergo rotation as well as bodies that undergo translation, the energy principle may be written as in Chapter 7,

$$\left\{\begin{array}{c}\text{Work done or energy} \\ \text{supplied from the outside}\end{array}\right\} = (K_2 - K_1) + (V_2 - V_1) + W_f,$$

provided that kinetic energy of rotation is included, along with kinetic energy by translation, within the symbol K.

Example: A cord is wrapped around the rim of a flywheel 2 ft in radius and a steady pull of 10 lb is exerted on the cord.   The wheel is mounted in frictionless bearings on a horizontal shaft through its center.   The moment of inertia of the wheel is 1.5 slug-ft^2. What is the angular velocity of the wheel after 20 ft of cord are unwound?

The work done by the outside agent exerting the steady pull of 10 lb in unwinding 20 ft of cord is

$$W = 20 \text{ ft} \times 10 \text{ lb} = 200 \text{ ft-lb}.$$

Assuming the wheel to start from rest, the increase of kinetic energy is

$$K_2 - K_1 = \tfrac{1}{2}I\omega^2 = \tfrac{1}{2} \times 1.5 \text{ slug-ft}^2 \times \omega^2.$$

From the principle of conservation of energy,

$$W = K_2 - K_1$$

or

$$200 = \tfrac{1}{2} \times 1.5\omega^2,$$

$$\omega = 16.3 \text{ rad/sec.}$$

10-5 Angular momentum and angular impulse.   Fig. 10-8(a) represents a small body of mass m moving in the plane of the diagram with a velocity v and a momentum mv.   We define its *angular momentum* about an axis through O perpendicular to the plane of the diagram, as the product of its linear momentum and the perpendicular distance from the axis to its line of motion.   That is,

$$\left\{ \begin{array}{l} \text{Angular momentum} \\ \text{of a particle} \end{array} \right\} = mvr.$$

It will be seen that angular momentum is defined in the same way as the moment of a force and it is often referred to as *moment of momentum*.

Fig. 10-8(b) represents a body of finite size rotating in the plane of the diagram about an axis through O.   The velocity v of a small element of the body is related to the angular velocity of the body by $v = \omega r$.   The

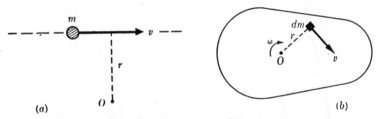

Fig. 10-8.   Angular momentum.

angular momentum of the element is therefore $mvr = \omega mr^2$, and the total angular momentum of the body is $\Sigma \omega mr^2 = \omega \Sigma mr^2$.   But Σmr^2 is the moment of inertia of the body about its axis of rotation.   Hence the angular momentum can be written as $I\omega$.   In this form it is completely analogous to linear momentum mv.   Thus

$$\left\{ \begin{array}{l} \text{Angular momentum} \\ \text{of a rotating body} \end{array} \right\} = I\omega.$$

Fig. 10-9(a) represents two disks with moments of inertia I and I', respectively, rotating with angular velocities ω_0 and ω_0'. Suppose at moment t_0 the two disks engage and, after a very short interval of time, say $t - t_0$, the disks have the same final angular velocity ω, as in Fig. 10-8(b). (Subscript zero means before engaging and the absence of a subscript, after.) During the very short time interval necessary to cause these changes in angular velocity, the larger disk exerts a torque τ on the smaller, and the smaller exerts a torque τ' on the larger. From Newton's third law τ and τ' are at all times equal in magnitude and oppositely directed. That is, $\tau = -\tau'$. Both τ and τ' vary during the contact. Both are zero before contact, both are small at the first instant of contact, then both increase to a maximum, and both decrease and become zero when the disks attain their final angular velocity.

A torque that varies with the time in this manner is called an *impul-*

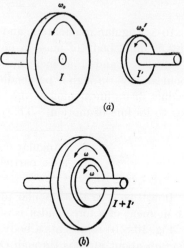

(a)

(b)

Fig. 10-9. An impulsive torque acts when two rotating disks engage.

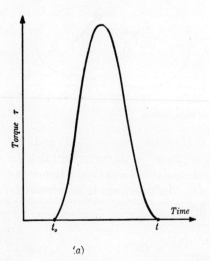

(a)

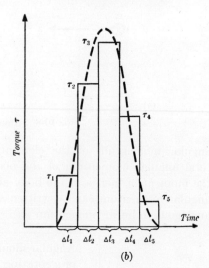

(b)

Fig. 10-10.

sive torque and is plotted on a torque-time diagram in Fig. 10-10(a) and is seen to have the same characteristics as those of the impulsive force shown in Fig. 8-2(a) on page 127. Suppose the total time interval $t - t_0$ is subdivided into any number of parts $\Delta t_1, \Delta t_2, \ldots$, and rectangles are drawn as in Fig. 10-10(b) whose jagged outline approximates the smooth curve. As before, the larger the number of subdivisions, the more closely will the smooth curve be approximated and the more closely will the sum of the areas of the rectangles approach the area under the smooth curve.

Let us therefore replace the continuously varying impulsive torque by a torque which remains constant at the value τ_1 during the time interval Δt_1, then jumps to the value τ_2, maintaining this value for a time Δt_2, and so on. If the angular velocity of the disk of moment of inertia I changes from its original value ω_0 to the value ω_1 at the end of the first time interval, we have, from Eq. (10-9)

$$\tau_1 = I \frac{\omega_1 - \omega_0}{\Delta t_1}$$

or

$$\tau_1 \Delta t_1 = I\omega_1 - I\omega_0,$$

and similarly for all the other intervals

$$\tau_2 \Delta t_2 = I\omega_2 - I\omega_1,$$
$$\tau_3 \Delta t_3 = I\omega_3 - I\omega_2,$$
$$\tau_4 \Delta t_4 = I\omega_4 - I\omega_3,$$
$$\tau_5 \Delta t_5 = I\omega - I\omega_4,$$

where ω is the angular velocity at the end of the last time interval. Adding these equations, we get

$$\Sigma\tau\Delta t = I\omega - I\omega_0. \tag{10-16}$$

If we now imagine the total time interval subdivided into a larger and larger number of steps, the left-hand member of Eq. (10-16) becomes the area under the smooth curve, while the right-hand member remains unaffected. We have, therefore, the result that

$$\left\{ \begin{matrix} \text{Area under the} \\ \tau\text{-}t \text{ curve} \end{matrix} \right\} = I\omega - I\omega_0. \tag{10-17}$$

Similarly

$$\left\{ \begin{matrix} \text{Area under the} \\ \tau'\text{-}t \text{ curve} \end{matrix} \right\} = I'\omega - I'\omega_0'. \tag{10-18}$$

In conformity with the terminology employed in the case of an impulsive force, we call the left-hand member of (10-17) or (10-18) an *angular impulse*. Thus

$$\text{Angular impulse} = \left\{\begin{array}{l}\text{Area under the} \\ \tau{-}t \text{ curve}\end{array}\right\}.$$

Eq. (10-17) or (10-18) may therefore be stated verbally as follows: *The angular impulse acting on either body is equal to the change in angular momentum of that body about the same axis.*

10-6 Conservation of angular momentum. Since the torque τ acting on the smaller disk of Fig. 10-9 is at all times equal in magnitude and opposite in direction to the torque τ' acting on the larger disk, we have

$$\left\{\begin{array}{l}\text{Area under the} \\ \tau{-}t \text{ curve}\end{array}\right\} = -\left\{\begin{array}{l}\text{Area under the} \\ \tau'{-}t \text{ curve}\end{array}\right\}$$

and therefore, from Eqs. (10-17) and (10-18),

$$I\omega - I\omega_0 = -(I'\omega - I'\omega_0')$$

or

$$I\omega_0 + I'\omega_0' = (I + I')\omega. \tag{10-19}$$

The left side of Eq. (10-19) is the total angular momentum of the system (consisting of both disks) before engaging, and the right side is the total angular momentum after engaging. We have therefore derived the important result that the total angular momentum of the whole system is unaltered. When both disks are regarded as one system, then the torques τ and τ' are *internal* torques and during the engaging process no external torque acts. We therefore have the result that *if the resultant external torque on a system is zero, the angular momentum of the system remains constant*; and hence any interaction between the parts of a system cannot alter its total angular momentum. This is the *principle of conservation of angular momentum*, and it ranks with the principles of conservation of linear momentum and conservation of energy as one of the most fundamental of physical laws.

Examples. (1) A disk weighing 10 lb, with a radius of gyration of 9 inches, and rotating with an angular velocity of 120 rpm engages with another disk of weight 15 lb, radius of gyration 12 inches, originally rotating in the same direction as the first with an angular velocity of 40 rpm. What is the final angular velocity of both disks?

$$I = \frac{w}{g} k^2 = \frac{10}{32} \left(\frac{9}{12}\right)^2 = 0.176 \text{ slug-ft}^2,$$

$$I' = \frac{w'}{g} k'^2 = \frac{15}{32} (1)^2 = 0.468 \text{ slug-ft}^2,$$

$$\omega_0 = \frac{120 \times 2\pi}{60} = 4\pi \text{ rad/sec},$$

$$\omega_0' = \frac{40 \times 2\pi}{60} = \frac{4}{3} \pi \text{ rad/sec}.$$

Since

$$I\omega_0 + I'\omega_0' = (I + I')\omega,$$

$$\omega = \frac{0.176 \times 4\pi + 0.468 \times \frac{4}{3}\pi}{0.176 + 0.468}$$

$$= 2.19\pi \text{ rad/sec}$$

$$= 65.7 \text{ rpm}.$$

(2) A man stands at the center of a turntable, holding his arms extended horizontally with a 10-lb weight in each hand. He is set rotating about a vertical axis with an angular velocity of one revolution in 2 sec. Find his new angular velocity if he drops his hands to his sides. The moment of inertia of the man may be assumed constant and equal to 4 slug-ft². The original distance of the weights from the axis is 3 ft, and their final distance is 6 inches.

If friction in the turntable is neglected, no external torques act about a vertical axis and the angular momentum about this axis is constant. That is,

$$I\omega = (I\omega)_0 = I_0\omega_0,$$

where I and ω are the final moment of inertia and angular velocity, and I_0 and ω_0 are the initial values of these quantities.

$$I = I_{\text{man}} + I_{\text{weights}},$$

$$I = 4 + 2\left(\frac{10}{32}\right)\left(\frac{1}{2}\right)^2 = 4.16 \text{ slug-ft}^2,$$

$$I_0 = 4 + 2\left(\frac{10}{32}\right)(3)^2 = 9.63 \text{ slug-ft}^2,$$

$$\omega_0 = \pi \text{ rad/sec},$$

$$\omega = \omega_0 \frac{I_0}{I} = 2.31 \pi \text{ rad/sec}.$$

That is, the angular velocity is more than doubled. This experiment is easily performed with a piano stool as a turntable. The results are most surprising.

10-7 Vector representation of angular quantities. It was mentioned briefly in Sec. 9-5 that any quantity associated with an axis, such as angular velocity, angular acceleration, etc., could be represented by a vector along the axis. The sense of the vector is usually considered to be that in which a nut would advance along the axis if threaded on it with a right-hand thread and rotated in the direction of the angular quantity to be represented. Evidently torque, angular impulse, and angular momentum can all be represented in this way.

Example: A couple consisting of the two forces P and P', each equal to 4 lb, is applied for 3 sec to a disk of radius 1.5 ft and moment of inertia 20 slug-ft^2, pivoted about an axis through its center as in Fig. 10-11. The initial angular velocity of the disk is 5 rad/sec. Show in a vector diagram the torque, the initial angular momentum, and the final angular momentum.

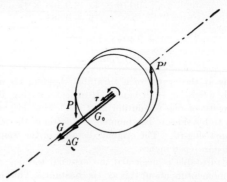

Fig. 10-11. Vector ΔG is the change in angular momentum produced by the couple P-P'.

From the preceding discussion, the vectors representing the torque τ due to the couple, and the initial angular momentum G_0, are directed as in Fig. 10-11. The magnitude of the initial angular momentum is

$$G_0 = I\omega_0 = 20 \times 5 = 100 \text{ slug-ft}^2/\text{sec.}$$

The angular impulse, which was defined as the area under the torque-time curve, is in this problem merely the product of the constant torque τ and the time interval Δt. Since this must equal the change in angular momentum, we have

$$\tau \Delta t = I\omega - I\omega_0 = \Delta(I\omega) = \Delta G.$$

But $\tau = 4$ lb $\times$ 3 ft $= 12$ lb-ft, and $\Delta t = 3$ sec.
Hence

$$\Delta G = 12 \times 3 \text{ lb-ft-sec}$$

$$= 36 \frac{\text{slug-ft}^2}{\text{sec}}.$$

This increase has been represented by the vector ΔG in Fig. 10-11.

The final angular momentum, G, is the vector sum of G_0 and ΔG. Since both are in the same direction, the vector sum is simply the arithmetic sum. That is

$$G = G_0 + \Delta G = 136 \frac{\text{slug-ft}^2}{\text{sec}} \, .$$

10-8 Precession. The disk shown in Fig. 10-12 is rotating about a shaft which coincides with the X-axis. A couple consisting of the forces P and P' is applied to the *shaft*, and we wish to find the resulting motion of the disk. The problem will be solved by the same method used in the preceding example. The initial angular momentum is represented by the vector G_0. The effect of the forces P and P' is to produce a torque τ about the Z-axis, perpendicular to the X-Y plane in which the forces act. In the time interval Δt, the change in angular momentum produced by this torque is $\tau \Delta t$ and this change is represented by the vector ΔG in the figure. The final angular momentum is the vector sum of G_0 and ΔG and is represented by the vector G.

It will be seen that the situation is exactly analogous to that of Fig. 10-11, the only difference being that in the first case the direction of the applied torque vector is the same as the initial angular momentum vector, so that the vectors G_0 and ΔG are in the same line, while in the second case the torque vector is perpendicular to the initial angular momentum vector, and hence G_0 and ΔG are at right angles to one another. The new angular

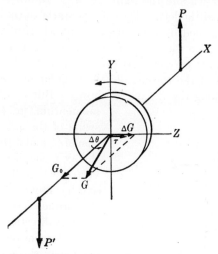

FIG. 10-12. Vector ΔG is the change in angular momentum produced by the couple P-P'. Compare with Fig. 10-11.

momentum, G, will be seen to lie in the horizontal (X-Z) plane but displaced from the original angular momentum by an angle $\Delta\theta$.

Finally, since an angular momentum vector in a given direction implies rotation in a plane perpendicular to that direction, it follows that the plane of the spinning disk must also have rotated through an angle $\Delta\theta$. That is, the vector G must lie along the new axis of rotation. This leads to the very unexpected result that the forces P and P', instead of forcing the further end of the shaft up and the nearer end down, as would be the case if the disk were not spinning, cause the further end of the shaft to move to the left and the nearer end to move to the right, perpendicular to the directions in which P and P' are acting.

. If we assume that the forces P and P' follow the motion of the shaft as it turns in the X-Z plane, the shaft and spinning disk will rotate about the vertical Y-axis with a uniform angular velocity, say Ω (capital ω). This type of motion is called *precession*, and Ω is the precessional velocity.

Precessional effects are familiar to everyone who has ridden a bicycle. When one is riding straight ahead, the angular momentum vector G_0 of the front wheel is horizontal and points to the left. Suppose that a torque is now applied to the handlebars (and hence to the shaft of the front wheel) in such a direction as to turn the front wheel to the right. The corresponding torque vector points vertically down, as does the change in angular momentum, ΔG, produced by it. The new angular momentum vector, G, now points to the left and downward, which means that the left end of the front axle points down and the right end up. In other words, the bicycle and rider tip toward the left. Thus if one starts to tip in either direction, balance can be regained by turning the front wheel in that direction.

Fig. 10-13 is a top view of the vector diagram of Fig. 10-12. This diagram is not strictly correct. At the first instant when P and P' start to act, the directions of the torque and the angular momentum change produced by it are along the Z-axis, as shown. But this change in angular momentum immediately causes a swing of the axis toward the direction of G, and if the forces move with the axis, the direction of the torque vector swings also. By the time the axis has moved to the direction of G, the torque vector is at right angles to this new direction. Hence Fig. 10-13 must be considered to apply to an extremely short time interval only,

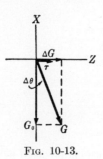

Fig. 10-13.

while the axis swings from its initial position through a very small angle $\Delta\theta$. If the angle is small, the length of G is practically the same as that of G_0, and the only effect of the change is to alter the direction of G_0 slightly. In other words, the couple P–P' changes the direction of the angular momentum but not its magnitude. (This is exactly analogous to the effect produced by centripetal force in circular motion. The centripetal force changes the direction of the tangential velocity but not its magnitude.)

If the angle $\Delta\theta$ in Fig. 10-13 is small, its value in radians is very nearly

$$\Delta\theta = \frac{\Delta G}{G} = \frac{\tau\Delta t}{G}.$$

(Since G_0 and G are numerically equal, let G represent the magnitude of either.)

The precessional velocity, Ω, is

$$\Omega = \frac{\Delta\theta}{\Delta t} = \frac{\tau}{G}, \quad \text{or}$$

$$\tau = \Omega G.$$

Finally, replacing G by $I\omega$, we obtain

$$\boxed{\tau = I\omega\Omega.} \qquad (10\text{-}20)$$

In this equation, τ is the torque necessary to produce an angular velocity of precession Ω in a rotating system of angular momentum $I\omega$. Both Ω and ω are to be expressed in rad/sec, and τ and I in appropriate units.

Eq. (10-20) may help to make clear, in part, the stabilizing properties of the gyroscope. If we write it as $\Omega = \tau/I\omega$, it is seen that for a given torque τ the precessional velocity Ω will be small if the product $I\omega$ is large, and this product can be made very large indeed, even in a gyroscope of small mass and dimensions, by running it at a high angular velocity ω. Hence, for a couple at right angles to its axis of spin, the gyroscope behaves like a body of very large inertia.

Example: The moment of inertia of a bicycle wheel is approximately 0.2 slug-ft². At a forward speed of 15 mi/hr, its angular velocity ω is about 20 rad/sec. If a torque of 4 lb-ft is applied through the handlebars, what is the angular velocity of precession?

$$\Omega = \frac{\tau}{I\omega}$$

$$= \frac{4}{0.2 \times 20}$$

$$= 1 \text{ rad/sec.}$$

10-9 The gyroscope. Another illustration of precessional motion is afforded by the gyroscope. As well as being an interesting and puzzling toy, it finds important technical applications in the gyro compass, the directional gyro, the artificial hori-
zon, the turn indicator, and in the stabilization of ships.

The usual mounting of a toy gyroscope is shown in Fig. 10-14. The forces acting on the gyroscope are its weight w and the upward push of the pivot P. If these forces are equal they constitute a couple, and since the effect of a couple is the same wherever it may be applied, the arrangement of forces in

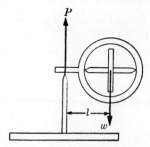

FIG. 10-14. The forces P and w, equal and oppositely directed, constitute a couple.

Fig. 10-14 is entirely equivalent to that in Fig. 10-12. The gyroscope will not "fall" under these circumstances because the resultant vertical force acting on it is zero!

The torque produced by the couple is wl. Hence the precessional velocity is

$$\Omega = \frac{wl}{I\omega}. \tag{10-21}$$

If the gyroscope is held with its axis of rotation at rest, say by supporting the free end with the finger, the upward push P and the upward force exerted by the finger will each equal $w/2$. If the finger is suddenly removed, the forces on the gyroscope do not constitute a couple, since the downward force is w and the upward force only $w/2$. The center of gravity of the gyroscope therefore starts to fall, and at the same time precession begins, but with a smaller precessional velocity than that given by Eq. (10-21), since the resultant torque is smaller. The effect of the motion of the gyroscope is such as to increase the magnitude of P to a value larger than w. This causes the axis to rise again, after which the motion repeats itself.   The resulting motion is one of precession combined with an up and down oscillation of the axis of rotation.   This motion is called *nutation* and its complete analysis is too lengthy to be carried out here.

If it is desired to start the gyroscope off with a motion of pure precession after releasing it, it is necessary to give the free end a push in the direction in which it will naturally precess.   The effect of the horizontal push is to cause the pivoted end to bear down on the pivot, thus increasing the force P.   At the instant when P has increased to equal w, the precessional velocity of the gyroscope will have reached its proper value.   The outer end may then be released and the motion will continue.

Problems — Chapter 10

10-1. (a) Compute the torque developed by an airplane engine whose output is 2000 hp at an angular velocity of 2400 rpm. (b) If a drum 18 inches in diameter were attached to the motor shaft, and the power output of the motor were used to raise a weight hanging from a rope wrapped around the shaft, how large a weight could be lifted? (c) With what velocity would it rise?

10-2. An automobile engine delivers 20 horsepower at 1200 rpm to the transmission of a car. The ratio of engine speed to that of the driveshaft is 1:1 in high gear and 3:1 in low gear. The ratio of drive shaft speed to rear axle is 4:1. Each rear wheel has a diameter of 28 inches (6.00 × 16 tire). If the overall efficiency of the power transmitting system is 80% at all gear ratios, find (a) the power delivered to the rear wheels when in high gear and when in low gear, (b) the torque delivered to the rear wheels when in high gear and when in low gear, and (c) the tangential force exerted by the rear wheels on the road when in high gear and when in low gear.

10-3. Find the moment of inertia of a rod 4 cm in diameter and 2 m long, of mass 8 kgm, (a) about an axis perpendicular to the rod and passing through its center; (b) about an axis perpendicular to the rod and passing through one end; (c) about a longitudinal axis through the center of the rod.

10-4. The inner radius of a hollow cylinder is 3 inches, the outer radius is 4 inches, and the length is 6 inches. What is the radius of gyration of the cylinder about its axis?

10-5. The four bodies shown in Fig. 10-15 have equal masses M. Body A is a solid cylinder of radius R. Body B is a hollow thin cylinder of radius R. Body C is a solid square with length of side = $2R$. Body D is the same size as C, but hollow

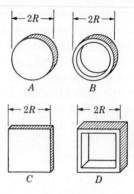

Fig. 10-15

(i.e., made up of four thin sticks). The bodies have axes of rotation perpendicular to the page and through the center of gravity of each body. (a) Which body has the smallest moment of inertia? (b) Which body has the largest moment of inertia?

10-6. A grindstone in the form of a solid cylinder has a radius of 2 ft and weighs 96 lb. (a) What torque will bring it from rest to an angular velocity of 300 rpm in 10 sec? (b) What is its kinetic energy when rotating at 300 rpm?

10-7. The flywheel of a motor weighs 640 lb and has a radius of gyration of 4 ft. The motor develops a constant torque of 1280 lb-ft, and the flywheel starts from rest. (a) What is the angular acceleration of the flywheel? (b) What will be its angular velocity after making 4 revolutions? (c) How much work is done by the motor during the first 4 revolutions?

10-8. The flywheel of a punch press has a moment of inertia of 15 slug-ft² and it runs at 300 rpm. The flywheel supplies all the energy needed in a quick punching operation. (a) Find the speed in rpm to which the flywheel will be reduced by a sudden punching operation requiring 4500 ft-lb of work. (b) What must be the constant power supply to the flywheel in horsepower to bring it back to its initial speed in 5 sec?

10-9. The flywheel of a gasoline engine is required to give up 380 ft-lb of kinetic energy while its angular velocity decreases from 600 rpm to 540 rpm. What moment of inertia is required?

10-10. A flywheel 3 ft in diameter is pivoted on a horizontal axis. A rope is wrapped around the outside of the flywheel and a steady pull of 10 lb is exerted on the rope. It is found that 24 ft of rope are unwound in 4 sec. (a) What was the angular acceleration of the flywheel? (b) What was its final angular velocity? (c) What was its final kinetic energy? (d) What is its moment of inertia?

10-11. A light rigid rod 100 cm long has a small block of mass 50 gm attached at one end. The other end is pivoted and the rod rotates in a vertical circle. At a certain instant the rod makes an angle of 53° with the vertical, and the tangential speed of the block is 400 cm/sec. (a) What are the horizontal and vertical components of the velocity of the block? (b) What is the moment of inertia of the system? (c) What is the radial acceleration of the block? (d) What is the tangential acceleration of the block? (e) What is the tension or compression in the rod?

10-12. A man sits on a piano stool holding a pair of dumbbells at a distance of 3 ft from the axis of rotation of the stool. He is given an angular velocity of 2 rad/sec, after which he pulls the dumbbells in until they are but 1 ft distant from the axis. The moment of inertia of the man about the axis of rotation is 3 slug-ft² and may be considered constant. The dumbbells weigh 16 lb each and may be considered point masses. Neglect friction. (a) What is the initial angular momentum of the system? (b) What is the angular velocity of the system after the dumbbells are pulled in toward the axis? (c) Compute the kinetic energy of the sys-

tem, before and after the dumbbells are pulled in. Account for the difference, if any.

10-13. A small block weighing 8 lb is attached to a cord passing through a hole in a horizontal frictionless surface. The block is originally revolving in a circle of radius 2 ft about the hole with a tangential velocity of 12 ft/sec. The cord is then pulled slowly from below, shortening the radius of the circle in which the block revolves. The breaking strength of the cord is 144 lb. What will be the radius of the circle when the cord breaks?

10-14. A uniform rod of mass 30 gm and 20 cm long rotates in a horizontal plane about a fixed vertical axis through its center. Two small bodies, each of mass 20 gm, are mounted so that they can slide along the rod. They are initially held by catches at positions 5 cm on each side of the center of the rod, and the system is rotating at 15 rpm. Without otherwise changing the system, the catches are released and the masses slide outward along the rod and fly off at the ends. (a) What is the angular velocity of the system at the instant when the small masses reach the ends of the rod? (b) What is the angular velocity of the rod after the small masses leave it?

10-15. A turntable rotates about a fixed vertical axis, making one revolution in 10 sec. The moment of inertia of the turntable about this axis is 720 slug-ft². A man weighing 160 lb, initially standing at the center of the turntable, runs out along a radius. What is the angular velocity of the turntable when the man is 6 ft from the center?

10-16. The pedal of a bicycle is being pushed down with a force of 5 lb when in the position shown in Fig. 10-16. (a) Assuming that the bicycle is moving with constant velocity, what is the friction force exerted by the bicycle on the ground? Make any simplifying assumptions you feel are necessary. (b) The force on the pedal is now increased to 100 lb. What

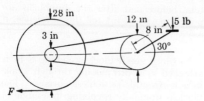

FIG. 10-16

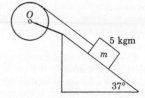

FIG. 10-18

rurther information must we have in order to calculate the acceleration of the bicycle?

10-17. A disk of mass M and radius R is pivoted about a horizontal axis through its center, and a small body of mass M is attached to the rim of the disk. If the disk is released from rest with the small body at the end of a horizontal radius, find the angular velocity when the small body is at the bottom.

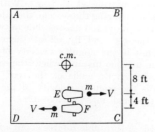

FIG. 10-17

10-18. The rectangle $ABCD$ of Fig. 10-17 is a top view of a large wooden platform resting on the frictionless surface of a frozen lake. Two guns, E and F, fastened to the platform and pointed in opposite directions simultaneously fire two cannon balls of mass $m = 5$ slugs with velocities V of 800 ft/sec. The moment of inertia of platform plus guns, about an axis through the center of gravity and perpendicular to the diagram, is 8000 slug-ft². (a) What is the linear velocity of the center of gravity of the platform after the guns are fired? (b) What is the angular velocity of the platform after the guns are fired?

10-19. A block of mass $m = 5$ kgm slides down a surface inclined 37° to the horizontal as shown in Fig. 10-18. The coefficient of sliding friction is 0.25. A string attached to the block is wrapped around a flywheel on a fixed axis at O. The flywheel has a mass $M = 20$ kgm, an outer radius $R = 0.2$ m, and a radius of gyration with respect to the axis $k_0 = 0.1$ m. (a) What is the acceleration of the block down the plane? (b) What is the tension in the string?

10-20. Disks A and B are mounted on a shaft SS and may be connected or disconnected by clutch C, as in Fig. 10-19. The moment of inertia of disk A is one-half that of disk B. With the clutch disconnected, A is brought up to an angular velocity ω_0. The accelerating torque is

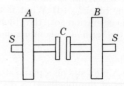

FIG. 10-19

then removed from A and it is coupled to disk B by the clutch. Bearing friction may be neglected. It is found that 3000 ft-lb of heat are developed in the clutch when the connection is made. What was the original kinetic energy of disk A?

10-21. The stabilizing gyroscope of a ship weighs 50 tons, its radius of gyration is 5 ft, and it rotates about a vertical axis with an angular velocity of 900 rpm.

(a) How long a time is required to bring it up to speed, starting from rest, with a constant power input of 100 hp? (b) Find the righting moment exerted on the ship, in lb-ft, when the axis is forced to precess in a vertical fore-and-aft plane at the rate of 1 degree/sec.

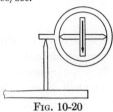

Fig. 10-20

10-22. The mass of the rotor of a toy gyroscope is 150 gm and its moment of inertia about its axis is 1500 gm-cm². The mass of the frame is 30 gm. The gyroscope is supported on a single pivot as in Fig. 10-20 with its center of gravity distant 4 cm horizontally from the pivot, and is precessing in a horizontal plane at the rate of 1 revolution in 6 sec. (a) Find the upward force exerted by the pivot. (b) Find the angular velocity with which the rotor is spinning about its axis, expressed in rpm. (c) Copy the diagram, and show by vectors the angular velocity of the rotor and the angular velocity of precession.

CHAPTER 11

ELASTICITY

11-1 Introduction. In the preceding chapters we have developed the principles by which the engineer can compute the tensile or compressive forces in the various members of a structure. It is not enough, however, to know how much force each part of a structure will exert. One must also know how large a cable or strut is needed to withstand this force, and how much the structure will distort under load. The subject of elasticity is the study of the way in which actual materials such as wood, steel, concrete, etc., are changed in shape by forces applied to them. In engineering work this part of mechanics is called "Strength of Materials."

All real substances are found to yield somewhat under the influence of a force. Some materials return to their original form when the force is removed, while others remain more or less distorted. A *perfectly elastic* material is one which returns exactly to its original form when the distorting force is removed; a *perfectly inelastic* material is one which does not return at all. Many substances are nearly perfectly elastic up to a certain maximum distortion but do not recover completely if distorted beyond this point, which is known as the *elastic limit*.

The elastic properties of materials are described in terms of two concepts known as *stress* and *strain*. These terms are used loosely in everyday life, often as synonyms, but like other terms, such as force and work, they are given a very restricted meaning in physics.

11-2 Stress. Fig. 11-1 (a) represents a bar subjected at its ends to equal and opposite pulls of magnitude F. The bar is in equilibrium under the action of these forces, and hence every part of it is also in equilibrium. Imagine the bar to be cut at the dotted section, and consider the portion of the bar at the left of the cut. (Fig. 11-1(b).) Since this portion was in equilibrium before the cut was made, the portion of the bar at the right of the section must have been exerting a force on it,

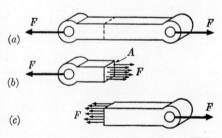

Fig. 11-1. Tensile stress.

equal to F and directed toward the right.   If the cut is not too near the end of the bar, this force will be distributed uniformly over the cross section as indicated by the small arrows.

Let A represent the cross sectional area of the bar.   The ratio of the distributed force to the cross sectional area is called the *stress* in the bar, and the bar is said to be in a state of stress (in this particular case, in *tensile* stress).   Since the cut may be made at any point along the bar the entire bar is in a state of stress.

Stress is a force per unit area, and the units of stress in our three systems are lb/ft², newtons/m², and dynes/cm².   It is almost universal engineering practice, however, to express a stress in lb/in².

Some engineering texts use the term "stress" for the *total* force F acting across a section, and the term "unit stress" for the force per unit area.

It is evident that the portion of the bar shown in Fig. 11-1(b) must itself be exerting a force toward the left, on the right-hand portion of the bar.   This force, shown in Fig. 11-1(c), is the reaction to the distributed force in 11-1(b) and hence is also equal in magnitude to F.   The concept of stress is considered to include both of these distributed forces.   If, for example, the force F is 1000 pounds and the area A is two square inches, the stress at the section is $1000/2 = 500$ lb/in².   One cannot say, however, in which direction the stress acts.   The portion of the bar at the left of the section is being pulled toward the right, and that at the right of the section is being pulled toward the left.

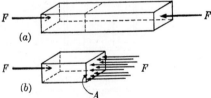

F ——— F
(a)

F ——— F
(b)
A

Fig. 11-2.   Compressive stress.

If a member, such as a column or strut, is subject to compression, a similar state of affairs exists at every cross section, except that a push instead of a pull acts across the section. The portion of the member at either side of the section exerts a push on that portion at the other side as in Fig. 11-2.   The stress in the member is defined in the same way, as the ratio of the force to the area, and is called a *compressive* stress.

A third type of stress is illustrated in Fig. 11-3.   The lower face of the block is being pulled to the left and the upper face to the right.   The force which the portion above any horizontal plane exerts on the portion below that plane is shown in Fig. 11-3(b).   This force is also distributed over the cross section of the block, but it is parallel to the plane of the cross section instead of being perpendicular to it as in tensile or compressive stress.   A stress of this type is called a *shearing stress* or simply a *shear*.

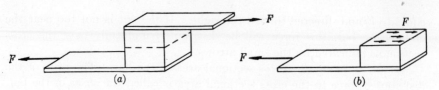

Fig. 11-3. Shearing stress.

Since the lower half of the block is in equilibrium[1], the distributed force at its top face must equal the force F, and, as before, the shearing stress is defined as the ratio of this force to the cross sectional area.

Still another type of stress is illustrated in Fig. 11-4. Fig. 11-4(a) represents a cylinder provided with a tightly fitting piston and filled with a liquid. A force F presses down on the piston, compressing the liquid in the cylinder. Let A be the cross section of the piston. The *pressure* exerted on the liquid by the piston is defined as the ratio of the force F to the area A. It is well known that the side walls and bottom of the cylinder press inward on the liquid with a pressure equal to that exerted by the piston, so that the liquid is subjected to a uniform inward pressure over its entire surface.

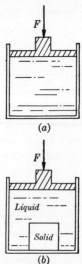

Fig. 11-4. Both liquid and solid are under a hydrostatic pressure.

If a solid block is placed in the liquid and pressure applied as in Fig. 11-4(b), the same uniform inward pressure is exerted over the entire surface of the block.

A stress of this sort is called a *hydrostatic pressure*, and, like other types of stress, is expressed in force units per unit of area. Like other stresses also, it is not confined to the surface of the liquid or solid. Across any imagined area within either one a force is exerted by that part of the body at one side of the area, on the part at the other side.

---

[1] The two forces F in Fig. 11-3(a) constitute a couple, and by themselves would produce clockwise rotation. Since a couple can only be balanced by another couple of opposite sign, there must be other forces on the block for complete equilibrium, but we shall ignore them here.

11-3 Strain. The term *strain* refers to the relative change in dimensions or shape of a body which is subjected to stress. Associated with each type of stress described in the preceding section is a corresponding type of strain.

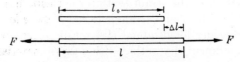

Fig. 11-5. Longitudinal strain.

Fig. 11-5 shows a bar whose natural length is l_0 and which elongates to a length l when equal and opposite pulls are exerted at its ends. The elongation, of course, does not occur at the ends only, but every element of the bar stretches in the same proportion as does the bar as a whole. The *tensile strain* in the bar is defined as the ratio of the increase in length to the original length.

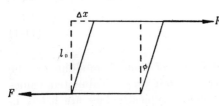

Fig. 11-6. Shearing strain.

$$\text{Tensile strain} = \frac{l - l_0}{l_0} = \frac{\Delta l}{l_0}.$$

The *compressive strain* of a bar in compression is defined in the same way, as the ratio of the decrease in length to the original length.

Fig. 11-6 illustrates a shearing strain. The block whose original rectangular shape is shown by the dotted lines is subjected to a shearing stress and becomes distorted as shown. In this type of strain it is the change in shape, rather than the change in size, which is of interest, and the strain is defined as the angle ϕ. In all cases of practical interest the angle is small and hence is nearly equal to the ratio of the displacement Δx to the dimension l_0.

$$\text{Shearing strain} = \phi \text{ (radians)} = \frac{\Delta x}{l_0}.$$

In both longitudinal and shearing strain, the displacements Δl or Δx and the dimension l_0 are to be expressed in the same unit. (Any unit may be used.) Since a strain is the ratio of one length to another, both expressed in the same unit, it is a pure number.

The strain produced by a hydrostatic pressure is defined as the ratio of the change in volume to the original volume. If we call the original volume V_0 and the change in volume ΔV, the strain is the ratio $\Delta V/V_0$. Like other strains it is a pure number.

11-4 Elastic modulus. The ratio of a stress to the corresponding strain is called an elastic modulus, and provided the elastic limit is not exceeded this ratio is found experimentally to be constant, characteristic of a given material. In other words, the stress is directly proportional to the strain, or is a linear function of the strain (within the elastic limit). This linear relationship between stress and strain is called *Hooke's law*.

Let us first consider longitudinal (i.e. tensile or compressive) stresses and strains. Experiment shows that with a given material, a given longitudinal stress produces a strain of the same magnitude whether the stress is a compression or a tension. Hence the ratio of tensile stress to tensile strain, for a given material, equals the ratio of compressive stress to compressive strain. This ratio is called the *stretch modulus* or *Young's modulus* of the material and will be denoted by Y.

$$Y = \frac{\text{tensile stress}}{\text{tensile strain}} = \frac{\text{compressive stress}}{\text{compressive strain}}$$

or

$$Y = \frac{F/A}{\Delta l/l_0}. \tag{11-1}$$

Since a strain is a pure number, the units of Young's modulus are the same as those of stress, namely, force per unit area. Tabulated values are usually in lb/in^2 or dynes/cm^2. Some typical values are listed in Table 11-1.

TABLE 11-1.—ELASTIC CONSTANTS
(Representative values)

Material	Young's Modulus		Shear Modulus		Bulk Modulus	
	dynes/cm^2	lb/in^2	dynes/cm^2	lb/in^2	dynes/cm^2	lb/in^2
Aluminum	7×10^{11}	10×10^6	2.4×10^{11}	3.4×10^6	7×10^{11}	10×10^6
Brass.........	9	13	3.5	5.1	6.1	8.5
Copper........	10–12	14–18	4	6	12	17
Iron, cast.....	8–10	12–14			9.6	14
Iron, wrought.	18–20	26–29			15	21
Lead..........	1.5	2.3	0.5	0.8	0.8	1.1
Steel	19–21	27–30	8	12	16	23

The ratio of a shearing stress to the corresponding shearing strain is called the *shear modulus* of a material and will be represented by M. It is also called the *modulus of rigidity* or the *torsion modulus*.

$$M = \frac{\text{shearing stress}}{\text{shearing strain}}$$

$$= \frac{F/A}{\phi} = \frac{F/A}{\Delta x/l_0}. \tag{11-2}$$

(Refer to Fig. 11-6 for the meaning of ϕ, Δx, and l_0.)   The shear modulus of a material is also expressed in force per unit area.   For most materials it is one-half to one-third as great as Young's modulus.

The modulus relating an increase in hydrostatic pressure to the corresponding decrease in volume is called the *bulk modulus* and we shall represent it by B.

$$B = -\frac{\Delta p}{\Delta V/V_0}. \tag{11-3}$$

The minus sign is included in the definition of B since an increase of pressure always causes a decrease in volume.   That is, if Δp is positive ΔV is negative.   By including a minus sign in its definition the bulk modulus itself is a positive quantity.

The reciprocal of the bulk modulus is called the *compressibility*, k. Tables of physical constants often list the compressibility rather than the bulk modulus.   From its definition,

$$k = \frac{1}{B} = -\frac{1}{\Delta p}\frac{\Delta V}{V_0}, \tag{11-4}$$

$$\Delta V = -kV_0\Delta p. \tag{11-5}$$

The ratio $\Delta V/V_0$ is the fractional change in volume.   Hence the compressibility of a substance may be defined as its fractional change in volume per unit increase in pressure.

TABLE 11-2.—COMPRESSIBILITY OF LIQUIDS

Liquid	Compressibility (atm^{-1})
Carbon disulphide................	66×10^{-6}
Ethyl alcohol...................	112
Glycerine.......................	22
Mercury.........................	3.8
Water...........................	50

The units of a bulk modulus, from Eq. (11-3), are the same as those of pressure, and the units of compressibility, from Eq. (11-4), are those of a reciprocal pressure. In tabulating compressibilities, the pressure is often expressed in atmospheres. (1 atmosphere = 14.7 lb/in².) The corresponding units of compressibility are therefore "reciprocal atmospheres" or atm⁻¹. For example, the statement that the compressibility of water (see Table 11-2) is 50×10^{-6} atm⁻¹, or 50×10^{-6} per atmosphere, means that the volume decreases by 50 one-millionths of the original volume for each atmosphere increase in pressure.

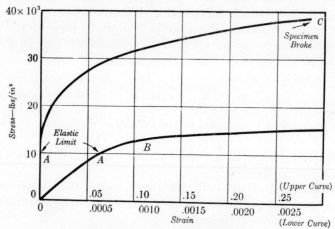

FIG. 11-7. Stress-strain diagram.

When a metal rod is subjected to an increasing tensile stress, the strain is found to change as in Fig. 11-7. The first part of the curve, from O to A, is a straight line. That is, in this region there is a linear relationship between stress and strain and the material obeys Hooke's law. If the stress is not carried beyond that corresponding to point A the specimen returns to its original length when the stress is removed. In other words, the portion of the curve from O to A is the region of perfect elasticity.

If the stress is increased to a value corresponding to point B and then removed, the specimen does not return to its original length but retains a *permanent strain* or a *set*. Point A is called the *elastic limit* or the *yield point* of the material. (Actual materials may show some small irregularities at this point which are omitted for simplicity.) Finally, when the stress is increased sufficiently, the specimen breaks at point C.

Examples. (1) In an experiment to measure Young's modulus, a load of 1000 lb hanging from a steel wire 8 ft long, of cross section 0.025 in², was found to stretch the wire 0.12 inch above its no-load length. What were the stress, the strain, and the value of Young's modulus for the steel of which the wire was composed?

$$\text{Stress} = \frac{F}{A} = \frac{1000}{.025} = 40{,}000 \text{ lb/in}^2.$$

$$\text{Strain} = \frac{\Delta l}{l_0} = \frac{.010}{8} = .00125.$$

$$Y = \frac{\text{stress}}{\text{strain}} = \frac{40{,}000}{.00125} = 32 \times 10^6 \text{ lb/in}^2.$$

(2) A brass plate 2 ft square and $\frac{1}{4}$ inch thick is rigidly fastened to the floor along one edge as in Fig. 11-8. A flat strip S is brazed to its top edge. How large a force is needed to pull the top edge a distance of 0.01 inch to the right? The shear modulus for this brass is 5×10^6 lb/in^2.

The force F is applied to the strip over an area of $24 \times \frac{1}{4} = 6$ in^2.   Hence

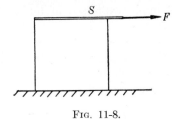

Fig. 11-8.

Shearing stress $= F/6$ lb/in^2.

Also, $\Delta x = 0.01$ inch, $l_0 = 24$ inches.

Shearing strain $= \Delta x/l_0 = \dfrac{.01}{24} = 0.000417.$

Shear modulus $M = \dfrac{\text{stress}}{\text{strain}}.$

$$5 \times 10^6 = \frac{F/6}{.000417},$$

$$F = 12{,}500 \text{ lb}.$$

(3) The volume of oil contained in a certain hydraulic press is 5 ft^3. Find the decrease in volume of the oil when subjected to a pressure of 2000 lb/in^2. The compressibility of the oil is 20×10^{-6} per atm.

The volume decreases by 20 parts per million for a pressure increase of one atm. Since 2000 lb/in$^2 = 136$ atm, the volume decrease is $136 \times 20 = 2720$ parts per million. Since the original volume is 5 ft^3, the actual decrease is

$$\frac{2720}{1{,}000{,}000} \times 5 = 0.0136 \text{ ft}^3 = 23.5 \text{ in}^3.$$

Or, from Eq. (11-5),

$$\Delta V = -kV_0\Delta p = -20 \times 10^{-6} \times 5 \times 136$$
$$= -0.0136 \text{ ft}^3.$$

11-5 The force constant. The various elastic moduli are quantities which describe the elastic properties of a particular *material* and do not directly indicate how much a given rod, cable, or spring constructed of the material will distort under load. If Eq. (11-1) is solved for F one obtains

$$F = \frac{YA}{l_0}\,\Delta l$$

or, if YA/l_0 is replaced by a single constant k, and the elongation Δl is represented by x,

$$F = kx. \tag{11-6}$$

In other words, the elongation of a body in tension above its no-load length, is directly proportional to the stretching force. Hooke's law was originally stated in this form, rather than in terms of stress and strain.

When a helical spring is stretched, the actual distortion of the wire composing it is a combination of stretching, bending, and torsion. It is nevertheless true that the elongation of the spring as a whole is directly proportional to the stretching force, provided the elastic limit is not exceeded. That is, an equation of the form $F = kx$ still applies, although the proportionality constant k cannot be simply expressed in terms of elastic moduli.

The constant k, or the ratio of the force to the elongation, is called the *force constant* or the *coefficient of stiffness* of the spring, and is expressed in pounds per foot, newtons per meter, or dynes per centimeter. It is equal numerically to the force required to produce unit elongation.

Problems — Chapter 11

11-1. A steel wire 10 ft long and 0.1 square inch in cross section, is found to stretch 0.01 ft under a tension of 2500 lb. What is Young's modulus for this steel?

11-2. The elastic limit of a steel elevator cable is 40,000 lb/in². Find the maximum upward acceleration which can be given a 2-ton elevator when supported by a cable whose cross section is one-half a square inch, if the stress is not to exceed $\frac{1}{4}$ of the elastic limit?

11-3. A copper wire 12 ft long and 0.036 inch in diameter was given the test below. A load of 4.5 lb was originally hung from the wire to keep it taut. The position of the lower end of the wire was read on a scale.

Added load (lb)	Scale reading (in)
0	3.02
2	3.04
4	3.06
6	3.08
8	3.10
10	3.12
12	3.14
14	3.65

Make a graph of these values, plotting the increase in length horizontally and the added load vertically. Calculate the value of Young's modulus. What was the stress at the elastic limit?

11-4. A steel wire has the following properties:

Length = 10 ft
Cross section = .01 square inch
Young's modulus = 30,000,000 lb/in²
Shear modulus = 10,000,000 lb/in²
Elastic limit = 60,000 lb/in²
Breaking stress = 120,000 lb/in²

The wire is fastened at its upper end and hangs vertically. (a) How great a load can be supported without exceeding the elastic limit? (b) How much will the wire stretch under this load? (c) What is the maximum load that can be supported?

11-5. A copper rod of length 3 ft and cross-sectional area 0.5 in² is fastened end-to-end to a steel rod of length L and cross-sectional area 0.2 in². The compound rod is subjected to equal and opposite pulls of magnitude 6000 lb at its ends. (a) Find the length L of the steel rod if the elongations of the two rods are equal. (b) What is the stress in each rod? (c) What is the strain in each rod?

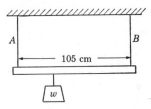

Fig. 11-9

11-6. A rod 105 cm long, whose weight is negligible, is supported at its ends by wires A and B of equal length. The cross section of A is 1 mm², that of B is 2 mm². Young's modulus for wire A is 30×10^6 lb/in² and for B it is 20×10^6 lb/in². At what point along the bar should a weight w be suspended in order to produce (a) equal stresses in A and B, (b) equal strains in A and B? (Fig. 11-9.)

11-7. A bar of length L, cross-sectional area A, Young's modulus Y, is subjected to a tension F. Represent the stress in the bar by S and the strain by P. Derive the expression for the elastic potential energy, per unit volume, of the bar in terms of S and P.

11-8. The compressibility of sodium is to be measured by observing the displacement of the piston in Fig. 11-4(b) when a force is applied. The sodium is immersed in an oil which fills the cylinder below the piston. Assume that the piston and walls of the cylinder are perfectly rigid, that there is no friction, and no oil leak. Compute the compressibility of the sodium in terms of the applied force F, the piston displacement x, the piston area A, the initial volume of the oil V_0, the initial volume of the sodium v_0, and the compressibility of the oil k_0.

11-9. Two strips of metal are riveted together at their ends by four rivets, each of diameter 0.25 inch. What is the maximum tension that can be exerted by the riveted strip if the shearing stress on the rivets is not to exceed 10,000 lb/in²? Assume each rivet to carry one-quarter of the load.

11-10. Find the weight-density of ocean water at a depth where the pressure is 4700 lb/ft². The weight-density at the surface is 64 lb/ft³.

11-11. Compute the compressibility of steel, in reciprocal atmospheres, and compare with that of water. Which material is the more readily compressed?

11-12. A steel post 6 inches in diameter and 10 ft long is placed vertically and is required to support a load of 20,000 lb. (a) What is the stress in the post? (b) What is the strain in the post? (c) What is the change in length of the post?

11-13. In Fig. 11-10, A and B are two short steel rods, of 0.5 in² cross-sectional area. The lower ends of A and B are welded to the fixed plate CD. The upper end of A is welded to the L-shaped piece EFG, which can slide without friction on the upper end of B. A horizontal pull of

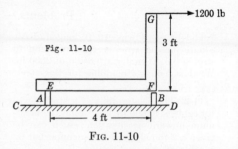

Fig. 11-10

Fɪɢ. 11-10

1200 lb is exerted at G. Neglect the weight of EFG. (a) Compute the shearing stresses in rods A and B. (b) Compute the longitudinal stress in A. Is the stress a tension or a compression? (c) Compute the longitudinal stress in B. Is it a tension or a compression?

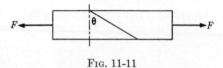

Fɪɢ. 11-11

11-14. A bar of cross section A is subjected to equal and opposite tensile forces F at its ends. Consider a plane through the bar making an angle θ with a plane at right angles to the bar (Fig. 11-11). (a) What is the tensile (normal) stress at this plane, in terms of F, A, and θ? (b) What is the shearing (tangential) stress at the plane, in terms of F, A, and θ? (c) For what value of θ is the tensile stress a maximum? (d) For what value of θ is the shearing stress a maximum?

CHAPTER 12

HARMONIC MOTION

12-1 Introduction. The motion of a body when acted upon by a constant force was considered in detail in Chaps. 5 and 6. The motion is one of constant acceleration, and it was found useful to derive expressions for the position and velocity of the body at any time, and for its velocity in any position. In the present chapter we are to study the motion of a body when the resultant force on it is not constant, but varies during the motion. Naturally, there are an infinite number of ways in which a force may vary and hence no general expressions can be given for the motion of a body when acted on by a variable force, except that the acceleration at each instant must equal the force at that instant divided by the mass of the body. There is, however, one particular mode of variation which is met with in practice so frequently that it is worth while to develop formulas for this special case. The force referred to is an elastic restoring force, brought into play whenever a body is distorted from its normal shape. When released, the body will be found to vibrate about its equilibrium position.

Examples of this sort of motion are the up-and-down motion which ensues when a weight hanging from a spring is pulled down and released; the vibrations of the strings or air columns of musical instruments; the vibration of a bridge or building under impact loads; and the oscillation of the balance wheel of a watch or of a clock pendulum. Furthermore, many reciprocating motions such as those of the crosshead in a steam engine or the piston of an automobile engine, while not exactly of this type, do approximate it quite closely.

It turns out that the equations of motion involve sines or cosines, and the term *harmonic* is applied to expressions containing these functions. This type of vibratory motion is therefore called *harmonic motion*.

12-2 Elastic restoring forces. It has been shown in Chap. 11 that when a body is caused to change its shape, the distorting force is proportional to the amount of the change, provided the elastic limit is not exceeded. The change may be in the nature of an increase in length, as of a rubber band or a coil spring; or a decrease in length; or a bending as of a flat spring; or a twisting of a rod about its axis; or of many other forms. The term "force" is to be interpreted liberally as the force, or torque, or pressure, or whatever may be producing the distortion. If we restrict the discussion to the case of a push or a pull, where the distortion is simply the displacement of the point of application of the force, the force and displacement are related by Hooke's law,

$$F = kx,$$

where k is a proportionality constant called the force constant and x is the displacement from the equilibrium position.

In this equation, F stands for the force which must be exerted *on* an elastic body to produce the displacement x. We shall find it more convenient to work with the reaction to this force, that is, the force with which the distorted body pulls back. This force is called the *restoring force* and is given by

$$F = -kx.$$

12-3 Definitions. To fix our ideas, suppose that a flat strip of steel such as a hacksaw blade is clamped vertically in a vise and a small mass is attached to its upper end as in Fig. 12-1. We shall assume that the strip is sufficiently long and the displacement sufficiently small so that the motion is essentially along a straight line. The mass of the strip itself is negligible.

Let the top of the spring be pulled to the right a distance A as

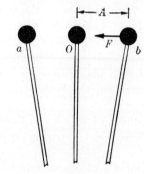

FIG. 12-1. Motion under an elastic restoring force.

in Fig. 12-1 and released. The attached mass is then acted on by a restoring force exerted by the steel strip and directed toward the equilibrium position O. It therefore accelerates in the direction of this force, and moves in toward the center with increasing speed. The *rate* of increase (i.e. the acceleration) is not constant, however, since the accelerating force becomes smaller as the body approaches the center.

When the body reaches the center the restoring force has decreased to zero, but because of the velocity which has been acquired, the body "overshoots" the equilibrium position and continues to move toward the left. As soon as the equilibrium position is passed the restoring force again comes into play, directed now toward the right. The body therefore decelerates, and at a rate which increases with increasing distance from O. It will therefore be brought to rest at some point to the left of O, and repeat its motion in the opposite direction.

Both experiment and theory show that the motion will be confined to a range $\pm A$ on either side of the equilibrium position, each to-and-fro movement taking place in the same length of time. If there were no loss of energy by friction the motion would continue indefinitely once it had been started. This type of motion, under the influence of an elastic restoring force and in the absence of all friction, is called *simple* harmonic motion, often abbreviated *SHM*.

Any sort of motion which repeats itself in equal intervals of time is called *periodic*, and if the motion is back and forth over the same path it is also called *oscillatory*.

A *complete vibration* or *oscillation* means one round trip, say from a to b and back to a, or from O to b to O to a and back to O.

The *periodic time*, or simply the *period* of the motion, represented by T, is the time required for one complete vibration.

The *frequency*, f, is the number of complete vibrations per unit time. Evidently the frequency is the reciprocal of the period, or

$$T = \frac{1}{f}.$$

The *displacement*, x, at any instant, is the distance away from the equilibrium position or center of the path at that instant.

The *amplitude*, A, is the maximum displacement. The total range of the motion is therefore $2A$.

12-4 Equations of simple harmonic motion. We now wish to find expressions for the displacement, velocity, and acceleration of a body moving with simple harmonic motion, just as we found those for a body moving with constant acceleration. It must be emphasized that the equations of motion with *constant* acceleration cannot be applied, since the acceleration is continually changing.

Fig. 12-2 represents the vibrating body of Fig. 12-1 at some instant when its displacement is x. The resultant force on it is simply the elastic restoring force, $-kx$, and from Newton's second law,

$$F = -kx = ma,$$

or

$$a = -\frac{k}{m}x, \qquad (12\text{-}1)$$

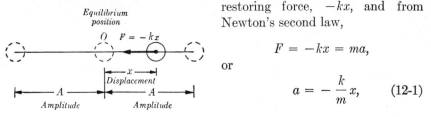

FIG. 12-2.

where m is the mass of the body.

Since k and m are both constants, the ratio k/m is constant. Hence the acceleration is directly proportional to the displacement and, because of the minus sign, is in the opposite direction to the displacement. That is, when the body is at the right of its equilibrium position, its acceleration is toward the left and vice versa. Another way of stating this is that the acceleration is always directed toward the center of the path. With the help of calculus, the equation above can be solved at once to find the desired expressions for displacement and velocity. However, we shall make use of a simple geometrical method of deducing these equations.

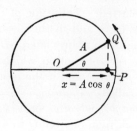

FIG. 12-3. Coordinate of a body in simple harmonic motion.

Consider a type of motion determined as follows. Let Q, Fig. 12-3, be a point revolving in a circle of radius A with a constant angular velocity of ω rad/sec. Let P be a point on the horizontal diameter of the circle, directly below Q. Point P is called the projection of Q onto the diameter. Point Q is referred to as the *reference point*, and the circle in which it moves as the *reference circle*.

As the reference point revolves, the point P moves back and forth along a horizontal line, keeping always directly below (or above) Q. We shall show that the motion of P is the same as that of a body moving under the influence of an elastic restoring force in the absence of friction.

The displacement of P at any time t is the distance OP or x, and if θ represents the angle which OQ makes with the horizontal diameter,

$$x = A \cos \theta.$$

The angle θ is called the *phase angle*, or simply the *phase* of the motion. *If point Q is at the extreme right-hand end of the diameter at time $t = 0$, the angle θ may be written*

$$\theta = \omega t.$$

Hence

$$x = A \cos \omega t.$$

Now ω, the angular velocity of Q in radians per second, is related to f, the number of complete revolutions of Q per second, by

$$\omega = 2\pi f,$$

since there are 2π radians in one complete revolution. Furthermore, the

point P makes one complete vibration for each revolution of Q. Hence
f may also be interpreted as the number of vibrations per second or the
frequency of vibration of point P.   Replacing ω by $2\pi f$, we have

$$x = A \cos 2\pi ft. \qquad\qquad (12\text{-}2)$$

Eq. (12-2) gives the displacement of point P at any time t after the
start of the motion, and thus corresponds to

$$x = v_0 t + \tfrac{1}{2}at^2$$

for a body moving with constant acceleration.   Note carefully that x, in
Eq. (12-2), represents the *distance from the center of the path*, not the distance from the starting point.

The instantaneous velocity of P may be found with the aid of Fig.
12-4.   The reference point Q moves with a tangential velocity

$$v_T = \omega A = 2\pi fA.$$

Since point P is always directly below or above the reference point,
the velocity of P at each instant
must equal the X-component of the
velocity of Q.   That is, from Fig.
12-4,

$$v = v_T \sin \theta = -2\pi fA \sin \theta$$

or

$$v = -2\pi fA \sin 2\pi ft. \qquad (12\text{-}3)$$

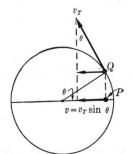

Fig. 12-4. Velocity in simple harmonic
motion.

The minus sign is introduced since the
direction of the velocity is toward
the left.   When Q is below the horizontal diameter, the velocity of P will
be toward the right, but since $\sin \theta$ is negative at such points, the minus
sign is still needed.   Eq. (12-3) gives the velocity of point P at any time,
and corresponds to

$$v = v_0 + at$$

for motion with constant acceleration.

Since $\sin \theta = \sqrt{1 - \cos^2 \theta}$ and $\cos \theta = \dfrac{x}{A}$, Eq. (12-3) may be written

$$v = \pm 2\pi f A \sqrt{1 - \frac{x^2}{A^2}},$$

$$v = \pm 2\pi f \sqrt{A^2 - x^2}. \qquad (12\text{-}4)$$

The symbol $\pm$ is required, since at any given displacement x the point may be moving either toward the right or left. Eq. (12-4) gives the velocity of P at any *displacement*. It thus corresponds to

$$v^2 = v_0{}^2 + 2ax$$

for constant acceleration.

Finally, the acceleration of point P may be found, making use again of the fact that since P is always directly below or above Q its acceleration must equal the X-component of the acceleration of Q. Point Q, since it moves in a circular path with a constant angular velocity ω, has at each instant an acceleration toward the center given by

$$a_R = \omega^2 A = 4\pi^2 f^2 A.$$

From Fig. 12-5, the X-component of this acceleration is

$$a = a_R \cos \theta, \quad \text{or}$$

$$a = -4\pi^2 f^2 A \cos 2\pi f t, \qquad (12\text{-}5)$$

and since $A \cos 2\pi f t = x$,

$$a = -4\pi^2 f^2 x. \qquad (12\text{-}6)$$

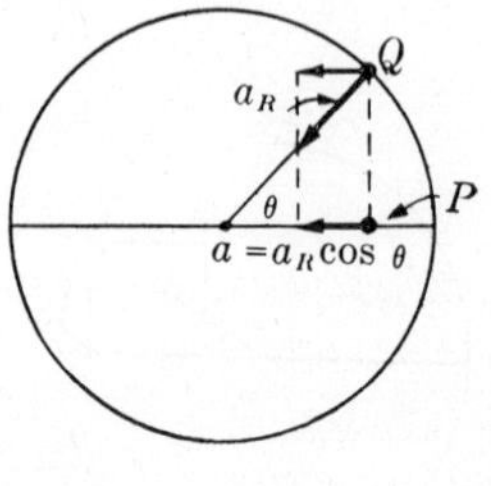

FIG. 12-5. Acceleration in simple harmonic motion.

The minus sign is introduced since the acceleration is toward the left.

When Q is at the left of the center the acceleration of P is toward the right, but since $\cos \theta$ is negative at such points, the minus sign is still required. Eqs. (12-5) and (12-6) give the acceleration of P at any time and at any displacement. There are no corresponding equations in motion with constant acceleration except the extremely simple one

$$a = \text{constant.}$$

Eq. (12-6) states that the acceleration of point P, moving in the manner described, is proportional to the displacement x and is in the direction opposite to x. But 'this is just the condition which must be fulfilled by a body moving under the influence of an elastic restoring force (Eq. 12-1). Hence it may be concluded that Eqs. (12-2) to (12-6) describe the motion of a body when acted on by such a force, and are the equations which we set out to find.

In order that the motion of point P may coincide in all respects with that of a given vibrating body, the radius A of the reference circle must equal the amplitude A of the actual vibration, and the frequency of revolution of Q must be the same as the frequency of the actual vibration. The proper value of the latter may be found by combining Eq. (12-1),

$$a = -\frac{k}{m}x,$$

which gives the acceleration of the vibrating body at any displacement, and Eq. (12-6)

$$a = -4\pi^2 f^2 x,$$

which gives the acceleration of point P at any displacement. Since these accelerations must be the same,

$$\frac{k}{m} = 4\pi^2 f^2,$$

and therefore

$$f = \frac{1}{2\pi}\sqrt{\frac{k}{m}}. \tag{12-7}$$

Eq. (12-7) may be used to find the vibration frequency of a body of given mass when vibrating under the influence of an elastic restoring force of given force constant.

Since the period is the reciprocal of the frequency, Eq. (12-7) may also be written

$$T = 2\pi\sqrt{\frac{m}{k}}. \tag{12-8}$$

In using Eqs. (12-7) or (12-8), m must be expressed in slugs, kilograms, or grams, and k in lbs/ft, newtons/meter, or dynes/cm. The frequency f will then be in vibrations per second, and the period T in seconds per vibration.

A somewhat unexpected conclusion to be drawn from these equations is that the period does not depend on the amplitude, but on the mass and force constant alone.

The equations for simple harmonic motion may be conveniently summarized by comparing them with similar equations for motion with constant linear acceleration, as shown in the first two columns of Table 12-1.

TABLE 12-1

Motion with constant linear acceleration	Simple harmonic motion $\left(\text{in terms of } \dfrac{k}{m}\right)$	Simple harmonic motion $\left(\text{using } 2\pi f = \sqrt{\dfrac{k}{m}}\right)$
$a = \text{const.}$	$a = -\dfrac{k}{m}x$ $a = -\dfrac{k}{m}A\cos\sqrt{\dfrac{k}{m}}\,t$	$a = -4\pi^2 f^2 x$ $a = -4\pi^2 f^2 A \cos 2\pi f t$
$v^2 = v_0^2 + 2ax$ $v = v_0 + at$	$v = \pm\sqrt{\dfrac{k}{m}}\sqrt{(A^2 - x^2)}$ $v = -\sqrt{\dfrac{k}{m}}A\sin\sqrt{\dfrac{k}{m}}\,t$	$v = \pm 2\pi f\sqrt{(A^2 - x^2)}$ $v = -2\pi f A \sin 2\pi f t$
$x = v_0 t + \frac{1}{2}at^2$	$x = A\cos\sqrt{\dfrac{k}{m}}\,t$	$x = A\cos 2\pi f t$

It is helpful in visualizing harmonic motion to represent the position, velocity, and acceleration of the vibrating body graphically. Graphs of these quantities against time are given in Fig. 12-6, which may be considered as a graph of Eqs. (12-2), (12-3), and (12-5). Notice that the velocity is a maximum when the displacement is zero, that is, at the center; while the velocity is zero when the displacement is a maximum. The acceleration, on the other hand, is zero at the center and a maximum at the ends of the path.

Fig. 12-7 is a multiflash photograph of the motion of a mass suspended from a coil spring and set into vertical vibration. The camera was rotated about a vertical axis while the photographs were taken so that each image is displaced laterally from the preceding image. In effect this introduces a horizontal time scale into the motion and the body traces out its own sinusoidal displacement-time graph corresponding to the upper diagram in Fig. 12-6. By comparing the *vertical* separation of successive images, it is seen that the velocity is greatest at the center of the path and zero at the ends, while the acceleration is greatest at the ends and zero at the center.

Examples.   (1) A flat steel strip is mounted as in Fig. 12-1.   By attaching a spring balance to the end of the strip and pulling it sidewise, it is found that a force of 1 lb

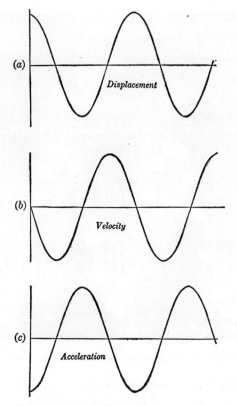

(a) *Displacement*

(b) *Velocity*

(c) *Acceleration*

FIG. 12-6. Graphs of position, velocity, and acceleration.

will produce a deflection of 6 inches. A 4-lb body is attached to the end of the strip, pulled aside a distance of 8 inches, and released.

(a) Compute the force constant of the spring.

A force of 1 lb produces a displacement of 6 inches or $\frac{1}{2}$ ft. Hence

$$k = \frac{F}{x} = \frac{1}{\frac{1}{2}} = 2 \text{ lb/ft.}$$

(b) Compute the period of vibration.

$$T = 2\pi \sqrt{\frac{m}{k}} = 2\pi \sqrt{\frac{4/32}{2}} = \frac{\pi}{2} \text{ sec.}$$

(c) Compute the maximum velocity attained by the vibrating body.

Fig. 12-7. Simple harmonic motion of a mass suspended from a spring.

The maximum velocity occurs at the center, where the displacement is zero. From Eq. (12-4),

$$v = \pm 2\pi f \sqrt{A^2 - x^2}, \text{ and when } x = 0,$$

$$v_{max} = \pm 2\pi fA,$$

$$f = \frac{1}{T} = \frac{2}{\pi} \text{ vibrations per sec,}$$

$$A = 8 \text{ in.} = \frac{2}{3} \text{ ft,}$$

$$\therefore v = \pm 2\pi \times \frac{2}{\pi} \times \frac{2}{3} = \pm \frac{8}{3} \text{ ft/sec.}$$

(d) Compute the maximum acceleration.

The maximum acceleration occurs at the ends of the path where $x = \pm A$. From Eq. (12-6),

$$a_{max} = \mp 4\pi^2 f^2 A$$

$$= \mp 4\pi^2 \times \left(\frac{2}{\pi}\right)^2 \times \frac{2}{3}$$

$$= \mp \frac{32}{3} \text{ ft/sec}^2.$$

(e) Compute the velocity and acceleration when the body has moved halfway **in** toward the center from its initial position.

At this point, $x = \dfrac{A}{2} = \dfrac{1}{3}$ ft,

$$v = -2\pi \times \frac{2}{\pi}\sqrt{\left(\frac{2}{3}\right)^2 - \left(\frac{1}{3}\right)^2} = -\frac{4}{\sqrt{3}} \text{ ft/sec,}$$

$$a = -4\pi^2 \times \left(\frac{2}{\pi}\right)^2 \times \frac{1}{3} = -\frac{16}{3} \text{ ft/sec}^2.$$

(f) How long a time is required for the body to move halfway in to the center from its initial position?

Note that the motion is neither one of constant velocity nor of constant acceleration. The simplest method of handling a problem involving the time required to move from one point to another in harmonic motion is to make use of the reference circle. While the body moves halfway in, the reference point revolves through an angle of 60° (Fig. 12-8). Since the reference point moves with constant angular velocity and makes one complete revolution in $\pi/2$ sec (in this particular example), the time to rotate through 60° is $\dfrac{1}{6} \times \dfrac{\pi}{2} = \pi/12$ sec.

The time may also be computed directly from the equation

$x = A \cos 2\pi ft,$

$$\frac{A}{2} = A \cos\left(2\pi \times \frac{2}{\pi} \times t\right),$$

$$\cos 4t = \frac{1}{2},$$

$$4t = \cos^{-1}\frac{1}{2} = \frac{\pi}{3},$$

$$\therefore t = \frac{\pi}{12} \text{ sec.}$$

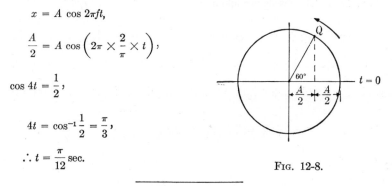

Fig. 12-8.

12-5 The simple pendulum. A simple pendulum consists of a mass of small dimensions suspended by an inextensible weightless string. When pulled to one side of its equilibrium position and released, the pendulum bob vibrates about this position with motion which is both periodic and oscillatory. We wish to discover if the motion is simple harmonic.

The necessary condition for simple harmonic motion is that the restoring force, F, shall be directly proportional to the displacement, x, and oppositely directed. The path of the bob is, of course, not a straight line, but the arc of a circle of radius L, where L is the length of the supporting cord. The displacement refers to distances measured along this arc. (See Fig. 12-9.) Hence if $F = -kx$ the motion will be simple harmonic, or since $x = L\theta$, the requirement may be written $F = -kL\theta$.

Fig. 12-9 shows the forces on the bob at an instant when its displacement is x. Choose axes tangent to the circle and along the radius, and resolve the weight into components. The restoring force F is

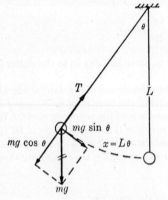

$$F = -mg \sin \theta. \qquad (12\text{-}9)$$

The restoring force is therefore *not* proportional to θ but to $\sin \theta$, so the motion is *not* simple harmonic. However, *if the angle θ is small*, $\sin \theta$ is very nearly equal to θ and Eq. (12-9) becomes

$$F = -mg\theta = -mg\frac{x}{L},$$

or

$$F = -\frac{mg}{L}x.$$

FIG. 12-9. The simple pendulum.

The restoring force is then proportional to the displacement *for small displacements*, and the constant $\dfrac{mg}{L}$ represents the force constant k. The period of a simple pendulum when its amplitude is small is therefore

$$T = 2\pi \sqrt{\frac{m}{k}} = 2\pi \sqrt{\frac{m}{mg/L}},$$

or

$$T = 2\pi \sqrt{\frac{L}{g}}. \qquad (12\text{-}10)$$

What constitutes a "small" amplitude? It can be shown that the general equation for the time of swing, when the maximum angular displacement is α, is

$$T = 2\pi \sqrt{\frac{L}{g}} \left(1 + \frac{1}{4} \sin^2 \frac{\alpha}{2} + \frac{9}{64} \sin^4 \frac{\alpha}{2} + \cdots \right).$$

The time may be computed to any desired degree of precision by taking enough terms in the infinite series. When $\alpha = 15°$ (on either side of the central position), the true period differs from that given by the approximate Eq. (12-10) by less than one-half of one percent.

The utility of the pendulum as a timekeeper is based on the fact that the period is practically independent of the amplitude. Thus, as a clock runs down and the amplitude of the swings becomes slightly smaller, the clock will still keep very nearly correct time.

The simple pendulum is also a precise and convenient method of measuring the acceleration of gravity, g, without actually resorting to free fall, since L and T may readily be measured. More complicated pendulums find considerable application in the field of geophysics. Local deposits of ore or oil, if their density differs from that of their surroundings, affect the local value of

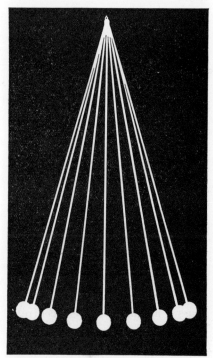

FIG. 12-10. A single swing of a simple pendulum.

"g," and precise measurements of this quantity over an area which is being prospected often furnish valuable information regarding the nature of underlying deposits.

Fig. 12-10 is a multiflash photograph of a single swing of a simple pendulum. The motion is evidently of the simple harmonic type with maximum speed at the center and maximum acceleration at the ends of the swing.

12-6 Angular harmonic motion. Angular harmonic motion results when a body which is pivoted about an axis experiences a restoring torque proportional to the angular displacement from its equilibrium position.

This type of vibration is very similar to linear harmonic motion, and the corresponding equations may be written down immediately from the analogies between linear and angular quantities.   The oscillatory motion of the balance wheel of a watch is a common example of angular harmonic motion.

A restoring torque proportional to angular displacement is expressed by

$$\tau = -k\theta. \tag{12-11}$$

The moment of inertia of the pivoted body corresponds to the mass of a body in linear motion.   Hence the period formula for angular harmonic motion is

$$T = 2\pi \sqrt{\frac{I}{k}} \tag{12-12}$$

where k is the constant in Eq. (12-11).

The equations for angular displacement, angular velocity, and angular acceleration can be obtained by comparison with the corresponding equations in Sec. 12-4.

12-7 The physical pendulum.   A so-called "physical" pendulum is any real pendulum, as contrasted with a simple pendulum in which all of the mass is assumed to be concentrated at a point.   Let Fig. 12-11 represent a body of irregular shape pivoted about a horizontal frictionless axis and displaced from the vertical by an angle θ.   The distance from the pivot to the center of gravity is l, the moment of inertia of the pendulum about an axis through the pivot is I, and the mass of the pendulum is m.   The restoring torque in the position shown in the figure is

$$\tau = -mgl \sin \theta.$$

If θ is small we may replace $\sin \theta$ by θ, and

$$\tau = -mgl\theta.$$

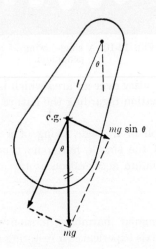

Fig. 12-11.   The physical pendulum.

Hence the pendulum is acted on, in effect, by an elastic restoring torque with $k = mgl$. The period of vibration is therefore

$$T = 2\pi \sqrt{\frac{I}{k}} = 2\pi \sqrt{\frac{I}{mgl}} \text{ (for small amplitudes).} \qquad (12\text{-}13)$$

Examples. (1) Let the body in Fig. 12-11 be a meter stick pivoted at one end. Then if L stands for the length of 1 meter,

$$I = \frac{1}{3} mL^2, \quad l = \frac{L}{2}, \quad g = 9.8 \text{ m/sec}^2,$$

$$T = 2\pi \sqrt{\frac{\frac{1}{3} mL^2}{mg \dfrac{L}{2}}} = 2\pi \sqrt{\frac{2}{3} \frac{L}{g}}$$

$$= 2\pi \sqrt{\frac{2}{3} \frac{1}{9.8}} = 1.65 \text{ sec.}$$

(2) Eq. (12-12) may be solved for the moment of inertia I, giving

$$I = \frac{T^2 mgl}{4\pi^2}. \qquad (12\text{-}14)$$

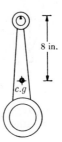

8 in.

c.g

FIG. 12-12.

The quantities on the right of the equation are all directly measurable. Hence the moment of inertia of a body of any complex shape may be found by suspending the body as a physical pendulum and measuring its period of vibration. The location of the center of gravity can be found by balancing. Since T, m, g, and l are known, I can be computed. For example, Fig. 12-12 illustrates a connecting rod pivoted about a horizontal knife edge. The connecting rod weighs 4 lb and its center of gravity has been found by balancing to be 8 inches below the knife edge. When set into oscillation, it is found to make 100 complete vibrations in 120 sec, so that $T = 120/100 = 1.2$ sec. Therefore

$$I = \frac{(1.2)^2 \times 4 \times \frac{2}{3}}{4\pi^2}$$

$$= 0.097 \text{ slug-ft}^2.$$

12-8 Center of oscillation. It is always possible to find an *equivalent* simple pendulum whose period is equal to that of a given physical pendulum. If L_0 is the length of the equivalent simple pendulum,

$$T = 2\pi \sqrt{\frac{L_0}{g}} = 2\pi \sqrt{\frac{I}{mgl}}$$

or

$$L_0 = \frac{I}{ml}. \qquad (12\text{-}15)$$

Thus, as far as its period of vibration is concerned, the mass of a physical pendulum may be considered to be concentrated at a point whose distance from the pivot is $L_0 = I/ml$. This point is called the *center of oscillation* of the pendulum.

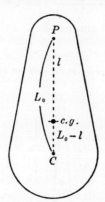

FIG. 12-13. Point C is the center of oscillation.

Fig. 12-13 shows a body pivoted about an axis through P and whose center of oscillation is at point C. The center of oscillation and the point of support have the following interesting property, namely, if the pendulum is pivoted about a new axis through point C its period is unchanged and point P becomes the new center of oscillation. The point of support and the center of oscillation are said to be *conjugate* to one another.

12-9 Center of percussion. Everyone knows that there is one point on a baseball bat or golf club where the ball may be struck and no "sting" will be felt. This point is called the *center of percussion* and its position may be found as follows. Let Fig. 12-14 represent a baseball bat held or pivoted at the point O and struck at its center of percussion with a blow of impulse J. Let l be the distance from O to the center of gravity and L the distance from O to the center of percussion.

In order that no sting may be felt, it is necessary that there shall be no tendency for point O to move to the right or left while the blow is struck. In other words, the bat must start to pivot about point O.

The linear momentum acquired by the bat is found from the relation

$$J = m\bar{v}$$

where $\bar{v}$ is the velocity of the center of gravity of the bat, marked c. g. in Fig. 12-14; and the angular momentum about an axis through O from the relation

$$JL = I\omega.$$

Since the instantaneous axis passes through O,

$$\bar{v} = \omega l.$$

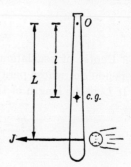

FIG. 12-14. Center of percussion.

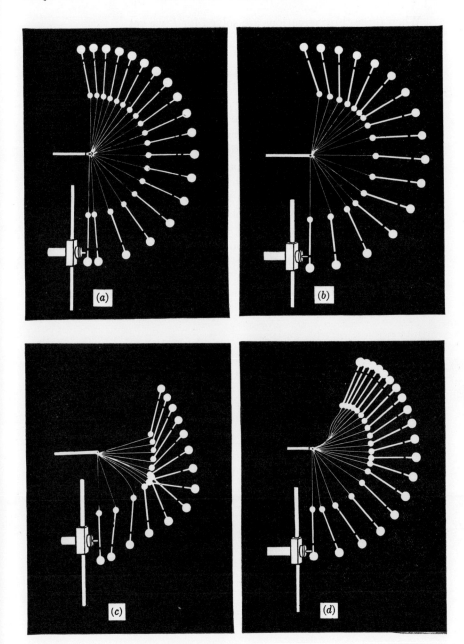

FIG. 12-15.   Center of percussion.

When these three equations are solved for L we get

$$L = \frac{I}{ml}.$$ (12-16)

Comparison with Eq. (12-15) shows that the center of percussion coincides with the center of oscillation. Note, however, that the position of either center depends on the location of the pivot.

It is easy to show that the pivot and the center of percussion are interchangeable. That is, if the bat in Fig. 12-14 were to be held at the point at which it is being struck, the proper place to hit a ball would be at O.

Fig. 12-15 is a series of multiflash photographs illustrating the motion of a body suspended by a cord when the body is struck a horizontal blow. The *center of gravity* is marked by a black band. In (a), the body is struck at its center of percussion relative to a pivot at the upper end of the cord, and it starts to swing smoothly about this pivot. In (b), the body is struck at its center of gravity. Note that it does not start to rotate about the pivot, but that its initial motion is one of pure translation. That is, the center of percussion does not coincide with the center of gravity. In (c), the body is struck above, and in (d) below its center of percussion.

Problems — Chapter 12

12-1. A body is vibrating with simple harmonic motion of amplitude 15 cm and frequency 4 vibr/sec. Compute (a) the maximum values of the acceleration and velocity, (b) the acceleration and velocity when the displacement is 9 cm, (c) the time required to move from the equilibrium position to a point 12 cm distant from it.

12-2. A body of mass 10 gm moves with simple harmonic motion of amplitude 24 cm and period 4 sec. The displacement is $+24$ cm when $t = 0$. Compute (a) the position of the body when $t = 0.5$ sec, (b) the magnitude and direction of the force acting on the body when $t = 0.5$ sec, (c) the minimum time required for the body to move from its initial position to the point where $x = -12$ cm, (d) the velocity of the body when $x = -12$ cm.

12-3. The motion of the piston of an automobile engine is approximately simple harmonic. (a) If the stroke of an engine (twice the amplitude) is 4 inches and the angular velocity is 3600 rpm, compute the acceleration of the piston at the end of its stroke. (b) If the piston weighs 1 lb, what resultant force must be exerted on it at this point? (c) What is the velocity of the piston, in mi/hr, at the midpoint of its stroke?

12-4. A 4-lb weight hung from a spring is found to stretch the spring 8 inches. (a) What is the force constant of the spring? (b) What would be the period of vibration of the 4-lb weight, if suspended from this spring? (c) What would be the period of an 8-lb weight hanging from the same spring?

12-5. The scale of a spring balance reading from zero to 32 lb is 6 inches long. A body suspended from the balance is observed to oscillate vertically at 1.5 vibr/sec. What is the weight of the body?

12-6. A body of mass 100 gm hangs from a long spiral spring. When pulled down 10 cm below its equilibrium position and released, it vibrates with a period of 2 seconds. (a) What is its velocity as it passes through the equilibrium position? (b) What is its acceleration when it is 5 cm above the equilibrium position? (c) When it is moving upward, how long a time is required for it to move from a point 5 cm below its equilibrium position to a point 5 cm above it? (d) How much will the spring shorten if the body is removed?

12-7. Two bodies of equal mass are hung from separate springs having force constants k_1 and k_2. k_2 is greater than k_1. The two bodies oscillate with amplitudes such that the maximum velocities are equal. For which system is the amplitude of motion greater? Give reasons.

12-8. A block suspended from a spring vibrates with simple harmonic motion. At an instant when the displacement of the block is equal to one-half the amplitude, what fraction of the total energy of the system is kinetic and what fraction is potential?

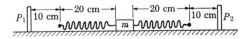

Fig. 12-16

12-9. Two springs, each of unstretched length 20 cm but having different force constants k_1 and k_2, are attached to opposite ends of a block of mass m on a level frictionless surface. The outer ends of the springs are now attached to the two pins P_1 and P_2, 10 cm from the original positions of the springs. Let $k_1 = 1000$ dynes/cm, $k_2 = 300$ dynes/cm, $m = 100$ gm. (See Fig. 12-16.) (a) Find the length of each spring when the block is in its new equilibrium position, after the springs have been attached to the pins. (b) Show that the effective force constant of the combination is 4000 dynes/cm. (c) Find the period of vibration of the block if it is slightly displaced from its new equilibrium position and released.

12-10. a) With what additional force must a vertical spring carrying an 8-lb body in equilibrium be stretched so that, when released, it will perform 48 complete oscillations in 32 seconds with an amplitude of 3 inches? (b) What force is exerted by the spring on the body when it is at the lowest point, the middle, and the highest point of the path? (c) What is the kinetic energy of the system when the body is 1 inch below the middle of the path? its potential energy?

12-11. A load of 320 lb suspended from a wire whose unstretched length L_0 is 10 ft, is found to stretch the wire by 0.12 inch. The cross-sectional area of the wire, which can be assumed constant, is 0.016 square inch. (a) If the load is pulled down a small additional distance and released, find the frequency at which it will vibrate. (b) Compute Young's modulus for the wire.

12-12. Find the length of a simple pendulum whose period is exactly 1 sec at a point where $g = 32.2$ ft/sec².

12-13. A pendulum clock which keeps correct time at a point where $g = 980.0$ cm/sec² is found to lose 10 sec per day at a higher altitude. Find the value of g at the new location.

12-14. A simple pendulum with a supporting steel wire of cross-sectional area 0.01 cm² is observed to have a period of 2 sec when a 10 kgm lead bob is used. The lead bob is replaced by an aluminum bob of the same dimensions having a mass of 2 kgm, and the period is remeasured. (a) What was the length of the pendulum with the lead bob? (b) By what fraction is the period changed when the aluminum bob is used? Is it an increase or decrease?

12-15. The balance wheel of a watch vibrates with an angular amplitude of π radians and with a period of 0.5 sec. (a) Find its maximum angular velocity. (b) Find its angular velocity when its displacement is one-half its amplitude. (c) Find its angular acceleration when its displacement is 45°.

12-16. A monkey wrench is pivoted at one end and allowed to swing as a physical pendulum. The period is 0.9 sec and the pivot point is 6 inches from the center of gravity. (a) What is the radius of gyration of the wrench about an axis through the pivot? (b) If the wrench was initially displaced 0.1 radian from its equilibrium position, what is the angular velocity of the wrench as it passes through the equilibrium position?

12-17. A meter stick is pivoted at one end. At what distance below the pivot should it be struck in order that it start swinging smoothly about the pivot?

CHAPTER 13

HYDROSTATICS

13-1 Introduction. The term "hydrostatics" is applied to the study of fluids at rest, and "hydrodynamics" to fluids in motion. The special branch of hydrodynamics relating to the flow of gases and of air in particular is called "aerodynamics."

A fluid is a substance which can flow. Hence the term includes both liquids and gases. A liquid, while it adapts its shape to that of the containing vessel, has a definite volume. A gas, on the other hand, completely fills the volume of any container, however large, in which it may be placed. Liquids and gases differ markedly in their compressibilities, a gas being easily compressed while a liquid is practically incompressible. The small volume changes of a liquid under pressure can usually be neglected in this part of the subject.

Fluids also differ from one another in viscosity. Liquids like glycerine, molasses, or heavy oil, have much larger viscosities than water, alcohol, and kerosene. The viscosity of a gas is extremely small. A substance like pitch is on the borderline between a liquid and a solid. A lump of pitch will fracture under a blow like a solid, but in the course of time a lump of it placed on a horizontal surface will spread out into a thin sheet. It may be described as a liquid of very great viscosity. For the present, we shall assume that liquids are nonviscous and incompressible.

13-2 Pressure in a fluid. A fluid (liquid or gas) confined in a vessel exerts forces against the walls of the vessel, and by Newton's third law the walls exert oppositely directed forces on the confined fluid. The magnitude of *the pressure at any point* is defined as the ratio of the force ΔF exerted on a small area ΔA, including the point, to the area ΔA.

$$p = \frac{\Delta F}{\Delta A}, \quad \Delta F = p\Delta A. \tag{13-1}$$

Pressure is expressed in lb/ft², newtons/m², or dynes/cm² in our three systems of units.

If a fluid is at rest, the force exerted by it against any infinitesimal wall area is at right angles to that area, and the force exerted by the wall on the fluid is also at right angles to the wall. That this is so is evident when we realize that a fluid cannot permanently support a shearing stress. Any sidewise or tangential force exerted on the fluid by the walls would constitute a shearing stress and cause a flow parallel to the wall. If the liquid is at rest, there is no such flow, hence there is no tangential force and the force is normal to the surface at every point.

The same is true for any imagined area within the fluid. A small cube of the fluid, in any orientation, is subjected to inward forces at right angles to all of its faces. Conversely, at each face of the cube the fluid within it exerts a force at right angles to the face on the surrounding fluid. A state of stress, similar to the longitudinal stress in a bar under compression, exists therefore throughout the fluid, with the important difference that the forces at any imagined plane in the fluid, whatever the orientation of the plane, are normal to that plane. This is what is meant by the statement sometimes made that "the pressure in a fluid acts in all directions." Pressure is not a vector quantity and no direction can be assigned to it, but the *force* exerted by the fluid at one side of the plane, on the fluid at the other side of the plane, is at right angles to the plane whatever the orientation of the plane.

Let us compute the pressure at a point below the surface of a liquid in an open tank. Consider a portion of the liquid in the shape of a cylinder of cross-sectional area A. Let the top of the cylinder be at the surface of the liquid where the pressure is p_0, and the bottom at a depth y, as shown in Fig. 13-1. Isolating the cylindrical portion of liquid, the horizontal forces must add up to zero because of symmetry. Only the vertical forces are shown in the figure and these are $p_0 A$ down on the upper face, pA up on the lower face and the weight w down. Since the cylinder is in equilibrium,

$$\Sigma Fy = pA - p_0 A - w = 0.$$

The weight of the cylinder is, however, equal to the product of its weight density ρg and its volume yA, or

$$w = \rho gyA.$$

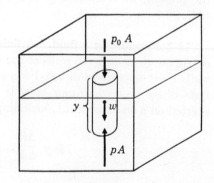

Fig. 13-1. Vertical forces on a cylindrical portion of a fluid.

Hence

$$p = p_0 + \rho g y.$$ (13-2)

That is, the pressure p at any depth y below the surface of a liquid equals the pressure p_0 at the surface plus the product of "weight-density" times depth. Notice that the shape of the containing vessel does not affect the pressure, and that the pressure is the same at all points at the same depth. It also follows from Eq. (13-2) that if the pressure p_0 is increased in any way, say by inserting a piston on the top surface and pressing down on it, the pressure p at any depth must increase by exactly the same amount. This fact was stated by the French scientist Blaise Pascal (1623–1662) in 1653 and is called "Pascal's law." It is often stated: "Pressure applied to an enclosed fluid is transmitted undiminished to every portion of the fluid and the walls of the containing vessel." We can see now that it is not an independent principle but a necessary consequence of the laws of mechanics.

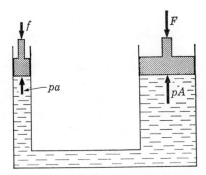

Fig. 13-2.   The hydraulic press

Pascal's law is applied in the operation of a hydraulic press, shown in Fig. 13-2. A piston of small cross-sectional area a is used to exert a small force f directly on a liquid such as oil. The pressure $p = f/a$ is transmitted through the connecting pipe to a larger cylinder equipped with a larger piston of area A. Since the pressure is the same in both cylinders

$$p = \frac{f}{a} = \frac{F}{A}$$

and

$$F = \frac{A}{a} \times f.$$

It follows that the hydraulic press is a force multiplying device with an ideal mechanical advantage equal to the ratio of the areas of the two pistons. Barber chairs, dentist chairs, car lifts, and hydraulic brakes are all devices that make use of the principle of hydraulic press.

13-3 The hydrostatic paradox. If a number of vessels of different shapes are interconnected as in Fig. 13-3, it will be found that a liquid poured into them will stand at the same level in each. Before the principles of hydrostatics were completely understood, this seemed a very puzzling phenomenon and was called the "hydrostatic paradox." It would appear

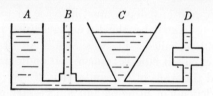

FIG. 13-3.   Liquid stands at the same level   FIG. 13-4.
in each vessel.

at first sight, for example, that vessel C should develop a greater pressure at its base than should B, and hence that liquid would be forced from C into B.

Eq. (13-2), however, states that the pressure depends only on the depth below the liquid surface and not at all on the shape of the containing vessel. Since the depth of the liquid is the same in each vessel, the pressure at the base of each is the same and hence the system is in equilibrium.

A more detailed explanation may be helpful in understanding the situation. Consider vessel C in Fig. 13-4. The forces exerted against the liquid by the walls are shown by arrows, the force being everywhere perpendicular to the walls of the vessel. The inclined forces at the sloping walls may be resolved into horizontal and vertical components. The weight of the liquid in the sections lettered A is supported by the vertical components of these forces. Hence the pressure at the base of the vessel is due only to the weight of the liquid in the cylindrical column B. Any vessel, regardless of its shape, may be treated the same way.

13-4 Pressure gauges. The simplest type of pressure gauge is the open tube manometer, illustrated in Fig. 13-5 (a). It consists of a U-shaped tube containing a liquid, one end of the tube being at the pressure p which it is desired to measure, while the other end is open to the atmosphere. The lowest point of the U may be thought of as at the bottom of either column of the U. The pressure due to the left column is

$$p + \rho g y_0,$$

while that due to the right column is

$$p_0 + \rho g (y_0 + y)$$

(ρ is the density of the liquid in the manometer). Since these pressures both refer to the same point, they are equal. Hence

$$p + \rho g y_0 = p_0 + \rho g (y_0 + y),$$

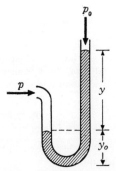

FIG. 13-5 (a). The open tube manometer.

and

$$p - p_0 = \rho g y. \;\; \checkmark$$

The difference in height between the liquid columns is therefore proportional to the difference between the pressure p and the atmospheric pressure p_0. This difference, $p - p_0$, is called the *gauge pressure*, while the pressure p is the *absolute pressure*.

The *mercurial barometer* is simply a *U*-tube with one arm sealed off and evacuated, so that the pressure at the top of that arm is zero. (Fig. 13-5 (b).) It is easy to show that

$$p_0 = \rho g y,$$

FIG. 13-5 (b).   The barometer.

where p_0 is the atmospheric pressure and y the difference in level between the tops of the mercury columns in the barometer arms. Since the pressure is proportional to the height y, it is customary to express atmospheric pressure (and other pressures also) as so many "inches of mercury" or "centimeters of mercury." Note, however, that an "inch of mercury" is *not* a unit of pressure. (Pressure is the ratio of force to area.)

Example: Compute the atmospheric pressure on a day when the height of the barometer is 76.0 cm.

The height of the mercury column depends on ρ and g as well as the atmospheric pressure. Hence both the density of mercury and the local acceleration of gravity must be known. The density varies with the temperature, and g with the latitude and elevation above sea level. All accurate barometers are provided with a thermometer and with a table or chart from which corrections for temperature and elevation can be found. If we assume $g = 980$ cm/sec^2 and $\rho = 13.6$ gm/cm^3,

$$p_0 = \rho g y = 13.6 \times 980 \times 76$$
$$= 1{,}013{,}000 \text{ dynes/cm}^2.$$

(About a million dynes per square centimeter.)

In English units,

$$76 \text{ cm} = 30 \text{ in.} = 2.5 \text{ ft,}$$

$$\rho g = 850 \text{ lb/ft}^3,$$

$$p_0 = 2120 \text{ lb/ft}^2 = 14.7 \text{ lb/in}^2.$$

A pressure of 1.013×10^6 dynes/cm^2, or 14.7 lb/in^2, is called *one atmosphere.* A pressure of exactly one million dynes per square centimeter is called one *bar,* and a pressure one one-thousandth as great is one *millibar.* Evidently, 1 bar = 1000 millibars. Atmospheric pressures are of the order of 1000 millibars, and are now stated in terms of this unit by the United States Weather Bureau.

Unfortunately, workers in the field of acoustics have adopted the term "bar" to mean a pressure of 1 dyne/cm^2. This need cause little confusion, however, since it is usually obvious which definition is being used.

The Bourdon type pressure gauge is more convenient for most purposes than a liquid manometer. It consists of a flattened brass tube closed at one end and bent into a circular form. The closed end of the tube is connected by a gear and pinion to a pointer which moves over a scale. The open end of the tube is connected to the apparatus, the pressure within which is to be measured. When pressure is exerted within the flattened tube it straightens slightly just as a bent rubber hose straightens when water is admitted. The resulting motion of the closed end of the tube is transmitted to the pointer.

13-5 Archimedes' principle. It is a fact of common experience that a body, when wholly or partly immersed in a fluid, is buoyed up by the fluid. Like Pascal's principle, the explanation of this effect follows directly from the laws of mechanics and does not depend on any special properties of a fluid. Fig. 13-6 represents a body in the shape of a right cylinder of height h and cross section A, submerged in a fluid of density ρ. The horizontal forces exerted on the cylinder by the fluid evidently add up to zero and are not shown. At the upper end of the cylinder the liquid exerts a downward force F_1 given by

$$F_1 = p_1 A = (p_0 + \rho g y_0)A,$$

where y_0 is the depth of the upper end below the surface. Similarly,

$$F_2 = p_2 A = [p_0 + \rho g(y_0 + y)]A.$$

The net upward force, or the buoyant force, is

$$F_2 - F_1 = \rho g y A.$$

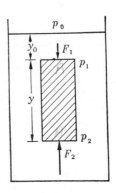

But yA is the volume of the body, and ρg is the weight per unit volume of the fluid. Hence, $\rho g y A$ is the weight of a volume of the fluid equal to the volume of the body, or, as it is called, the "weight of the displaced fluid." Hence,

Fɪɢ. 13-6.   Buoyant force equals weight of fluid displaced.

A body immersed in a fluid is buoyed up with a force equal to the weight of the displaced fluid.

This is Archimedes' principle. Although derived from the special case of a right cylinder, it can be shown to hold regardless of the shape of the body. According to legend, Archimedes (287–212 B.C.) discovered this relation when given the problem of determining whether a crown of King Hero was or was not pure gold.

If the body is not wholly submerged in the fluid, the buoyant force is equal to the weight of a volume of fluid equal to the volume of the submerged portion of the body. If a body can displace its own weight of fluid before it is completely submerged, it will float. Otherwise it will sink in the fluid.

When making "weighings" with a sensitive analytical balance, correction must be made for the buoyant force of the air if the density of the body being "weighed" is very different from that of the standard "weights," which are usually of brass. For example, suppose a block of wood of density 0.4 gm/cm³ is balanced on an equal-arm balance by brass "weights" of 20 gm, density 8.0 gm/cm³. The apparent weight of each body is the difference between its true weight and the buoyant force of the air. If ρ_w, ρ_b, and ρ_a are the densities of the wood, brass, and air, and V_w and V_b

are the volumes of the wood and brass, the apparent weights, which are equal, are

$$\rho_w V_w g - \rho_a V_w g = \rho_b V_b g - \rho_a V_b g.$$

The true mass of the wood is $\rho_w V_w$, and the true mass of the standard is $\rho_b V_b$. Hence,

$$\text{True mass} = \rho_w V_w = \rho_b V_b + \rho_a (V_w - V_b)$$

$$= \text{mass of standard} + \rho_a (V_w - V_b).$$

In the specific example cited

$$V_w = \frac{20}{0.4} = 50 \text{ cm}^3 \text{ (very nearly)},$$

$$V_b = \frac{20}{8} = 2.5 \text{ cm}^3, \quad \rho_a = 0.0013 \text{ gm/cm}^3.$$

Hence

$$\rho_a (V_w - V_b) = .0013 \times 47.5 = 0.062 \text{ gm.}$$

$$\text{True mass} = 20.062 \text{ gm.}$$

If measurements are being made to one one-thousandth of a gram, it is obvious that the correction of 62 thousandths is of the greatest importance.

Example: A tank filled with water is placed on a spring scale, which registers a total weight W. A stone of weight w is hung from a string and lowered into the water without touching the sides or bottom of the tank. [Fig. 13-7(a).] What will be the reading on the spring scale?

First, isolating the stone, the forces are shown in Fig. 13-7(b), where B is the buoyant force and T the tension in the string. Since $\Sigma Y = 0$,

$$T + B = w.$$

Next, isolating the tank with the water and stone in it, the forces are shown in Fig. 13-7(c), where S is the force exerted by the spring scale on the isolated system and, by Newton's third law, is equal in magnitude and opposite in direction to the force exerted on the scale. The condition for equilibrium yields the equation

$$T + S = w + W.$$

Subtracting the first equation from the second, we get

$$S = W + B$$

or the reading of the spring scale has been increased by an amount equal to the buoyant force.

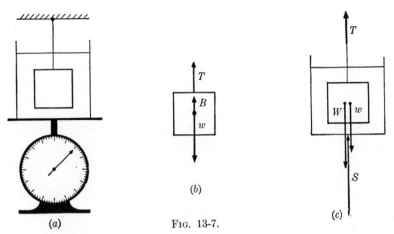

(a)   Fig. 13-7.

(b)

(c)

13-6 Stability of a ship. Archimedes' principle gives the magnitude of the buoyant force but not its line of action. It can be shown that the latter passes through the center of gravity of the displaced fluid. This has an important bearing on the stability of a floating object such as a ship. Fig. 13-8 represents a section of the hull of a ship, when on an even keel and when heeled over. The weight w and the buoyant force B give rise to a couple in such a direction as to right the ship.

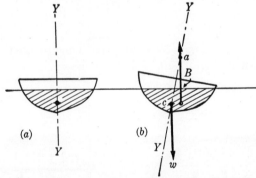

FIG. 13-8.   Forces on a ship.   Point a is the metacenter.

Point a, at which the line of action of the buoyant force intersects the line YY, is called the *metacenter*, and the distance ca is the *metacentric height*. The greater the metacentric height, the greater will be the stability. The righting couple is the same as though the ship were hung from a pivot at the metacenter.

If the line of action of B intersects YY at a point below the center of gravity, the ship is unstable and will capsize.

13-7 Surface tension. A liquid flowing slowly from the tip of a medicine dropper does not emerge as a continuous stream but as a succession of drops. A metal needle whose density may be as much as ten times that of water, if placed carefully on a water surface, makes a small depression in the surface and rests there without sinking. When a clean glass tube of small bore is dipped into water, the water rises in the tube, but if the tube is dipped in mercury, the mercury is depressed. All these phenomena, and many others of a similar nature, are associated with the existence of a boundary surface between a liquid and some other substance.

All surface phenomena indicate that the surface of a liquid is under tension, with properties similar (in many respects but not in all) to those of a stretched membrane. When a wire is under tension, a small element of the wire is in equilibrium under the action of two opposing pulls exerted by neighboring elements on each side. The magnitude of either of these forces is the tension of the wire. Similarly, in the case of a surface under tension, an element of area is pulled in all directions by neighboring elements, the vector sum of these forces, of course, being equal to zero. Consider for the sake of simplicity the square element of area of a surface shown in Fig. 13-9. Any one of the forces F, divided by the length l of the side perpendicular to the action line of the force is defined as the *surface tension S*. Thus,

$$S = \frac{F}{l}.$$

(13-3)

The reality of a surface force may be demonstrated by the simple apparatus shown in Fig. 13-10, which anyone can construct with a few

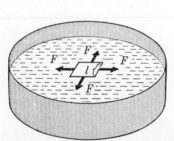

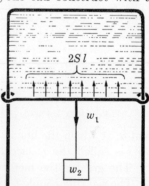

FIG. 13-9. A square element of area of a surface is in equilibrium under the action of surface forces. The surface tension $S = F/l$.

FIG. 13-10. The horizontal slide-wire is in equilibrium under the action of the upward surface force $2S\,l$ and the downward pull $w_1 + w_2$.

pieces of copper wire. The wire is
bent into the shape of a U and another piece of length l is used as a
slider. Upon dipping into a soap
solution, two surface films are
formed, with liquid between them.
To maintain the slide-wire in equilibrium, a downward force w_2, in
addition to its weight w_1, must be
exerted on it. If no additional
downward force is supplied, the
slide-wire will be accelerated upward by action of the unbalanced
force $2Sl - w_1$.

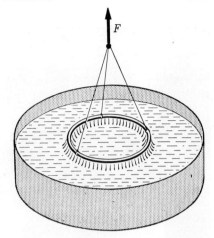

Another less spectacular way of
showing a surface force is embodied
in the actual apparatus, shown in
Fig. 13-11, that is often used to
measure surface tension. A circular

Fig. 13-11. Lifting a circular wire of
length l out of a liquid requires an additional force F to balance the surface forces
$2Sl$. This method is commonly used to
measure surface tension.

wire whose circumference is of length l is lifted out from the body of a
liquid. The additional force F needed to balance the surface forces $2Sl$
due to the two surface films on each side is measured either by the stretch
of a delicate spring or by the twist of a torsion wire. The surface tension
is then given by

$$S = \frac{F}{2l} .$$

TABLE 13-1

EXPERIMENTAL VALUES OF SURFACE TENSION

Liquid in contact with air	Temperature °C	Surface tension in dynes/cm
Benzene...............	20	28.9
Carbon tetrachloride......	20	26.8
Ethyl alcohol............	20	22.3
Glycerine...............	20	63.1
Mercury................	20	465
Olive oil................	20	32.0
Soap solution............	20	25.0
Water..................	0	75.6
Water..................	20	72.8
Water..................	60	66.2
Water..................	100	58.9

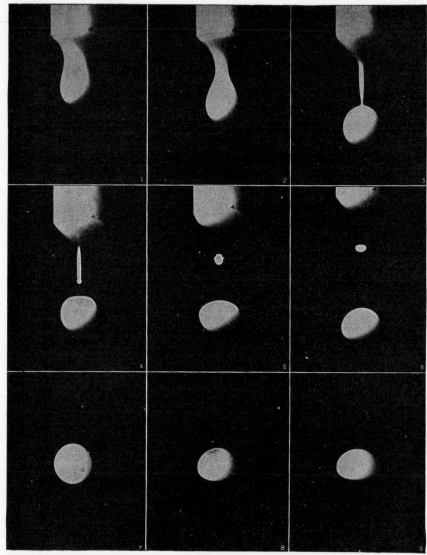

FIG. 13-12.   Successive stages in the formation of a drop.

The usual unit of surface tension is the dyne/cm. Other methods of measuring surface tension will be apparent in what is to follow. Some typical values are shown in Table 13-1.

The surface tension of a liquid surface in contact with its own vapor or with air is found to depend only on the nature of the liquid and on the temperature. The values for water in Table 13-1 are typical of the general result that surface tension decreases as the temperature increases. Measurements of the surface tension of an extremely thin layer of oil on the surface of water indicate that, in this case, the surface tension depends on the area of the oil film as well as on the temperature.

13-8 The physics of surfaces. Any surface under tension tends to contract until it occupies the minimum area consistent with the boundaries of the surface. A small volume of heavy engine oil injected into the center of a mixture of alcohol and water whose density is the same as that of the oil, will therefore contract until it has the smallest surface area consistent with its volume. The shape of such a surface is spherical.

A more interesting situation is depicted in Fig. 13-12 showing a series of high-speed photographs of successive stages in the formation of a drop of milk at the end of a vertical tube. The photographs were taken by Dr. Edgerton of M.I.T. It will be seen that the process, if examined in detail, is exceedingly complex. An interesting feature is the small drop that follows the larger one. Both drops execute a few oscillations after their formation (4, 5, and 6) and eventually assume a spherical shape (7) which would be retained but for the effects of air resistance as shown in (8) and (9). The drop in (9) has fallen 14 ft.

A beautiful photograph of the splash made by a drop of milk falling on a hard surface is reproduced in Fig. 13-13. It also was taken by Dr. Edgerton.

Surface films may be used to solve problems in mathematics whose analytic solution presents great difficulties. If it is required to find the minimal surface (surface of minimum area) bounded by a wire framework bent into an arbitrary shape, the problem may be solved by dipping the wire framework into a soap solution and waiting a few seconds for the film to contract.

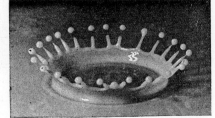

Fig. 13-13. A drop of milk splashes on a hard surface.

The results for a framework in the

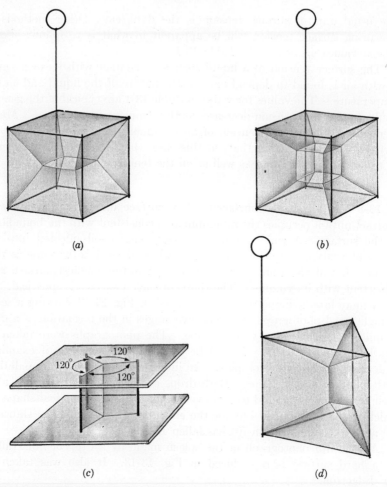

FIG. 13-14. Solution of mathematical problems involving minimal surfaces by means of surface films. (a) Cubical wire framework dipped once. (b) Cubical wire framework dipped twice to entrap an air bubble in the center. (c) Two plastic plates connected by three wires form three plane surface films at angles of 120° to each other. (d) A wire framework in the form of a prism shows that at most three surface films can intersect in a line, and that at most four edges can intersect at a point.

form of a cube and one in the form of a tetrahedron are shown in Fig. 13-14. These results could hardly have been guessed, and their prediction by purely mathematical methods would have been attended by considerable difficulty. For further details, the student is referred to a fascinating book called *What is Mathematics* by Courant and Robbins.

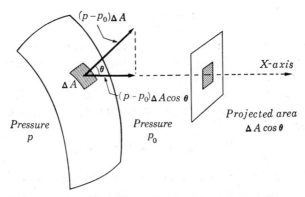

FIG. 13-15. The force in the X-direction is the difference of pressure multiplied by the *projected* area in the X-direction.

A soap bubble consists of two spherical surface films very close together, with liquid in between. If we isolate one-half of the bubble and apply the principles of statics to the study of the equilibrium of this half bubble, we may obtain a simple relation between the surface tension and the difference in pressure of the air inside and that outside the bubble. Consider first a small element of a surface ΔA shown in Fig. 13-15. Suppose the air pressure on the left of this element is p and that on the right is p_0. The force normal to the element is therefore $(p - p_0)\Delta A$. The component of this force in the X-direction is

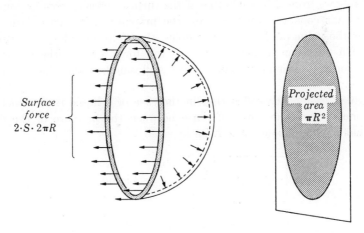

FIG. 13-16. Equilibrium of half of a soap bubble. The force exerted by the other half is $2 \cdot S \cdot 2\pi R$, and the net force exerted by the air inside and outside the bubble is the pressure difference times the projected area, or $(p - p_0)\pi R^2$.

$$(p - p_0)\Delta A \cos \theta.$$

But $\Delta A \cos \theta$ is the area projected on a plane perpendicular to the X-axis. *The force in the X-direction is therefore the difference of pressure multiplied by the projected area in the X-direction.*

Now consider the half bubble shown in Fig. 13-16. The other half exerts a force to the left equal to twice the surface tension times the perimeter or

$$F \text{ (to the left)} = 2S \times 2\pi R.$$

The force to the right is equal to the pressure difference $p - p_0$ multiplied by the area obtained by projecting the half bubble on a plane perpendicular to the direction in question. Since this projected area is πR^2,

$$F \text{ (to the right)} = (p - p_0)\pi R^2.$$

Since the half-bubble is in equilibrium,

$$(p - p_0)\pi R^2 = 4\pi RS,$$

or

$$\boxed{p - p_0 = \frac{4S}{R}.} \qquad \text{(Soap bubble.)} \qquad (13\text{-}4)$$

It follows from this result that if the surface tension remains constant (this means constant temperature), the pressure difference is larger the smaller the value of R. If two bubbles, therefore, are blown at opposite ends of a pipe the smaller of the two will force air into the larger. In other words, the smaller one will get still smaller, and the larger will increase.

It may easily be verified that in the case of a liquid drop which has only one surface film, the difference between the pressure of the liquid and that of the outside air is given by

$$\boxed{p - p_0 = \frac{2S}{R}.} \qquad \text{(Liquid drop.)} \qquad (13\text{-}5)$$

Example: Calculate the excess pressure inside a drop of mercury whose temperature is 20° C and whose diameter is 4 mm.

$$p - p_0 = \frac{2S}{R}$$

$$= \frac{2 \times 465 \text{ dyne/cm}}{0.4 \text{ cm}}$$

$$= 2325 \frac{\text{dyne}}{\text{cm}^2} \cdot$$

13-9 Capillarity. Some of the most interesting and important phenomena take place near the boundary between a surface and a solid wall. These phenomena are associated with short range forces that are exerted on a small particle of liquid by the rest of the liquid on the one hand, and by the wall on the other. Forces of attraction that exist among particles of a liquid are called *forces of cohesion*. Those between a particle of liquid and a solid wall are called *forces of adhesion*. In the case of water and glass, the adhesive force is greater than the cohesive force. For mercury and glass, however, cohesion is much greater than adhesion. We shall see that the relation between cohesion and adhesion determines the curvature of the liquid surface near the wall. Gravitational forces are negligibly small in comparison with cohesive and adhesive forces.

In Fig. 13-17(a) water is in contact with a silver wall. In this case cohesion and adhesion are approximately equal. A particle of liquid near the boundary between surface and wall is in equilibrium under the action of three forces: (1) the ad-

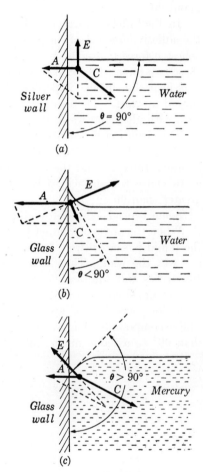

Fig. 13-17. The surface of a liquid near a solid wall is perpendicular to the equilibrant E of the cohesive and adhesive force.

hesive force A toward the wall, (2) the cohesive force C toward the main body of liquid, and (3) the equilibrant E, which is a force of repulsion between the particle in question and neighboring particles near the surface. The liquid near the wall automatically adjusts itself until the surface is perpendicular to the equilibrant of the cohesive and adhesive forces. When C and A are approximately equal, E is almost vertical and the surface remains approximately horizontal. The angle between the wall and the surface, *measured in the liquid*, known as the *contact angle θ*, is therefore about 90°.

In Fig. 13-17(b) water is in contact with a glass wall. In this case, the adhesive force A of the glass on a particle of water is greater than the cohesive force C exerted by other water particles. The equilibrant E of these two forces, provided by repulsion between the particle and its neighbors near the surface, is perpendicular to the surface, which is seen to be curved upward. The contact angle θ is less than 90° and, as a matter of fact, with glass and water it is so small that it can be taken to be zero.

The situation that exists when mercury is in contact with a glass wall is shown in Fig. 13-17(c). Here the cohesive force C is greater than the adhesive force A, and the equilibrant E is seen to be in such a direction as to cause the surface to be curved downward. The contact angle is greater than 90°.

Some typical values of contact angle are given in Table 13-2.

When the angle of contact between a liquid surface and a wall is small, the liquid is said to wet the wall. If the angle is large, however, it does not wet the wall. Thus water wets clean glass but mercury does not. Impurities and adulterants present in or added to a liquid may alter the contact angle considerably. In recent years a number of chemicals have been developed which are very potent as *wetting agents* or *detergents*. These compounds change the contact angle from a large value greater than 90° to a value much smaller than 90°. Conversely, waterproofing

TABLE 13-2

Contact Angles

Liquid	Wall	Contact angle, in degrees
Alcohol............	Glass	0
Ether.............	Glass	0
Glycerin...........	Glass	0
Mercury...........	Glass	140
Water.............	Glass	0
Water.............	Paraffin	107

agents applied to a cloth cause the contact angle of water in contact with the cloth to be larger than 90°.

The effect of a detergent on a drop of water resting on a block of paraffin is shown in Fig. 13-18.

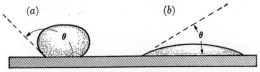

Block of paraffin

FIG. 13-18. Action of a detergent added to a drop of water. (a) Before the detergent is added, the contact angle is large. (b) Afterwards, the contact angle is much smaller.

The most familiar surface effect is the elevation of a liquid in an open tube of small cross section. The term "capillarity," used to describe effects of this sort, originates from the description of such tubes as "capil-

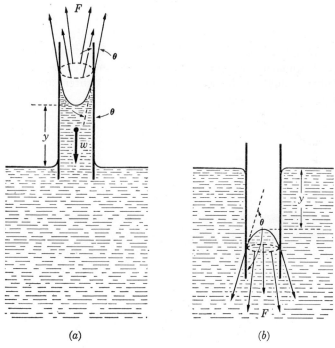

(a)   (b)

FIG. 13-19. Capillarity. (a) Rise of liquid in a capillary when the contact angle θ is less than 90°. (b) Depression of a liquid in a capillary where the contact angle is greater than 90°.

lary" or "hairlike."   In the case of a liquid that wets the tube, the contact angle is less than 90° and the liquid rises until an equilibrium height y is reached, as shown in Fig. 13-19(a).   If the tube radius is r, the liquid makes contact with the tube along a line of length $2\pi r$.   Isolating the cylinder of liquid of height y and radius r, the total upward force is

$$F = 2\pi r S \cos \theta.$$

The downward force is the weight of the cylinder w, which is equal to the weight density ρg times the volume $\pi r^2 y$, or

$$w = \rho g \pi r^2 y.$$

The condition for equilibrium is

$$\rho g \pi r^2 y = 2\pi r S \cos \theta,$$

or

$$y = \frac{2S \cos \theta}{\rho g r}.$$

The same equation holds for the capillary depression, shown in Fig. 13-19(b).   Capillarity accounts for the rise of ink in blotting paper, the rise of lighting fluid in the wick of a cigarette lighter, and many other common phenomena.

Problems — Chapter 13

13-1. The piston of a hydraulic automobile lift is 12 inches in diameter. What pressure, in lb/in², is required to lift a car weighing 2400 lb?

13-2. The expansion tank of a household hot-water heating system is open to the atmosphere and is 30 ft above a pressure gauge attached to the furnace. What is the gauge pressure, in lb/in²?

13-3. The submarine Squalus sank at a depth of 240 ft. Compute the absolute pressure at this depth, in lb/in² and lb/ft². The specific gravity of sea water is 1.025.

13-4. A piece of gold-aluminum alloy weighs 10 lb. When suspended from a spring balance and submerged in water, the balance reads 8 lb. What is the weight of gold in the alloy if the specific gravity of gold is 19.3 and the specific gravity of aluminum is 2.5?

13-5. The densities of air, helium, and hydrogen (at standard conditions) are respectively 0.00129 gm/cm³, 0.000178 gm/cm³, and 0.0000899 gm/cm³. What is the volume in cubic feet displaced by a hydrogen-filled dirigible which has a total "lift" of 10 tons? What would be the "lift" if helium were used instead of hydrogen?

13-6. A piece of wood is 2 ft long, 1 ft wide, and 2 inches thick. Its specific gravity is 0.6. What volume of lead must be fastened underneath so that the wood in calm water so that its top is just even with the water level?

13-7. Block A in Fig. 13-20 hangs by a cord from spring balance D and is submerged in a liquid C contained in beaker B. The weight of the beaker is 2 lb, the weight of the liquid is 3 lb. Balance D reads 5 lb and balance E reads 15 lb. The

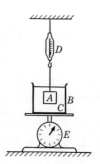

Fig. 13-20

volume of block A is 0.1 ft³. (a) What is the "weight-density" of the liquid? (b) What will each balance read if block A is pulled up out of the liquid?

13-8. A hollow sphere of inner radius 9 cm and outer radius 10 cm floats half submerged in a liquid of specific gravity 0.8. (a) Calculate the density of the material of which the sphere is made. (b) What would be the density of a liquid in which the hollow sphere would just float completely submerged?

13-9. Two spherical bodies having the same diameter are released simultaneously from the same height. If the mass of one is ten times that of the other and if the air resistance on each is the *same*, show that the heavier body will arrive at the ground first.

13-10. When a life preserver having a volume of 0.75 ft³ is immersed in sea water (specific gravity 1.1) it will just support a 160-lb man (specific gravity 1.2) with 2/10 of his volume above water. What is the weight density of the material composing the life preserver?

13-11. An object in the shape of a truncated cone weighs 1000 lb in vacuum and is suspended by a rope in an open tank of liquid of density 2 slugs/ft³ as in Fig. 13-21. (a) Find the total downward force

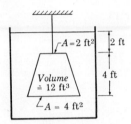

FIG. 13-21

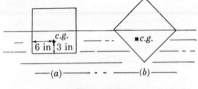

FIG. 13-23

exerted by the liquid on the top of the object, of area 2 ft². (b) Find the total upward force exerted by the liquid on the bottom of the object, of area 4 ft². (c) Find the tension in the cord supporting the object.

13-12. A 3200-lb cylindrical can buoy floats vertically in salt water (specific gravity = 1.03). The diameter of the buoy is 3 ft. Calculate (a) the additional distance the buoy will sink when a 150-lb man stands on top, (b) the period of the resulting vertical simple harmonic motion when the man dives off.

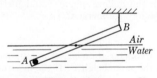

FIG. 13-22

13-13. A uniform rod AB, 12 ft long, weighing 24 lb, is supported at end B by a flexible cord and weighted at end A with a 12-lb lead weight. The rod floats as shown in Fig. 13-22 with one-half its length submerged. The buoyant force on the lead weight can be neglected. (a) Show in a diagram all of the forces acting on the rod. (b) Find the tension in the cord. (c) Find the total volume of the rod.

13-14. A cubical block of wood 1 ft on a side is weighted so that its center of gravity is at the point shown in Fig. 13-23 (a), and it floats in water with one-half its volume submerged. Compute the right-

ing moment and the metacentric height when the block is "heeled" at an angle of 45° as in Fig. 13-23(b).

13-15. Compare the tension of a soap bubble with that of a rubber balloon in the following respects: (a) Has each a surface tension? (b) Does the surface tension depend on area? (c) Is Hooke's law applicable?

13-16. Water can rise to a height y in a certain capillary. Suppose that this tube is immersed in water so that only a height $y/2$ is above the surface. Will you have a fountain or not? Explain.

13-17. A capillary tube is dipped in water with its lower end 10 cm below the water surface. Water rises in the tube to a height of 4 cm above that of the surrounding liquid, and the angle of contact is zero. What gauge pressure is required to blow a hemispherical bubble at the lower end of the tube?

13-18. A glass tube of inside diameter 1 mm is dipped vertically into a container of mercury, with its lower end 1 cm below the mercury surface. (a) What must be the gauge pressure of air in the tube to blow a hemispherical bubble at its lower end? (b) To what height will mercury rise in the tube if the air pressure in the tube is 3×10^4 dynes/cm² below atmospheric? The angle of contact between mercury and glass is 140°.

13-19. On a day when the atmospheric pressure is 950 millibars, (a) what would be the height of the mercury column in a barometric tube of inside diameter 2 mm?

(b) what would be the height in the absence of any surface tension effects? (c) what is the minimum diameter a barometric tube may have in order that the correction for capillary depression shall be less than 0.01 cm of mercury?

13-20. (a) Derive the expression for the height of capillary rise in the space between two parallel plates dipping in a liquid. (b) Two glass plates, parallel to each other and separated by 0.5 mm, are dipped in water. To what height will the water rise between them? Assume zero angle of contact.

13-21. A tube of circular cross section and outer radius 0.14 cm is closed at one end. This end is weighted and the tube floats vertically in water, heavy end down. The total mass of the tube and weights is 0.20 gm. If the angle of contact is zero, how far below the water surface is the bottom of the tube?

13-22. A glass tube of inside diameter 1 mm and wall thickness 0.5 mm is aligned coaxially within a larger tube of inside diameter 2.5 mm. When the tubes are dipped below the flat surface of a liquid, the liquid rises to a height of 1.2 cm in the inner tube. To what height does it rise in the annular space between the tubes? The angle of contact between the liquid and the glass is 10° and the specific gravity of the liquid is 0.80.

13-23. Find the gauge pressure, in dynes/cm², in a soap bubble 5 cm in diameter. The surface tension is 25 dynes/cm.

13-24. Two large glass plates are clamped together along one edge and separated by spacers a few millimeters thick along the opposite edge to form a wedge-shaped air film. These plates are then placed vertically in a dish of colored liquid. Show that the edge of the liquid forms an equilateral hyperbola.

13-25. A soap bubble may be drawn out into a cylinder by touching to it a ring of the same diameter as the tube from which the bubble is blown, and then "stretching" the bubble between the tube and the ring. By isolating half of the cylindrical surface, show that the gauge pressure within the bubble is given by S/R where R is the radius of the cylindrical surface.

CHAPTER 14

HYDRODYNAMICS AND VISCOSITY

14-1 Streamline flow. Hydrodynamics is the study of fluids in motion. It is one of the most complex branches of mechanics, as will be realized by considering such common examples of fluid flow as a river in flood or a swirling cloud of cigarette smoke. While it must be true that $F = ma$ at each instant for each drop of water or each smoke particle, imagine attempting to write their equations of motion! However, the problem is not as hopeless as it seems at first sight.

When the proper conditions are fulfilled, the flow of a fluid is of a relatively simple type called *streamline* or *steady* flow. Fig. 14-1 represents a portion of a pipe in which a fluid is flowing from left to right. If the flow is of the streamline type, every particle passing a point such as a, follows exactly the same path as the preceding particles which passed the same point. These paths are called *lines of flow* or *streamlines*

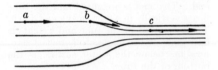

FIG. 14-1.   Streamline or steady flow.

and three of them are shown in the figure. If the cross section of the pipe varies from point to point, the velocity of any one particle will vary along its line of flow, but at any fixed point in the pipe the velocity of the particle which happens to be at that point is always the same. The particle which is now at a in the figure will be a moment later at point b, traveling in a different direction with a different speed, and a moment later yet it will be at c, having again changed its velocity. However, if we fix our attention on the point of space marked b, then each successive particle as it passes through b will be traveling in exactly the same direction and with the same speed as is the particle which is at that point now.

Any real fluid, because of its viscosity, will have a higher velocity at the center of the pipe than at the outside. For the present we shall assume the fluid to be nonviscous and the velocity to be the same at all points of a transverse cross section.

The flow of a fluid is of the streamline type provided the velocity is not too great and the obstructions, constrictions, or bends in the pipe are not such as to cause the lines of flow to change their direction too abruptly. If these conditions are not fulfilled, the flow is of a much more complicated type called *turbulent*.

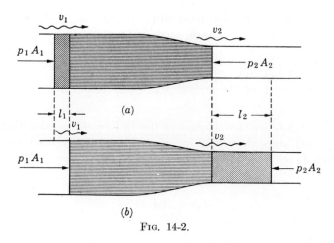

$$(a)$$

$$(b)$$

Fɪɢ. 14-2.

14-2 Bernoulli's equation. The fundamental equation of hydrodynamics is Bernoulli's equation, which is a relation between the pressure, velocity, and elevation at points along a line of flow. Fig. 14-2 represents a portion of a pipe line in which an incompressible, nonviscous fluid is flowing with streamline flow. The portion of the pipe shown in the figure has a uniform cross section A_1 at the left, followed by a region of diminishing cross section, and then a length of uniform but smaller cross section A_2. Focussing our attention on a portion of the fluid represented by both cross shading and horizontal shading (hereafter called the "system"), let us consider the motion of this system from the position shown in (a) to that in (b).

At all points in the wide part of the pipe, the pressure is p_1 and the velocity v_1. At all points in the narrow part, the pressure is p_2 and the velocity v_2. Since the left end of the system advances a distance l_1 parallel to an external force p_1A_1, it follows that the

$$\left\{ \begin{matrix} \text{Work done } on \\ \text{the system} \end{matrix} \right\} = p_1A_1l_1.$$

The right end advances a distance l_2 while an external force p_2A_2 in the opposite direction is acting. Therefore

$$\left\{ \begin{matrix} \text{Work done } by \\ \text{the system} \end{matrix} \right\} = p_2A_2l_2.$$

To move the system from position (a) to position (b), a net amount of work must be done by an outside agent (a pump, in this case) equal to

$$\left\{ \begin{array}{l} \text{Net work done} \\ \text{on the system} \end{array} \right\} = p_1 A_1 l_1 - p_2 A_2 l_2.$$

But $A_1 l_1$ and $A_2 l_2$ are the volumes of the two cross-shaded regions, which must be equal, since the fluid is incompressible. If m is the mass of either cross-shaded region, and ρ is the density of the fluid, then

$$A_1 l_1 = A_2 l_2 = \frac{m}{\rho},$$

and, finally,

$$\text{Net work} = (p_1 - p_2) \frac{m}{\rho}.$$

Since the kinetic energy of the horizontally shaded portion undergoes no change whatever in the transition from (a) to (b), it follows that the total change of kinetic energy of the system is the change in the cross-shaded portions only, or

$$\left\{ \begin{array}{l} \text{Net change of} \\ \text{kinetic energy} \end{array} \right\} = \frac{1}{2} m v_2{}^2 - \frac{1}{2} m v_1{}^2.$$

Applying the principle of conservation of energy, the net work done on the system equals the sum of the increases in its kinetic energy and its gravitational potential energy. In Fig. 14-2, where the pipe is horizontal, there is no increase in potential energy. In general, the cross-shaded portion in (b) will be at a different elevation from that of the cross-shaded portion in (a), and the

$$\left\{ \begin{array}{l} \text{Net change of} \\ \text{potential energy} \end{array} \right\} = m g y_2 - m g y_1,$$

where y_2 and y_1 are the respective elevations of the cross-shaded regions above some arbitrary zero level. Equating the net work done to the sum of the increases in kinetic and potential energy, we get

$$(p_1 - p_2)\frac{m}{\rho} = (\tfrac{1}{2}mv_2{}^2 - \tfrac{1}{2}mv_1{}^2) + (mgy_2 - mgy_1).$$

After cancelling m and rearranging terms, we obtain

$$p_1 + \tfrac{1}{2}\rho v_1{}^2 + \rho gy_1 = p_2 + \tfrac{1}{2}\rho v_2{}^2 + \rho gy_2, \qquad (14\text{-}2)$$

and since the subscripts 1 and 2 refer to *any* two points along the pipe line we may write

$$p + \tfrac{1}{2}\rho v^2 + \rho gy = \text{constant.} \qquad (14\text{-}3)$$

Either Eq. (14-2) or Eq. (14-3) may be considered Bernoulli's equation.

Note carefully: p is the *absolute* (not gauge) pressure and must be expressed in pounds per square foot, newtons per square meter, or dynes per square centimeter. The density ρ must be expressed in slugs per cubic foot, kilograms per cubic meter, or grams per cubic centimeter. It is shown in more advanced textbooks that Bernoulli's equation is still valid for a compressible fluid.

14-3 Discharge rate of a pipe. Fig. 14-3 represents the open end of a pipe line of cross section A, out of which is flowing a liquid with velocity v. The quantity of liquid discharged in time t is that contained in a cylinder of area A, extending back from the end of the pipe a distance vt. In other words, each point of the liquid which is now at the dotted section will, in time t, have just reached the end of the pipe, and all of the liquid between that section and the end of the pipe will have been discharged in the

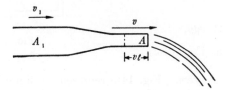

Fig. 14-3.   Discharge rate of a pipe.

meantime.　Hence a volume of liquid equal to Avt is discharged in a time interval t, and the discharge *rate*, Q, is

$$Q = \frac{Avt}{t} = Av. \tag{14-4}$$

Q is expressed in ft³/sec, m³/sec, or cm³/sec if the appropriate units are used for A and v.

If an incompressible liquid completely fills the pipe at all points, the same volume of liquid must pass every cross section in any given time as is discharged from the end of the pipe.　If that were not the case, the volume of liquid between that cross section and the end would be increasing or decreasing.　Hence if A_1 and v_1, Fig. 14-3, are the area and velocity at any other point along the pipe,

$$Q = Av = A_1 v_1 = \text{constant.} \tag{14-5}$$

This is known as the *equation of continuity*.　A consequence of this relation is that the velocity is greatest at points where the cross section is least and vice versa.

14-4 Applications of Bernoulli's equation.　(1) The equations of hydrostatics are special cases of Bernoulli's equation, when the velocity is everywhere zero.　For example, the variation of pressure with depth in an incompressible liquid may be found by applying Bernoulli's equation to points 1 and 2 in Fig. 14-4.　We have

$p_1 = p_0$ (atmospheric),　$v_1 = v_2 = 0$.

Let elevations be measured from the level of point 2.　Then

$$y_2 = 0, \quad y_1 = y,$$

and

$$p_0 + \rho g y = p_2,$$

or

$$p_2 = p_0 + \rho g y,$$

which is the same as Eq. (13-2).

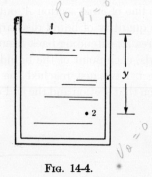

Fig. 14-4.

(2) *Torricelli's theorem.*　Fig. 14-5 represents a liquid flowing from an orifice in a tank at a depth y below the surface of the liquid in the tank. Take point 1 at the surface and point 2 at the orifice.　The pressure at each point is the atmospheric pressure, p_0, since both are open to the

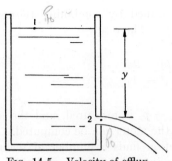

FIG. 14-5.   Velocity of efflux equals $\sqrt{2gy}$.

atmosphere. Take the reference level at the elevation of point 2. If the orifice is small, the level of liquid in the tank will fall only slowly. Hence v_1 is small and we shall assume it zero. Then

$$p_0 + \rho gy = p_0 + \tfrac{1}{2}\rho v_2{}^2,$$

or

$$v_2{}^2 = 2gy. \qquad (14\text{-}6)$$

This is Torricelli's theorem. Note that the velocity of discharge is the same as that which would be acquired by a body falling freely from rest through a height y.

If A is the area of the opening, the discharge rate Q is

$$Q = Av = A\sqrt{2gy}. \qquad (14\text{-}7)$$

Because of the converging of the streamlines as they approach the orifice, the cross section of the stream continues to diminish for a short distance outside the tank. It is the area of smallest cross section, known as the *vena contracta* which should be used in Eq. (14-7). For a sharp-edged circular opening, the area of the *vena contracta* is about 65% as great as the area of the orifice.

(3) *The Venturi meter.* The Venturi meter, illustrated in Fig. 14-6, consists of a constriction or throat inserted in a pipe line, and having properly designed tapers at inlet and outlet to avoid turbulence and assure streamline flow. Bernoulli's equation, applied to the wide and to the constricted portions of the pipe, becomes

$$p_1 + \tfrac{1}{2}\rho v_1{}^2 = p_2 + \tfrac{1}{2}\rho v_2{}^2$$

(the "y" terms drop out if the pipe is level).

Since v_2 is greater than v_1, it follows that p_2 is less than p_1. That is, the pressure in the throat is smaller than in the main pipe line. The

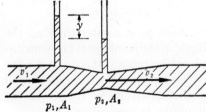

FIG. 14-6.   The Venturi meter.

pressure difference may be measured by attaching vertical side tubes as shown in the diagram. If y is the difference in height of the liquid in the tubes, then

$$p_1 - p_2 = \rho gy.$$

The discharge rate, Q, may be obtained by combining Bernoulli's equation with the equation of continuity.   The result is

$$Q = A_1 A_2 \sqrt{\frac{2(p_1 - p_2)}{\rho(A_1{}^2 - A_2{}^2)}}.$$

Hence, if the pressure difference $p_1 - p_2$ is measured, and the areas A_1 and A_2 are known, the flow through the meter can be computed.

The reduced pressure at a constriction finds a number of technical applications. Gasoline vapor is drawn into the intake manifold of an internal combustion engine by the low pressure produced in a Venturi throat to which the carburetor is connected. The aspirator pump is a Venturi throat through whch water is forced. Air is drawn into the low pressure water rushing through the constricted portion. The injection pump used on a steam locomotive to draw water from the tender makes use of the same principle.

(4) *The pitot tube.* A pitot tube is shown in Fig. 14-7 as it would be used to measure the velocity of a gas flowing in a tube or pipe. An open tube manometer is connected as shown to the tube in which the gas is flowing. The pressure at the left arm of the manometer, whose opening is parallel to the direction of flow, is equal to the pressure in the gas stream. The pressure in the right arm, whose opening is at right angles to the stream, may be computed by applying Bernoulli's equation to the points a and b. Let v be the velocity of the stream, ρ the density of the gas, and p_a the pressure at point a. The velocity at point b, of course, is zero. Then

$$p_b = p_a + \tfrac{1}{2}\rho v^2.$$

Since p_b is greater than p_a, the liquid in the manometer becomes displaced as shown. If ρ_0 is the density of the liquid in the manometer and y the difference in height of the liquid in its arms, then

$$p_b = p_a + \rho_0 g y.$$

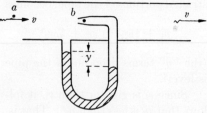

FIG. 14-7.   The pitot tube.

When this is combined with the preceding equation we get

$$\rho_0 g y = \tfrac{1}{2}\rho v^2,$$

from which v may be expressed in terms of measurable quantities.

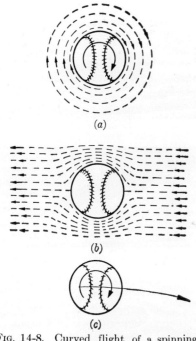

(a)

(b)

(c)

FIG. 14-8.   Curved flight of a spinning ball.

(5) *The curved flight of a spinning ball.* Fig. 14-8(a) represents a top view of a ball spinning about a vertical axis.   Because of friction between the ball and the surrounding air, a thin layer of air is dragged around by the spinning ball.

Fig. 14-8(b) represents a stationary ball in a blast of air moving from right to left.   The motion of the air stream around and past the ball is the same as though the ball were moving through still air from left to right.   If the ball is moving from left to right and spinning at the same time, the actual velocity of the air at any point is the resultant of the velocities at the same point in (a) and (b). At the top of the diagram the two velocities are in opposite directions, while the reverse is true at the bottom of the diagram.   The top is a region of low velocity and high pressure, while the bottom is a region of high velocity and low pressure. There is therefore an excess pressure forcing the ball down in the diagram, so that if moving from left to right and spinning at the same time, it deviates from a straight line as shown in the top view in Fig. 14-8(c).

(6) *Lift on an airplane wing.*   Fig. 14-9 is a photograph of streamline flow around a section in the shape of an airplane wing or an airfoil, at three different angles of attack.   The apparatus consists of two parallel glass plates spaced about 1 mm apart.   The wing section, whose thickness equals the separation of the plates, is inserted between them and alternate streams of clear water and ink flow by gravity between the plates and past the section.   The photographs have been turned through 90° to give the effect of horizontal air flow past an airplane wing. Because the fluid is water flowing relatively slowly, the nature of the flow pattern is not identical with that of air moving at high speed past an actual wing.

Consider the first photograph, which corresponds to a plane in level flight.   It will be seen that there is relatively little disturbance of the flow below the wing, but because of the shape of the airfoil there is a marked crowding together of the streamlines above it, much as if they were being forced through the throat of a Venturi. Hence the region above the wing is one of increased velocity and reduced pressure, while below the wing the pressure is nearly atmospheric. It is this pressure differential between upper and lower wing surfaces which gives rise to the lift on the wing. The wing is not simply forced up by air blowing against its lower surface.

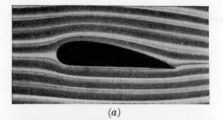

(a)

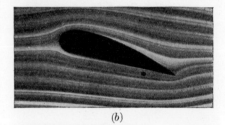

(b)

There is a mistaken impression that the flow around an airplane wing results in an upward "pull" on the upper surface of the wing. Of course this cannot happen. The air presses against all portions of the wing surface, but the reduction below atmospheric pressure, at the upper surface, usually exceeds the increase above atmospheric pressure at the lower surface.

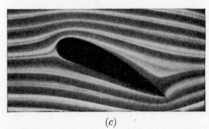

(c)

Fig. 14-9.   Lines of flow around an airfoil.

The second and third photographs show how, as the angle of attack is increased, the streamlines above the wing have to change direction sharply to follow the contour of the wing surface and join smoothly with the streamline flow below the wing. While the slowly moving water in Fig. 14-9 does retain its streamline form even at the large angle of attack in the third photograph, it is much more difficult for the air moving rapidly past an airplane wing to do so. As a consequence, if the angle of attack is too great, the streamline flow in the region above and behind the wing breaks down and a complicated system of whirls and eddies known as *turbulence* is set up. Bernoulli's equation no longer applies, the pressure above the wing rises, and the lift on the wing decreases and the plane stalls.

14-5 Viscosity.   Viscosity may be thought of as the internal friction of a fluid. Because of viscosity, a force must be exerted to cause one layer of a fluid to slide past another, or to cause one surface to slide past another

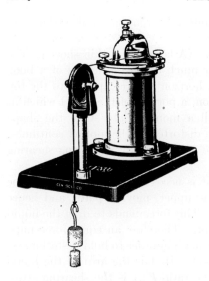

FIG. 14-10.   One type of viscosimeter.
(*Courtesy of Central Scientific Co.*)

if there is a layer of fluid between the surfaces. Both liquids and gases exhibit viscosity, although liquids are much more viscous than gases. In developing the fundamental equations of viscous flow, it will be seen that the problem is very similar to that of the shearing stress and strain in a solid.

Fig. 14-10 illustrates one type of apparatus for measuring the viscosity of a liquid. A cylinder is pivoted on nearly frictionless bearings so as to rotate concentrically within a cylindrical vessel. The liquid whose viscosity is to be measured is poured into the annular space between the cylinders. A torque can be applied to the inner cylinder by the weight-pulley system. When the weight is released, the inner cylinder accelerates momentarily but very quickly comes up to a constant angular velocity and continues to rotate at that velocity as long as the torque acts. It is obvious that this velocity will be smaller with a liquid such as glycerin in the annular space than it will be if the liquid is water or kerosene. From a knowledge of the torque, the dimensions of the apparatus, and the angular velocity, the viscosity of the liquid may be computed.

To reduce the problem to its essential terms, imagine that the cylinders are of nearly the same size so that the liquid layer between them is small. A short arc of this layer will then be approximately a straight line. Fig. 14-11 shows a portion of the liquid layer between the moving inner wall and the stationary outer wall. The liquid in contact with the moving surface is found to have the same velocity as that surface; the liquid adjacent to the stationary inner wall is at rest. The velocities of inter-

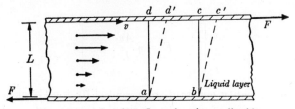

FIG. 14-11.   Laminar flow of a viscous liquid.

mediate layers of the liquid increase uniformly from one wall to the other as shown by the arrows.

Flow of this type is called *laminar*. (A lamina is a thin sheet.) The layers of liquid slide over one another much as do the leaves of a book when it is placed flat on a table and a horizontal force applied to the top cover. As a consequence of this motion, a portion of the liquid which at some instant has the shape *abcd*, will a moment later take the shape *abc'd'*, and will become more and more distorted as the motion continues. In other words, the liquid is in a state of continually increasing shearing strain.

In order to maintain the motion, it is necessary that a force shall be continually exerted to the right on the upper, moving plate, and hence indirectly on the upper liquid surface. This force tends to drag the liquid and the lower plate as well to the right. Therefore an equal force must be exerted toward the left on the lower plate in order to hold it stationary. These forces are lettered F in Fig. 14-11. If A is the area of the liquid over which these forces are applied, the ratio F/A is the shearing stress exerted on the liquid.

When a shearing stress is applied to a solid, the effect of the stress is to produce a certain displacement of the solid such as dd'. The shearing strain is defined as the ratio of this displacement to the transverse dimension L, and within the elastic limit the shearing stress is proportional to the shearing strain. With a fluid, on the other hand, the shearing strain increases without limit as long as the stress is applied, and the stress is found by experiment to be proportional, not to the shearing strain, but to its *rate of change*. The strain in Fig 14-11 at the instant when the volume of fluid has the shape $abc'd'$ is dd'/ad, or dd'/L. Since L is constant, the rate of change of strain equals $1/L$ times the rate of change of dd'. But the rate of change of dd' is simply the velocity of point d', or the velocity v of the moving wall. Since shearing stress is proportional to rate of change of shearing strain,

$$\frac{F}{A} \propto \frac{v}{L}, \quad \text{or} \quad \frac{F}{A} = \eta \frac{v}{L},$$

or

$$F = \eta \frac{Av}{L}. \tag{14-8}$$

The proportionality constant, represented by the Greek letter η (eta), is called the *coefficient of viscosity*, or simply the *viscosity*. It is small for liquids which flow readily like kerosene, and larger for liquids like molasses or glycerin.

From Eq. (14-8), the unit of viscosity is that of force times distance divided by area times velocity, or, in the cgs system, 1 dyne-sec/cm². A viscosity of 1 dyne-sec/cm² is called a *poise*. Small viscosities are usually expressed in centipoises (1 cp = 10^{-2} poise) or micropoises (1 μp = 10^{-6} poise). Some typical values of viscosity are given in Table 14-1.

TABLE 14-1

Viscosities of Liquids and Gases

(1 cp = 10^{-2} poise, 1 μp = 10^{-6} poise)

Liquids	t (° C)	η (cp)
Alcohol, ethyl..........................	20	16
Glycerin.............................	20	830
Machine Oil:		
Heavy............................	15	660
Light............................	15	113
Mercury.............................	20	1.55
Water..............................	20.20	1.0000

Gases	t (° C)	η (μp)
Air................................	20	181
Argon.............................	23	221
Carbon dioxide......................	20	148
Helium.............................	23	196
Hydrogen...........................	20	88
Mercury (vapor).....................	380	654
Neon...............................	15	312
Nitrogen............................	23	177
Oxygen.............................	15	196

The coefficient of viscosity is markedly dependent on temperature, increasing for gases and decreasing for liquids as the temperature is increased.

A common technical method of measuring viscosity makes use of a small container in the bottom of which is an orifice of specified dimensions. A specified volume of liquid is poured into the container and the time required for the liquid to run out through the orifice is measured. The viscosity is then computed by an empirical formula.

Viscosities of lubricating oils are commonly expressed on an arbitrary scale established by the Society of Automotive Engineers. An oil whose SAE number is 10 has a viscosity at 130° F between about 160 and 220 centipoise; the viscosity of SAE 20 is between 230 and 300 centipoise, and that of SAE 30 is between 360 and 430 centipoise.

14-6 Stokes' law. When a viscous fluid flows past a sphere with streamline flow or when a sphere moves through a viscous fluid at rest, a resisting force is exerted on the sphere. (A force is, of course, experienced by a body of any shape but only for a sphere is the expression for the force readily calculable.) Analysis which is beyond the scope of this book shows that the resisting force is given by

$$F = 6\pi\eta r v, \tag{14-9}$$

where η is the viscosity of the fluid, r the radius of the sphere, and v the relative velocity of sphere and fluid. This relation was first deduced by Sir George Stokes in 1845 and is called *Stokes' Law*. We shall consider it briefly in relation to a sphere falling through a viscous fluid.

If the sphere is released from rest ($v = 0$), the viscous force at the start is zero. The other forces on the sphere are its weight and the buoyant force of the fluid. If ρ is the density of the sphere and ρ_0 the density of the fluid,

$$\text{weight} = mg = \frac{4}{3}\,\pi r^3 \rho g, \quad \text{buoyant force} = \frac{4}{3}\,\pi r^3 \rho_0 g.$$

Since there is a net downward force on the sphere, it is accelerated and, as a result of this acceleration, the sphere acquires a downward velocity and therefore experiences a retarding force given by Stokes' law. As the velocity increases, the retarding force also increases in direct proportion, and eventually a velocity is reached such that the downward force and the retarding force are equal. The sphere then ceases to accelerate and moves with a constant velocity called its *terminal velocity*. This velocity can be found by setting the downward force equal to the retarding force.

$$\frac{4}{3}\,\pi r^3\,(\rho - \rho_0)\,g = 6\pi\eta r v,$$

or

$$v = \frac{2}{9}\frac{r^2 g}{\eta}\,(\rho - \rho_0). \tag{14-10}$$

The relation above holds provided the velocity is not so great that turbulence sets in. When this occurs the retarding force is much greater than that given by Stokes' law.

Example: Find the terminal velocity of a steel ball bearing 2 mm in radius, falling in a tank of glycerin.

ρ_{steel} = (about) 8 gm/cm³, $\rho_{glycerin}$ = (about) 1.3 gm/cm³, $\eta_{glycerin}$ = (about) 8.3 poise

$$v = \frac{2}{9}\frac{(.2)^2 \times 980}{8.3}\,(8 - 1.3) = 7 \text{ cm/sec.}$$

This velocity is attained in a very short distance from the start of the motion. The experiment above is used as one method of measuring viscosity.

Problems — Chapter 14

14-1. A circular hole 1 inch in diameter is cut in the side of a large standpipe, 20 ft below the water level in the standpipe. Find the velocity of efflux and the discharge rate. Neglect the contraction of the stream lines after emerging from the hole

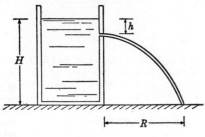

FIG. 14-12

14-2. Water stands at a depth H in a large open tank whose side walls are vertical. (Fig 14-12.) A hole is made in one of the walls at a depth h below the water surface. (a) At what distance R from the foot of the wall does the emerging stream of water strike the floor? (b) At what height above the bottom of the tank could a second hole be cut so that the stream emerging from it would have the same range?

14-3. A tank of large area is filled with water to a height of one foot. A hole of 1 in² cross section in the bottom allows water to drain out in a *continuous stream*. (a) What is the rate at which water flows out of the tank, in ft³/sec? Neglect the convergence of the stream lines. (b) At what distance below the bottom of the tank is the cross-sectional area of the stream equal to one-half the area of the hole?

14-4. A sealed tank containing sea water to a height of 5 ft also contains air above the water at a gauge pressure of 580 lb/ft². Water flows out from a hole at the bottom. The cross-sectional area of the hole is 1.6 in². (a) Calculate the efflux velocity of

the water. (b) Calculate the reaction force on the tank exerted by the water in the emergent stream.

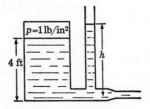

FIG. 14-13

14-5. Sea water (weight density 64 lb/ft³) stands to a height of 4 ft in a tank. The tank contains compressed air at a gauge pressure of 1 lb/in². The horizontal outlet pipe has cross-sectional areas of 2.88 in² and 1.44 in² at the larger and smaller sections (Fig. 14-13). (a) What is the discharge rate from the outlet? (b) To what height h does water stand in the open end pipe? (c) If now the tank is punctured at the top and the gauge pressure drops to zero, what will be the height h?

14-6. A large open tank is filled with water to a depth h_0. The tank has two openings in its bottom, each of cross-sectional area A_0. One of these leads directly to the air. The other is connected to a garden hose having a nozzle with a variable opening of area A_1 at its end. The nozzle is at a distance h_1 below the bottom of the tank. (a) If $A_0 = A_1$, will more or less water flow through the hose than through the other opening? (b) What should be the area A_1 of the nozzle so that there will be the same total flow through each of the holes in the tank?

14-7. The water level in a tank on the top of a building is 100 ft above the ground. The tank supplies water, through pipes of 0.02 ft² cross-sectional area, to the various apartments. Each faucet through which the water emerges has an orifice of 0.01 ft² effective area. (a) How long will it take to fill a 1 ft³ pail in an apartment 75 ft above the ground? (b) What is the gauge pressure in a water pipe (not in the faucet) on the ground level when the faucet is closed? (c) What is the gauge pressure in a pipe on the ground level when the faucet is open?

14-8. Sea water of weight density 64 lb/ft³ flows through a horizontal pipe of cross-sectional area 1.44 in². At one section the cross-sectional area is 0.72 in². The pressure difference between the two sections is 0.048 lb/in². How many cubic feet of water will flow out of the pipe in one minute?

14-9. Water flows from a reservoir to a turbine 330 ft below. The efficiency of the turbine is 80 percent and it receives 100 ft³ of water per minute. Neglecting friction in the pipe, compute the horsepower output of the turbine.

14-10. Assume that air is streaming horizontally past an airplane wing such that the velocity is 100 ft/sec over the top surface and 80 ft/sec past the bottom surface. If the wing weighs 600 lb and has an area of 40 ft², what is the net force on the wing?

14-11. Sea water with a weight density of 64 lb/ft³ is siphoned from an open tank through a tube of cross-sectional area 0.5 in². The highest point in the tube is 15 ft above the water surface and the outlet is 9 ft below the water surface. (a) What is the discharge rate in ft³/sec? (b) What is the gauge pressure in lb/in² at the highest point in the tube?

14-12. Two very large open tanks, A and F (Fig. 14-14), both contain the same liquid. A horizontal pipe BCD having a constriction at C leads out of the bottom of tank A, and a vertical pipe E opens into the constriction at C and dips into the liquid in tank F. Assume streamline flow and no viscosity. If the cross section

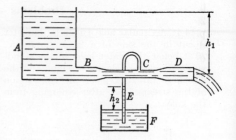

Fig. 14-14

at C is one-half that at D, and if D is at a distance h_1 below the level of the liquid in A, to what height h_2 will liquid rise in pipe E? Express your answer in terms of h_1. Neglect changes in atmospheric pressure with elevation.

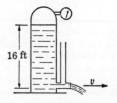

Fig. 14-15

14-13. Water in an enclosed tank stands at a level of 16 ft above a short efflux pipe at the base (Fig. 14-15). (a) What pressure (gauge) of compressed air above the tank will result in a velocity of efflux from the pipe of 40 ft/sec? (b) A manometer tube is attached to the efflux pipe close to the tank. To what height will water rise in this tube?

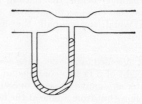

Fig. 14-16

14-14. The section of pipe shown in Fig. 14-16 has a cross section of 0.04 ft² at the wider portions and 0.01 ft² at the constriction. One cubic foot of water is discharged from the pipe in 5 sec. (a) Find the velocities at the wide and the narrow portions. (b) Find the pressure difference between these portions. (c) Find the difference in height between the mercury columns in the U-tube.

14-15. With what terminal velocity will an air bubble 1 mm in diameter rise in a liquid of viscosity 150 cp and density 0.90 gm/cm³? What is the terminal velocity of the same bubble in water?

CHAPTER 15

TEMPERATURE—EXPANSION

15-1 Temperature. The temperature of a body is a measure of its relative hotness or coldness. When we touch a body our temperature sense enables us to make a rough estimate of its temperature in somewhat the same way that we can, by muscular effort, make a rough estimate of the magnitude of a force. It is evident, however, that the temperature sense is too limited in its range and not sufficiently precise to be of any value in engineering or scientific work. For the *measurement* of temperature we must make use of some measurable physical property which changes with temperature, just as for the measurement of a force we use some property of a body which changes with the force, as, for example, the length of a coil spring. Any instrument used for the measurement of temperature is called a *thermometer*.

15-2 Thermometers. Some common physical properties which change with temperature are the length of a rod, the volume of a liquid, the electrical resistance of a wire, or the color of a lamp filament, and, in fact, all of these changes are utilized in the construction of various types of thermometers.

We shall consider first the common *liquid-in-glass* thermometer. This instrument, illustrated in Fig. 15-1, consists of a thin walled glass bulb A, to the top of which is sealed a slender glass capillary tube B. A liquid such as mercury or colored alcohol partially fills the bulb and tube. The upper end of the tube is sealed off, and in most instances the air is removed from the space above the liquid. A scale for measuring the position of the top of the liquid column in the capillary is engraved on tube B, or a separate scale may be mounted behind the tube. As the temperature of the thermometer is increased, the volume of the liquid increases, and the volume of the

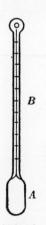

FIG. 15-1. Liquid-in-glass thermometer.

bulb and capillary increases also. If both expanded alike, the position of
the liquid in the capillary would not change, but actually the liquid expands
more rapidly than does the bulb. Hence the liquid level rises in the
capillary with increasing temperature and falls as the temperature is
lowered. This instrument, therefore, utilizes the *difference* between the
expansions of the liquid and the glass.

15-3 Temperature scales. In engineering work and in everyday life in
this country, the *fahrenheit* temperature scale is used. In scientific work
throughout the world, temperatures are expressed on the *centigrade* scale.
In defining each scale, two reference temperatures or so-called *fixed points*
are chosen, and arbitrary values are assigned to those temperatures, thus
fixing the position of the zero point and the size of the temperature unit.

One reference temperature, the *ice point*, is the temperature of a mixture
of air-saturated water and ice at a pressure of one atmosphere. The
other, the *steam* point, is the boiling temperature of pure water at a pressure of one atmosphere. On the centigrade scale, the ice point is numbered zero and the steam point, 100. On the fahrenheit scale, these temperatures are numbered 32 and 212.

With the aid of a liquid-in-glass thermometer, any other temperature, t,
is now defined (on the centigrade scale) as that temperature which produces
a relative volume change $t/100$ as great as the change between the ice and
steam points. If the capillary is of uniform cross section, this is equivalent
to the statement that the temperature is directly proportional to the length
of the liquid column above the ice point. In other words, if the position
of the top of the liquid is marked on the tube, first when the thermometer
is inserted in an ice-water mixture, and second when it is immersed in pure
water boiling at atmospheric pressure, the distance between these marks
may be divided into 100 equal parts and these divisions numbered from
zero to 100. The temperature interval corresponding to each of the divisions is called one centigrade degree, and the numbering may be extended
above 100 and below zero. The fahrenheit scale is obtained in a similar
way, by dividing the length of the column between ice and steam points
into 180 divisions, and extending the scale in either direction.

Since the same temperature interval is divided into 100 degrees on the
centigrade scale and 180 degrees on the fahrenheit scale, the temperature
range corresponding to one centigrade degree is $\frac{180}{100}$, or $\frac{9}{5}$ as great as that
corresponding to one fahrenheit degree.

The zero point on the fahrenheit scale is obviously 32 fahrenheit degrees
below the ice point. Temperatures below the zero of either scale are considered negative. The relation between the scales is best kept in mind

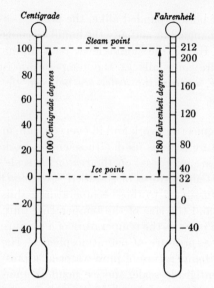

Fig. 15-2.   Relation between centigrade and fahrenheit scale.

by a diagram such as that of Fig. 15-2.

Note. Suppose the temperature of a beaker of water is raised from 20° C to 30° C, through a temperature interval of 10 centigrade degrees. It is desirable to distinguish between such a temperature interval and the actual temperature of 10 degrees above the centigrade zero. Hence we shall use the phrase "10 degrees centigrade," or "10° C," when referring to an *actual temperature*, and "10 centigrade degrees," or "10 C°" to mean a temperature *interval*. Thus there is an interval of 10 centigrade degrees between 20 degrees centigrade and 30 degrees centigrade.

The following process of reasoning may be used to convert a temperature expressed on one scale to its value on the other scale. A temperature of 30° C, for instance, means that there is an interval of 30 centigrade degrees between this temperature and the ice point. Since 1 C° = $\frac{9}{5}$ F° (*not* 1° C = $\frac{9}{5}$ °F), 30 C° = 30 × $\frac{9}{5}$ = 54 F°. Hence this temperature lies 54 fahrenheit degrees above the ice point. Since the temperature of the ice point is 32° F, the temperature corresponding to 30° C is 54 + 32, or 86° F. It will be left as an exercise to show that the reasoning above leads to the following relations

$$t_F = \tfrac{9}{5} t_C + 32, \quad t_C = \tfrac{5}{9}(t_F - 32),$$

where t_F and t_C refer to the same temperature on the fahrenheit and centigrade scales respectively. What is the relation between a given temperature *interval* on the fahrenheit and centigrade scales?

There is, of course, no reason why the numbering of either scale cannot be extended indefinitely both above and below zero. We shall see later however, that both theory and experiment show that there is a limit to the *lowest* temperature which can ever be attained, although there is no theoretical limit to the highest possible temperature. This lowest attainable temperature is known as *absolute* zero, and its location is at −273.2° C, or in round numbers, −273° C. For some purposes, it is found convenient to use a temperature scale whose zero point is at the absolute zero. Temperatures on this scale are called absolute temperatures, and both fahrenheit and centigrade absolute scales are used. The centigrade absolute is also called the Kelvin scale, in honor of Lord Kelvin who first suggested its use.   Temperatures on the Kelvin scale are numerically 273 degrees larger than those on the centigrade scale, so the temperature of the ice point is 273° K and that of the steam point is 373° K.

The temperature of absolute zero on the fahrenheit scale is $-460°$ F, and temperatures on the fahrenheit absolute scale are numerically 460° larger than on the fahrenheit scale.   The temperature of the ice point is thus 492° fahrenheit absolute, and that of the steam point is 672° fahrenheit absolute.

15-4 Other methods of thermometry. Mercury freezes at $-40°$C, and its vapor pressure becomes unduly high at temperatures much above 360° C.   Hence the mercury-in-glass thermometer is limited to this temperature range.   The lower range of liquid-in-glass thermometers can be extended by the use of liquids such as alcohol or pentane, which freeze at $-130°$ C and $-200°$ C respectively.

The *resistance thermometer* makes use of the fact that the electrical resistance of metals increases with increasing temperature.   The thermometer itself consists of a fine wire, usually of platinum, wound on a mica frame and enclosed in a thin-walled silver tube for protection.   Copper wires lead from the thermometer unit to a resistance measuring device which may be located at any convenient point.   Since resistance may be measured with a high degree of precision, the resistance thermometer is one of the most precise instruments for the measurement of temperature, a precision of 0.001° C being attainable.   The range of a platinum resistance thermometer is from the lowest attainable temperature to 1760° C, the melting point of platinum.

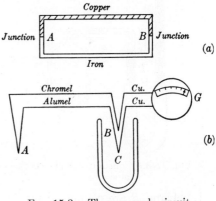

The *thermocouple* consists of an electrical circuit such as that shown in Fig. 15-3(a).   When wires of any two unlike metals are joined so as to form a complete circuit, it is found

FIG. 15-3.   Thermocouple circuit.

that an electromotive force exists in the circuit whenever the junctions A and B are at different temperatures.   The emf, for any given pair of metals, depends on the difference in temperature between the junctions. The thermocouple may be used as a thermometer by placing one junction in contact with the body whose temperature is to be measured, keeping the other junction at some known temperature (usually 0° C), and meas-

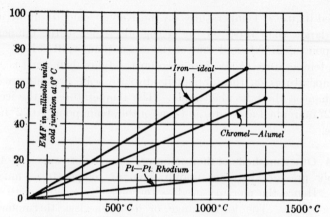

Fig. 15-4.   Emf's of some common thermocouples.

uring the emf.   The usual thermocouple circuit is shown in Fig. 15-3(b).
Junctions B and C are kept at 0° C by ice and water in a Dewar flask, and
junction A is placed in contact with the body whose temperature is to be
measured.   The emf is read on galvanometer G.   Fig. 15-4 shows the emf's
developed by some of the pairs of metals commonly used in thermocouples,

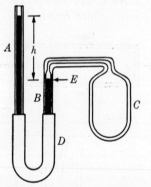

Fig. 15-5.   Constant volume gas thermometer.

for various temperatures of the "hot
junction," when the "cold junction"
is at 0° C.

The *constant volume gas thermometer*, shown in Fig. 15-5, makes
use of the pressure changes of a gas
kept at constant volume.   The gas,
usually hydrogen or helium, is contained in bulb C, and the pressure
exerted by it can be measured by the
open tube mercury manometer.   As
the temperature of the gas is increased, it expands, forcing the mercury down in tube B and up in tube
A. A and B are connected by the flexible rubber tube D, and by raising
A the mercury level in B may be brought back to the reference mark E.
The gas is thus kept at constant volume.

Any type of thermometer, such as a liquid-in-glass thermometer, a
resistance thermometer, a thermocouple or a gas thermometer may be
used to establish a scale of temperature.   That is, $t°$ C is defined for any
one thermometer as that temperature which produces $t/100$ as great a
change in the physical property used by that particular thermometer, as

the change occurring between 0° C and 100° C. The temperature scales of different kinds of thermometers do not agree. That is, liquid-in-glass thermometers filled with different liquids do not agree among themselves except at the fixed points of 0° C and 100° C, nor do any of the liquid-in-glass scales agree with the resistance thermometer scales, and so on. The least variation is found among gas thermometers using different kinds of gas, and by applying certain corrections which are beyond the scope of this book, it is possible to bring all gas thermometers into agreement. Furthermore, it can be shown that such corrected temperatures agree with the Kelvin temperature scale. The differences between the gas thermometer scale and other scales is not large and for many purposes can be neglected. Some typical values are given in Table 15-1.

TABLE 15-1

COMPARISON OF CONSTANT-VOLUME HYDROGEN THERMOMETER
WITH OTHER THERMOMETERS

Constant volume hydrogen thermometer	Mercury-in-glass thermometer	Platinum resistance thermometer	Platinum-pt-rhodium thermocouple
0° C	0° C	0° C	0° C
20	20.091	20.240	20.150
40	40.111	40.360	40.297
60	60.086	60.360	60.293
80	80.041	80.240	80.147
100	100	100	100

The *optical pyrometer*, illustrated in Fig. 15-6, consists essentially of a telescope, in the tube of which is mounted a filter A of red glass and a small electric lamp bulb B. When the pyrometer is directed toward a furnace, an observer looking through the telescope sees the dark lamp filament against the bright background of the furnace. The lamp filament is connected to a battery C and a rheostat D. By turning the rheostat knob the current in the filament, and hence its brightness, may be gradually increased until the brightness of the filament just matches the brightness of the background. From previous calibration of the instrument at known temperatures, the scale of the ammeter E in the

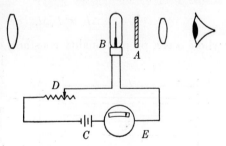

FIG. 15-6.   Principle of the optical pyrometer.

circuit may be marked to read the unknown temperature directly. Since no part of the instrument needs to come into contact with the hot body, the optical pyrometer may be used at temperatures above the melting points of resistance thermometers or of thermocouples.

The melting and boiling points of a large number of substances have been carefully measured and tabulated and these temperatures may now be used in the calibration of any type of thermometer. A number of such temperatures are listed in Table 15-2.

TABLE 15-2

TABLE OF FIXED POINTS

Hydrogen boiling point..........................	−252.78°C
Nitrogen boiling point...........................	−195.81
Mercury freezing point..........................	−38.87
Ice point.......................................	0.00
Steam point....................................	100.00
Sulfur boiling point.............................	444.60
Silver melting point.............................	960.5
Gold melting point..............................	1063.0

15-5 Linear expansion. With a few exceptions, the dimensions of all substances increase as the temperature of the substance is increased. If a given specimen is in the form of a rod or cable, one is usually interested in its change of *length* with changes in temperature. (The change in cross section is so small it may be neglected.) Fig. 15-7 represents a rod whose length is L_0 at some reference temperature t_0, and whose length is L at some higher temperature t. The difference $L - L_0 = \Delta L$ is the amount the rod has expanded on heating. It is found experimentally that the increase in length, ΔL, is proportional to the original length L_0, and very nearly proportional to the increase in temperature, $t - t_0$ or Δt. That is,

$$\Delta L \propto L_0 \Delta t, \quad \text{or} \quad \Delta L = \alpha L_0 \Delta t, \tag{15-1}$$

where α is a proportionality constant, different for different materials, and is called the *coefficient of linear expansion.*

Eq. (15-1) may be solved for α and written

$$\alpha = \frac{\Delta L}{L_0} \frac{1}{\Delta t}. \tag{15-2}$$

FIG. 15-7. Linear expansion.

The coefficient of linear expansion of a substance may therefore be described as the fractional change in length per degree rise in temperature. Another useful relation is obtained by replacing ΔL by $L - L_0$ and solving for L.

$$L = L_0(1 + \alpha \Delta t). \qquad\qquad (15\text{-}3)$$

Since L_0, L, and ΔL are all expressed in the same unit, the units of α are "reciprocal degrees" (centigrade or fahrenheit). Thus the coefficient of linear expansion of copper is written

$$\alpha = 14 \times 10^{-6} \text{ per centigrade degree}$$

or

$$\alpha = 14 \times 10^{-6} \text{ (C°)}^{-1}.$$

This means that a copper rod one centimeter long at 0° C, increases in length by 0.000014 cm when heated to 1° C. A rod one foot long at 0° C increases by 0.000014 ft, and so on.

Since the fahrenheit degree is only $\frac{5}{9}$ as large as the centigrade degree, coefficients of expansion per fahrenheit degree are $\frac{5}{9}$ as large as their values on the centigrade scale.

Example: An iron steam pipe is 200 ft long at 0° C. What will be its increase in length when heated to 100° C? $\alpha = 10 \times 10^{-6}$ per centigrade degree.

$L_0 = 200$ ft, $\alpha = 10 \times 10^{-6}$ per C°, $t = 100°$ C, $t_0 = 0°$ C.

$$\begin{aligned} \text{Increase in length} = \Delta L &= \alpha L_0 \Delta t \\ &= (10 \times 10^{-6})(200)(100) \\ &= 0.20 \text{ ft.} \end{aligned}$$

The coefficient of expansion of a substance in the form of a rod is measured by making two fine lines on the rod near its ends, and measuring the displacement of each line with a measuring microscope while the temperature of the rod is changed by a measured amount.

The *bimetallic* element is a device which has come into wide use in recent years, both as a thermometer and as a part of many thermostatic controls. It consists of two thin flat strips of different metals, welded or riveted together as in Fig. 15-8(a). If metal A has a larger coefficient of expansion than metal B, the compound strip, if originally straight, bends into a curve when heated as shown in Fig. 15-8(b). The transverse motion of the end of the strip is very much larger than the increase in length of either metal.

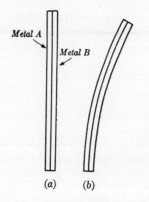

Metal A

Metal B

(a)   (b)

Fig. 15-8.   The bimetallic element.

When used as a thermostat, one end of the strip is fixed and the motion of the other end is made to open or close an electrical control circuit. The common oven thermometer consists of a bimetallic strip coiled in a helix. With changes in temperature the helix winds up or unwinds, and this motion is transmitted to a pivoted pointer which moves over a calibrated scale. Because of lost motion and friction, such thermometers are not precision instruments.

TABLE 15-3

COEFFICIENTS OF LINEAR EXPANSION

Substance	α (C°)$^{-1}$
Aluminum	24×10^{-6}
Brass	20
Copper	14
Glass	4–9
Steel	12
Invar	0.9
Quartz (fused)	0.4
Zinc	26

TABLE 15-4

COEFFICIENTS OF CUBICAL EXPANSION

Substance	β (C°)$^{-1}$
Alcohol, ethyl	0.745×10^{-3}
Carbon Disulphide	1.140
Glycerin	0.485
Mercury	0.182
Petroleum	0.899

15-6 Surface and volume expansion.   When a plate or sheet of material is heated, both the length and breadth of the plate increase. Consider a rectangular plate whose length and breadth at temperature t_0 are L_0 and b_0 respectively. When heated to a temperature t, these dimensions become

$$L = L_0(1 + \alpha \Delta t),$$

and

$$b = b_0(1 + \alpha \Delta t).$$

The original area of the plate was

$$A_0 = L_0 b_0$$

and the area after heating is

$$A = Lb = L_0 b_0 (1 + \alpha \Delta t)(1 + \alpha \Delta t)$$
$$= A_0 (1 + 2\alpha \Delta t + (\alpha \Delta t)^2).$$

But since α is a small quantity, α^2 will be extremely small and the term $(\alpha \Delta t)^2$ may be neglected. Hence

$$A = A_0 (1 + 2\alpha \Delta t).$$

If we now define a *surface* coefficient of expansion γ so that

$$A = A_0 (1 + \gamma \Delta t), \qquad (15\text{-}4)$$

it follows that

$$\boxed{\gamma = 2\alpha,}$$

and the coefficient of surface expansion is twice the coefficient of linear expansion. Although derived for the special case of a rectangular plate, the result holds for a plate of any shape whatever.

If the plate contains a hole, the area *of the hole* expands at the same rate as does the surrounding material. This remains true even if the hole becomes so large that the "plate" is reduced to nothing but a rim around the hole. Thus the area of the "hole" enclosed by a steel wagon tire expands at the same rate as would a disk of this size, if constructed of the same kind of steel as is the rim.

By considering a solid block of material in the form of a rectangular parallelepiped whose dimensions at t_0 are L_0, b_0, and c_0, it is easy to show by the same type of reasoning that

$$V = V_0 (1 + 3\alpha \Delta t) = V_0 (1 + \beta \Delta t) \qquad (15\text{-}5)$$

where V is the volume at the temperature t, V_0 is the volume at t_0, and

$$\boxed{\beta = 3\alpha}$$

is the *volume* coefficient or *cubical* coefficient of expansion. This equation holds regardless of the shape of the body.

It is also true that the volume enclosed by a solid, such as the volume of a tank, a flask, or thermometer bulb, expands at the same rate as would a solid body of the same material as that of which the walls are composed.

Eq. (15-5) may also be used to compute the expansion of a liquid. The linear and surface coefficients of expansion of a liquid are of little significance.

Example: The volume of the bulb of a mercury thermometer at $0°C$ is V_0 and the cross section of the capillary is A_0. The linear coefficient of expansion of the glass is α_G per $C°$ and the cubical coefficient of expansion of mercury is β_M per $C°$. If the mercury just fills the bulb at $0°$ C, what is the length of the mercury column in the capillary at a temperature of $t°$ C?

The volume of the bulb at a temperature t is

$$V = V_0(1 + \beta_G t),$$

where $\beta_G = 3\alpha_G$ is the cubical coefficient of expansion of the glass.

The volume of the mercury at a temperature t is

$$V_M = V_0(1 + \beta_M t).$$

The volume of mercury that has been expelled from the bulb is the difference between these, or

$$V_0(1 + \beta_M t) - V_0(1 + \beta_G t) = V_0 t(\beta_M - \beta_G).$$

This volume is also equal to the length l of the mercury column multiplied by the cross section A of the capillary, where

$$A = A_0(1 + 2\alpha_G t).$$

Table 15-3 shows that the linear coefficient of expansion of glass is of the order of 5×10^{-6} per $C°$. Hence even if t is as great as $300°$ C the term $2\alpha_G t$ is only 0.003. It may therefore be neglected in comparison with unity, which is equivalent to considering the cross section of the capillary constant. Then

$$lA_0 = V_0 t(\beta_M - \beta_G)$$

and

$$l = \frac{V_0}{A_0}(\beta_M - \beta_G)t.$$

The length of the mercury column is therefore proportional to the temperature and to the difference between the cubical coefficients of expansion of mercury and the glass of which the thermometer is constructed.

Water, in the temperature range from $0°$ C to $4°$ C, *decreases* in volume with increasing temperature, contrary to the behavior of most substances. That is, between $0°$ C and $4°$ C the coefficient of expansion of water is *negative*. Above $4°$ C, water expands when heated. Since the volume of a given mass of water is smaller at $4°$ C than at any other temperature, the density of water is a maximum at $4°$ C. This behaviour of water is the reason why lakes and ponds freeze first at their upper surface. Table 15-5 illustrates the anomalous expansion of water.

TABLE 15-5

DENSITY AND VOLUME OF WATER

$t°$ C	Density—gm/cm³	Volume of 1 gram, in cm³
0	0.99987	1.00013
2	0.99997	1.00003
4	1.00000	1.00000
6	0.99997	1.00003
10	0.99973	1.00027
20	0.99823	1.00177
50	0.98807	1.01207
75	0.97489	1.02576
100	0.95838	1.04343

15-7 Thermal stresses. If the ends of a rod are rigidly fixed so as to prevent expansion or contraction and the temperature of the rod is changed, tensile or compressive stresses, called *thermal stresses*, will be set up in the rod. These stresses may become very large, sufficiently so to stress the rod beyond its elastic limit or even beyond its breaking strength. Hence in the design of any structure which is subject to changes in temperature, some provision must, in general, be made for expansion. In a long steam pipe this is accomplished by the insertion of expansion joints or a section of pipe in the form of a U. In bridges, one end may be rigidly fastened to its abutment while the other rests on rollers.

It is a simple matter to compute the thermal stress set up in a rod which is not free to expand or contract. Suppose that a rod at a temperature t has its ends rigidly fastened, and that while they are thus held the temperature is reduced to a lower value, t_0.

The fractional change in length if the rod were free to contract would be

$$\frac{\Delta L}{L_0} = \alpha(t - t_0) = \alpha \Delta t. \tag{15-6}$$

Since the rod is not free to contract, the tension must increase by a sufficient amount to produce the same fractional change in length. But from the definition of Young's modulus (see page 193),

$$Y = \frac{F/A}{\Delta L/L_0},$$

and hence

$$F = AY \frac{\Delta L}{L_0}.$$

Introducing the expression for $\dfrac{\Delta L}{L_0}$ from Eq. (15-6), we have

$$F = A Y \alpha \Delta t, \qquad\qquad (15\text{-}7)$$

which gives the tension F in the rod. The *stress* in the rod is

$$\frac{F}{A} = Y \alpha \Delta t. \qquad\qquad (15\text{-}8)$$

Problems — Chapter 15

15-1. (a) What is the melting point of silver in degrees fahrenheit? (See Table 15-2.) (b) What is the coefficient of linear expansion of copper in $(F°)^{-1}$? (c) What is the coefficient of volume expansion of copper in $(C°)^{-1}$? (d) At what temperature do the fahrenheit and centigrade scales coincide?

15-2. The pendulum shaft of a clock is of aluminum. What is the fractional change in length of the shaft when it is cooled from 75°F to 45°F?

15-3. The length of Technology Bridge is about 2000 ft. Find the difference between its length on a winter day when the temperature is −20°F, and a summer day when the temperature is 100°F. Use the coefficient of expansion of steel.

15-4. A surveyor's 100-ft steel tape is correct at a temperature of 65°F. The distance between two points, as measured by this tape on a day when the temperature is 95°F, is 86.57 ft. What is the true distance between the points?

15-5. Give an example of a material having a negative coefficient of volume expansion.

15-6. A glass flask whose volume is exactly 1000 cm³ at 0°C is filled level full of mercury at this temperature. When flask and mercury are heated to 100°C, 15.2 cm³ of mercury overflow. If the cubical coefficient of expansion of mercury is 0.000182 per centigrade degree, compute the linear coefficient of expansion of the glass.

15-7. Steel rails 120 ft long are laid with their ends in contact on a day when the temperature is 110°F. What length gap will there be between rails on a day when the temperature is −20°F?

15-8. (a) A steel wire which is 10 ft long at 20°C is found to increase in length by ¾ inch when heated to 520°C. Compute its coefficient of linear expansion. (b) Find the stress in the wire if it is stretched taut at 520° and cooled to 20° without being allowed to contract.

15-9. A wire 60 cm long is bent into a circular ring, having a gap of 1.0 cm. The temperature of the wire is increased uniformly by 100°C. At the new temperature the gap is found to be 1.002 cm. What is the linear temperature coefficient of expansion of the wire? Assume no stresses within the wire before or after heating.

15-10. A watch with a balance wheel in the form of an annular brass ring (neglect the effect of the spokes) keeps correct time at a temperature of 30°C. By how many seconds per day will it be in error at a temperature of 15°C? Will it gain or lose?

15-11. A slender steel rod oscillates as a physical pendulum about a horizontal axis through one end. If the rod is 8 ft long at 30°C, compute the change in its period when the temperature is decreased to 0°C.

15-12. A steel rod 1.5 cm² in cross section is 70 cm long at 20°C. If it is heated to 520°C and cooled to 20°C without being allowed to contract, compute the stress in the rod.

15-13. The cross section of a steel rod is 1.5 in². What is the least force that will prevent it from contracting while cooling from 520°C to 20°C?

15-14. What hydrostatic pressure is necessary to prevent a copper block from expanding when its temperature is increased from 20°C to 30°C?

15-15. A steel bomb is filled with water at 10°C. If the whole is heated to 75°C and no water is allowed to escape, compute the increase in pressure in the bomb. Assume the bomb to be sufficiently strong so that it is not stretched by the increased pressure.

15-16. Steel railroad rails 60 ft long are laid on a winter day when the temperature is 20°F. (a) How much space must be left between rails if they are to just touch on a summer day when the temperature is 110°F? (b) If the rails were originally laid in contact, what would be the stress in them on a summer day when the temperature is 110°F?

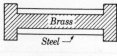

FIG. 15-9

15-17. A heavy brass bar has projections at its ends, as in Fig. 15-9. Two fine steel wires fastened between the projections are just taut (zero tension), when the whole system is at 0°C. What is the tensile stress in the steel wires when the temperature of the system is raised to 300°C? Make any simplifying assumptions you think are justified, but state what they are.

15-18. A liquid is enclosed in a metal cylinder provided with a piston of the same metal. The system is originally at atmospheric pressure and at a temperature of 80°C. The piston is forced down until the pressure on the liquid is increased by 100 atm, and it is then clamped in this position. Find the new temperature at which the pressure of the liquid is again 1 atmosphere. Assume that the cylinder is sufficiently strong so that its volume is not altered by changes in pressure, but only by changes in temperature. Compressibility of liquid $(k) = 50 \times 10^{-6}$ atm^{-1}. Cubical coefficient of expansion of liquid $(\beta) = 5.3 \times 10^{-4}$ °C^{-1}. Linear coefficient of expansion of metal $(\alpha) = 10 \times 10^{-6}$ °C^{-1}.

15-19. A steel rod of length 40 cm and a copper rod of length 36 cm, both of the same diameter, are placed end to end between two rigid supports, with no initial stress in the rods. The temperature of the rods is now raised 50 C°. What is the stress in either rod?

CHAPTER 16

QUANTITY OF HEAT

16-1 Heat, a form of energy. Heat was formerly thought to be an invisible weightless fluid called *caloric*, which was produced when a substance burned and which could be transmitted by conduction from one body to another. The abandonment of the caloric theory was a part of the general development of physics during the 18th and 19th centuries. The two men who were probably chiefly responsible for the views we hold today were Count Rumford (1753–1814) (a native of Woburn, Mass.) and Sir James Prescott Joule.

Rumford was engaged in supervising the boring of cannon for the government of Bavaria. To prevent overheating, the bore of the cannon was kept filled with water, and as this boiled away during the boring process the supply had to be continually replenished. It was admitted that caloric had to be supplied to water in order to boil it, and the continual production of caloric was explained by the hypothesis that when matter was more finely subdivided (as in the process of boring) its capacity for retaining caloric grew smaller and the caloric thus released was what caused the water to boil.

Rumford noted, however, that the cooling water continued to boil away even when his boring tools became so dull that they were no longer cutting. That is, even a dull boring tool was apparently an inexhaustible supply of caloric *as long as mechanical work was being done to rotate the tool*.

Now one of the features which justifies our acceptance of many abstract ideas in physics is that they obey a "conservation principle." Here was a process in which *two* quantities failed to be conserved. Mechanical energy was not conserved since work was continually being expended, and caloric was not conserved since it was continually being created. Although Rumford did not express his ideas in just this way, he saw the opportunity to eliminate two cases of nonconservation and at the same time to extend the principle of conservation of energy as it was then understood. He asserted that what had formerly been thought a separate entity, namely caloric, was in reality merely energy in another form. The process was not the continual disappearance of one thing and the appearance of another, but merely the transformation of energy from one form to another. As we would say today, mechanical energy was continually being transformed into heat, the process being one example of conservation of energy.

Rumford made some measurements of the quantities of work done and of cooling water boiled away, but his experiments were not of great precision. When Joule, in the period from 1843 to 1878, showed that whenever a given quantity of mechanical energy was converted to heat the *same* quantity of heat was always developed, the equivalence of heat and work as two forms of energy was definitely established.

There are, of course, processes for whose explanation the caloric theory is entirely satisfactory. When heat flows from one body to another by conduction, or when substances at different temperatures are mixed in a calorimeter, heat is conserved, and for such processes the caloric theory would serve perfectly well.

16-2 Quantity of heat. Heat, like mechanical energy, is an intangible thing and a unit of heat is not something that can be preserved in a Standards laboratory. The quantity of heat involved in a process is measured by some change which accompanies the process, and a unit of heat is defined as the heat necessary to produce some standard, agreed-on change. Three such units are in common use, the kilogram-calorie, the gram-calorie, and the British thermal unit (Btu).

One kilogram-calorie is the quantity of heat which must be supplied to one kilogram of water to raise its temperature through one centigrade degree.

One gram-calorie is the quantity of heat which must be supplied to one gram of water to raise its temperature through one centigrade degree.

One Btu is the quantity of heat which must be supplied to one pound of water to raise its temperature through one fahrenheit degree.[1]

Evidently, 1 kilogram-calorie = 1000 gram-calories.

Since 454 gm = 1 lb, and since 1 F° = $\frac{5}{9}$ C°, the Btu may be defined as the quantity of heat which must be supplied to 454 gm (.454 kgm) of water to raise its temperature through $\frac{5}{9}$ C°, which is 454 × $\frac{5}{9}$ = 252 gm-cal or 0.252 kgm-cal.   Hence

$$1 \text{ Btu} = 252 \text{ gm-cal} = 0.252 \text{ kgm-cal}.$$

The gram-calorie is much more widely used in physics and chemistry than is the kilogram-calorie, and from now on, unless stated otherwise, we shall use the term calorie to mean gram-calorie.

---

[1] In this part of the subject we shall depart from the English gravitational system of units which we used throughout mechanics, and adopt as a mass unit the *mass of the standard pound*. This unit is also called one pound, and is equal to a mass of 454 grams, or (about) $\frac{1}{32}$ slug. Also, for simplicity, we shall confine metric units chiefly to the cgs system.

The heat units here defined vary somewhat with the location of the degree, i.e., whether it is from 0° to 1°, 47° to 48°, etc. It is generally agreed to use the temperature interval from 14.5° C to 15.5° C (the "15° calorie"), and in English units to use the temperature interval from 63° F to 64° F. For most purposes this variation is small enough to be neglected.

It is essential that the distinction between "quantity of heat" and "temperature" shall be clearly understood. The terms are commonly misused in everyday life. Suppose that two pans, one containing a small and the other a large amount of water, are placed over identical gas burners and heated for the same length of time. It is obvious that at the end of this time the temperature of the small amount of water will have risen higher than that of the large amount. In this instance, equal quantities of heat have been supplied to each pan of water, but the increases in temperature are not equal.

On the other hand, suppose the two pans are both initially at a temperature of 60° F and that both are to be heated to 212° F. It is evident that more heat must be supplied to the pan containing the larger amount of water. The temperature change is the same for both but the quantities of heat supplied are very different.

We shall represent a quantity of heat by the letter Q.

16-3 Internal energy. A body may be warmed either by placing it in contact with a second body at a higher temperature, or by doing mechanical work on the body. For example, the air in a bicycle pump becomes hotter when the piston is pushed down, although it could also be heated by placing it in a furnace.

If one were given a sample of hot air, it would be impossible to tell by any tests whether it had been heated by compression or by heat flow from a hotter body. This raises the question as to whether one is justified in speaking of the "heat in a body," since the present state of the body may have been brought about either by adding heat to it or by doing work on it. We shall show later that the proper term to use is "internal energy," and that the expression "heat energy of a body" is meaningless.

From the atomic point of view, the internal energy of a body is the sum total of the kinetic and potential energies of its atoms, apart from any kinetic or potential energy of the body as a whole. Not enough is known at present about the atomic structure of matter to be able to express internal energies wholly in terms of an atomic model. To a first approximation, the internal energy of a gas at low pressure may be identified with the aggregate kinetic energy of its atoms.

Even though the details of the atomic picture of matter are not fully understood, we do have definite evidence that atomic energies and velocities, whether in a solid, liquid, or gas, increase with increasing temperature. Such statements as "the heat in a body is the energy of motion of its atoms" should, however, be avoided.

16-4 The mechanical equivalent of heat. Energy in mechanical form is usually expressed in ergs, joules, or foot-pounds; energy in the form of heat is expressed in calories or Btu. The relative magnitudes of the "heat units" and the "mechanical units" can be found by an experiment in which a measured quantity of mechanical energy is completely converted into a measured quantity of heat. The first accurate experiments were performed by Joule, using an apparatus in which falling weights rotated a set of paddles in a container of water. The energy transformed was computed in mechanical units from a knowledge of the weights and their height of fall, and in heat units from a measurement of the mass of water and its rise in temperature. In more recent methods, which are also more precise, electrical energy is converted to heat in a resistance wire immersed in water. The best results to date give:

$$778 \text{ ft-lb} = 1 \text{ Btu.}$$
$$4.186 \text{ joules} = 1 \text{ gm-cal.}$$
$$4186 \text{ joules} = 1 \text{ kgm-cal.}$$

That is, 778 ft-lb of mechanical energy, when converted to heat, will raise the temperature of 1 lb of water through 1 F°, etc.

These relations are often expressed by the statement that *the mechanical equivalent of heat* is 4.186 joules/gm-cal, or 778 ft-lb/Btu. The phraseology is a carry-over from the early days when the equivalence of mechanical energy and heat was being established.

The precise value of the mechanical equivalent of heat depends on the particular temperature interval used in the definition of the calorie or Btu. To avoid this confusion, an International commission has agreed to *define* 1 kgm-cal as *exactly* 1/860 kilowatt-hour. Then by definition, 1 gm-cal = 4.18605 joules and 1 Btu = 778.26 ft-lb. It follows that 1 Btu = 251.996 gm-cal.

16-5 Heat capacity. Specific heat. Materials differ from one another in the quantity of heat required to produce a given elevation of temperature in a given mass. Suppose that a quantity of heat Q is supplied to a given body, resulting in a temperature rise Δt. The ratio of the heat supplied to the corresponding temperature rise is called the *heat capacity* of the body.

$$\text{heat capacity} = \frac{Q}{\Delta t}. \tag{16-1}$$

Heat capacities are ordinarily expressed in calories per centigrade degree, or Btu per fahrenheit degree. If we set $\Delta t = 1$ degree in Eq. (16-1), it will be seen that the heat capacity of a body is numerically equal to the quantity of heat which must be supplied to it to increase its temperature by one degree.

To obtain a figure which is characteristic of the material of which a body is composed, the *specific heat capacity*, abbreviated *specific heat*, of a material is defined as the *heat capacity per unit mass* of a body composed of the material. We shall represent specific heat capacity by the letter c.

$$c = \frac{\text{Heat capacity}}{\text{mass}} = \frac{Q/\Delta t}{m} = \frac{Q}{m\Delta t}. \tag{16-2}$$

Specific heat capacity is expressed in calories per gram-centigrade degree, or Btu per pound-fahrenheit degree.

The specific heat capacity of a material is numerically equal to the quantity of heat which must be supplied to *unit mass* of the material to increase its temperature through 1 degree. The specific heat capacities of a few common materials are listed in Table 16-1.

It follows from Eq. (16-2) that the heat which must be supplied to a body of mass m, whose specific heat capacity is c, to increase its temperature through an interval Δt, is

$$Q = mc\Delta t = mc(t_2 - t_1). \tag{16-3}$$

Strictly speaking, Eq. (16-2) defines the *average* specific heat capacity

TABLE 16-1

Substance	Specific heat	Temperature interval
Aluminum	0.217	17–100° C
Brass	0.094	15–100
Copper	0.093	15–100
Glass	0.199	20–100
Ice	0.55	−10–0
Iron	0.113	18–100
Lead	0.031	20–100
Mercury	0.033	0–100
Silver	0.056	15–100

over the temperature range Δt. It is found, however, that the quantity of heat required to raise the temperature of a material through a small interval varies with the location of the interval in the temperature scale. The *true* specific heat capacity of a material at any temperature is defined from Eq. (16-2) by considering Δt to be a very small temperature rise.

At ordinary temperatures, and over temperature intervals which are not too great, specific heats may be considered constant. At extremely low temperatures, approaching absolute zero, all specific heats decrease and for certain substances approach zero.

It should be pointed out that the significance of the word "capacity" in "heat capacity" is not the same as when one speaks of the "capacity" of a bucket. The bucket can hold just so much water and no more, while heat can be added to a body indefinitely with, of course, a corresponding rise in temperature.

For some purposes, particularly in dealing with gases, it is more convenient to express specific heat capacities on the basis of one gram-atomic weight rather than one gram. It was first noted in 1819 by Dulong and Petit that the specific heat capacities of the metals, expressed in this way, were all very nearly equal to 6 cal/gm-atomic wt-C°. This fact is known as the *Dulong and Petit law*.

16-6 Calorimetry. The term calorimetry relates to the measurement of quantities of heat. Two types of calorimeter, the *water calorimeter* and the *continuous flow calorimeter*, will be described.

The water calorimeter in its simple form consists of a thin walled metal can A, (Fig. 16-1), whose capacity is about two liters, and whose outer surface is nickel plated. The can contains a measured quantity of water, and is provided with a cover through which passes thermometer B. Heat losses are further reduced by surrounding the can with the heat-insulating jacket C. If the thermometer is read before and after an unknown quantity of heat Q is introduced into the calorimeter, Q may be found from the measured rise in temperature.

The water calorimeter may be used to measure specific heat as follows: a sample of the material whose

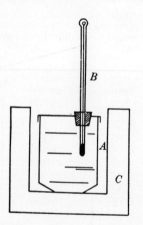

Fig. 16-1. The water calorimeter.

specific heat is desired is heated in a furnace or steam bath to a known temperature, say t_s. Let the mass of the sample be m_s and its specific heat c_s.

The water in the calorimeter is thoroughly stirred and its temperature is measured. The sample is then quickly transferred to the calorimeter, the water is again thoroughly stirred, and the new temperature of the water is recorded. Let t_1 and t_2 be the initial and final temperatures of the water, m_w the mass of the water, m_c the mass of the calorimeter can and c_c its specific heat.

If no heat is lost from the calorimeter during the experiment, the heat given up by the sample in cooling from t_s to t_2 must equal the heat gained by the water and the calorimeter can. Hence

$$m_s c_s (t_s - t_2) = m_w \times 1 (t_2 - t_1) + m_c c_c (t_2 - t_1)$$
$$= (m_w + m_c c_c)(t_2 - t_1)$$

and c_s may be found, since the other factors are known.

The effect of the heat capacity of the calorimeter, $m_c c_c$, is evidently equivalent to increasing the mass of the water by an amount $m_c c_c$ and using a calorimeter of zero heat capacity. The product $m_c c_c$ is called the *water equivalent* of the calorimeter.

Actually the calorimeter will gain (or lose) heat from its surroundings during an experiment unless special precautions are taken. One way of minimizing the heat transfer is to start with the calorimeter somewhat cooler than its surroundings and finish with its temperature the same amount higher than the surroundings. Then the heat gained during the first part of the experiment offsets the heat lost in the latter part. Another method (the so-called "adiabatic jacket") is to heat the jacket by an electric heating coil so that its temperature rises at the same rate as does that of the calorimeter. If both temperatures are always equal there will be no gain or loss of heat.

It should be noted that this method of measuring specific heat gives only the *average* specific heat over the temperature range from t_s to t_2. Much more elaborate apparatus is required to measure the true specific heat at any desired temperature.

The *continuous flow* calorimeter, as used to measure the mechanical equivalent of heat, is illustrated in Fig. 16-2. A continuous stream of water enters the apparatus at A, flows through the tube B around the resistance wire C, and leaves at D. Thermometers T_1 and T_2 read the temperatures t_1 and t_2 at inlet and outlet, and the electrical power expended is measured by the ammeter and voltmeter.

To use the calorimeter, the water is started flowing and the heating current is turned on. Thermometers T_1 and T_2 are read at intervals of

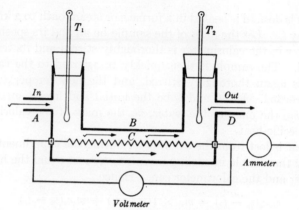

FIG. 16-2. A continuous flow calorimeter.

say, one minute, and their temperatures recorded. After sufficient time has elapsed, both thermometer readings become constant. Of course the temperature t_2 at the outlet is higher than the temperature t_1 at the inlet. When this steady state has been reached the apparatus itself is absorbing no heat, since its temperature remains constant. Heat is therefore being carried away by the flowing water at exactly the same rate as it is developed by the heating coil.

If then the mass of water passing through the calorimeter in a certain time is found, usually by catching the water in a beaker placed below the outlet, the quantity of heat developed can be computed from the rise in temperature of this mass of water. The energy input in the same time can be found from the ammeter and voltmeter readings.

A modified form of continuous flow calorimeter is used to measure the heat of combustion of gas, the flowing water being heated by a gas flame instead of an electrical heater.

16-7 Heat of combustion. The heat of combustion of a substance is the quantity of heat liberated per unit mass, or per unit volume, when the substance is completely burned. Heats of combustion of solid and liquid fuels are usually expressed in Btu/lb or in cal/gm. The heat of combustion of gases is commonly expressed in Btu/ft^3. Some values are given in Table 16-2.

Heats of combustion of solid and liquid fuels are measured with a *bomb calorimeter*. A measured mass of the fuel is inserted in a strong steel bomb which is filled with oxygen under pressure to ensure complete combustion. The bomb is placed in a water calorimeter and the fuel ignited by sending a momentary electric current through a fine heater

TABLE 16-2

HEATS OF COMBUSTION

Coal gas.............................	600 Btu/ft³
Natural gas...........................	1000–2500 Btu/ft³
Coal.................................	11,000–14,000 Btu/lb
Ethyl alcohol........................	14,000 Btu/lb
Fuel oil.............................	20,000 Btu/lb

wire. From the measured temperature rise, the mass of water, and the water equivalent of calorimeter and bomb, the heat of combustion can be computed.

The heat of combustion of gaseous fuels is usually measured with a type of continuous flow calorimeter, illustrated in Fig. 16-3.

16-8 Change of phase. The term *phase* as used here relates to the fact that matter exists either as a solid, liquid or gas. Thus the chemical substance H_2O exists in the *solid phase* as ice, in the *liquid phase* as water, and in the *gaseous phase* as steam. Provided they do not decompose at high temperatures, all substances can exist in any of the

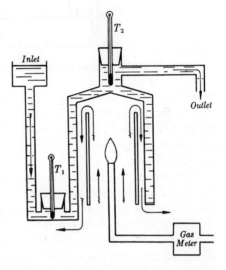

FIG. 16-3. Continuous flow calorimeter used to measure the heat of combustion of gaseous fuel.

three phases under the proper conditions of temperature and pressure. Transitions from one phase to another are accompanied by the absorption or liberation of heat and usually by a change in volume.

As an illustration, suppose that ice is taken from a refrigerator where its temperature was, say −25° C. Let the ice be crushed quickly, placed in a container, and a thermometer inserted in the mass. Imagine the container to be surrounded by a heating coil which supplies heat to the ice at a uniform rate, and suppose that no other heat reaches the ice. The temperature of the ice would be observed to increase steadily as shown by the portion of the graph (Fig. 16-4) from *a* to *b*, or until the temperature has risen to 0° C. As soon as this temperature is reached, some liquid water will be observed in the container. In other words, the ice begins to melt. The melting process is a *change of phase*, from the solid phase to the liquid phase. The thermometer, however, will show no *increase in*

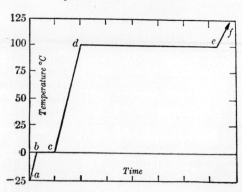

Fig. 16-4. The temperature remains constant during each change of phase.

temperature, and even though heat is being supplied at the same rate as before, the temperature will remain at 0° C until all of the ice is melted (point *c*, Fig. 16-4). (The ice and water mixture must be kept thoroughly stirred, otherwise the temperature of that part of the water closest to the heater will rise above 0° C.)

As soon as the last of the ice has melted, the temperature begins to rise again at a uniform rate, from *c* to *d*, Fig. 16-4, although this rate will be slower than that from *a* to *b* because the specific heat of water is greater than that of ice. When a temperature of 100° C is reached, (point *d*) bubbles of steam (gaseous water or water vapor) start to escape from the liquid surface, or the water begins to boil. The temperature remains constant at 100° C until all of the water has boiled away. Another change of phase has therefore taken place, from the liquid phase to the gaseous phase.

If all of the water vapor had been trapped and not allowed to diffuse away (a very large container would be needed), the heating process could be continued as from *e* to *f*. The gas would now be called "superheated steam."

Although water was chosen as an example in the process just described, the same type of curve as in Fig. 16-4 is obtained for many other substances. Some, of course, decompose before reaching a melting or boiling point, and others, such as glass or pitch, do not change state at a definite temperature but become gradually softer as their temperature is raised. Crystalline substances, such as ice, or a metal, melt at a definite temperature. Glass and pitch are actually supercooled liquids of very high viscosity.

The temperature at which a crystalline solid melts when heat is supplied to it at atmospheric pressure is called its *normal melting point,* and the temperature at which a liquid boils when heat is supplied to it at

TABLE 16-3

Substance	Normal Melting Point		Heat of Fusion		Normal Boiling Point		Heat of Vaporization	
	° C	° F	cal/gm	Btu/lb	° C	° F	cal/gm	Btu/lb
Lead...........	327	621	5.86	10.59				
Mercury	−39	−38	2.82	5.08	357	675	65	117
Nitrogen.......	−210	−346	6.09	10.95	−196	321	48	87
Oxygen........	−219	−363	3.30	5.95	−183	297	51	92
Platinum.......	1775	3232	27.2	49.0				
Silver..........	961	1762	21.1	38.0				
Sulphur........	119	246	13.2	23.8	444	831		
Water.........	0	32	79.7	144	100	212	539	970
Ethyl alcohol...	−114	−174	24.9	44.8	78	172	204	368
Sulfur dioxide..	−85.6	−122			−10	14	93	167

atmospheric pressure is called its *normal boiling point*. The quantity of heat per unit mass that must be supplied to a material at its melting point to convert it completely to a liquid at the same temperature, is called the *heat of fusion* of the material. The quantity of heat per unit mass that must be supplied to a material at its boiling point to convert it completely to a gas at the same temperature, is called the *heat of vaporization* of the material. Heats of fusion and vaporization are expressed in calories per gram, or Btu per pound. Thus the heat of fusion of ice is about 80 cal/gm or 144 Btu/lb. The heat of vaporization of water (at 100° C) is 539 cal/gm or 970 Btu/lb. Some heats of fusion and vaporization are listed in Table 16-3.

When heat is removed from a gas its temperature falls, and at the same temperature at which it boiled it returns to the liquid phase, or *condenses*. In so doing it gives up to its surroundings the same quantity of heat which was required to vaporize it. The heat so given up, per unit mass, is called the *heat of condensation* and is equal to the heat of vaporization. Similarly, a liquid returns to the solid phase, or freezes, when cooled to the temperature at which it melted, and gives up heat called *heat of solidification* exactly equal to the heat of fusion. Thus the melting point and the freezing point are at the same temperature, and the boiling point and condensation point are at the same temperature.

Whether a substance, at its melting point, is freezing or melting depends on whether heat is being supplied or removed. That is, if heat is supplied to a beaker containing both ice and water at 0° C some of the ice will melt; if heat is removed, some of the water will freeze; the temperature in either case remains at 0° C as long as both ice and water are present. If heat is *neither supplied nor removed,* no change at all takes place and the relative amounts of ice and water, and the temperature, all remain constant.

This furnishes, then, another point of view which may be taken regarding the melting point. That is, the melting (or freezing) point of a substance is *that temperature at which both the liquid and solid phases can exist together.* At any higher temperature, the substance can only be a liquid; at any lower temperature, it can only be a solid.

The general term *heat of transformation* is applied both to heats of fusion and heats of vaporization, and both are designated by the letter L. Since L represents the heat absorbed or liberated in the change of phase of unit mass, the heat Q absorbed or liberated in the change of phase of a mass m is

$$Q = mL. \tag{16-4}$$

The household steam heating system makes use of a boiling-condensing process to transfer heat from the furnace to the radiators. Each pound of water which is turned to steam in the furnace absorbs 970 Btu (the heat of vaporization of water) from the furnace, and gives up 970 Btu when it condenses in the radiators. (This figure is correct if the steam pressure is one atmosphere. It will be slightly smaller at higher pressures.) Thus the steam-heating system does not need to circulate as much water as a hot-water heating system. If water leaves a hot-water furnace at 140° F and returns at 100° F, dropping 40 F°, about 24 lb of water must circulate to carry the same heat as is carried in the form of heat of vaporization by one pound of steam.

Under the proper conditions of temperature and pressure, a substance can change directly from the solid to the gaseous phase without passing through the liquid phase. The transfer from solid to vapor is called *sublimation,* and the solid is said to *sublime.* "Dry ice" (solid carbon dioxide) sublimes at atmospheric pressure. Liquid carbon dioxide can not exist at a pressure lower than about 73 lb/in².

Heat is absorbed in the process of sublimation, and liberated in the reverse process. The quantity of heat per unit mass is called the *heat of sublimation.*

16-9 Measurement of heats of fusion and vaporization. The method of mixtures is used to measure heats of fusion and of vaporization. For example, the heat of fusion of ice may be found by dropping a weighed sample of ice at 0° C into a calorimeter containing a measured amount of water, and observing the temperature of the water before and after the addition of the ice. Let a mass m_i of ice at 0° C be dropped in a calorimeter containing a mass m_w of water, lowering the temperature of the water from t_1 to t_2. We shall assume that all of the ice melts, and neglect the heat capacity of the calorimeter. Then if L represents the heat of fusion of the ice, the ice absorbs a quantity of heat $m_i L$ on melting (this converts it to water at $0°$ C) and a further quantity of heat $m_i t_2$ on warming up to the final temperature t_2. The water in the calorimeter gives up a quantity of heat $m_w(t_1 - t_2)$. Hence,

$$m_w(t_1 - t_2) = m_i(L + t_2),$$

so that L can be found if the other quantities are known.

The heat of condensation ($=$ heat of vaporization) of steam can be measured in a similar way, by allowing steam from a boiler to condense within a calorimeter. The condensation usually takes place in a coiled tube immersed in the calorimeter, so that the amount of steam condensing may be found by weighing the coil before and after the experiment. We have

Heat given up by condensing steam $= m_s L$.

$$\left[\begin{matrix} \text{Heat given up by condensed steam} \\ \text{(water at } 100° \text{ C) cooling to } t_2 \end{matrix} \right] = m_s(100 - t_2).$$

Heat absorbed by calorimeter $= m_w(t_2 - t_1)$.

The heat of vaporization may be found by equating heat loss to heat gain.

16-10 Effect of dissolved substances on freezing and boiling points. The freezing point of a liquid is lowered when some other substance is dissolved in the liquid. A common example is the use of an "anti-freeze" to lower the freezing point of the water in the cooling system of an automobile engine.

The freezing point of a saturated solution of common salt in water is about $-20°$ C. To understand why a mixture of ice and salt may be used as a freezing mixture, let us make use of the definition of the freezing point as the only temperature at which the liquid and solid phases can exist in equilibrium. When a concentrated salt solution is cooled, it freezes at $-20°$ C, and crystals of ice (pure H_2O) separate from the solution. In other words, ice crystals and a salt solution can only exist in equilibrium at $-20°$ C, just as ice crystals and pure water can only exist together at $0°$ C.

When ice at $0°$ C is mixed with a salt solution at $20°$ C, some of the ice melts, abstracting its heat of fusion from the solution until the temperature falls to 0° C. But ice and salt solution cannot remain in equilibrium at 0° C, so that the ice continues to melt. Heat is now supplied both by the ice and the solution, and both cool down until the equilibrium temperature of −20° C is reached. If no heat is supplied from outside, the mixture remains unchanged at this temperature. If the mixture is brought in contact with a warmer body, say an ice cream mixture at 20° C, heat flows from the ice cream mixture to the cold salt solution, melting more of the ice but producing no rise in temperature as long as any ice remains. The flow of heat from the ice cream mixture lowers its temperature to its freezing point (which will be below 0° C since it is itself a solution). Further loss of heat to the ice-salt mixture causes the ice cream to freeze.

The boiling point of a liquid is also affected by dissolved substances, but may be either increased or decreased. Thus the boiling point of a water-alcohol solution is *lower* than that of pure water, while the boiling point of a water-salt solution is *higher* than that of pure water.

Both boiling and freezing points are affected by the external pressure, a matter which will be taken up in Chap. 19.

Problems — Chapter 16

16-1. How many cubic feet of a coal gas must be burned to heat 40 gallons of water from 50°F to 150°F, assuming 25% stack loss? (There are 7.5 gallons in a cubic foot.)

16-2. A certain Diesel engine consumes 20 lb of fuel oil per hour. The heat of combustion of the oil is 20,000 Btu/lb. If the over-all efficiency of the engine is 30%, (a) how many Btu/hr are converted into mechanical work? (b) How many Btu are wasted? (c) What horsepower does the engine develop?

16-3. An automobile weighing 2000 lb is traveling at 10 ft/sec. How many Btu are developed in the brakes when it is brought to rest?

16-4. An aluminum can of mass 500 gm contains 117.5 gm of water at a temperature of 20°C. A 200-gm block of iron at 75°C is dropped into the can. (a) Find the final temperature, assuming no heat loss to the surroundings. (b) What is the water equivalent of the calorimeter?

16-5. A casting weighing 100 lb is taken from an annealing furnace where its temperature was 900°F and plunged into a tank containing 800 lb of oil at a temperature of 80°F. The final temperature is 100°F, and the specific heat of the oil is 0.5. What was the specific heat of the casting? Neglect the heat capacity of the tank itself and any heat losses.

16-6. Compute from Table 16-1 the heat capacities of one gram atomic weight of Al, Cu, Pb, Hg, and Ag, and compare with the values predicted by the Dulong and Petit law.

16-7. Compare the heat capacities of equal *volumes* of water, copper, and lead.

16-8. A lead bullet of mass 5 gm, traveling with a kinetic energy of 12.6 joules, strikes a target and is brought to rest. What would be the rise in temperature of the bullet if none of the heat developed were lost to the surroundings?

16-9. How much heat is required to convert 1 gm of ice at −10°C to steam at 100°C?

16-10. A beaker whose heat capacity is negligible contains 500 gm of water at a temperature of 80°C. How many grams of ice at a temperature of −20°C must be dropped in the water so that the final temperature of the system will be 50°C?

16-11. Ice cubes at 0°C are dropped into a jug of salt water at 0°C. It is observed that the temperature of the mixture drops below 0°C. What happens to the heat that is released by the salt water when its temperature decreases?

16-12. An aluminum canteen whose mass is 500 gm contains 750 gm of water and 100 gm of ice. The canteen is dropped from an airplane to the ground. After landing, the temperature of the canteen is found to be 25°C. Assuming that no energy is given to the ground in the impact, what was the velocity of the canteen just before it landed?

16-13. A calorimeter contains 500 gm of water and 300 gm of ice, all at a temperature of 0°C. A block of metal of mass 1000 gm is taken from a furnace where its temperature was 240°C and is dropped quickly into the calorimeter. As a result, all of the ice is just melted. What would the final temperature of the system have been if the mass of the block had been twice as great? Neglect heat loss from the calorimeter, and the heat capacity of the calorimeter.

16-14. An ice cube whose mass is 50 gm is taken from a refrigerator where its temperature was −10°C, and dropped into a glass of water at 0°C.   If no heat is gained or lost from outside, how much water will freeze onto the cube?

16-15. A copper calorimeter can, having a heat capacity of 30 cal/deg, contains 50 gm of ice.   The system is initially at 0°C.   12 gm of steam at 100°C and 1 atm pressure are run into the calorimeter. What is the final temperature of the calorimeter and its contents?

16-16. A vessel whose walls are thermally insulated contains 2100 gm of water and 200 gm of ice, all at a temperature of 0°C.   The outlet of a tube leading from a boiler, in which water is boiling at atmospheric pressure, is inserted in the water. How many grams of steam must condense to raise the temperature of the system to 20°C?   Neglect the heat capacity of the container.

16-17. Inspect the following data sheet, which was prepared for an experiment to measure the heat of vaporization of water. Describe the experiment performed.   Fill in the blank spaces and use the data to calculate the heat of vaporization of water. What would you say about the experimental error?

Mass of empty beaker.......   50 grams
Mass of filled beaker......... 150 grams
 Mass of water.............
 _____

Initial temperature of water...... 25°C
Final temperature of water........ 45°C
 Change in temperature of
  water......................
  _____

Mass of water, beaker, and
  condensed steam........ 154 grams
 Mass of condensed steam...

CALCULATED HEAT OF
 VAPORIZATION OF
 WATER

16-18. A 2-kgm iron block is taken from a furnace where its temperature was 650°C and placed on a large block of ice at 0°C. Assuming that all of the heat given up by the iron is used to melt the ice, how much ice is melted?

16-19. A steel cylinder of cross-sectional area 0.1 ft², contains 0.4 ft³ of glycerin. The cylinder is equipped with a tightly fitting piston which supports a load of 6000 lb.   The cylinder is heated from 60°F to 160°F.   Neglect the expansion of the steel cylinder.   Find (a) the increase in volume of the glycerin, (b) the mechanical work done against the 6000-lb force by the glycerin, (c) the amount of heat added to the glycerin (specific heat of glycerin = 0.58), (d) the change in internal energy of the glycerin (i.e., the mechanical equivalent of the heat added minus the work done).

16-20. A "solar house" has storage facilities for 1 million Btu.   Compare the space requirements for this storage on the assumption (a) that the heat is stored in water heated from a minimum temperature of 80°F to a maximum at 120°F, and (b) that the heat is stored in Glauber salt ($Na_2SO_4 \cdot 10\ H_2O$) heated in the same temperature range.

Properties of Glauber salt:

Specific heat (solid)	0.46
Specific heat (liquid)	0.68
Specific gravity	1.6
Melting point	90°F
Heat of fusion	104 Btu/lb

CHAPTER 17

TRANSFER OF HEAT

17-1 Conduction.   If one end of a metal rod is placed in a flame while the other is held in the hand, that part of the rod one is holding will be felt to become hotter and hotter, although it was not itself in direct contact with the flame.   Heat is said to reach the cooler end of the rod by *conduction* along or through the material of the rod.   The atoms at the hot end of the rod increase the violence of their vibration as the temperature of the hot end increases.   Then, as they collide with their more slowly moving neighbors farther out on the rod, some of their energy of motion is shared with these neighbors and they in turn pass it along to those farther out from the flame.   Hence energy of thermal motion is passed along from one atom to the next, while each individual atom remains at its original position.

It is well known that metals are good conductors of electricity and also good conductors of heat.   The ability of a metal to conduct an electric current is due to the fact that there are within it so-called "free" electrons, that is, electrons that have become detached from their parent atoms. The free electrons also play a part in the conduction of heat, and the reason metals are such good heat conductors is because the free electrons, as well as the atoms, share in the process of handing on thermal energy from the hotter to the cooler portions of the metal.

Conduction of heat can only take place in a body when different parts of the body are at different temperatures, and the direction of heat flow is always from points of higher, to points of lower temperature.   The phenomenon of heat flow is sometimes made the basis for the definition of temperature equality or inequality.   That is, if heat flows from one body to another when the two are in contact, the temperature of the first, by definition, is higher than that of the second.   If there is no heat flow, the temperatures are equal.

Fig. 17-1 represents a slab of material of cross section A and thickness L.   Let the whole of the left face of the slab be kept at a temperature t_2, and the whole of the right face at a lower temperature t_1.   The direction of the heat current is then from left to right through the slab.

After the faces of the slab have been kept at the temperatures t_1 and t_2 for a sufficient length of time, the temperature at points within the slab is found to decrease uniformly with distance from the hot to the cold face.

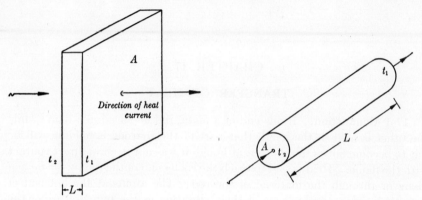

FIG. 17-1.   Conduction of heat through   FIG. 17-2   Conduction of heat along a
              a slab.   rod.

At each point, however, the temperature remains constant with time.
The slab is said to be in a "steady state."   (Non-steady state problems in
heat conduction involve mathematical methods beyond the scope of this
book.)

It is found by experiment that the rate of flow of heat through the slab
in the steady state is proportional to the area A, proportional to the
temperature difference $(t_2 - t_1)$, and inversely proportional to the thickness
L.   Let H represent the quantity of heat flowing through the slab per unit
time.   Then

$$H \propto \frac{A(t_2 - t_1)}{L}.$$

This proportion may be converted to an equation on multiplication by
a constant K whose numerical value depends on the material of the slab.
The quantity K is called the *coefficient of thermal conductivity* or simply the
thermal conductivity of the material.

$$H = \frac{KA(t_2 - t_1)}{L}.$$
(17-1)

Eq. (17-1) may also be used to compute the rate of heat flow along a
rod whose side walls are thermally insulated.   See Fig. 17-2, where the
letters have the same meaning as in Fig. 17-1.

In some circumstances, either because of non-steady conditions or
because of the geometry of the conductor, the temperature in a body
through which heat is flowing does not decrease uniformly along the direction of heat flow as it did in the slab of Fig. 17-1.   We can then consider

TABLE 17-1

THERMAL CONDUCTIVITY

	K (cal-cm/sec-cm^2-C°)	K (Btu-in/hr-ft^2-F°)
Metals:		
Aluminum...............	0.49	
Brass..................	0.26	
Copper.................	0.92	
Lead...................	0.083	
Mercury................	0.020	
Silver.................	0.97	
Steel..................	0.12	
Various Solids:		
(Representative values)		
Fire Brick.............	0.0025	8
Insulating Brick.......	0.00035	1
Red Brick..............	0.0015	4
Concrete...............	0.002	6
Cork...................	0.0001	0.3
Felt...................	0.0001	0.3
Glass..................	0.002	6
Ice....................	0.004	12
Rock Wool..............	0.0001	0.3
Wood....		0.003–0.001
Gases:		
Air....................	0.000057	
Argon..................	0.000039	
Helium.................	0.00034	
Hydrogen...............	0.00033	
Oxygen.................	0.000056	

a thin slab of thickness Δx between whose faces the temperature difference is Δt, and Eq. (17-1) becomes

$$H = -KA \frac{\Delta t}{\Delta x}. \tag{17-2}$$

The minus sign is introduced since if the temperature increases from left to right, the direction of the heat current is from right to left. Eq. (17-2) is the general equation of heat conduction. The ratio $\Delta t/\Delta x$ is called the *temperature gradient*. Eq. (17-1) evidently relates to a special case in which the temperature gradient is constant and equal to $(t_2 - t_1)/L$.

The cgs unit of rate of heat flow, or heat current, is one calorie per second. Temperatures are expressed on the centigrade scale. The units of A and L are obvious. The thermal conductivities of commercial insulating materials such as cork or rock wool are usually stated in a "hybrid" system in which areas are in square feet, temperatures in fahrenheit degrees, thicknesses in inches, and the rate of flow of heat in Btu per hour. In any system of units, H and K are numerically equal when A = one unit of area, $t_2 - t_1$ = one degree, and L = one unit of length. Thus in the commercial system, the thermal conductivity of a material is numerically equal to the number of Btu that flow in one hour through a slab one inch thick and one square foot in cross section, when the temperature difference between the faces of the slab is one fahrenheit degree.

It is evident from Eq. (17-1) that the larger the thermal conductivity K, the larger the heat current, other factors being equal. A material for which K is large is therefore a good heat conductor, while if K is small, the material is a poor conductor or a good insulator. There is no such thing as a "perfect heat conductor" ($K = \infty$) or a "perfect heat insulator" ($K = 0$). However, it will be seen from Table 17-1, which lists some representative values of thermal conductivity, that the metals as a group have much greater thermal conductivities than the nonmetals.

17-2 Convection. The term *convection* is applied to the transfer of heat from one place to another by the actual motion of hot material. The hot-air furnace and the hot-water heating system are examples. If the heated material is forced to move by a blower or pump, the process is called *forced convection;* if the material flows due to differences in density, the process is called *natural* or *free* convection. To understand the latter, consider a U-tube as illustrated in Fig. 17-3.

In (a), the water is at the same temperature in both arms of the U and hence stands at the same level in each. In (b), the right side of the U has been heated. The water in this side expands and therefore, being of smaller density, a longer column is needed to balance the pressure produced by the cold water in the left column. The stopcock may now be opened and water will flow from the top of the warmer column into the

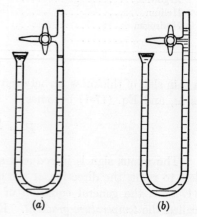

Fig. 17-3. Convection is brought about by differences in density.

colder column. This increases the pressure at the bottom of the U produced by the cold column, and decreases the pressure at this point due to the hot column. Hence at the bottom of the U, water is forced from the cold to the hot side. If heat is continually applied to the hot side and removed from the cold side, the circulation continues of itself. The net result is a continual transfer of heat from the hot to the cold side of the column. In the common household hot-water heating system, the "cold" side corresponds to the radiators and the "hot" side to the furnace.

The anomalous expansion of water which was mentioned in Chap. 15 has an important effect on the way in which lakes and ponds freeze in winter. Consider a pond at a temperature of, say, 20° C throughout, and suppose the air temperature at its surface falls to $-10°$ C. The water at the surface becomes cooled to, say, 19° C. It therefore contracts, becomes more dense than the warmer water below it, and sinks in this less dense water, its place being taken by water at 20° C. The sinking of the cooled water causes a mixing process, which continues until all of the water has been cooled to 4° C. Now, however, when the surface water cools to 3° C, it expands, is less dense than the water below it, and hence floats on the surface. Convection and mixing then cease, and the remainder of the water can only lose heat by *conduction*. Since water is an extremely poor heat conductor, cooling takes place very slowly after 4° C is reached, with the result that the pond freezes first at its surface. Then, since the density of ice is even smaller than that of water at 0° C, the ice floats on the water below it, and further freezing can only result from heat flow upward by conduction.

The mathematical theory of heat convection is quite involved. There is no simple equation for convection as in the case of conduction. This arises from the fact that the heat lost or gained by a surface at one temperature in contact with a fluid at another temperature depends on many circumstances, such as

1. Whether the surface is flat or curved.

2. Whether the surface is horizontal or vertical.

3. Whether the fluid in contact with the surface is a gas or a liquid.

4. The density, viscosity, specific heat, and thermal conductivity of the fluid.

5. Whether the velocity of the fluid is small enough to give rise to laminar flow or large enough to cause turbulent flow.

6. Whether evaporation, condensation, or formation of scale takes place.

The procedure adopted in practical calculations is first to define a *convection coefficient h* by means of the equation

$$H = hA\Delta t,$$

(17-3)

where H is the heat convection current (the heat gained or lost by convection by a surface per unit of time), A is the area of the surface, and Δt is the temperature difference between the surface and the main body of fluid. The next step is the determination of numerical values of h that are appropriate to a given piece of equipment. Such a determination is accomplished partly by reasoning known as *dimensional analysis* and partly by an elaborate series of experiments. An enormous amount of research in this field has been done in recent years so that, by now, there are in existence fairly complete tables and graphs from which the physicist or engineer may obtain the convection coefficient appropriate to certain standard types of apparatus.

A case of common occurrence is that of natural convection from a wall or a pipe at a constant temperature, surrounded by air at atmospheric pressure and differing in temperature by an amount Δt. The convection coefficients applicable in this situation are given in Table 17-2. As an example of a problem involving natural convection to and from a vertical wall, consider the following.

The air in a room is at a temperature of $25°$ C, and the outside air is at $-15°$ C. How much heat is transferred per unit area of a glass windowpane of thermal conductivity 2.5×10^{-3} cgs units and of thickness 2 mm?

TABLE 17-2

COEFFICIENTS OF NATURAL CONVECTION IN AIR AT ATMOSPHERIC PRESSURE

Equipment	Convection coefficient h in $\dfrac{\text{cal}}{\text{sec-cm}^2\text{-deg}}$
Horizontal plate, facing upward	$0.595 \times 10^{-4}(\Delta t)^{1/4}$
Horizontal plate, facing downward	$0.314 \times 10^{-4}(\Delta t)^{1/4}$
Vertical plate	$0.424 \times 10^{-4}(\Delta t)^{1/4}$
Horizontal or vertical pipe $\left(\dfrac{\text{diameter}}{D}\right)$	$1.00 \times 10^{-4}\left(\dfrac{\Delta t}{D}\right)^{1/4}$

To assume that the inner surface of the glass is at 25° C and the outer surface is at −15° C is entirely erroneous, as anyone can verify by touching the inner surface of a glass windowpane on a cold day. One must expect a much smaller temperature difference across the windowpane, so that in the steady state, the rates of transfer of heat (1) by convection in the room, (2) by conduction through the glass, and (3) by convection in the outside air, are all equal.

As a first approximation in the solution of this problem, let us assume that the window is at a uniform temperature t. If $t = 5°$ C, then the temperature difference between the inside air and the glass is the same as that between the glass and the outside air, or 20 deg. Hence the convection coefficient in both cases is

$$h = 0.424 \times 10^{-4} \, (20)^{1/4} \, \frac{\text{cal}}{\text{sec-cm}^2\text{-deg}} \, ,$$

$$= 0.895 \times 10^{-4} \, \frac{\text{cal}}{\text{sec-cm}^2\text{-deg}} \, ,$$

and, from Eq. (17-3), the heat transferred per unit area is

$$\frac{H}{A} = 0.895 \times 10^{-4} \times 20 = 17.9 \times 10^{-4} \, \frac{\text{cal}}{\text{sec-cm}^2}$$

The glass, however, is not at a uniform temperature; there must be a temperature difference Δt across the glass sufficient to provide heat conduction at the rate of 17.9×10^{-4} cal/sec-cm^2. Using the conduction equation, Eq. (17-1),

$$\Delta t = \frac{L}{K} \times \frac{H}{A}$$

$$= \frac{0.2}{2.5 \times 10^{-3}} \times 17.9 \times 10^{-4} \, \text{deg}$$

$$= 0.14 \, \text{deg}.$$

With sufficient accuracy we may therefore say that the inner surface is at 5.07° C and the outer surface is at 4.93° C.

17-3 Radiation. When one's hand is placed in direct contact with the surface of a hot-water or steam radiator, heat reaches the hand by *conduction* through the radiator walls. If the hand is held above the radiator but not in contact with it, heat reaches the hand by way of the upward-moving *convection* currents of warm air. If the hand is held at one side of the radiator it still becomes warm, even though conduction through the air is negligible and the hand is not in the path of the convection currents. Energy now reaches the hand by *radiation*.

The term radiation refers to the continual emission of energy from the surface of all bodies. This energy is called *radiant energy* and is in the form of electromagnetic waves. These waves travel with the velocity of light and are transmitted through a vacuum as well as through air. (Better, in fact, since they are absorbed by air to some extent.) When they fall on a body which is not transparent to them, such as the surface of one's hand or the walls of the room, they are absorbed and their energy converted to heat.

The radiant energy emitted by a surface, per unit time and per unit area, depends on the nature of the surface and on its temperature. At low temperatures the rate of radiation is small and the radiant energy is chiefly of relatively long wave length. As the temperature is increased, the rate of radiation increases very rapidly, in proportion to the 4th power of the absolute temperature. For example, a copper block at a temperature of 100° C (373° K) radiates about 300,000 ergs/sec or 0.03 watt from each square centimeter of its surface. At a temperature of 500° C (773° K) it radiates about 0.54 watt from each square centimeter, and at 1000° C (1273° K) it radiates about 4 watts per square centimeter. This rate is 130 times as great as that at a temperature of 100° C.

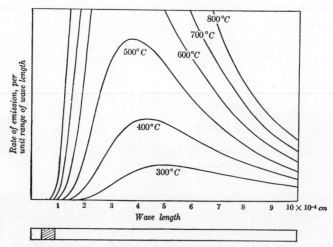

FIG. 17-4. Rate of emission of radiant energy by a blackbody, per unit of wave length, as a function of wave length. Shaded area indicates visible spectrum.

At each of these temperatures the radiant energy emitted is a mixture of waves of different wave lengths. At a temperature of 300° C the most intense of these waves has a wave length of about 5×10^{-4} cm; for wave lengths either greater or less than this value the intensity decreases as shown by the curve in Fig. 17-4. The corresponding distribution of energy at higher temperatures is also shown in the figure. The area between each curve and the horizontal axis represents the total rate of radiation at that temperature. It is evident that this rate increases rapidly with increasing temperature, and also that the wave length of the most intense wave shifts toward the left, or toward shorter wave lengths with increasing temperature.

At a temperature of 300° C, practically all of the radiant energy emitted by a body is carried by waves longer than those corresponding to red light. Such waves are called *infrared*, meaning "beyond the red." At a temperature of 800° C a body emits enough visible radiant energy to be self-luminous and appears "red hot." By far the larger part of the energy emitted, however, is still carried by infrared waves. At 3000° C, which is about the temperature of an incandescent lamp filament, the radiant energy contains enough of the shorter wave lengths so that the body appears nearly "white hot."

17-4 Stefan's law. Experimental measurements of the rate of emission of radiant energy from the surface of a body were made by John Tyndall (1820–1893) and on the basis of these Josef Stefan (1835–1893), in 1879, concluded that the rate of emission could be expressed by the relation

$$R = e\sigma T^4, \tag{17-4}$$

which is *Stefan's law*. R is the rate of emission of radiant energy per unit area and is expressed in ergs per second per square centimeter, in the cgs system, and in watts per square meter in the mks system. The constant σ has a numerical value of 5.672×10^{-5} in cgs units and 5.672×10^{-8} in mks units. T is the Kelvin temperature of the surface and e is a quantity called the emissivity of the surface. The emissivity lies between zero and unity, depending on the nature of the surface. The emissivity of copper, for example, is about 0.3. (Strictly speaking, the emissivity varies somewhat with temperature even for the same surface.) In general, the emissivity is larger for rough and smaller for smooth, polished surfaces.

It may be wondered why it is, if the surfaces of all bodies are continually emitting radiant energy, that all bodies do not eventually radiate away all of their internal energy and cool down to a temperature of absolute zero (where $R = 0$ by Eq. (17-4)). The answer is that they would do so, if energy were not supplied to them in some way. In the case of a Sunbowl heater element or the filament of an electric lamp, energy is supplied electrically to make up for the energy radiated. As soon as this energy supply is cut off, these bodies do, in fact, cool down very quickly to room temperature. The reason that they do not cool further is that their surroundings (the walls, and other objects in the room) are also radiating, and some of this radiant energy is intercepted, absorbed, and converted into internal energy. The same thing is true of all other objects in the room—each is both emitting and absorbing radiant energy simultaneously. If any object is hotter than its surroundings, its rate of emission will exceed its rate of absorption. There will thus be a net loss of energy and the body will cool down unless heated by some other method. If a body is at a lower temperature than its surroundings, its rate of absorption will be larger than its rate of emission and its temperature will rise. When the body is at the same temperature as its surroundings the two rates become equal, there is no net gain or loss of energy, and no change in temperature.

If a small body of emissivity e is completely surrounded by walls at a temperature T, the rate of *absorption* of radiant energy per unit area by the body is

$$R = e\sigma T^4.$$

Hence for such a body at a temperature T_1, surrounded by walls at a temperature T_2, the *net* rate of loss (or gain) of energy per unit area by radiation is

$$R_{\text{net}} = e\sigma T_1{}^4 - e\sigma T_2{}^4$$
$$= e\sigma(T_1{}^4 - T_2{}^4). \tag{17-5}$$

17-5 The ideal radiator. Imagine that the walls of the enclosure in Fig. 17-5 are kept at the temperature T_2 and a number of different bodies having different emissivities are suspended one after another within the enclosure. Regardless of their temperature when they were inserted, it will be found that eventually each comes to the same temperature as that of the walls, T_2, even if the enclosure is evacuated. If the bodies are small compared to the size of the enclosure, radiant energy from the walls strikes the surface of each body at the same rate. Of this energy, a part is reflected and the remainder absorbed. In the absence of any other process, the energy absorbed will raise the temperature of the absorbing body,

but since the temperature is observed *not* to change, each body
must *emit* radiant energy at the same
rate as it *absorbs* it. Hence a good
absorber is a good emitter, and a
poor absorber is a poor emitter.
But since each body must either absorb or reflect the radiant energy
reaching it, a poor absorber must
also be a good reflector. Hence a
good reflector is a *poor emitter.*

This is the reason for silvering

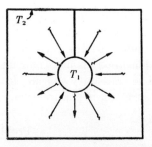

Fig. 17-5. In thermal equilibrium, the
rate of emission of radiant energy equals
the rate of absorption. Hence a good absorber is a good emitter.

the walls of vacuum ("thermos")
bottles. A vacuum bottle is constructed with double glass walls, the space
between the walls being evacuated so that heat flow by conduction and
convection is practically eliminated. To reduce the radiant emission to as
low a value as possible, the walls are covered with a coating of silver which
is highly reflecting and hence is a very poor emitter.

Since a good absorber is a good emitter, the *best* emitter will be that
surface which is the best absorber. But no surface can absorb more than
all of the radiant energy which strikes it. Any surface which does absorb
all of the incident energy will be the best emitting surface possible. Such
a surface would reflect no radiant energy, and hence would appear black
in color (provided its temperature is not so high that it is self-luminous).
It is called an *ideally black surface*, and a body having such a surface is
called an ideal blackbody, an ideal radiator, or simply a *blackbody.*

No actual surface is ideally black, the closest approach being lamp-
black, which reflects only about 1%. Blackbody conditions can be closely
realized, however, by a small opening in the walls of a closed container.
Radiant energy entering the opening is in part absorbed by the interior
walls. Of the part reflected, only a very little escapes through the opening, the remainder being eventually absorbed by the walls. Hence the
opening behaves like an ideal absorber.

Conversely, the radiant energy emitted by the walls or by any body
within the enclosure, and escaping through the opening, will, if the walls
are of uniform temperature, be of the same nature as that emitted by an
ideal radiator. This fact is of importance when using an optical pyrometer,
described on page 267. The readings of such an instrument are correct
only when it is sighted on a blackbody. If used to measure the temperature of a red hot ingot of iron in the open, its readings will be too low,
since iron is a poorer emitter than a blackbody. If, however, the pyrom-

eter is sighted on the iron while still in the furnace, where it is surrounded by walls at the same temperature, "blackbody conditions" are fulfilled and the reading will be correct. The failure of the iron to emit as effectively as a blackbody is just compensated by the radiant energy which it reflects.

The emissivity e of an ideally black surface is equal to unity. For all real surfaces, it is a fraction, less than one.

Problems — Chapter 17

17-1. A long rod, insulated to prevent heat losses, has one end immersed in boiling water (at atmospheric pressure) and the other end in a water-ice mixture. The rod consists of 100 cm of copper (one end in steam) and a length, L_2, of steel (one end in ice). Both rods are of cross-sectional area 5 cm². The temperature of the copper-iron junction is 60°C, after a steady state has been set up. (a) How many calories per second flow from the steam bath to the ice-water mixture? (b) How long is L_2?

17-2. A rod is initially at a uniform temperature of 0°C throughout. One end is kept at 0°C and the other is brought into contact with a steam bath at 100°C. The surface of the rod is insulated so that heat can flow only lengthwise along the rod. The cross-sectional area of the rod is 2 cm², its length is 100 cm, its thermal conductivity is 0.8 cal-cm/sec-cm²-C°, its density is 10 gm/cm³, and its specific heat capacity is 0.10 cal/gm-C°. Consider a short cylindrical element of the rod 1 cm in length. (a) If the temperature gradient at one end of this element is 200 C°/cm, how many calories flow across this end per second? (b) If the average temperature of the element is increasing at the rate of 5 C°/sec, what is the temperature gradient at the other end of the element?

17-3. Rods of copper, brass, and steel are welded together to form a Y-shaped figure. The cross-sectional area of each rod is 2 cm². The end of the copper rod is maintained at 100°C and the ends of the brass and steel rods at 0°C. Assume there is no heat loss from the surfaces of the rods. The lengths of the rods are: copper, 46 cm; brass, 13 cm; steel, 12 cm. (a) What is the temperature of the junction point? (b) What is the heat current in the copper rod?

17-4. A container of wall area 5000 cm² and thickness 2 cm is filled with water in which there is a stirrer. The outer surface of the walls is kept at a constant temperature of 0°C. The thermal conductivity of the walls is 0.000478 cal-cm/sec-cm²-C°, and the effect of edges and corners can be neglected. The power required to run the stirrer at an angular velocity of 1800 rpm is found to be 100 watts. What will be the final steady-state temperature of the water in the container? Assume that the stirrer keeps the entire mass of water at a uniform temperature.

17-5. A boiler with a steel bottom 1.5 cm thick rests on a hot stove. The area of the bottom of the boiler is 1500 cm². The water inside the boiler is at 100°C and 750 gm are evaporated every 5 minutes. Find the temperature of the lower surface of the boiler, which is in contact with the stove.

17-6. A cubical box 2 ft on an edge is constructed of insulating wallboard of thermal conductivity 0.4 Btu-in/hr-ft²-F°, and of thickness ½ inch. Mounted within the box is an electric heater developing 600 watts. Find the temperature difference between inner and outer surfaces of the walls of the box after the steady state has been reached.

17·7. An icebox, having wall area of 2 m² and thickness 5 cm, is constructed of insulating material having a thermal conductivity of 10^{-4} cal/sec-cm-C°. The outside temperature is 20°C, and the inside of the box is to be maintained at 5°C by ice. The melted ice leaves the box at a temperature of 15°C. If ice costs one cent per kgm, what will it cost to run the icebox for one hour?

17-8. A flat wall is maintained at a constant temperature of 100°C, and the air on both sides is at atmospheric pressure and at 19°C. How much heat is lost by natural convection from 1 sq meter of wall (both sides) in one hour if (a) the wall is vertical, (b) the wall is horizontal?

17-9. A vertical steam pipe of outside diameter 7.5 cm and height 4 meters has its outer surface at the constant temperature of 140°C. The surrounding air is at atmospheric pressure and at 20°C. How much heat is delivered to the air by natural convection in one hour?

17-10. The operating temperature of a tungsten filament in an incandescent lamp is 2450°K and its emissivity is 0.30. Find the surface area of the filament of a 25-watt lamp.

17-11. A blackened solid copper sphere of radius 2 cm is placed in an evacuated enclosure whose walls are kept at 100°C. At what rate must energy be supplied to the sphere to keep its temperature constant at 127°C?

17-12. A cylindrical metal can 10 cm high and 5 cm in diameter contains liquid helium at 4°K, at which its heat of vaporization is 5 cal/gm. Completely surrounding the helium can are walls maintained at the temperature of liquid nitrogen, 80°K, the intervening space being evacuated. How much helium is lost per hour? Assume the emissivity to be 1.

CHAPTER 18

THE FIRST LAW OF THERMODYNAMICS

18-1 External work. We have seen that when the temperature of a body is raised, many different effects may take place: gases expand, solids and liquids usually expand but in rare instances they may contract, thermocouples develop an electromotive force, wires undergo a change of resistance, and many other phenomena occur. In such processes there is usually a flow of heat, and also the application of a force which undergoes a displacement, thereby bringing about the performance of work. The study of these phenomena and the energy changes involved in the flow of heat and performance of work constitute a subject known as *thermodynamics*.

Thermodynamics is an intensely practical subject. It concerns itself with a clearly defined *system* (a gas contained in a cylinder, a pound of steam moving through a nozzle, etc.), which is caused to interact directly with its surroundings and, by such interaction, to perform some useful function. It does not concern itself with minute interior effects which do not affect the outside and which cannot be used or measured.

If a system as a whole exerts a force on its surroundings and a displacement takes place, the work that is done either by or on the system is called *external work*. Thus, a gas confined in a cylinder and at uniform pressure, while expanding and imparting motion to a piston, does external work on its surroundings.

Work done by one part of a system on another part of the same system is called *internal work*. The interactions of molecules or electrons on one another constitute internal work. *Internal work has no place in thermodynamics*.

18-2 Work in changing the volume. Imagine any solid or fluid contained in a cylinder equipped with a movable piston on which the system and the surroundings may act. Suppose that the cylinder has a cross-sectional area A and that the pressure exerted by the system at the piston face is p. The force on the piston is therefore pA. If the piston moves out a very small distance Δx, the system performs a very small amount of work ΔW equal to

$$\Delta W = pA\Delta x.$$

But

$$A\Delta x = \Delta V,$$

where ΔV is the change of volume.   Therefore

$$\Delta W = p\Delta V. \qquad (18\text{-}1)$$

If the pressure remains constant while the volume changes a finite amount, say from V_1 to V_2, then the work W is

$$W = p(V_2 - V_1) \text{ (constant pressure only)}. \qquad (18\text{-}2)$$

If, on the other hand, the pressure decreases as the volume increases, then we may imagine that the whole series of changes consists of a small volume change ΔV_1 while the pressure is p_1, then another small volume change ΔV_2 while the pressure is p_2, and so on.   The work will then be

$$W = p_1 \Delta V_1 + p_2 \Delta V_2 + \cdots.$$

Suppose that the pressure is plotted along the Y-axis and the volume along the X-axis.   The changes of pressure and volume will then be indicated by a smooth curve such as that shown in Fig. 18-1(a).   If the total volume change $V_2 - V_1$ is divided into a number of small steps ΔV_1, ΔV_2, etc., as shown in Fig. 18-1(b), then the smooth curve may be approximated with any desired degree of accuracy by a jagged curve where the pressure is p_1 only during the volume change ΔV_1, and is p_2 only during ΔV_2, and so on.   The total work, $p_1 \Delta V_1 + p_2 \Delta V_2 + \cdots$, is thus seen to be the sum of the areas of all the rectangles which make up the total area under

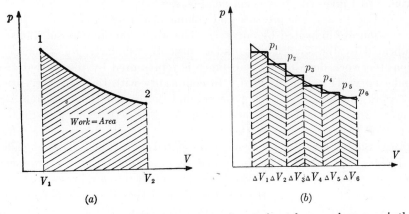

(a)   (b)

Fig. 18-1.   The work done when a substance changes its volume and pressure is the area under the curve on a p-V diagram.

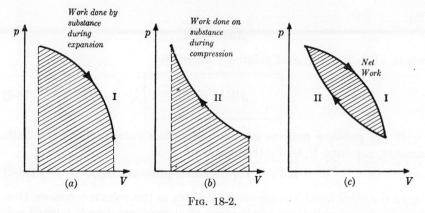

Fig. 18-2.

the jagged curve. If now the number of steps is increased indefinitely, the area under such a jagged curve approaches the area under the smooth curve, and we have the result that

$$W = \begin{Bmatrix} \text{Area under a curve} \\ \text{on a } p\text{–}V \text{ diagram} \end{Bmatrix}. \qquad (18\text{-}3)$$

Notice that this method of finding the work done by a varying pressure is the same as that for finding the work done by a varying force, as explained in Sec. 7-11.

It is an accepted convention that work done *by* a substance is positive; that done *on* a substance is negative. Thus, if a substance expands from 1 to 2 in Fig. 18-1(a), the area is regarded as positive. The compression from 2 to 1 gives rise to a negative area.

In Fig. 18-2(a) the pressure and volume changes of a substance during expansion are indicated by curve I. The work done by the substance is indicated by the shaded area under curve I. Similarly, for a compression, the work done on the substance is represented by the shaded area under curve II in Fig. 18-2(b). In conformity with the sign convention for work, the area under I is positive, and that under II is negative. In Fig. 18-2(c), curves I and II are drawn together so that they constitute a series of processes whereby the substance is brought back to its initial state. Such a series of processes, represented by a closed figure, is called a *cycle*. The area within the closed figure is obviously the difference between the areas under curves I and II and therefore represents the *net* work done in the cycle. It should be noticed that the cycle is traversed in such a direction that the net work is positive. If the direction were reversed, the net work would be negative.

18-3 Work depends on path. On
the $p - V$ diagram depicted in Fig.
18-3 an initial state 1 (characterized
by pressure p_1 and volume V_1) and a
final state 2 (characterized by pressure p_2 and volume V_2) are represented by the two points 1 and 2.
There are many ways in which the
system may be taken from 1 to 2.
For example, the pressure may be
kept constant from 1 to 3 (isobaric
process) and then the volume kept
constant from 3 to 2 (isovolumic
process), in which case the work

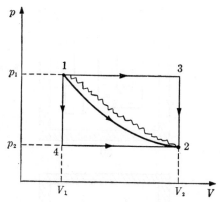

Fig. 18-3.   Work depends on the path.

done is equal to the area under the line $1 \rightarrow 3$.   Another possibility is
the path $1 \rightarrow 4 \rightarrow 2$, in which case the work is the area under the line
$4 \rightarrow 2$.   The jagged line and the continuous curve from 1 to 2 represent
other possibilities, in each of which the work done is different.   We can
see, therefore, that *the work done by a substance depends not only on the
initial and final states but also on the intermediate states, i.e., on the path.*

18-4 Work and heat.   We have seen how a substance may be caused to
go from state 1 to state 2 by any number of processes, all of which involve
the performance of work.   There are other means, however, of changing
the state of a substance.   Consider, for example, the four situations
depicted in Fig. 18-4.   In (a) the system is a composite one consisting
of some water and a paddle wheel, which is caused to rotate and churn
the water by means of a falling weight.   In (b) both the water and an
electric resistance wire embedded in the water constitute the system.   An
electric current in the resistor is maintained by a generator turned by
means of a falling weight.   In both cases the state of the system is caused
to change and, since the agency for changing the state of the system is a
falling weight, *both processes involve the performance of work.*

In (c) and (d), however, the situation is quite different.   The system
in both cases is some water in a heat-conducting container.   In (c) the
system is in contact with the burning gases from a Bunsen burner, i.e.,
with another body at a higher temperature, whereas in (d) the system is
near but not in contact with an electric lamp whose temperature is much
higher than that of the water.   In both cases the state of the system is
caused to change, but in neither case can the agency for the change be
described by mechanical means.   *In these cases there is a flow of heat.*

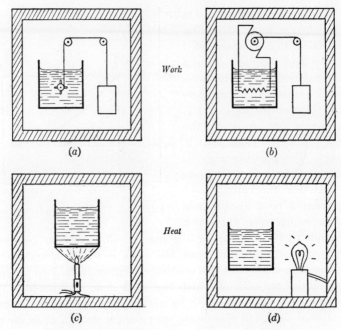

Fig. 18-4.   Distinction between work and heat.

It is important to observe that the decision as to whether a particular change of state involves the performance of work or the transfer of heat requires first an unequivocal answer to the questions "What is the system?" and "What are the surroundings?"   For example, in Fig. 18-4(b), if the resistor is regarded as the system and the water as the surroundings, then there is a transfer of heat from the resistor by virtue of the temperature difference between the resistor and the water.   Also, if a small part of the water is regarded as the system, the rest of the water being the surroundings, then again there is a transfer of heat.   Regarding, however, the composite system composed of both the water and the resistor, the surroundings do not contain any object whose temperature differs from that of the system, and hence no heat is transferred between *this composite system* and its surroundings.

The flow of heat is a *nonmechanical energy transfer* brought about by a temperature difference between two bodies, and we say that heat flows from one place to another.   When the flow has ceased, there is no longer any occasion to use the word heat.   The performance of work and the flow of heat are methods of supplying energy to a body or extracting energy from a body. We have seen that, in general, the work done on or by a substance depends on the path by which the system was brought from the initial to the final state. Exactly the same is true of the heat transferred to or from a body. *Heat also depends on the path.*

It would be just as incorrect to refer to the "heat in a body" as it would be to speak about the "work in a body." For suppose we assigned an arbitrary value to "the heat in a body" in some standard reference state. The "heat in the body" in some other state would then equal the "heat" in the reference state plus the heat added when the body is carried to the second state. But the heat added depends entirely on the path by which we go from one state to the other, and since there are an infinite number of paths which might be followed, there are an infinite number of values which might equally well be assigned to the "heat in the body" in the second state. Since it is not possible to assign any one value to the "heat in the body" we conclude that this concept is meaningless, or at any rate useless.

18-5 The first law of thermodynamics. Suppose a substance is caused to change from state 1 to state 2 along a definite path and that the heat absorbed Q and the work W done by the substance are measured. Expressing both Q and W either in thermal units or in mechanical units we may then calculate the difference $Q - W$. If now we do the same thing over again for many different paths (between the same states 1 and 2), the important result is obtained that $Q - W$ *is the same for all paths connecting 1 and 2.* But Q is the energy that has been added to a substance by the transfer of heat and W is equal to the energy that has been extracted from the substance by the performance of work. The difference $Q - W$, therefore, must represent the internal energy change of the substance. It follows that *the internal energy change of a substance is independent of the path,* and is therefore equal to the energy of the substance in state 2 minus the energy in state 1, or $U_2 - U_1$.

$$U_2 - U_1 = Q - W.$$

If some arbitrary value is assigned to the internal energy in some standard reference state, its value in any other state is uniquely defined, since $Q - W$ is the same for all processes connecting the states.

The simple algebraic statement of these facts in the form

$$\boxed{Q = U_2 - U_1 + W} \tag{18-4}$$

is known as *the first law of thermodynamics.* In applying the law in this form it must be remembered that (1) all quantities must be expressed in the same units, (2) Q is positive when heat goes into the system, (3) W is positive when work goes out of the system.

18-6 Adiabatic process. A process that takes place in such a manner that no heat enters or leaves a system is called an *adiabatic process*. This may be accomplished either by surrounding the system with a thick layer of heat insulating material (such as cork, asbestos, firebrick, or any light, porous powder) or by performing the process quickly. The flow of heat is a fairly slow process, so that any process performed quickly enough will be practically adiabatic. Applying the first law to an adiabatic process, we get

$$-W = U_2 - U_1 \quad \text{(Adiabatic process)},$$

which shows that all the work done *on* the substance is converted into internal energy. A rise of internal energy is usually accompanied by an increase of temperature. Conversely, if the substance undergoes an adiabatic process in such a direction that work is done *by* the substance, there will be a decrease of internal energy numerically equal to the work, and usually an accompanying temperature drop.

The compression of the mixture of gasoline vapor and air that takes place during the compression stroke of a gasoline engine is an example of an approximately adiabatic process involving a temperature rise. The expansion of the combustion products during the power stroke of the engine is an approximately adiabatic process involving a temperature decrease. Adiabatic processes, therefore, play a very important role in mechanical engineering.

18-7 Isovolumic process. If a substance undergoes a process in which the volume remains unchanged, the process is called *isovolumic*. The rise of pressure and temperature produced by a flow of heat into a substance contained in a nonexpanding chamber is an example of an isovolumic process. If the volume does not change, no work is done and, therefore, from the first law,

$$Q = U_2 - U_1 \quad \text{(Isovolumic process)},$$

or all the heat that has been added has served to increase the internal energy. The very sudden increase of temperature and pressure accompanying the explosion of gasoline vapor and air in a gasoline engine may be treated mathematically as though it were an isovolumic addition of heat.

18-8 Isobaric process. A process taking place at constant pressure is called an *isobaric process*. When water enters the boiler of a steam engine and is heated to its boiling point, vaporized, and then the steam is superheated, all of these processes take place isobarically. Such processes play an important rôle in mechanical engineering and also in chemistry.

Consider the change of phase of a mass m of liquid to vapor at constant pressure and temperature. If V_L is the volume of liquid and V_V the volume of vapor, the work done in expanding from V_L to V_V at constant pressure p is

$$W = p(V_V - V_L).$$

The heat absorbed by each unit of mass is the heat of vaporization L. Hence

$$Q = mL.$$

From the first law,

$$mL = (U_V - U_L) + p(V_V - V_L). \tag{18-5}$$

Example: One gram of water (1 cm³) becomes 1671 cm³ of steam when boiled at a pressure of 1 atm. The heat of vaporization at this pressure is 539 cal/gm. Compute the external work and the increase in internal energy.

External work $= p(V_V - V_L)$
$\qquad\qquad\quad = 1.013 \times 10^6(1671 - 1)$
$\qquad\qquad\quad = 1.695 \times 10^9$ ergs
$\qquad\qquad\quad = 169.5$ joules
$\qquad\qquad\quad = 41$ calories.

From Eq. (18-5)

$$U_V - U_L = mL - W = 539 - 41$$
$$= 498 \text{ calories.}$$

Hence the external work, or the external part of the heat of vaporization, equals 41 calories, and the increase in internal energy, or the internal part of the heat of vaporization, is 498 calories.

18-9 Free expansion.   Imagine a vessel with rigid walls and covered with asbestos. Suppose the vessel is divided into two parts by a thin partition, and that one part contains a gas while the other is evacuated. If the partition is suddenly broken, the gas rushes into a vacuum, undergoing what is known as a *free expansion*. Since the walls of the container are rigid, no external work is done, and since the vessel is heat-insulated, the process is adiabatic. Thus, $Q = 0$ and $W = 0$. Hence, from the first law,

$$U_1 = U_2 \quad \text{(Free expansion)},$$

or the initial and final internal energies are equal.

The magnitude of the temperature change (if any) that takes place as a result of a free expansion is of some theoretical interest and, as a result, many attempts have been made to perform an experiment of this sort. The experimental difficulties, however, are enormous and no one has really succeeded so far. From a practical point of view a free expansion is of no importance whatever.

18-10 Throttling process. A throttling process is one in which a fluid, originally at a constant high pressure, seeps through a porous wall or a narrow opening (needle valve or throttling valve) into a region of constant lower pressure, without a transfer of heat taking place. The experiment is sometimes called the porous plug experiment. Fig. 18-5(a) will help to make the process clear. A fluid is discharged from a pump at a high pressure, then passes through a throttling valve into a pipe which leads directly to the intake or low-pressure side of the pump. Every successive unit of mass of fluid undergoes the throttling process in a continuous stream.

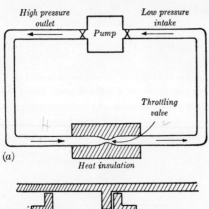

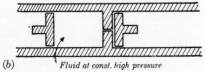

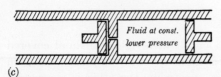

Fig. 18-5.   Throttling process.

Consider just one unit of mass enclosed between the piston and throttling valve of Fig. 18-5(b). Suppose this piston to move toward the right and another piston on the other side of the valve to move to the right also at such rates that the pressure on the left remains at a constant high value and that on the right at a constant lower value. After all the fluid has been forced through the valve, the final state is that of Fig. 18-5(c).

The net work done in this process is the difference between the work done by the fluid in forcing the right-hand piston out and the work done on the fluid in forcing the left-hand piston in.   Let

p_1 = high pressure (on the left),

V_1 = volume of unit mass of fluid at the high pressure,

p_2 = lower pressure (on the right),

V_2 = volume of unit mass of fluid at the low pressure.

Since the low pressure fluid changes in volume from zero to V_2 at the constant pressure p_2, the work done by the fluid is

$$p_2(V_2 - 0),$$

and since the high pressure fluid changes in volume from V_1 to zero at the constant high pressure p_1, the work done is

$$p_1(0 - V_1).$$

This is negative because it is done *on* the fluid.   The net work W is therefore
$$W = p_2 V_2 - p_1 V_1.$$

Since the process is adiabatic, $Q = 0$, and hence from the first law,

$$0 = U_2 - U_1 + (p_2 V_2 - p_1 V_1)$$

or

$$U_1 + p_1 V_1 = U_2 + p_2 V_2.$$

This result is of great importance in steam engineering and in refrigeration.   The sum $U + pV$, called the *enthalpy*, is tabulated for steam and for many refrigerants.   The throttling process plays the main rôle in the action of a refrigerator since this is the process that gives rise to the drop in temperature needed for refrigeration.   Liquids that are about to evaporate (saturated liquids) always undergo a drop in temperature and partial vaporization as a result of a throttling process.   Gases, however, may undergo a temperature rise or drop depending on the initial temperature and pressure and on the final pressure.

Problems — Chapter 18

18-1. A gas contained in a cylinder surrounded by a thick layer of felt is quickly compressed, the temperature rising several degrees. (a) Has there been a transfer of heat? (b) Has work been done?

18-2. A resistor, immersed in running water, carries an electric current. Regarding the resistor as the system under consideration, (a) is there a flow of heat into the resistor? (b) is there a flow of heat into the water? (c) is work done on the resistor? (d) Assuming the state of the resistor to remain unchanged, apply the first law to this process.

18-3. In a certain process, 500 cal of heat are supplied to a system and at the same time 100 joules of work are done on the system. What is the increase in its internal energy?

18-4. A cylinder is equipped with a tightly fitting piston. The cylinder is filled with 500 cubic inches of gas at a pressure of 50 lb/in². How much work is required to compress the gas to 490 cubic inches? Assume the pressure of the gas remains practically unchanged.

18-5. The heat of vaporization of water is 970 Btu/lb at 212°F and 14.7 lb/in²,

and one pound of steam at this temperature occupies a volume of 27 ft³. Calculate the external work in ft-lb when one pound of steam is formed at this temperature.

18-6. When water is boiled under a pressure of 2 atm the heat of vaporization is 946 Btu/lb, the boiling point is 250°F, one pound of steam occupies a volume of 14 ft³, and one lb of water a volume of 0.017 ft³. (a) Compute the external work, in ft-lb and in Btu, when 1 lb of steam is formed at this temperature. (b) Compute the increase in internal energy, in Btu.

18-7. A substance undergoes a series of processes which bring it back to its initial state. In this cycle, heat Q_2 is absorbed by the substance and heat Q_1 is rejected. What is the net amount of work done?

18-8. A cylinder is filled with 10 gm of gas and is compressed from a volume of 500 in³ to 100 in³. During the compression process, 100 calories of heat are removed from the gas, and at the end of the process the temperature of the gas has increased by 5 C°. Compute the specific heat of the gas for this process.

CHAPTER 19

THERMAL PROPERTIES OF MATTER

19-1 Boyle's law. The behaviour of a gas is governed by simpler laws than those applying to liquids and solids. Robert Boyle, in 1660, reported on one of the first quantitative experiments relating to gaseous behaviour. He found that if the temperature of a fixed mass of gas was held constant while its volume was varied over wide limits, the pressure exerted by the gas varied also, and in such a way that the product of pressure and volume remained essentially constant. Mathematically,

$$pV = \text{constant.} \qquad \begin{cases} \text{const. temp.} \\ \text{const. mass} \end{cases} \qquad (19\text{-}1)$$

This relation is *Boyle's law.* (*p* represents the *absolute* pressure.)

If the subscripts 1 and 2 refer to two different states of the gas at the same temperature, Boyle's law may also be written,

$$p_1V_1 = p_2V_2. \qquad \begin{cases} \text{States 1 and 2} \\ \text{at same temp.} \end{cases} \qquad (19\text{-}2)$$

The pV product, while nearly constant at a given temperature, does vary somewhat with the pressure. We therefore find it convenient to postulate an imaginary substance called an *ideal gas* which *by definition* obeys Boyle's law exactly at all pressures. Real gases at low pressure closely approximate an ideal gas.

The relation between the pressure and volume of an ideal gas at constant temperature is shown by the curves of Fig. 19-1, where p is plotted vertically and V horizontally. The curves are equilateral hyperbolas, asymptotic to the p and V axes. Each curve corresponds to a different temperature. That is, while $pV = a$ *constant* at any one temperature, the constant is larger the higher the temperature.

It should be pointed out that in order to be able to speak of *the* pressure or *the* temperature of a gas (or of any other body) it is necessary that all parts be at the *same* pressure or temperature. When its pressure and temperature are the same throughout, the gas is said to be in *equilibrium*. For example, a gas in a tank which is being heated by a blowtorch directed against one side is not in equilibrium, and it is meaningless to speak of *the* temperature of the gas.   Only when the gas has been left to itself for a long enough time for its tempera-

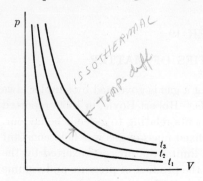

ture to be the same throughout can we associate any one temperature with it.

Each of the curves in Fig. 19-1 can be considered to represent a *process* through which the gas is carried, for example, a process in which the gas is compressed from a large to a small volume in a bicycle pump. We shall show later that in order to keep the temperature constant in such a compression it would be necessary to remove heat from the gas, and therefore the

Fig. 19-1.   The product of the pressure and volume of an ideal gas is constant at constant temperature.

process would have to be carried out slowly in order to keep the temperature the same throughout the gas.   Such a slow compression carries the gas through a series of states, each of which is very nearly an equilibrium state, and it is called a *quasi-static*, or a "nearly static" process. Unless stated otherwise, we shall assume in what follows that all processes are to be carried out in this way, so that at each stage of the process the gas is, for all practical purposes, in an equilibrium state.

Any process in which the temperature remains constant is called *isothermal*, and the curves in Fig. 19-1 are the isothermal curves, or, more briefly, the *isotherms* of an ideal gas.

19-2 Gay-Lussac's law.   The first accurate statement of the law connecting the volume changes of a gas with changes in its temperature was published by Joseph Louis Gay-Lussac in 1802.   Earlier work on the subject had been carried on by many other investigators, among them being Jacques A. C. Charles, whose name is often associated with Gay-Lussac's in connection with the law.

Gay-Lussac measured what we would now call the cubical coefficient of expansion of a number of different gases, and was apparently the first to recognize that when making such measurements with gases it is essential that the pressure be kept constant.   If this is not done, the volume changes due to changes in pressure will obscure those due to temperature alone.

The quantity measured was therefore the cubical coefficient of expansion *at constant pressure*. The experimental results can be expressed by the following relation

$$V = V_0[1 + \beta(t - t_0)], \tag{19-3}$$

where V_0 is the volume at some reference temperature t_0 and V is the volume at temperature t. The coefficient β is the cubical coefficient of expansion, expressed in reciprocal degrees. Its numerical value depends on the size of the degree (i.e., whether fahrenheit or centigrade) and on the reference temperature t_0. If, as is usually the case, the reference temperature is taken as 0° C, Eq. (19-3) becomes

$$V = V_0(1 + \beta_0 t). \tag{19-4}$$

The symbol β_0 indicates that the reference temperature is 0° C.

The first point of interest is that the volume is a *linear* function of the temperature. The second, which is more surprising, is that the coefficient of expansion, β_0, has *very nearly the same value for all gases*. (Compare with the coefficients of expansion of liquids and solids which differ widely for different materials.) By measuring β_0 for a number of gases in a series of measurements at different pressures, it is found that the lower the pressure the more closely do the values of β_0 agree for different gases. Extrapolating such a series of measurements to zero pressure gives the following value, common to all gases,

$$\beta_0 = 0.003660 \text{ per centigrade degree.}$$

We accordingly extend our definition of an ideal gas, and state that, in addition to obeying Boyle's law at all pressures, it obeys Gay-Lussac's law with $\beta_0 = 0.003660$ per centigrade degree.

The decimal 0.003660 is very nearly equal to 1/273, and the experimental facts above are often stated: the volume of a fixed mass of any gas kept at constant pressure increases by 1/273 of its value at 0° C for each centigrade degree increase in temperature. The linear relation between volume and temperature, at constant pressure, is illustrated in Fig. 19-2.

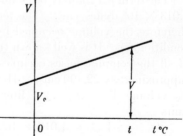

FIG. 19-2. At constant pressure the volume of an ideal gas is a linear function of the temperature.

19-3 The equation of state of an ideal gas. We may now combine the laws of Boyle and Gay-Lussac to obtain a single equation connecting the pressure, volume, and temperature of an ideal gas. The analysis is best understood with the help of a diagram in the p-V plane. The coordinates of point 1 in Fig. 19-3 represent the pressure and volume of a certain mass of an ideal gas at a pressure $p_0 = 1$ atm and a temperature $t_0 = 0°$ C. Point 2 is any other point at which the pressure is p, the volume V, and the temperature $t°$ C. Consider a process shown by the heavy lines, in which the gas is first expanded from its initial state to another (point 3) at the same pressure but at a temperature t; and second, compressed isothermally to point 2.

Since points 1 and 3 are at the same pressure, it follows from Gay-Lussac's law that

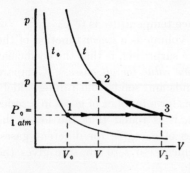

FIG. 19-3.

$$V_3 = V_0(1 + \beta_0 t). \quad (19\text{-}5)$$

Since points 3 and 2 are at the same temperature, it follows from Boyle's law that

$$pV = p_0 V_3. \quad (19\text{-}6)$$

When the expression for V_3 from Eq. (19-5) is substituted in (19-6) we obtain

$$pV = p_0 V_0 (1 + \beta_0 t)$$

which can be written

$$pV = p_0 V_0 \beta_0 \left(t + \frac{1}{\beta_0} \right). \quad (19\text{-}7)$$

The term $p_0 V_0 \beta_0$ may be evaluated as follows: the pressure p_0 is 1 atm = 1.013×10^6 dynes/cm². The temperature $t_0 = 0°$ C. The volume V_0 is therefore the volume occupied by the gas at 1 atm and 0° C ("standard conditions"). It is well known that at standard conditions one gram-mole of all the common gases occupies a volume of 22.415 liters or 22,415 cm³ (approximately 22,400 cm³). Hence if the sample comprises n gram-moles, its volume $V_0 = n \times 22.4$ liters $= n \times 22,400$ cm³. Therefore in cgs units

$$p_0 V_0 \beta_0 = 1.013 \times 10^6 \times n \times 22,400 \times .00366$$
$$= n \times 8.31 \times 10^7 \text{ dyne-cm/C° or ergs/C°,}$$

and in a common hybrid system in which the pressure unit is 1 atm and the volume unit is 1 liter,

$$p_0 V_0 \beta_0 = 1 \times n \times 22.4 \times .00366$$
$$= n \times 0.08207 \text{ liter-atm/C}°.$$

The coefficients 8.31×10^7 or 0.08207 are the same for all gases; their numerical value is determined by the choice of units. Both are represented by the letter R, referred to as the *universal gas constant*.

$$\left.\begin{array}{l} R = 8.31 \times 10^7 \text{ ergs/mole C}° \\ = .08207 \text{ liter-atm/mole C}° \end{array}\right\} \qquad (19\text{-}8)$$

Consider next the term in parentheses in Eq. (19-7), $\left(t + \dfrac{1}{\beta_0}\right)$. Since β_0 is in reciprocal centigrade degrees, $1/\beta_0$ is in centigrade degrees and represents a temperature. The addition of this temperature to the centigrade temperature t is equivalent to expressing temperatures on a new scale whose zero point is lower than the centigrade zero by $1/\beta_0$ degrees, but in which *the unit temperature interval is the same as on the centigrade scale*. Temperatures on this scale are called *centigrade absolute* or *Kelvin* temperatures and will be represented by T.

$$T = t + \frac{1}{\beta_0} = t + \frac{1}{.00366} = t + 273.2. \qquad (19\text{-}9)$$

Eq. (19-7) may now be written

$$\boxed{pV = nRT,} \qquad (19\text{-}10)$$

where if p is in atmospheres, V in liters, n in gram-moles and T in degrees Kelvin, $R = 0.08207$ lit-atm/mole K°, and if p is in dynes/cm², V in cm³, n in gram-moles and T in degrees Kelvin, $R = 8.31 \times 10^7$ ergs/mole K°. Eq. (19-10) is known as *the equation of state of an ideal gas*.

Notice that nothing in the foregoing discussion precludes the existence of temperatures lower than zero on the Kelvin scale. It is true, from Eq. (19-10), that the volume of an ideal gas kept at constant pressure would become zero at the Kelvin zero of temperature, or the pressure of an ideal gas kept at constant volume would become zero at this temperature. These consequences alone do not imply that still lower temperatures would be unattainable. The true significance of absolute zero as the lower limit of attainable temperatures can only be brought out in the light of reasoning based on the second law of thermodynamics. This will be done in Chapter 20.

The number of moles n in a sample of gas equals the mass m of the gas divided by its molecular weight. If the latter is represented by M, then

$$n = \frac{m}{M}.$$

Hence we may write,

$$pV = m \frac{R}{M} T. \tag{19-11}$$

By definition, the density of the gas, ρ, is

$$\rho = \frac{m}{V},$$

and therefore Eq. (19-10) may be written

$$p = \rho \frac{R}{M} T \quad \text{or} \quad \rho = \frac{pM}{RT}. \tag{19-12}$$

The density of a gas is seen to depend on its pressure and temperature as well as on its molecular weight. Hence in tabulating gas densities the pressure and temperature must be specified. The densities of a few common gases are listed in Table 19-1.

The molar volume is defined as the volume per mole, V/n. This is also represented by v and in terms of it Eq. (19-10) becomes

$$pv = RT. \tag{19-13}$$

(It is not worth-while to attempt to memorize these various forms of the ideal gas equation. Eq. (19-10) is sufficient.)

TABLE 19-1

DENSITIES OF GASES

(grams per cm³ at 1 atm and 0° C)

Air...	1.2929×10^{-3}
Argon...	1.7832
Carbon dioxide.............................	1.9769
Helium.......................................	0.1785
Hydrogen....................................	0.0899
Nitrogen.....................................	1.2506
Oxygen......................................	1.4290

A more familiar form of the ideal gas equation may be obtained by writing Eq. (19-10) in the form

$$\frac{pV}{T} = nR. \tag{19-14}$$

If a fixed mass of gas is carried through any sort of process, the right side of Eq. (19-14) will have the same value at all stages of the process. Hence if subscripts 1 and 2 refer to any two states,

$$\boxed{\frac{p_1 V_1}{T_1} = \frac{p_2 V_2}{T_2}.} \qquad (19\text{-}15)$$

Examples: (1) How many kilograms of O_2 are contained in a tank whose volume is 2 ft³ when the gauge pressure is 2000 lb/in² and the temperature is 27° C? Assume the ideal gas laws to hold. The molecular weight of oxygen is 32 gm/mole.

$$2 \text{ ft}^3 = 2 \times 28.3 = 56.6 \text{ liters.}$$

$$p_{abs} = 2015 \text{ lb/in}^2 = \frac{2015}{14.7} = 137 \text{ atm.}$$

$$T = t + 273 = 300° \text{ K.}$$

Hence, from Eq. (19-10),

$$n = \frac{pV}{RT} = \frac{137 \times 56.6}{.082 \times 300}$$

$$= 315 \text{ moles.}$$

$$m = 315 \times 32 = 10,100 \text{ gm}$$

$$= 10.1 \text{ kgm.}$$

(2) What volume would be occupied by this gas if it were allowed to expand to atmospheric pressure at a temperature of 50° C?

Since we are dealing with a fixed mass of gas, we may write

$$\frac{p_1 V_1}{T_1} = \frac{p_2 V_2}{T_2},$$

$$V_2 = V_1 \frac{p_1}{p_2} \frac{T_2}{T_1}$$

$$= 2 \times \frac{137}{1} \times \frac{323}{300}$$

$$= 295 \text{ ft}^3.$$

19-4 Molecular theory of matter. The fact that matter is compressible suggests that all substances have a granular or spongy structure with spaces into which the granules can penetrate when the external pressure is increased. The ease with which liquids can flow and gases can diffuse points more to a collection of tiny particles than to a spongelike structure. Thousands of physical and chemical facts support the contention that matter in all phases is composed of tiny particles called *molecules*. The

molecules of any one substance are identical.   They have the same structure, the same mass, and the same mechanical and electrical properties.
Many of the large-scale properties of matter which have been discussed
heretofore, such as elasticity, surface tension, condensation, vaporization,
etc., can be comprehended with deeper understanding of their significance
in terms of the molecular theory.   For this purpose we may conceive of a
molecule as a rigid sphere, like a small billiard ball, capable of moving,
of colliding with other molecules or with a wall, and of exerting attractive
or repulsive forces on neighboring molecules.   In other parts of physics
and chemistry it is important to consider the structure of the molecule,
but this is not necessary at this point.

One of the outstanding characteristics of a molecule is the force that
exists between it and a neighbor.   There is, of course, a force of gravitational attraction between every pair of molecules, but it turns out that
this is negligible in comparison with the forces we are now considering.
The forces that hold the molecules of a liquid (or solid) together are, in
part at least, of electrical origin and do not follow a simple inverse square
law.   When the separation of the molecules is large, as in a gas, the force
is extremely small and is an attraction.   The attractive force increases
as a gas is compressed and its molecules brought closer together.   But
since tremendous pressures are needed to compress a liquid, i.e. to force
its molecules closer together than their normal spacing in the liquid state,
we conclude that at separations only slightly less than the dimensions
of a molecule the force is one of repulsion and is relatively large.   The
force must then vary with separation in somewhat the fashion shown in
Fig. 19-4.   At large separations the
force is one of attraction but is extremely small.   The force of attraction at first increases as the separation decreases, then passes through
zero and changes to a large force of
repulsion when the separation is less
than r_0.

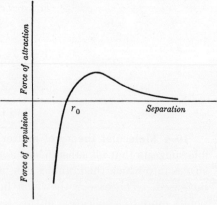

A single pair of molecules could
remain in equilibrium at a center-to-
center spacing equal to r_0 in Fig.
19-4.   If they were separated slightly
the force between them would be
attractive and they would be drawn
together.   If they were forced closer

FIG. 19-4.   Intermolecular force as a
function of separation.

together than the distance r_0 the force would be one of repulsion and they would spring apart.   If they were either pulled apart or pushed together, and then released, they would oscillate about their equilibrium separation r_0.

If the only property of a molecule were the force of attraction between it and its neighbors, all matter would eventually coalesce into the liquid or solid phase.   The existence of gases points to another property which enables molecules to stay apart.   This is accomplished by molecular motion.   The more vigorous the motion the less chance there is for condensation into the liquid or solid phase.   In solids the molecules execute vibratory motion about more or less fixed centers.   This vibratory motion is relatively weak and the centers remain fixed at regularly spaced positions which comprise a *space lattice*.   This gives rise to the extraordinary regularity and symmetry of crystals.   In liquids the molecules execute vibratory motion of greater energy about centers which are free to move but which remain at approximately the same distance from one another. The molecules of gases have the greatest kinetic energy.   The motion is linear until collision takes place either with another molecule or with a wall. The average distance between molecules of a gas is so great that only small attractive forces exist.

A common substance like water exists in the solid phase at low temperatures.   When the temperature is raised beyond a definite value, the liquid phase results, and when the temperature of the liquid is raised further, the water exists in the gaseous phase.   That is, from a large-scale or *macroscopic* point of view, the transition from solid to liquid to gas is in the direction of increasing temperature.   From a molecular point of view this transition is in the direction of increasing molecular kinetic energy.   Evidently, *there must be some connection between temperature and molecular kinetic energy.*

The preceding paragraphs may be conveniently summarized by means of Table 19-2.

The reason that the surface of a liquid behaves somewhat like a mem-

TABLE 19-2

Phase	Attractive forces among molecules	Molecular kinetic energy	Temperature
Solid..............	Strong	Small	Low
Liquid............	Moderate	Moderate	Medium
Gas...............	Weak	Large	High

brane under tension may be understood in terms of the attractive forces among molecules. A molecule of the surface is much closer to a neighboring molecule in the liquid phase than to a molecule in the gaseous phase above the liquid. It is therefore attracted downward until it is close enough to its neighbors to give rise to a repulsion which is large enough to cause equilibrium. An increase in kinetic energy is attended by a greater average intermolecular distance and therefore a weaker "skin effect" or surface tension. Hence an increase in temperature always causes a decrease in surface tension.

19-5 Kinetic theory of an ideal gas. If the molecules of a gas are, on the average, far enough apart, the forces of attraction are exceedingly weak. We define an ideal gas as one whose molecules exert no forces on one another, except when they collide. Collisions are assumed to be perfectly elastic, so that the total kinetic energy of two molecules before collision is the same as that after a collision. Let us suppose that the gas is in a container which, for the sake of simplicity, is a cube of volume V.

The pressure exerted by the gas is due to molecular collisions with the walls of the container. For an elastic impact, a molecule approaching a wall with momentum mv will recede from the wall with momentum $-mv$. The change in momentum of the molecule will therefore be $-2mv$. To determine the pressure of the gas, we must first calculate the force exerted on one of the six walls of the cube and then divide this force by the area A of the wall.

In general, a molecule near the center of the container will undergo many collisions with other molecules before it arrives at a wall. For a given temperature and pressure there exists an average distance that a molecule may traverse before it collides with another molecule. This is called its *mean free path*. Imagine a plane situated at any distance from one wall less than the mean free path. Between this plane and the wall all molecules that happen to be moving perpendicularly toward the wall will reach it without colliding with other molecules on the way. In this space let

v_1 = a velocity component perpendicular to the wall,

N_1 = the number of molecules per unit volume which have the velocity component v_1.

t = the average time it takes such a molecule to reach the wall.

Then the number of molecules striking the wall in time t is equal to

$$\frac{N_1}{2} A v_1 t,$$

since only half are moving *toward* the wall. Each of these molecules undergoes a change of momentum upon collision equal to $-2mv$. Therefore, the rate of change of momentum of these molecules equals

$$\frac{\dfrac{N_1}{2} A v_1 t \times (-2mv_1)}{t}$$

and, by Newton's second law, this must represent the force exerted by the wall on these molecules. From Newton's third law, however, this is equal in magnitude but opposite in direction to the force exerted *on* the wall. The pressure, therefore, due to the collision of these molecules only is equal to

$$p_1 = \frac{\dfrac{N_1}{2} A v_1 t \times (2mv_1)}{At}$$

or

$$p_1 = N_1 m v_1^2.$$

Consider now another group of molecules, N_2 per unit volume, that have a different velocity component v_2 perpendicular to the wall. Their collisions with the wall will give rise to an additional pressure

$$p_2 = N_2 m v_2^2.$$

The total pressure p due to all the molecules is therefore equal to

$$p = N_1 m v_1^2 + N_2 m v_2^2 + N_3 m v_3^2 + \cdots, \qquad (19\text{-}16)$$

where all possible values of the velocity component perpendicular to the wall are taken into account.

If we regard the direction perpendicular to the wall as that of the X-axis, we may define an average of the squares of the X-components of velocity by the expression

$$\overline{v_x^2} = \frac{N_1 v_1^2 + N_2 v_2^2 + N_3 v_3^2 + \cdots}{N},$$

in which N represents the total number of molecules per unit volume. Substituting this value of $\overline{v_x^2}$ into the expression for the pressure, Eq. (19-16), we get

$$p = N m \overline{v_x^2}. \qquad (19\text{-}17)$$

If v is the magnitude of the velocity of any one molecule, then v may be expressed in terms of its X-, Y-, and Z-components, as follows:

$$v^2 = v_x{}^2 + v_y{}^2 + v_z{}^2.$$

Averaging over all the molecules, we get

$$\overline{v^2} = \overline{v_x{}^2} + \overline{v_y{}^2} + \overline{v_z{}^2}.$$

But the gas is uniform throughout the container. The average of the squares of the velocity components in any one direction is the same as that for any other direction. Therefore

$$\overline{v_x{}^2} = \overline{v_y{}^2} = \overline{v_z{}^2}$$

and

$$\overline{v^2} = 3\overline{v_z{}^2}.$$

Substituting this result in Eq. (19-17), we get finally

$$p = \frac{1}{3} N m \overline{v^2}. \qquad (19\text{-}18)$$

If $\mathbf{N}$ is the total number of molecules in the container of volume V, then $N = \mathbf{N}/V$ and

$$p = \frac{1}{3} \frac{\mathbf{N}}{V} m \overline{v^2}$$

or

$$pV = \frac{2}{3} \mathbf{N} \times \frac{1}{2} m \overline{v^2}. \qquad (19\text{-}19)$$

The kinetic energy of a single molecule is $\frac{1}{2} m v^2$. The average kinetic energy per molecule is therefore $\frac{1}{2} m \overline{v^2}$. We have already come to the conclusion that molecular kinetic energy is somehow connected with temperature, so let us assume, in the case of an ideal gas, that

$$\frac{1}{2} m \overline{v^2} = \frac{3}{2} kT, \qquad (19\text{-}20)$$

where k is a universal constant, known as *Boltzmann's constant*. It follows therefore that

$$pV = \frac{2}{3} \mathbf{N} \times \frac{3}{2} kT,$$

or

$$pV = \mathbf{N}kT. \qquad (19\text{-}21)$$

Comparing this equation with the equation of state of an ideal gas, namely,

$$pV = nRT,$$

we see that all ideal gases at the same temperature and pressure and oc-cupying the same volume have not only the same number of moles but also the same number of molecules. This result was first announced by Avogadro and therefore the universal constant N_0, equal to the number of molecules per mole, is known as *Avogadro's number*. Thus

$$\mathbf{N} = nN_0.$$

Rewriting Eq. (19-21), we get

$$pV = nN_0kT,$$

which shows that the universal gas constant R is the product of Avogadro's number N_0 and Boltzmann's constant k.

We have therefore derived the equation of state of an ideal gas from the laws of mechanics with the aid of the assumptions that

(1) An ideal gas consists of identical, "rigid sphere," elastic molecules.

(2) The molecules move with uniform linear motion between impacts.

(3) The molecules exert no forces on one another, except during impact.

(4) The average kinetic energy per molecule is proportional to the Kelvin temperature.

Since there are no attractive forces among the molecules of an ideal gas, these molecules have no potential energy. The total energy U of an ideal gas is therefore entirely kinetic. Since the average kinetic energy per molecule is $3/2kT$, we have

$$U = \frac{3}{2}\mathbf{N}kT$$

or

$$U = \frac{3}{2}nRT, \qquad (19\text{-}22)$$

which says that *the energy of an ideal gas is proportional to the Kelvin temper-ature* and depends on temperature only, independent of the pressure and of the volume. It must be emphasized that Eq. (19-22) is of *very restricted validity*. It holds only for an aggregate of rigid, "billiard-ball" molecules which exert no forces on one another, which do not rotate, vibrate, or dissociate. Equation (19-22) will therefore be expected to break down at very low temperatures where the molecules get close enough to exert forces on one another, and also at high temperatures where molecules start to vibrate, dissociate, or undergo electronic rearrangements. We *cannot* infer from Eq. (19-22) that, at absolute zero, the kinetic energy of the molecules equals zero, because long before absolute zero is approached the molecules begin to attract one another, condensation takes place, and Eq. (19-22) breaks down.

It is shown in advanced textbooks that the energy of a substance in a condensed phase is a very complicated function of the temperature, in no way resembling Eq. (19-22). This function has the property that, as the temperature approaches zero, *the energy does not approach zero*, but approaches a constant value, known as the *zero-point energy*. In the case of helium at low temperature, the zero-point energy is so large that the molecules of liquid cannot get close enough together to form a solid, unless the pressure is raised to about 25 atmospheres. In the absence of this high pressure, helium would remain a liquid down to absolute zero.

19-6 Specific heats of an ideal gas. The temperature of a gas may be raised under a variety of conditions. The volume may be kept constant, or the pressure may be kept constant, or they both may be allowed to vary in some definite manner. In each of these cases, the amount of heat necessary to cause unit rise of temperature in unit mass would be different. In other words, a gas has many different heat capacities. Only two, however, are of practical use, namely, at constant volume and at constant pressure.

Let us choose as a convenient unit of mass the number of grams equal to the molecular weight, that is, a mole. The corresponding heat capacity is called the molar heat capacity. If we have n moles of an ideal gas with a molar heat capacity at constant volume C_v and we raise its temperature at constant volume from T_1 to T_2, then the heat transferred is $nC_v(T_2 - T_1)$ and the work done is zero. From the first law we get

$$nC_v(T_2 - T_1) = U_2 - U_1 + 0. \tag{19-23}$$

If the same amount of the same gas were heated at constant pressure p until the temperature changed the same amount, then the heat transferred would be $nC_p(T_2 - T_1)$, where C_p is the molar heat capacity at constant pressure. In this process, however, the gas would expand, say, from volume V_1 to V_2 and an amount of work $p(V_2 - V_1)$ would be done. Therefore, using the first law,

$$nC_p(T_2 - T_1) = U_2' - U_1' + p(V_2 - V_1). \tag{19-24}$$

Now U_1 and U_1' are the internal energies, respectively, of an ideal gas at the same temperature T_1 but at different pressures. Since the energy of an ideal gas is a function of temperature only, $U_1 = U_1'$, and similarly, $U_2 = U_2'$.

Subtracting Eq. (19-23) from Eq. (19-24) we get

$$n(C_p - C_v)(T_2 - T_1) = p(V_2 - V_1). \qquad (19\text{-}25)$$

But

$$pV_1 = nRT_1,$$

and

$$pV_2 = nRT_2,$$

so that

$$p(V_2 - V_1) = nR(T_2 - T_1).$$

Substituting this result in Eq. (19-17), we get

$$n(C_p - C_v)(T_2 - T_1) = nR(T_2 - T_1),$$

or finally

$$\boxed{C_p - C_v = R.} \qquad (19\text{-}26)$$

This equation shows that the molar heat capacity at constant pressure of an ideal gas is always larger than that at constant volume, the difference being the universal gas constant R. Of course R must be expressed in the same units as C_p and C_v, usually cal/mole C°. Since $R = 8.31$ joules/mole C° and 4.19 joules $= 1$ cal,

$$R = \frac{8.31}{4.19} = 1.99 \; \frac{\text{cal}}{\text{mole C}°}$$

or very nearly 2 cal/mole C°.

Eq. (19-26) is strictly true only for an ideal gas but is very nearly true for real gases at moderate pressures. Measured values of C_p and C_v are given in Table 19-3 for some real gases at low pressures, and the difference is seen to be very nearly 2 cal/mole C°.

In the last column of Table 19-3 are listed the values of the ratio C_p/C_v denoted by the greek letter γ (gamma). It is seen that γ is 1.67 for monatomic gases, and is very nearly 1.40 for the so-called permanent diatomic gases. There is no simple regularity for polyatomic gases.

Solids and liquids also expand when heated, if free to do so, and hence perform work. The coefficients of volume expansion of solids and liquids are, however, so much smaller than those of gases that the external work is small.   The internal energy of a solid or liquid *does* depend on its volume as well as its temperature and this must be considered when evaluating the difference between specific heats of solids or liquids.   It turns out that here also $C_p > C_v$, but the difference is small and is not expressible as simply as that for a gas.   Because of the large stresses set up when solids or liquids are heated and *not* allowed to expand, most heating processes involving them take place at constant pressure and hence C_p is the quantity usually measured for a solid or liquid.

TABLE 19-3

MOLAR HEAT CAPACITIES OF GASES AT LOW PRESSURE

Type of Gas	Gas	C_p in $\dfrac{cal}{mole\ C°}$	C_v in $\dfrac{cal}{mole\ C°}$	$C_p - C_v$	$\gamma = \dfrac{C_p}{C_v}$
Monatomic	He	4.97	2.98	1.99	1.67
"	A	4.97	2.98	1.99	1.67
Diatomic	H_2	6.87	4.88	1.99	1.41
"	N_2	6.95	4.96	1.99	1.40
"	O_2	7.03	5.04	1.99	1.40
"	CO	6.97	4.98	1.99	1.40
Polyatomic	CO_2	8.83	6.80	2.03	1.30
"	SO_2	9.65	7.50	2.15	1.29
"	H_2S	8.37	6.2	2.1	1.34

19-7 Adiabatic compression or expansion of an ideal gas.   When an ideal gas is compressed adiabatically, the work done on the gas serves to increase the internal energy.   Since the internal energy is a function of the temperature only, the temperature therefore rises.   Conversely, in an adiabatic expansion of an ideal gas, the temperature decreases.

In Fig. 19-5, the heavy curves represent adiabatic curves on a p-V diagram.   The dashed curves represent isotherms for comparison.   The adiabatic curves, at any point, have a somewhat steeper slope than the isothermal curve passing through the same point.   That is, as one follows along an adiabatic from right to left (compression process) the curve

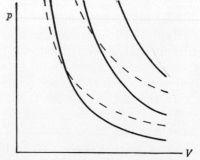

FIG. 19-5.   Adiabatic curves (full lines) vs isothermal curves (dashed lines).

continually cuts across isotherms of higher and higher temperatures, in agreement with the fact that the temperature continually increases in an adiabatic compression. It can be shown that the equation of an adiabatic curve for an ideal gas is

$$pV^\gamma = \text{const,} \quad ADIABATIC$$

where γ is the ratio of the heat capacities listed in the last column of Table 19-3.

19-8 Liquefaction of gases. An ideal gas, if compressed isothermally, remains a gas no matter how great a pressure is applied to it; the volume decreases continually with increasing pressure according to Boyle's Law. All real gases, however, become liquids when the pressure is increased sufficiently (provided the temperature is below a certain value known as the critical temperature.)

The difference between the behaviour of an ideal and a real gas in an isothermal compression is illustrated in Fig. 19-6(a) and (b). Imagine the gases to be contained within two similar cylinders each provided with a piston and a pressure gauge. The volume at each stage of the compression process is proportional to the distance of the piston from the closed end of the cylinder, and the pressure at each stage may be read from the gauge. Several stages of the compression are illustrated in each part of the figure, and corresponding pressures and volumes are plotted in the p-V diagrams. Each gas is initially at the same pressure and volume (point a), and the temperature of each is held constant throughout by the removal of heat.

As the piston in (a) is forced to the left, the reading of the pressure gauge rises steadily, and the relation between p and V is the familiar Boyle's Law. As the volume of the real gas is decreased, in Fig. 19-6(b), the pressure rises at first along the curve a-b in a manner not very different from that of the ideal gas. When point b is reached, however, a sharp break occurs in the curve, and the volume continues to decrease *without further increase of pressure*. At the same time, drops of liquid begin to appear on the walls of the cylinder. In other words, the process of *liquefaction* or *condensation* begins at point b.

As the volume is further reduced, from b to c and d, the quantity of liquid in the cylinder increases and the quantity of gas decreases. At point e, all of the substance has been converted into the liquid phase. Of course, during the transition from b to e, it was necessary to remove from the substance its heat of condensation.

Since liquids are nearly incompressible, a very large pressure increase

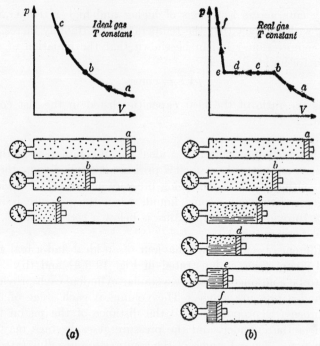

FIG. 19-6.   Isothermal compression of (a) an ideal gas; (b) a real gas.

is necessary to reduce the volume below that at point e.   That is, the curve rises nearly vertically from e to f, having a very small inclination toward the left.

As an example, if cylinder (b) had initially contained one gram of steam at 100° C, at a pressure of about $\frac{1}{2}$ atm and a volume of about 3000 cm³ (point a), condensation would begin when the pressure had increased to 1 atm and the volume decreased to 1670 cm³ (point b).   The pressure would remain constant at 1 atm from b to e, while the volume decreased from 1670 cm³ to 1 cm³.   529 cal would have to be removed during the condensation process.   To produce a further decrease in volume of 0.001 cm³, it would be necessary to increase the pressure to about 20 atm (point f).

If the experiment illustrated in Fig. 19-6(b) is repeated, starting at higher and higher temperatures, it is found that greater and greater pressures must be exerted on the gas before condensation begins.   Fig. 19-7 illustrates the curves obtained.   It will be seen that point b moves toward the left and point e toward the right until at the particular temperature lettered T_c in Fig. 19-7 the two points coincide. Above this temperature there is no straight horizontal portion to the curve. In other words, there is no stage in the compression process at which the substance separates into two distinct portions, one of which is a gas while the other is a liquid. The temperature T_c is called the *critical* temperature, and it is now evident why a gas must be first cooled below its critical temperature before it can be liquefied by compression.

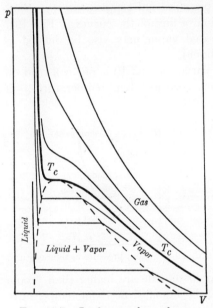

FIG. 19-7. Isotherms of a real gas.

It is customary to refer to a gas below its critical temperature as a *vapor*, although this distinction is not rigidly adhered to. Critical temperatures of some common gases are given in Table 19-4.

The dotted line in Fig. 19-7 divides the p-V plane into three regions. At all values of p, V, and T underneath this line, the substance is partly in the liquid and partly in the vapor phase. At the right of the curve it is a vapor or gas, at the left of the curve it is a liquid.

An examination of Fig. 19-7 shows that at any given temperature below the critical temperature there is one pressure and one pressure only at which the substance can exist in either the liquid or the vapor phase,

TABLE 19-4

CRITICAL TEMPERATURES, PRESSURES AND VOLUMES

Substance	Critical temperature (°C)	Critical pressure (atm)	Critical volume (cm³/gm)
Ammonia.	132	112	4.25
Argon.	−122	48	1.88
Carbon dioxide.	31	73.0	2.17
Helium.	−268	2.26	14.4
Hydrogen.	−240	12.8	32.3
Oxygen.	−119	49.7	2.33
Sulphur dioxide.	157	77.7	1.92
Water.	374	218	3.14

or in both phases simultaneously. This is the pressure corresponding to the horizontal portion of the isothermal curve for that particular temperature. If the pressure is any higher than that at the horizontal portion, the substance can only be a liquid. If the pressure is any lower, it can only be a vapor. Precisely at this pressure both liquid and vapor can exist together. The pressure at which a liquid and its vapor can exist in equilibrium, at any given temperature, is called the *vapor pressure* at that temperature. A vapor whose pressure and temperature are those corresponding to the horizontal portion of any of the curves in Fig. 19-7 is called a *saturated vapor*. A saturated vapor may also be defined as one which is in equilibrium with its liquid.

From the straight portions of the curves of Fig. 19-7, one can read off a series of vapor pressures and their corresponding temperatures. If these are plotted as in Fig. 19-8, one obtains the *vapor pressure curve* of the substance. All vapor pressure curves are similar in form to that of Fig. 19-8, rising with a continually increasing slope and ending at the critical point. An abridged table of the vapor pressure of water is given in Table 19-5.

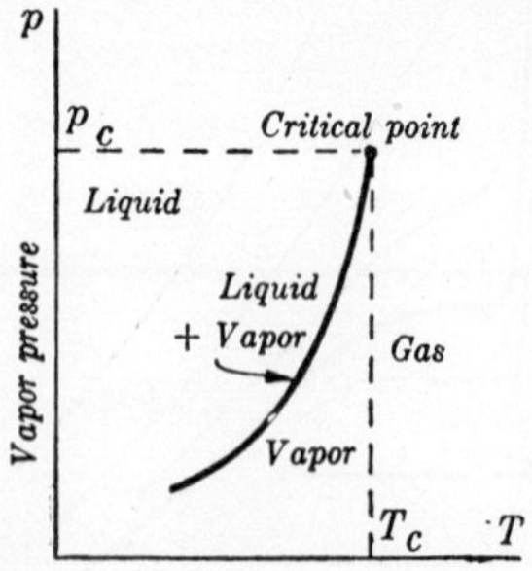

Reference to Table 19-4 will show that the critical temperatures

Fig. 19-8. Vapor pressure vs temperature.

of carbon dioxide, ammonia, and sulphur dioxide are higher than "room temperature." Hence these gases can be liquefied at room temperature without precooling, simply by increasing the pressure. Oxygen, nitrogen, or hydrogen, however, must evidently be precooled below room temperature before they can be liquefied. The Linde process for producing liquid air (or liquid oxygen or nitrogen) will be described briefly. See Fig. 19-9.

Compressor A maintains a continuous circulation of air as shown by the arrows. At B, the air leaving the compressor is at high pressure and high temperature. It enters cooling coils C, where it is cooled by air or water, and, still at high pressure, escapes through the small orifice or nozzle D, performing a *throttling* process. If air were an ideal gas, no temperature change would result from a throttling process. Real gases, however, undergo marked temperature changes in such a process, and if not too hot to begin with, are cooled in passing through the orifice. The pressure in E and F is kept low by the pump, and the cooled air passes up through E and F and repeats the cycle. The cooled air in E, circulating around the incoming air in D, cools it still further, hence an even

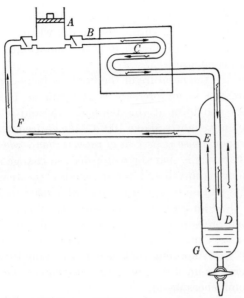

Fig. 19-9. Schematic diagram of Linde process for producing liquid air.

lower temperature is reached by the air escaping from D, until eventually the temperature falls sufficiently so that some of the air liquefies as it leaves the nozzle. The liquid air collects at G, where it may be drawn off.

19-9 Effect of pressure on boiling and freezing points. A pan of water exposed to the air of the room will evaporate, whatever its temperature, provided only that there is opportunity for the vapor to diffuse away, or to be removed in some manner from above the water surface. If the temperature of the water is increased to 100° C (at normal atmospheric pressure) the nature of the evaporation process changes completely. Vapor is formed not only at the liquid surface but throughout the entire volume of the liquid, which becomes violently agitated by the bubbles of vapor which rise through it and break at the surface. What distinguishes this violent process of *boiling* from the slow evaporation which goes on at temperatures below the boiling point?

It will be recalled that every liquid has a certain *vapor pressure* which depends on the temperature of the liquid. If, keeping the temperature constant, an attempt is made to increase the pressure *above* the vapor pressure, the vapor immediately condenses. The water in a vessel open to the atmosphere is subjected to atmospheric pressure. Say that the temperature of the water is 80° C. Its vapor pressure, from Table 19-5, is then 355 mm of mercury or 6.87 lb/in². Hence if a small bubble of vapor should chance to form within the liquid, where it is subjected to a pressure of 760 mm or 14.7 lb/in², it would immediately collapse under the pressure and condense.

Suppose now the temperature of the liquid is increased to 100° C. At this temperature the vapor pressure is 760 mm or 14.7 lb/in². Hence bubbles of vapor can form at this temperature, and if the temperature were to increase only slightly above 100° C, the entire mass of water would change to the vapor phase *if its heat of vaporization could be supplied to it*. What actually happens is that the water does so change as fast as heat is supplied. As long as any liquid water remains, the temperature cannot rise above 100° C and all of the heat supplied is used to produce a *change of phase* rather than an *increase in temperature*.

If the external pressure is suddenly increased above 14.7 lb/in², boiling immediately ceases, since the pressure is higher than the vapor pressure of water at 100° C. Assuming that heat is still supplied to the water, its temperature increases until the vapor pressure equals the applied pressure when boiling commences again.

It is evident that under an external pressure less than atmospheric, boiling will take place at a temperature below 100° C. From Table 19-5,

TABLE 19-5

VAPOR PRESSURE OF WATER (ABSOLUTE)

t (° C)	Vapor Pressure		t (° F)
	mm of mercury	lb/in²	
0	4.58	.0886	32
5	6.51	.126	41
10	8.94	.173	50
15	12.67	.245	59
20	17.5	.339	68
40	55.1	1.07	104
60	149	2.89	140
80	355	6.87	176
100	760	14.7	212
120	1490	28.8	248
140	2710	52.4	284
160	4630	89.6	320
180	7510	145	356
200	11650	225	392
220	17390	336	428

if the pressure is reduced to .339 lb/in^2, water will boil at room temperature (20° C).

The boiling point of a liquid is that temperature at which the vapor pressure of the liquid is equal to the external pressure.

Freezing points as well as boiling points are affected by external pressure. The freezing point of a substance like water, which expands on solidifying, is *lowered* by an increase in pressure. The reverse is true for substances which contract on solidifying. The change in the freezing point temperature is much smaller than is that of the boiling point, an increase of one atmosphere lowering the freezing point of water by only about 0.007° C.

The lowering of the freezing point of water (or the melting point of ice) can be demonstrated by passing a loop of fine wire over a block of ice and hanging a weight of a few pounds from each end of the loop. Suppose that the main body of the ice is at 0° C and at atmospheric pressure. The temperature of the small amount of ice directly under the wire decreases until it achieves the melting point appropriate to the pressure under the wire. During this increase of pressure and decrease of temperature, a small amount of melting takes place. The water thus formed is squeezed out from under the wire and, coming to the top of the wire where the pressure is atmospheric, it refreezes and liberates heat which passes through the wire and serves to melt the next bit of ice below the wire.

The wire thus sinks farther and farther into the block, eventually cutting its way completely through, but leaving a solid block of ice behind it. The phenomenon is known as *regelation* (refreezing). Since heat is conducted from the top to the bottom of the wire while the wire is cutting through the ice, the greater the thermal conductivity of the wire, the faster will the wire cut through the ice. Even a perfectly conducting wire would not cut through the ice very rapidly, however, because of the very low thermal conductivity of the water film which is always present beneath the wire.

19-10 The triple point. The vapor pressure curve of Fig. 19-8 can be considered to represent the pressure and temperature at which a change of phase from liquid to vapor will occur, or as the pressure and temperature at which both phases can remain in equilibrium with one another. There exist similar curves representing the pressure and temperature at which solid and liquid can be in equilibrium, and at which solid and vapor can be in equilibrium. These curves are shown in Fig. 19-10 and they intersect at a common point, called the *triple point*, at which all three phases can exist simultaneously.

The three curves in Fig. 19-10 divide the p-T plane into three regions. At any point (i.e. any pair of values of p and T) within one of these regions, the substance can exist in one phase only: solid, liquid, or vapor. Along each line, two phases can exist together, while only at the triple point can all three phases coexist.

For example, the triple-point temperature of CO_2 is $-56.6°$ C and the triple-point pressure is 5.11 atm.

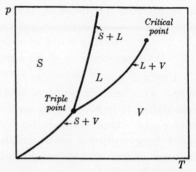

FIG. 19-10.   Pressure-temperature diagram

It is evident from Fig. 19-11 (not to a uniform scale) that at atmospheric pressure CO_2 can exist only as a solid or a vapor.   Hence solid CO_2 (dry ice) transforms directly to CO_2 vapor when open to the atmosphere, without passing through the liquid state.   This direct transition from solid to vapor is called *sublimation*.   Liquid CO_2 can only exist at a pressure greater than 5.11 atm.   The steel tanks in which CO_2 is commonly stored contain liquid and vapor.   The pressure in these tanks is the vapor pressure of CO_2 at the temperature of the tank.   If the latter is 20° C, the vapor pressure is about 56 atm or 830 lb/in².

While most substances increase in volume in the change of phase from solid to liquid, there are a few for which the reverse is true.   Water, of course, is one of the latter.   For such a substance an *increase* of pressure produces a *lowering* of the freezing point as shown in Fig. 19-12.   This effect was mentioned earlier in connection with regelation.

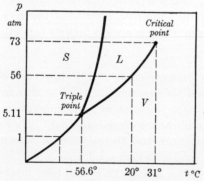

FIG. 19-11.   Pressure-temperature diagram of CO_2.   (Not to a uniform scale.)

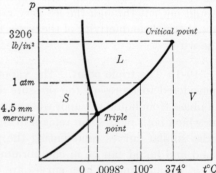

FIG. 19-12.   Pressure-temperature diagram of H_2O.   (Not to a uniform scale.)

19-11 Humidity.   Atmospheric air is a mixture of gases, consisting of about 80% nitrogen, 18% oxygen, and small amounts of carbon dioxide, water vapor, and other gases.   The mass of water vapor per unit volume is called the *absolute humidity*.   The total pressure exerted by the atmosphere is the sum of the pressures exerted by its component gases.   These pressures are called the *partial pressures* of the components.   It is found that the partial pressure of each of the component gases of a gas mixture is very nearly the same as would be the actual pressure of that component alone if it occupied the same volume as does the mixture, a fact known as *Dalton's Law*.   That is, each of the gases of a gas mixture behaves independently of the others.   The partial pressure of water vapor in the atmosphere is ordinarily a few millimeters of mercury.

It should be evident that the partial pressure of water vapor at any given air temperature can never exceed the vapor pressure of water at that particular temperature.   Thus at 10° C, from Table 19-5, the partial pressure cannot exceed 8.94 mm, or at 15° C it cannot exceed 12.67 mm.   If the concentration of water vapor, or the absolute humidity, is such that the partial pressure equals the vapor pressure, the vapor is said to be *saturated*.   If the partial pressure is less than the vapor pressure, the vapor is *unsaturated*.   The ratio of the partial pressure to the vapor pressure at the same temperature is called the *relative humidity*, and is usually expressed as a percentage.

$$\text{Relative humidity } (\%) = 100 \times \frac{\text{partial pressure of water vapor}}{\text{vapor pressure at same temperature}}$$

The relative humidity is 100% if the vapor is saturated and zero if no water vapor at all is present.

Example.   The partial pressure of water vapor in the atmosphere is 10 mm and the temperature is 20° C.   Find the relative humidity.

From Table 19-5, the vapor pressure at 20° C is 17.5 mm.   Hence,

$$\text{relative humidity} = \frac{10}{17.5} \times 100 = 57\%.$$

Since the water vapor in the atmosphere is saturated when its partial pressure equals the vapor pressure at the air temperature, saturation can be brought about either by increasing the water vapor content or by lowering the temperature.   For example, let the partial pressure of water vapor be 10 mm when the air temperature is 20° C, as in the preceding example.   Saturation or 100% relative humidity could be attained either by introducing enough more water vapor (keeping the temperature constant) to increase the partial pressure to 17.5 mm, *or by lowering the temperature* to 11.4° C, at which, by interpolation from Table 19-5, the vapor pressure is 10 mm.

If the temperature were to be lowered *below* 11.4° C, the vapor pressure would be less than 10 mm.   The partial pressure would then be higher than the vapor pressure and enough vapor would condense to reduce the partial pressure to the vapor pressure at the lower temperature.   It is this process which brings about the formation of clouds, fog, and rain. The phenomenon is also of frequent occurrence at night when the earth's surface becomes cooled by radiation.   The condensed moisture is called *dew*.   If the vapor pressure is so low that the temperature must fall below 0° C before saturation exists, the vapor condenses into ice crystals in the form of frost.

The temperature at which the water vapor in a given sample of air becomes saturated is called the *dew point*.   Measuring the temperature of the dew point is the most accurate method of determining relative humidity.   The usual method is to cool a metal container having a bright, polished surface, and to observe its temperature when the surface becomes clouded with condensed moisture.   Suppose the dew point is observed in this way to be 10° C, when the air temperature is 20° C.   We then know that the water vapor in the air is saturated at 10° C, hence its partial pressure, from Table 19-5, is 8.94 mm, equal to the vapor pressure at 10° C.   The pressure necessary for saturation at 20° C is 17.5 mm. The relative humidity is therefore

$$\frac{8.94}{17.5} \times 100 = 51\%.$$

A simpler but less accurate method of determining relative humidity employs a *wet-and-dry bulb thermometer*.   Two thermometers are placed side by side, the bulb of one being kept moist by a wick dipping in water. The lower the relative humidity, the more rapid will be the evaporation from the wet bulb, and the lower will be its temperature below that of the dry bulb.   The relative humidity corresponding to any pair of wet-and-dry bulb temperatures is read from tables.

The *hair hygrometer* makes use of the fact that human hair absorbs or gives up moisture from the air in an amount which varies with relative humidity, and changes its length slightly with moisture content.   Several strands of hair are wrapped around a small pivoted shaft to which is attached a pointer.   The hair is kept taut by a light spring, and changes in its length cause the shaft to rotate and move the pointer over a scale.

19-12 Thermodynamic surfaces. The equation of state of a substance is a relation among the three variables, p, V, and T. If these quantities are laid off on three mutually perpendicular axes, the equation of state defines a *surface* in the p-V-T space. All possible states of the substance are represented by points on this surface, and all processes through which the substance may be carried are represented by lines in the surface. An isothermal process is a line in the surface at all points of which T is constant, or in other words, it is the intersection of the surface with a plane perpendicular to the temperature axis. Similarly, processes at constant pressure or volume are intersections of the surface with planes perpendicular to the pressure or volume axes. Such a surface is called a thermodynamic surface, although other variables than p, V, and T are often used.

Fig. 19-13 illustrates the simplest of all p-V-T surfaces, that of an ideal gas. A few isotherms are indicated by the heavy lines. When this surface is viewed in a direction perpendicular to the p-V plane, the isotherms appear as in Fig. 19-1.

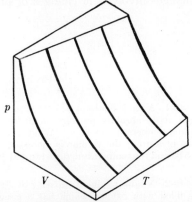

FIG. 19-13. p-V-T surface of an ideal gas

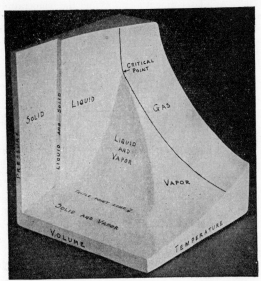

FIG. 19-14. p-V-T surface of a real substance.   (Not to a uniform scale.)

Fig. 19-14 is a photograph of the p-V-T surface of a real substance, not to a uniform scale. When viewed perpendicular to the p-V plane, the isotherms appear as in Fig. 19-7. The triple "point" is actually not a point but a line, since, although the pressure and temperature are fixed at that point, the volume is not. That is, the volume depends on the relative masses of the substance which are in each phase. If, for example, the substance is mostly in the vapor phase, with only small amounts of solid and liquid present, the volume will be large.

The surface is not constructed to scale because of the large volume changes involved in changes of phase.

Problems — Chapter 19

19-1. A tank contains 1.5 ft³ of nitrogen at an absolute pressure of 20 lb/in² and a temperature of 40°F. What will be the pressure if the volume is increased to 15 ft³ and the temperature raised to 440°F?

19-2. A tank having a capacity of 2 ft³ is filled with oxygen which has a gauge pressure of 60 lb per square inch when the temperature is 47°C. At a later time it is found that because of a leak the gauge pressure has dropped to 50 lb per square inch and the temperature has decreased to 27°C. Find: (a) The mass of the oxygen in the tank under the first set of conditions. (b) The amount of oxygen that has leaked out.

19-3. A flask of volume 2 liters, provided with a stopcock, contains oxygen at 300°K and atmospheric pressure. The system is heated to a temperature of 400°K, with the stopcock open to the atmosphere. The stopcock is then closed and the flask cooled to its original temperature. (a) What is the final pressure of the oxygen in the flask? (b) How many grams of oxygen remain in the flask?

19-4. A barrage balloon whose volume is 20,000 ft³ is to be filled with hydrogen at atmospheric pressure. If the hydrogen is stored in cylinders of volume 2 ft³ at an absolute pressure of 200 lb/in², how many cylinders are required?

19-5. A bubble of air rises from the bottom of a lake, where the pressure is 3.03 atmospheres (use 49/15), to the surface, where the pressure is 1 atmosphere. The temperature at the bottom of the lake is 7°C and the temperature at the surface is 27°C. What is the ratio of the size (i.e., the volume) of the bubble as it reaches the surface to the size of the bubble at the bottom?

19-6. Which is greater, the specific heat of a gas at constant pressure, or the specific heat at constant volume? Why?

19-7. Give an example of some process in which no heat is added to or removed from a system, but the temperature of the system decreases. If this is not possible, state why.

19-8. Give an example of some process in which heat is added to an object without changing its temperature.

19-9. 10 liters of air at atmospheric pressure is compressed isothermally to a volume of 2 liters. Show the process on a *p-V* diagram, carefully plotting the points. (You may assume that air is an ideal gas.) Approximately how much work is done by the gas during the compression? Find the answer directly from your *p-V* diagram. Tell how you obtained it. (You may give the answer in liter-atm.)

19-10. Ten cubic feet of air initially at 140°F expand at a constant gauge pressure of 20 lb/in² to a volume of 50 cubic feet, and then expand further adiabatically to a final volume of 80 cubic feet and a final gauge pressure of 3 lb/in². Sketch the process in a *p-V* diagram.

19-11. The cylinder of a pump compressing air from atmospheric pressure into a very large tank at 60 lb/in² gauge pressure is 10 inches long. (a) At what position in the stroke will air begin to enter the tank? Assume the compression to be adiabatic. (b) If the air is taken into the pump at 27°C, what is the temperature of the compressed air?

19-12. At the beginning of the compression stroke, the cylinder of a Diesel engine contains 48 cubic inches of air at atmospheric pressure and a temperature of 27°C. At the end of the stroke, the air has been compressed to a volume of 3 cubic inches, and the gauge pressure has increased to 600 lb per square inch. Compute the temperature, (a) in degrees Kelvin, (b) degrees Centigrade, (c) degrees Fahrenheit.

19-13. Derive from the equation of state an equation for the density of an ideal gas in terms of the pressure, temperature, and appropriate constants.

19-14. 2 moles of oxygen are initially at a temperature of 27°C and volume 20 liters. The gas is expanded first at constant pressure until the volume has doubled, and then adiabatically until the temperature returns to the original value. (a) What is the total increase in internal energy? (b) What is the final volume?

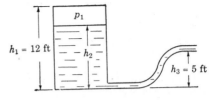

FIG. 19-15

19-15. A large tank of water has a hose connected to it, as shown in Fig. 19-15. The tank is sealed at the top and has compressed air between the water surface and the top. When the water height, h_2 is 10 ft, the gauge pressure, p_1, is 15 lb/in². Assume that the air above the water surface expands isothermally and take the weight density of water to be 64 lb/ft³. (a) What is the velocity of flow out of the hose when $h_2 = 10$ ft? (b) What is the velocity of flow of the hose when h_2 has decreased to 8 ft?

19-16. The volume of an ideal gas is 4 liters, the pressure 2 atm, and the temperature is 300°K. The gas first expands at constant pressure to twice its original volume, it is then compressed isothermally to its original volume, and finally cooled at constant volume to its original pressure. (a) Show the process in a *p-V* diagram. (b) Compute the temperature during the isothermal compression. (c) Compute the maximum pressure. (d) Explain how to find the *net* work done by the gas in the process.

19-17. Make two plots for a real gas, one showing pressure as a function of volume, and the other showing pressure as a function of temperature. Show on each graph the region in which the substance exists as (a) a gas or vapor, (b) a liquid, (c) a solid. Show also the triple point and the critical point.

19-18. A barometer is made of a tube 90 cm long and of cross section 1.5 cm². Mercury stands in this tube to a height of 75 cm. The room temperature is 27°C.

A small amount of nitrogen is introduced into the evacuated space above the mercury and the column drops to a height of 70 cm. How many grams of nitrogen were introduced?

19-19. The temperature in a room is 40°C. A can is gradually cooled by adding cold water. At 10°C the surface of the can clouds over. What is the relative humidity in the room?

19-20. A pan of water is placed in a sealed room of volume 60 m³ and at a temperature of 27°C. (a) What is the absolute humidity in gm/m³ after equilibrium has been reached? (b) If the temperature of the room is then increased 1 C° how many more grams of water will evaporate?

Molecular Data

N_0 = Avogadro's number = 6.02×10^{23} molecules/mole,

Mass of a hydrogen molecule = $2 \times 1.66 \times 10^{-24}$ gm,

Mass of a nitrogen molecule = $28 \times 1.66 \times 10^{-24}$ gm,

Mass of an oxygen molecule = $32 \times 1.66 \times 10^{-24}$ gm.

Diameter of a typical molecule = 3×10^{-8} cm.

19-21. Calculate Boltzmann's constant $k = R/N_0$ in ergs per molecule per degree.

19-22. Consider one mole of an ideal gas at 0°C and at 1 atm pressure. Imagine each molecule to be, on the average, at the center of a small cube. (a) What is the length of an edge of this small cube? (b) How does this distance compare with the diameter of a molecule?

19-23. A mole of liquid water occupies a volume of 18 cm³. Imagine each molecule to be, on the average, at the center of a small cube. What is the length of an edge of this small cube? How does this distance compare with the diameter of a molecule?

19-24. At what temperature is the velocity of an oxygen molecule equal to the velocity of a hydrogen molecule at a temperature of 27°C?

19-25. The velocity of sound in air at 27°C is about 1100 ft/sec. Compare this with the velocity of a nitrogen molecule at the same temperature.

CHAPTER 20

THE SECOND LAW OF THERMODYNAMICS

20-1 The second law of thermodynamics. The dominating feature of an industrial society is its ability to utilize, whether for wise or unwise ends, sources of energy other than the muscles of men or animals. Except for water power, where mechanical energy is directly available, most energy supplies are in the form of fuels such as coal or oil, where the energy is stored as internal energy. The process of combustion releases the internal energy and converts it to heat. In this form the energy may be utilized for heating habitations, for cooking, or for maintaining a furnace at high temperature in order to carry out other chemical or physical processes. But to operate a machine, or propel a vehicle or a projectile, the heat must be converted to mechanical energy, and one of the problems of the mechanical engineer is to carry out this conversion with the maximum possible efficiency.

There is only one type of process in which internal energy can be converted directly to mechanical energy, and that is when the chemical substances can be combined in an electrolytic cell. All other methods involve the intermediate step of transforming internal energy into heat. The changes may be represented schematically by

$$\text{Internal energy} \longrightarrow \text{Heat} \longrightarrow \text{Mechanical energy.}$$

The process represented by

$$\text{Internal energy} \longrightarrow \text{Heat}$$

presents few difficulties. The most common example is, of course, the combustion of coal, oil, or gas. The problem then reduces to

$$\text{Heat} \longrightarrow \text{Mechanical energy.}$$

It is evident in the first place that this transformation always requires the services of some sort of *engine*, such as a steam engine, gasoline engine, or Diesel engine.

At first sight the problem does not seem difficult, since we know that 1 Btu = 778 ft-lb, and it appears that every Btu of thermal energy should provide us with 778 ft-lb of mechanical energy. A pound of coal, for instance, develops about 13,000 Btu when burned, and might be expected to provide 13,000 × 778 ft-lb of mechanical work. Actual steam engines, however, furnish only from about 5% to about 30% of this value. What becomes of the remaining 70% to 95%?

Stack and friction losses account for only a small part, by far the largest part appearing as heat rejected in the exhaust. No one has ever constructed a heat engine which does not throw away in its exhaust a relatively large fraction of the heat supplied to it, and it is safe to say that no one ever will. The impossibility of constructing an engine which with no other outstanding changes will convert a given amount of heat *completely* into mechanical work is a fundamental law of Nature, known as *the second law of thermodynamics*. The first law, it will be recalled, is a statement of the principle of conservation of energy, and merely imposes the restriction that one can obtain *no more* than 778 ft-lb of mechanical work from every Btu of heat. It does not in itself restrict the fraction of a given amount of heat which an engine can convert into mechanical energy. The second law goes beyond the first, and states that 100% conversion is not possible by any form of engine. Of course, for that fraction of the heat supplied to it which an engine *does* convert to mechanical form, the equivalence expressed by the first law must hold true.

A young French engineer, Sadi Carnot, was the first to approach the problem of the efficiency of a heat engine from a truly fundamental standpoint. Improvements in steam engines, up to the time of Carnot's work in 1824, had either been along the lines of better mechanical design, or, if more basic improvements had been made, they had come about by chance or inspiration and had not been guided by any knowledge of basic principles. Carnot's contribution was a "theoretical" one, but it had more influence on the development of our industrial society in the 19th Century than the work of any of the "practical" men who had preceded him in this field.

Briefly, what Carnot did was to disregard the details of operation of a heat engine and focus attention on its truly significant features. These are, first, the engine is supplied with energy, in the form of heat, at a relatively high temperature. Second, the engine performs mechanical work. Third, the engine rejects heat at a lower temperature. In Carnot's time the caloric theory of heat as an indestructible fluid was still believed to be true, and Carnot pictured the flow of heat through an engine, from a higher to a lower temperature, as analogous to the flow of water through a water wheel or turbine from a higher to a lower elevation.

In any time interval, equal amounts of water enter the turbine and are discharged from it, but in the process some mechanical energy is abstracted from the water. Carnot believed that a similar process took place in a heat engine—some mechanical energy was abstracted from the heat but the amount of heat rejected by the engine in any time interval was equal to that delivered to the engine. We know now that this idea is incorrect, and that the heat rejected by the engine is less than the heat supplied to it by the amount that has been converted to mechanical work. In spite of his erroneous concept of the nature of heat, Carnot did in fact obtain the correct expression for the maximum efficiency of any heat engine operating between two given temperatures.

Since it is only heat and work that are of primary concern in a heat engine, we consider for simplicity an engine working in *closed cycles*. That is, the material that expands against a piston is periodically brought back to its initial condition so that in any one cycle the change in internal energy of this material, called the *working substance*, is zero. The condensing type of steam engine actually does operate in this way; the exhaust steam is condensed and forced back into the boiler so that the working substance (in this case, water) is used over and over again. The working substance then merely serves to transfer heat from one body to another, and, in virtue of its changes in volume, to convert some of the heat to mechanical work.

The energy transformations in a heat engine are conveniently represented schematically by the *flow diagram* of Fig. 20-1. The engine itself is represented by the circle. The heat Q_2 supplied to the engine is proportional to the cross section of the incoming "pipeline" at the top of the diagram. The cross section of the outgoing pipe line at the bottom is proportional to that portion of the heat, Q_1, which is rejected as heat in the exhaust. The branch line to the right represents that portion of the heat supplied which the engine converts to mechanical work, W. Since the working substance is periodically returned to its initial state and the change in its internal energy in any number of complete cycles is zero, it follows from the first law of thermodynamics that

$$W = Q_2 - Q_1.$$

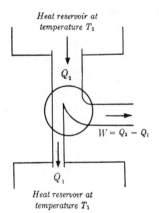

Heat reservoir at
temperature T_2

Q_2

$W = Q_2 - Q_1$

Q_1

Heat reservoir at
temperature T_1

FIG. 20-1. Schematic flow diagram of a heat engine.

That is, the mechanical work done equals the difference between the heat supplied and the heat rejected. (For convenience, W, Q_2, and Q_1 are all considered positive.)

The *thermal efficiency* E of the engine is the ratio of work output to heat input. The output is the mechanical work W. The exhaust heat is not considered a part of the output. The input is the heat Q_2. Hence

$$E = \frac{\text{Work output}}{\text{Heat input}},$$

$$= \frac{W}{Q_2},$$

$$\boxed{E = \frac{Q_2 - Q_1}{Q_2}.} \tag{20-1}$$

In terms of the flow diagram, the most efficient engine is the one for which the branch pipe line representing the work obtained is as large as possible, and the exhaust pipe line representing the heat rejected is as small as possible, for a given incoming pipe line or quantity of heat supplied.

We shall now consider, without going into the mechanical details of their construction, the internal combustion engine, the Diesel engine, and the steam engine.

20-2 The internal combustion engine. The common internal combustion engine is of the four-cycle type, so called because four processes take place in each cycle. Starting with the piston at the top of its stroke, an explosive mixture of air and gasoline vapor is drawn into the cylinder on the down-stroke, the inlet valve being open and the exhaust valve closed. This is the *intake* stroke. At the end of this stroke the inlet valve closes and the piston rises, performing an approximately adiabatic compression of the air-gasoline mixture. This is the *compression* stroke. At or near the top of this stroke a spark ignites the mixture of air and gasoline vapor, combustion taking place very rapidly. The pressure and temperature increase at nearly constant volume.

The piston is now forced down, the burned gases expanding approximately adiabatically. This is the *power stroke* or *working stroke*. At the end of the power stroke the exhaust valve opens. The pressure in the cylinder drops rapidly to atmospheric and the rising piston on the *exhaust stroke* forces out most of the remaining gas. The exhaust valve now closes, the inlet valve opens and the cycle is repeated.

For purposes of computation, the internal combustion cycle is approximated by the *air standard* or *Otto* cycle illustrated in Fig. 20-2.

Starting at point a, air at atmospheric pressure is compressed adiabatically in a cylinder to point b, heated at constant volume to point c, allowed to expand adiabatically to point d, and cooled at constant volume to point a, after which the cycle is repeated. Line ab corresponds to the compression stroke, bc to the explosion, cd to the working stroke,

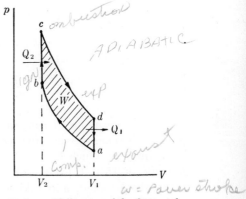

FIG. 20-2.   *p-V* diagram of the Otto cycle.

and da to the exhaust of an internal combustion engine. V_1 and V_2, in Fig. 20-2, are respectively the maximum and minimum volumes of the air in the cylinder. The ratio V_1/V_2 is called the *compression ratio*, and is about 7 for an internal combustion engine.

The work output in Fig. 20-2, is the shaded area enclosed by the figure *abcd*. The heat *input* is the heat supplied at constant volume along the line *bc*. The exhaust heat is removed along *da*. No heat is supplied or removed in the adiabatic processes *ab* and *cd*.

The heat input and the work output can be computed in terms of the compression ratio, assuming air to behave like an ideal gas. The result is

$$\text{Eff}(\%) = 100 \left(1 - \frac{1}{(V_1/V_2)^{\gamma-1}} \right),$$

where γ is the ratio of the specific heats.

For a compression ratio of 7 and a value of $\gamma = 1.4$, the efficiency is about 54%. It will be seen that the higher the compression ratio, the higher the efficiency. For an actual engine this ratio cannot be made much greater than 7 or pre-ignition and knocking will result.

Friction effects, turbulence, loss of heat to cylinder walls, etc., have been neglected. All these effects reduce the efficiency of an actual engine below the figure given above.

20-3 The Diesel engine. In the Diesel cycle, air is drawn into the cylinder on the intake stroke and compressed adiabatically on the compression stroke to a sufficiently high temperature so that fuel oil injected at the end of this stroke burns in the cylinder without requiring ignition by a spark. The combustion is not as rapid as in the gasoline engine, and the first part of the power stroke proceeds at essentially constant pressure. The remainder of the power stroke is an adiabatic expansion. This is followed by an exhaust stroke which completes the cycle.

The idealized air-Diesel cycle is shown in Fig. 20-3. Starting at point a, air is compressed adiabatically to point b, heated at constant pressure to point c, expanded adiabatically to point d, and cooled at constant volume to point a.

Since there is no fuel in the cylinder of a Diesel engine on the compression stroke, pre-ignition cannot occur and the compression ratio V_1/V_2 may be much higher than that of an internal combustion engine. A value of 15 is typical. The *expansion* ratio V_1/V_3 may be about 5. Using these values, and taking $\gamma = 1.4$, the efficiency of the air-Diesel cycle is about 56%. Hence somewhat higher efficiencies are possible than for the Otto cycle. Again, the actual efficiency of a real Diesel must be smaller than the value given above.

20-4 The steam engine. The condensing type of steam engine performs the following sequence of operations. Water is converted to steam in the boiler, and the steam thus formed is superheated above the boiler temperature. Superheated steam is admitted to the cylinder, where it expands against a piston, connection being maintained to the boiler for the first part of the working stroke, which thus takes place at constant pressure. The inlet valve is then closed and the steam expands adiabatically for the rest of the working stroke. The adiabatic cooling causes some of the steam to condense. The mixture of water droplets and steam (known as "wet" steam) is forced out of the cylinder on the return stroke and into the condenser, where the remaining steam is condensed into water. This water is forced into the boiler by the feed pump, and the cycle is repeated.

An idealized cycle (called the Rankine cycle) which approximates the actual steam cycle, is shown in Fig. 20-4. Starting with liquid water at

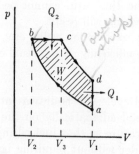

FIG. 20-3. p-V diagram of the Diesel cycle.

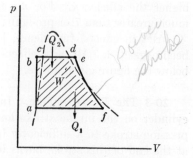

FIG. 20-4. The Rankine cycle.

low pressure and temperature (point *a*), the water is compressed adiabatically to point *b* at boiler pressure. It is then heated at constant pressure to its boiling point (line *bc*), converted to steam (line *cd*), superheated (line *de*), expanded adiabatically (line *ef*), and cooled and condensed (along *fa*) to its initial condition.

The efficiency of such a cycle may be computed in the same way as was done in the previous examples, by finding the quantities of heat taken in and rejected along the lines *be* and *fa*. Assuming a boiler temperature of 417° F (corresponding to a pressure of 300 lb in²), a superheat of 63° F above this temperature (480° F), and a condenser temperature of 102° F, the efficiency of a Rankine cycle is about 32%. Efficiencies of actual steam engines are, of course, considerably lower.

20-5 The second law of thermodynamics. Our experience with actual engines therefore leads us to the second law of thermodynamics which may be stated rigorously as follows:

It is impossible to construct an engine that, operating in a cycle, will produce no effect other than the extraction of heat from a source and the conversion of this heat completely into work.

If the second law were not true, it would be possible to drive a steamship across the ocean by extracting heat from the ocean or to run a power plant by extracting heat from the surrounding air. It should be noted that neither of these "impossibilities" violates the first law of thermodynamics. After all, both the ocean and the surrounding air contain an enormous store of internal energy, which, in principle, may be extracted in the form of a flow of heat. There is nothing in the first law to preclude the possibility of converting this heat completely into work. The second law, therefore, is not a deduction from the first but stands by itself as a separate law of nature, referring to an aspect of nature different from that contemplated by the first law. The first law denies the possibility of creating or destroying energy; the second denies the possibility of utilizing energy in a particular way.

The fact that work may be dissipated completely into heat, whereas heat may not be converted entirely into work expresses an essential one-sidedness of nature. All natural, spontaneous processes may be studied in the light of the second law, and in all such cases, this peculiar one-sidedness is found. Thus, heat always flows spontaneously from a hotter to a colder body; gases always seep through an opening spontaneously from a region of high pressure to a region of low pressure; gases and liquids left by themselves always tend to mix, not to unmix. Salt dissolves in water but a salt solution does not separate by itself into pure salt and pure water. Rocks weather and crumble; iron rusts; people grow old. These are all examples of *irreversible* processes that take place naturally in only one direction and, by their one-sidedness, express the second law of thermodynamics.

Irreversible, natural processes may be regarded from another point of view. A piece of pure salt and a volume of pure water represent an orderly arrangement of molecules. The solution of the salt in the water involves an increase in molecular disorder. If all the molecules of gas in a container were in one corner of the container, that would constitute an orderly arrangement. The uniform distribution of molecules throughout the container which actually exists is a much more disorderly arrangement. The sand that results from the weathering of rocks over a long period of time represents a greater disorder than the original well-formed rocks. Thus, the one-sidedness of nature may be redescribed by stating that *there is a tendency in nature to proceed toward a state of greater molecular disorder.*

20-6 The refrigerator. A refrigerator may be considered to be a heat engine operated in reverse. That is, a heat engine takes in heat from a *high* temperature source, converts a part of the heat into mechanical work output, and rejects the difference as heat in the exhaust at a *lower* temperature. A refrigerator takes in heat at a *low* temperature, the compressor supplies mechanical work *input*, and the sum is rejected as heat at a *higher* temperature.

The flow diagram of a refrigerator is given in Fig. 20-5. In terms of the processes in a household mechanical refrigerator, Q_1 represents the heat

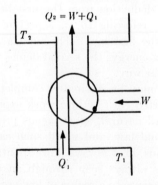

Fig. 20-5. Schematic flow diagram of
a refrigerator.

removed from the refrigerator by the cooling coils within it, W the work done by the motor, and Q_2 the heat delivered to the external cooling coils and removed by circulating air or water. It follows from the first law that

$$Q_2 = Q_1 + W.$$

That is, the circulating air or water must absorb both the heat "pumped" out of the refrigerator and the heat equivalent of the work done by the motor.

From an economic point of view, the best refrigeration cycle is one that removes the greatest amount of heat Q_1 from the refrigerator, for the least expenditure of mechanical work W. We therefore define the *coefficient of performance* (rather than the efficiency) of a refrigerator as the ratio Q_1/W, and since $W = Q_2 - Q_1$,

$$\text{Coefficient of performance} = \frac{Q_1}{Q_2 - Q_1}. \qquad (20\text{-}2)$$

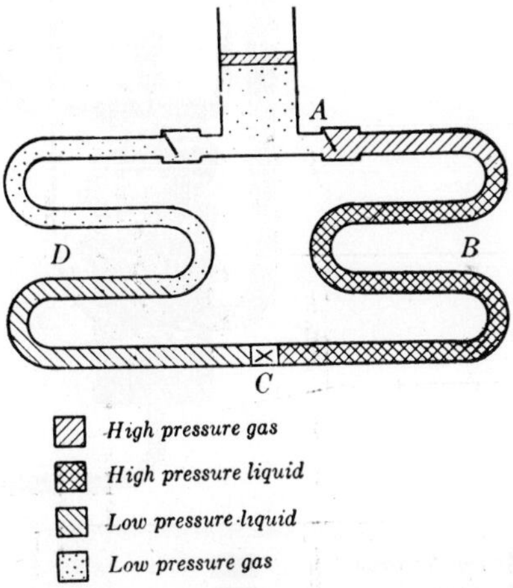

Fig. 20-6. Principle of the mechanical refrigeration cycle.

The principles of the common refrigeration cycle are illustrated schematically in Fig. 20-6. Compressor A delivers gas (SO_2, NH_3, etc.) at high temperature and pressure to coils B. Heat is removed from the gas in B by water or air cooling, resulting in condensation of the gas to a liquid, still under high pressure. The liquid passes through the throttling valve or expansion valve C, emerging as a mixture of liquid and vapor at a lower temperature. In coils D, heat is supplied that converts

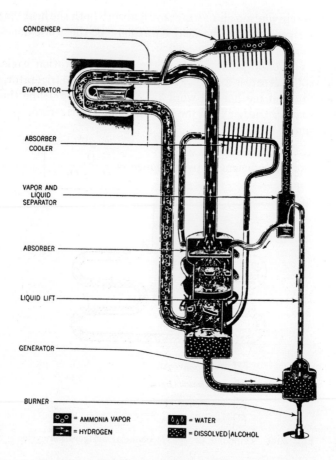

CONDENSER

EVAPORATOR

ABSORBER
COOLER

VAPOR AND
LIQUID
SEPARATOR

ABSORBER

LIQUID LIFT

GENERATOR

BURNER

$\overset{\circ\circ}{\circ}$ = AMMONIA VAPOR $\overset{\delta\,\delta\,\delta}{}$ = WATER

$\longrightarrow$ = HYDROGEN   = DISSOLVED|ALCOHOL

Fig. 20-7.   Simplified diagram of the gas refrigerator.
(*Courtesy of Servel-Electrolux.*)

the remaining liquid into vapor which enters compressor A to repeat the cycle.   In a domestic refrigerator, coils D are placed in the ice compartment, where they cool the refrigerator directly.   In a larger refrigerating plant, these coils are usually immersed in a brine tank, cooling the brine, which is then pumped to the refrigerating rooms.

A simplified diagram of the so-called *gas-refrigerator* is given in Fig. 20-7.   In the generator, a solution of ammonia in water is heated by a small gas flame.   Ammonia is driven out of solution and ammonia vapor rises in the liquid lift tube, carrying with it some of the water in the same way that water is raised in the central tube of a coffee percolator.   This water collects in the separator from which point it flows back through the absorber, while the ammonia vapor rises to the condenser.   Here the ammonia vapor is liquefied, its heat of condensation being removed by air circulating around the cooling vanes.   The liquid ammonia then flows into the evaporator, located in the cooling unit of the refrigerator, where it evaporates and in so doing absorbs heat from its surroundings.   The ammonia vapor continues on to the absorber where it dissolves in the water returning from the separator.   The ammonia-water solution then flows to the generator, completing the cycle.

The absorber and evaporator also contain hydrogen gas which is maintained in circulation by a convection process, brought about by the fact that the mixture of ammonia and hydrogen in the tube at the extreme left is denser than the pure hydrogen in the tube leading from the top of the absorber.   This current of hydrogen, entering at the top of the evaporator, sweeps the ammonia vapor out of the evaporator and aids in rapid evaporation.   Since ammonia is much more readily soluble in water than is hydrogen, most of the ammonia is dissolved in the water trickling down through the absorber while the hydrogen passes upward through the absorber.

It is necessary that heat be removed from the absorber as well as from the condenser because heat is liberated when ammonia vapor dissolves in water.   This is accomplished by the auxiliary circuit made up of the cooling coils around the absorber, and the absorber cooler.

If no work were needed to operate a refrigerator, the coefficient of performance (heat extracted divided by work done) would be infinite. Coefficients of performance of actual refrigerators vary from about 2 to about 6.   Experience shows that work is always needed to transfer heat from a colder to a hotter body.   This negative statement leads to another statement of the second law of thermodynamics, namely,

It is impossible to construct a refrigerator that, operating in a cycle, will produce no effect other than the transfer of heat from a cooler to a hotter body.

At first sight, this and the previous statement of the second law appear to be quite unconnected, but it can be shown that they are in all respects equivalent. Any device that would violate one statement would violate the other.

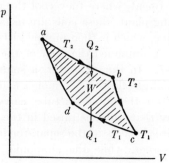

FIG. 20-8. The Carnot cycle.

20-7 The Carnot cycle. Although their efficiencies differ from one another, none of the heat engines which have been described has an efficiency of 100%. The question still remains open as to what is the maximum attainable efficiency, given a supply of heat at one temperature and a reservoir at a lower temperature for cooling the exhaust. An idealized engine which can be shown to have the maximum efficiency under these conditions was invented by Carnot and is called a *Carnot engine*. The *Carnot cycle*, shown in Fig. 20-8, differs from the Otto and Diesel cycles in that it is bounded by two *isothermals* and two adiabatics. Thus all the heat input is supplied at a *single* high temperature and all the heat output is rejected at a *single* lower temperature. (Compare with Figs. 20-2 and 20-3, in which the temperature is different at all points of the lines *bc* and *da*.)

This, however, is not the only feature of the Carnot cycle. There are no "one-way" processes in the Carnot cycle, such as explosions or throttling processes. The isothermal and adiabatic processes of the Carnot cycle may be imagined to proceed in either direction. In the direction shown in Fig. 20-8, heat Q_2 goes in, heat Q_1 goes out and work W is done by the engine. The arrows in the figure could be reversed, in which case the cycle would be a refrigeration cycle. Then heat Q_2 would go out, heat Q_1 would go in, and work W would have to be done on the refrigerator.

Suppose an engine (not a Carnot engine) were to operate between a source of heat at some temperature and a reservoir of heat at a lower temperature, thereby delivering to the outside an amount of work W. Suppose this work W were used to operate a Carnot refrigerator which extracted heat from the colder reservoir and delivered it to the warmer source. It can be shown that, if the first engine were more efficient than the Carnot engine that would result by operating the Carnot refrigerator backward, then the net effect would be a violation of the second law of thermodynamics.

Proceeding along these lines, it has been proved that:

No engine operating between two given temperatures can be more efficient than a Carnot engine operating between the same two temperatures,

and also

All Carnot engines operating between the same two temperatures have the same efficiency, irrespective of the nature of the working substance.

20-8 The Kelvin temperature scale. It was shown in the beginning of this chapter that the efficiency of any engine is equal to

$$E = \frac{W}{Q_2} = \frac{Q_2 - Q_1}{Q_2} = 1 - \frac{Q_1}{Q_2}.$$

If, therefore, the efficiencies of all Carnot engines operating between the same two temperatures are the same, irrespective of the working substance, the ratio Q_1/Q_2 must depend only on the two temperatures and on nothing else. Lord Kelvin proposed that this fact be used to define a temperature scale which would be independent of the properties of any particular substance, unlike the mercury scales and gas thermometer scales described in Chap. 15.

The Kelvin temperatures of the reservoir and the source between which a Carnot engine operates are defined by the relation

$$\frac{Q_1}{Q_2} = \frac{T_1}{T_2}, \tag{20-3}$$

where Q_1/Q_2 is the ratio of the heats rejected and absorbed, and T_1/T_2 is the ratio of the Kelvin temperatures of the reservoir and the source. The ratio alone does not completely fix the temperatures. If we arbitrarily set the difference between the Kelvin temperatures of the steam point and the ice point at 100 Kelvin degrees, then the scale is completely defined.

Suppose we denote temporarily the temperature that is measured with a gas thermometer by the symbol T'. Then, using the ideal gas equation $pV = nRT'$, we may compute the heat rejected, Q_1, and the heat absorbed, Q_2, when an ideal gas undergoes a Carnot cycle. The result of this calculation is that

$$\frac{Q_1}{Q_2} = \frac{T_1'}{T_2'},$$

where T_1' and T_2' are the absolute gas temperatures of the reservoir and source respectively. This, however, is exactly the same as the defining equation of the ratio of two Kelvin temperatures. Therefore, since the difference in the absolute gas temperatures of the steam and the ice point is also 100 degrees, we conclude that the absolute gas temperature and the Kelvin temperature are identical.

Now, the efficiency of a Carnot engine rejecting heat Q_1 to a reservoir at Kelvin temperature T_1 and absorbing heat Q_2 from a source at Kelvin temperature T_2 is, as usual,

$$E = 1 - \frac{Q_1}{Q_2}.$$

But, by definition of the Kelvin scale,

$$\frac{Q_1}{Q_2} = \frac{T_1}{T_2}.$$

Therefore, the efficiency of a Carnot engine is

$$E(\text{Carnot}) = 1 - \frac{T_1}{T_2}. \tag{20-4}$$

Eq. (20-4) points the way to the conditions which a real engine, such as a steam engine, must fulfill to approach as closely as possible the maximum attainable efficiency. These conditions are that the intake temperature T_2 must be made as high as possible and the exhaust temperature T_1 as low as possible.

The exhaust temperature cannot be lower than the lowest temperature available for cooling the exhaust. This is usually the temperature of the air, or perhaps of river water if this is available at the plant. The only recourse then is to raise the boiler temperature, T_2. Since the vapor pressure of all liquids increases rapidly with increasing temperature, a limit is set by the mechanical strength of the boiler. Another possibility is to use, instead of water, some liquid with a lower vapor pressure. Successful experiments in this direction have been made with mercury vapor replacing steam. At a boiler temperature of 200° C, at which the pressure in a steam boiler would be 225 lb/in², the pressure in a mercury boiler is only 0.35 lb/in².

20-9 Absolute zero. Imagine a series of Carnot engines operating in the following way: the first engine absorbs heat Q from a source, does work W and rejects a smaller amount of heat at a lower temperature; the

second engine absorbs the heat rejected by the first at the same temperature at which it was rejected, also does work, and rejects a still smaller
amount of heat at a still lower temperature; and so on.   The heats rejected by each Carnot engine represent a set of positive numbers which
get smaller as we go to each succeeding engine.   By definition of the
Kelvin scale, therefore, the temperatures at which each succeeding engine
rejects its heat get lower and lower, and these temperatures constitute a
set of decreasing positive numbers.   The limit of a set of positive decreasing numbers is zero and, therefore, a final engine can be imagined
which will reject no heat at a temperature which will be absolute zero.

*Absolute zero is the temperature of a reservoir to which no heat will be
rejected by a Carnot engine operating between this reservoir and a source at
higher temperature.*

This is the only definition of absolute zero that has a meaning in
thermodynamics.   It should be noted that the definition is in terms of
the properties of matter in general, but not of any particular substance.
Also, no reference is made to molecules or to molecular energy.

Problems — Chapter 20

20-1. The efficiency of an Otto cycle is 50% and $\gamma = 1.50$. What is the compression ratio?

20-2. A Carnot engine whose high temperature reservoir is at 127°C takes in 100 cal of heat at this temperature in each cycle, and gives up 80 cal to the low temperature reservoir. Find the temperature of the latter reservoir.

20-3. A Carnot engine whose low temperature reservoir is at 7°C has an efficiency of 40%. It is desired to increase the efficiency to 50%. By how many degrees must the temperature of the high temperature reservoir be increased?

20-4. A Carnot engine is operated between two heat reservoirs at temperatures of 400°K and 300°K. (a) If in each cycle the engine receives 1200 cal of heat from the reservoir at 400°K, how many calories does it reject to the reservoir at 300°K? (b) If the engine is operated in reverse, as a refrigerator, and receives 1200 cal of heat from the reservoir at 300°K, how many calories does it deliver to the reservoir at 400°K? (c) How many calories would be produced if the mechanical work required to operate the refrigerator in part (b) were converted directly to heat.

20-5. What is the efficiency of an engine which operates by taking an ideal monatomic gas through the following cycle? Let $C_v = 3$ cal/mole-C°. (a) Start with

n moles at p_0, V_0, T_0. (b) Change to $2p_0$, V_0 at constant volume. (c) Change to $2p_0$, $2V_0$ at constant pressure. (d) Change to p_0, $2V_0$ at constant volume. (e) Change to p_0, V_0 at constant pressure.

20-6. A Carnot refrigerator takes heat from water at 0°C and discards it to the room at a temperature of 27°C. 100 kgm of water at 0°C are to be changed to ice at 0°C. (a) How many calories of heat are discarded to the room? (b) What is the required work in joules?

20-7. A cylinder contains air at a pressure of 2 atm. The volume is 3 liters and the temperature is 300°K. The air is carried through the following processes:

(1) Heated at constant pressure to 500°K
(2) Cooled at constant volume to 250°K
(3) Cooled at constant pressure to 150°K
(4) Heated at constant volume to 300°K

(a) Show each process on a pressure-volume diagram giving the numerical values of p and V at the end of each process. (b) Calculate the net work done by the gas.

20-8. For the data in problem 20-7 find: (a) the number of moles of air in the cylinder. (b) For air $C_P = 7$ cal/mole-degree and $C_V = 5$ cal/mole-degree. Find the total heat input to the cylinder in processes 1 and 4. Express answer in calories. (c) What is the efficiency of this device as a heat engine?

CHAPTER 21

WAVE MOTION

21-1 Propagation of a disturbance in a medium. Imagine a medium consisting of a large number of particles, each connected or coupled to its neighbors by *elastic* material. If one end of the medium is disturbed or displaced in any way, the displacement will not occur immediately at all other parts of the medium. The original displacement will give rise to an elastic force in the material adjacent to it; then the next particle will be displaced; and then the next; and so on. In other words, *the displacement will be propagated along the medium with a definite speed.*

In Fig. 21-1(a) the medium is a spring, or just a wire under tension. If the left end is given a small displacement in a direction perpendicular to the medium, this transverse displacement will occur at successive intervals of time at each coil of the spring and there will result the propagation of a *transverse pulse* along the spring.

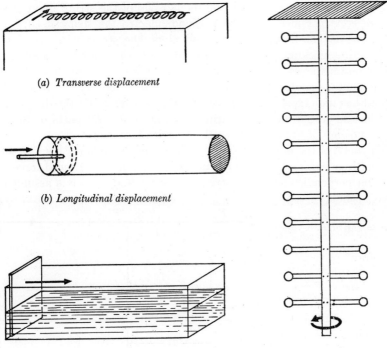

(a) *Transverse displacement*

(b) *Longitudinal displacement*

(c) *Longitudinal and transverse displacement*   (d) *Torsional displacement*

Fig. 21-1. Propagation of disturbances.

In Fig. 21-1(b) the medium is to be regarded as either a liquid or a gas contained in a tube closed at the right end with a rigid wall and at the left end with a movable piston. If the piston is moved slightly toward the right, a *longitudinal pulse* will be propagated through the medium in the tube.

In Fig. 21-1(c) the medium is a liquid contained in a shallow trough. The horizontal motion of a flat piece of wood at the left end will provide a displacement of the liquid which is both longitudinal and slightly transverse, and this disturbance will travel along the medium.

In Fig. 21-1(d) the medium is a set of "dumbbells" connected to a steel strip. A slight rotation of the lowest dumbbell constitutes a *torsional displacement* which will be propagated up the medium with a finite speed.

It will be shown in the next section that the speed of a pulse produced by a *small* displacement depends only on certain physical properties *of the medium itself* and not on the rapidity of the original displacement.

21-2 Calculation of the speed of a transverse pulse.

Consider the string depicted in Fig. 21-2(a) under a tension F, and with *linear density* (mass per unit length) μ. Imagine the left end of the string moving *with constant velocity* v in a direction perpendicular to the string itself. This transverse displacement is propagated along the string with speed u so that, as time goes on, more and more of the string becomes bent at the angle θ and achieves the perpendicular velocity v. Figure 21-2(b) shows the momentary configuration of the string after time t has elapsed. The left end has undergone the transverse displacement vt and the disturbance itself has advanced along the string a distance ut. All parts of the disturbed portion of the string have the transverse velocity v.

The mass of the moving portion of the string is the linear density times the length or μut, and the momentum is μutv. The unbalanced force in a direction perpendicular to the string is $F \sin \theta$, and since θ is assumed to be very small,

$$\sin \theta = \tan \theta = \frac{vt}{ut} = \frac{v}{u}.$$

Therefore

$$F \sin \theta = F \frac{v}{u}.$$

Since the impulse is equal to the change of momentum, we have

$$F \frac{v}{u})(t \qquad \mu utv,$$

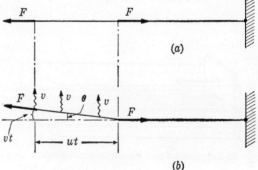

Fig. 21-2. Propagation of a transverse disturbance in a string.

and, after canceling vt from both sides, we get

$$u = \sqrt{\frac{F}{\mu}}. \qquad \text{(Transverse)} \qquad (21\text{-}1)$$

Thus it is seen that the velocity of propagation of a transverse pulse in a string depends only on the tension and the mass per unit length.

In numerical applications of Eq. (21-1), attention must be paid to the units employed. With cgs units, F must be expressed in dynes and μ in grams per centimeter. With mks units, F must be in newtons and μ in kilograms per meter. Finally, in British engineering units, F must be in pounds and μ in slugs per foot. The corresponding units of velocity will then be, respectively, centimeters per second, meters per second, and feet per second.

Example: Calculate the velocity of a transverse pulse in a string under a tension of 20 lb, if the string weighs 0.003 lb/ft.

$$F = 20 \text{ lb},$$

$$\mu = \frac{0.003}{32} \text{ slugs/ft},$$

$$u = \sqrt{\frac{20 \text{ lb} \times 32 \text{ ft/sec}^2}{0.003 \text{ lb/ft}}},$$

$$u = 461 \text{ ft/sec}.$$

21-3 Calculation of the speed of a longitudinal pulse. In Fig. 21-3(a) is shown an undisturbed portion of a fluid contained in a tube of constant cross-sectional area A and under a pressure p. Imagine the left end of the fluid moving with constant velocity v in the direction of the fluid. This longitudinal disturbance is propagated through the fluid with speed u, so that, as time goes on, more and more of the fluid achieves the pressure $p + \Delta p$ and the velocity v. Figure 21-3(b) shows the momentary configuration of the fluid after time t has elapsed. The left end has undergone the longitudinal displacement vt and the disturbance itself has advanced a distance ut. All parts of the disturbed portion of the fluid have the longitudinal velocity v.

The mass of the moving portion of the fluid is the density ρ times the volume Aut, or ρAut, and the momentum is $\rho Autv$. The unbalanced force is $A\Delta p$. Since the impulse is equal to the change in momentum,

$$A\Delta pt = \rho Autv$$

and therefore

$$u = \frac{\Delta p}{\rho v}. \qquad (21\text{-}2)$$

The bulk modulus B was defined in Chapter 11 as

$$B = \frac{\text{change in pressure}}{\text{fractional change in volume}},$$

or

$$B = \frac{\Delta p}{A v t / A u t} = \frac{\Delta p}{v} \times u.$$

Substituting for $\Delta p/v$ in Eq. (21-2) the value B/u given above, we get

$$u = \frac{B}{u\rho},$$

or

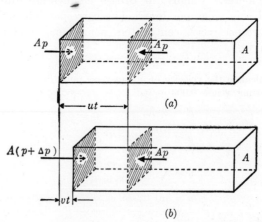

Fig. 21-3. Propagation of a longitudinal disturbance in a fluid confined in a tube.

$$\boxed{u = \sqrt{\frac{B}{\rho}}.}\qquad \text{(Longitudinal)} \qquad (21\text{-}3)$$

Suppose next that Fig. 21-3 refers to a solid bar that has been struck a blow at one end. The situation is somewhat different from that of a fluid confined in a tube of constant cross section, since the bar will expand slightly sidewise when it is compressed longitudinally. It can be shown by the same type of reasoning as that just given that the velocity of a longitudinal pulse in the bar is given by

$$\boxed{u = \sqrt{\frac{Y}{\rho}},}\qquad \text{(Longitudinal)} \qquad (21\text{-}4)$$

where Y is Young's modulus, defined in Chapter 11.

21-4 The motion of a wave. Up to this point we have considered the simplest type of disturbance that could be imparted to one end of a medium, namely, a single transverse or longitudinal displacement. Suppose now that one end of a medium is forced to vibrate periodically, the displacement y (either transverse or longitudinal) varying with the time according to the equation of simple harmonic motion:

$$y = A \cos 2\pi ft.$$

During half a cycle, a displacement in one direction is propagated through the medium, and during the other half, a displacement in the opposite direction is caused to proceed. The resulting continuous train of disturbances travelling with a speed depending on the properties of the medium is called a *wave*.

To fix our ideas, suppose that one end of a stretched string is forced to vibrate periodically in a transverse direction with simple harmonic motion of amplitude A, frequency f, and period $T = 1/f$. For the present we shall assume the string to be long enough so that any effects at the far end need not be considered. A *continuous train* of transverse sinusoidal waves then advances along the string. The shape of a portion of the string near the end, at intervals of $\frac{1}{8}$ of a period, is shown in Fig. 21-4 for a total time of one period. The string is assumed to have been vibrating for a sufficiently long time so that the

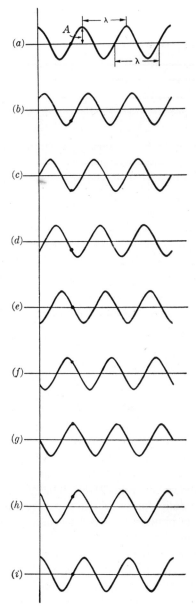

Fig. 21-4. A sinusoidal wave traveling toward the right, shown at intervals of $\frac{1}{8}$th period.

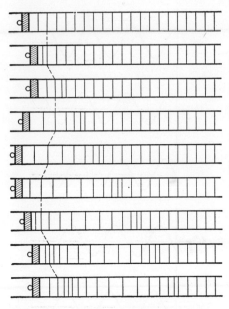

Fig. 21-5. Schematic diagram of a compressional wave in a gas.

shape of the string is sinusoidal for an indefinite distance from the driven end. It will be seen from the figure that the wave form advances steadily toward the right, while any one point on the string (see the black dot) oscillates about its equilibrium position with simple harmonic motion. It is important to distinguish between the motion of the *wave form*, which moves with constant velocity u along the string, and the motion of a *particle of the string*, which is simple harmonic and transverse to the string.

The distance between two successive maxima (or between any two successive points in the same phase) is the *wave length* of the wave and is denoted by λ. Since the wave form, travelling with constant velocity u, advances a distance of one wavelength in a time interval of one period, it follows that $u = \lambda/T$, or

$$u = f\lambda. \qquad (21\text{-}5)$$

That is, *the velocity of propagation equals the product of frequency and wave length.*

To understand the mechanics of a longitudinal wave, consider the long tube filled with a fluid and provided with a plunger at the left end, as shown in Fig. 21-5. The vertical lines represent layers of particles, equally spaced in the top diagram when the medium is at rest. Suppose the plunger is forced to undergo a simple harmonic vibration parallel to the direction of the tube. Every time the displacement is toward the right, a region whose pressure is above the equilibrium pressure (represented by vertical lines closely spaced) is formed, which advances along the medium and is known as a *condensation*. Every time the displacement is toward the left, a region whose pressure is lower than the equilibrium pressure (represented by vertical lines spaced farther apart) is caused to advance. This is a *rarefaction*. It is important in this case also to distinguish between the motion of the condensations and rarefactions, which move with constant velocity u through the medium, and the motion of a particle of the medium, which is simple harmonic and parallel to the direction of the wave.

The wave length is the distance between two successive condensations or two successive rarefactions, and the same fundamental equation, $u = f\lambda$, holds in this as in all types of waves.

21-5 Adiabatic character of a longitudinal wave. It is a familiar fact that compression of a fluid causes a rise in its temperature unless heat is withdrawn in some way. Conversely, an expansion is accompanied by a temperature decrease unless heat is added. As a longitudinal wave advances through a fluid, the regions which are compressed at any instant are slightly warmer than those that are expanded. The condition is present, therefore, for the conduction of heat from a condensation to a rarefaction. The quantity of heat conducted per second per unit area depends on the thermal conductivity of the fluid and upon the distance between a condensation and its adjacent rarefaction (half a wave length). Now for ordinary frequencies, say from 20 vibrations per second to 20,000 vibrations per second, and for even the best known heat conductors, the wave length is too large and the thermal conductivity too small for an appreciable amount of heat to flow. The compressions and rarefactions are therefore *adiabatic* rather than isothermal.

In the expression for the speed of a longitudinal wave in the fluid, $u = \sqrt{B/\rho}$, the bulk modulus B is defined by the relation

$$B = \frac{\text{change of pressure}}{\text{change of volume per unit volume}}$$

The change in volume produced by a given change of pressure depends upon whether the compression (or expansion) is adiabatic or isothermal. There are therefore two bulk moduli, the adiabatic bulk modulus B_{ad} and the isothermal bulk modulus. The rigorous expression for the speed of a longitudinal wave should therefore be written

$$u = \sqrt{\frac{B_{ad}}{\rho}} . \qquad (21\text{-}6)$$

In the case of an ideal gas, it can be shown that the adiabatic bulk modulus B_{ad} is equal to

$$B_{ad} = \gamma p, \quad \text{(Ideal gas)} \qquad (21\text{-}7)$$

where γ is the ratio of the heat capacity at constant pressure to the heat capacity at constant volume. Therefore

Fig. 21-6.

To use these diagrams, cut a slit about 4-¼″ long and about 1/16″ wide in a card. Place the card over the diagram and move it vertically with constant velocity. The portions of the curves that appear in the slit will correspond to the oscillations of the

FIG. 21-7.

particles in a longitudinal traveling wave in Fig. 21-6, and to a longitudinal standing wave in Fig. 21-7.

$$u = \sqrt{\frac{\gamma p}{\rho}}. \quad \text{(Ideal gas)} \qquad (21\text{-}8)$$

But, for an ideal gas,

$$\frac{p}{\rho} = \frac{RT}{M},$$

where R is the universal gas constant and M the molecular weight. Therefore

$$u = \sqrt{\frac{\gamma RT}{M}}, \quad \text{(Ideal gas)} \qquad (21\text{-}9)$$

and since for a given gas γ, R and M are constants, we see that the velocity of propagation is proportional to the square root of the absolute temperature.

Let us use Eq. (21-9) to compute the velocity of longitudinal waves in air. The mean molecular weight of air is 29, $\gamma = 1.40$, and $R = 8.3 \times 10^7$ ergs/mole-deg. Let $T = 300°$ K. Then

$$u = \sqrt{\frac{1.40 \times 8.3 \times 10^7 \times 300}{29}}$$

$$= 34{,}600 \text{ cm/sec} = 346 \text{ m/sec} = 1{,}130 \text{ ft/sec}.$$

This is in excellent agreement with the measured velocity at this temperature.

Longitudinal waves in air give rise to the sensation of sound. The ear is sensitive to a range of sound frequencies from about 20 to about 20,000 cycles/sec. From the relation $u = f\lambda$, the corresponding wavelength range is from about 56 ft, corresponding to a 20-cycle note, to about 0.056 ft or $\frac{5}{8}$ inch, corresponding to 20,000 cycles/sec.

21-6 Graphical representations of a wave. Suppose a medium extends indefinitely toward the positive x-direction. Since a periodic displacement started at the left end advances toward the right, eventually every particle of the medium will be executing simple harmonic motion. The displacement of the medium y will therefore be a *function of two variables*, x and t. *At a particular time*, every particle will have its own displacement. That is

$$y = f(x). \quad (t \text{ constant})$$

At a particular point in the medium, the displacement varies with the time.

Thus

$$y = f(t), \quad (x \text{ constant})$$

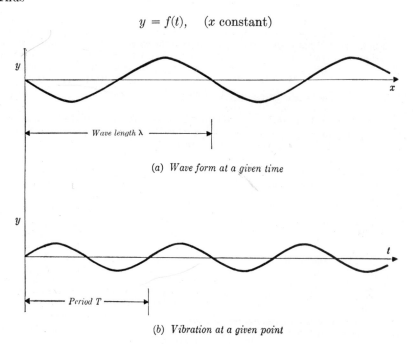

(a) *Wave form at a given time*

(b) *Vibration at a given point*

Fig. 21-8.   Graphical representation of a wave.

Fig. 21-8(a) represents the displacement of all parts of a string at a given moment, and is called a graph of the *wave form*.   Fig. 21-8(b) shows the displacement of one point of a string as a function of the time.   It is a graph of a *vibration*.

To represent completely the propagation of a wave in a medium, two graphs must be drawn.   Either

1. (a) The wave form at one moment, and
    (b) The wave form at a known time later;

or

2. (a) The wave form at a moment, and
    (b) The vibration at a point.

Problems — Chapter 21

21-1. A steel wire 6 m long has a mass of 60 gm and is stretched with a tension of 1000 newtons. What is the velocity of propagation of a transverse wave in the wire?

21-2. What must be the stress (F/A) in a stretched wire of a material whose Young's modulus is Y, in order that the velocity of longitudinal waves shall equal 10 times the velocity of transverse waves?

21-3. The velocity of longitudinal waves in water is approximately 1450 m/sec at 20°C. Compute the adiabatic compressibility $(1/B_{ad})$ of water and compare with the isothermal compressibility listed in Table 11-2.

21-4. Provided the amplitude is sufficiently great, the human ear can respond to longitudinal waves over a range of frequencies from about 20 vibrations per sec to about 20,000 vibrations per sec. Compute the wave lengths corresponding to these frequencies (a) for waves in air, (b) for waves in water. (See Problem 21-3.)

21-5. At a temperature of 27°C, what is the velocity of longitudinal waves in (a) argon, (b) hydrogen? Compare with the velocity in air at the same temperature.

21-6. What is the difference between the velocities of longitudinal waves in air at −3°C and at 57°C?

21-7. The sound waves from a loud speaker spread out nearly uniformly in all directions when their wave length is large compared with the diameter of the speaker. When the wave length is small compared with the diameter of the speaker, much of the sound energy is concentrated in the forward direction. For a speaker of diameter 10 inches, compute the frequency for which the wave length of the sound waves, in air, is (a) 10 times the diameter of the speaker, (b) equal to the diameter of the speaker, (c) 1/10 the diameter of the speaker.

21-8. A traveling transverse wave on a stretched string is represented by the equation

$$y = A \cos \frac{2\pi}{\lambda} (x - ut).$$

Let $A = 1$ in, $\lambda = 2$ in, and $u = (\frac{1}{4})$ in/sec. (a) At time $t = 0$, compute the transverse displacement y at $\frac{1}{4}$ inch intervals of x (i.e., at $x = 0$, $x = \frac{1}{4}$ in, $x = \frac{1}{2}$ in, etc.) from $x = 0$ to $x = 4$ inches. Show the results in a graph. This is the shape of the string at time $t = 0$. (b) Repeat the calculations, for the same values of x, at times $t = 1$ sec, $t = 2$ sec, $t = 3$ sec, and $t = 4$ sec. Show on the same graph the shape of the string at these instants. In what direction is the wave traveling?

21-9. Show that the equation in Problem 21-8 may be written

$$y = A \cos 2\pi \left(\frac{t}{T} - \frac{x}{\lambda} \right).$$

21-10. The equation of a transverse traveling wave on a string is

$$y = 2 \cos \left[\pi(0.5x - 200t) \right],$$

where x and y are in cm and t is in sec. (a) Find the amplitude, wave length, frequency, period, and velocity of propagation. (b) Sketch the shape of the string at the following values of t: 0, 0.0025, and 0.005 sec. (c) If the mass per unit length of the string is 5 gm/cm, find the tension.

CHAPTER 22

VIBRATING BODIES

22-1 Boundary conditions for a string. Let us now consider what will happen when a wave pulse or wave train, advancing along a stretched string, arrives at the end of the string. If fastened to a rigid support, the end must evidently remain at rest. The arriving pulse exerts a force on the support, and the reaction to this force "kicks back" on the string and sets up a *reflected* pulse traveling in the reversed direction. At the opposite extreme from a rigidly fixed end would be one which was perfectly free —a case of no great importance here (it may be realized by a string hanging vertically)—but which is of interest since its analogue does occur in other types of waves. At a free end the arriving pulse causes the string to "overshoot" and a reflected wave is also set up. The conditions which must be satisfied at the ends of the string are called *boundary conditions*.

The multiflash photograph of Fig. 22-1 shows the reflection of a pulse at a fixed end of a string. (The camera was tipped vertically while the photographs were taken so that successive images lie one under the other. The "string" is a rubber tube and it sags somewhat.) It will be seen that the pulse is reflected with its displacement and its velocity both reversed. When reflection takes place at a free end, the direction of the velocity is reversed but the direction of the displacement is unchanged.

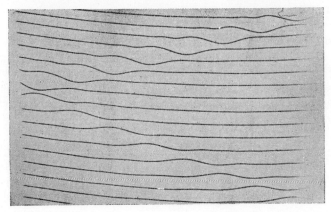

Fig. 22-1. A pulse starts in the upper right corner and is reflected from the fixed end of the string at the left.

375

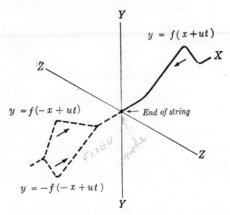

FIG. 22-2. A virtual pulse moves in from the left and combines with the original pulse to form the reflected pulse.

It is helpful to think of the process of reflection in the following way. Imagine the string to be extended indefinitely beyond its actual terminus. The actual pulse can be considered to continue on into the imaginary portion as though the support were not there, while at the same time a "virtual" pulse, which has been traveling in the imaginary portion, moves out into the real string and forms the reflected pulse. The nature of the reflected pulse depends on whether the end is fixed or free. The two cases are shown in Fig. 22-2. The upper dotted virtual pulse, which corresponds to reflection at a free end, has the same form as would the optical image of the incident pulse in a plane mirror in the Y-Z plane. The lower virtual pulse, which corresponds to reflection at a fixed end, is the mirror image of the upper in the X-Z plane.

The displacement at a point where the actual and virtual pulses cross one another is the algebraic sum of the displacements in the individual pulses. Figs. 22-3 and 22-4 show the shape of the end of the string for both types of reflected pulses. It will be seen that Fig. 22-3 corresponds to a free end and Fig. 22-4 to a fixed end. In the latter case, the incident and reflected pulses combine in such a way that the displacement of the end of the string is always zero.

22-2 Standing waves in a string. When a continuous train of waves arrives at a fixed end of a string, a continuous train of reflected waves appears to originate at the end and travel in the opposite direction. Provided the elastic limit of the string is not exceeded and the displacements are sufficiently small, the actual displacement of any point of the string is the algebraic sum of the displacements of the individual waves, a fact which is called the *principle of superposition*.   This principle is extremely important in all types of wave motion and applies not only to waves in a string but to sound waves in air, to light waves, and, in fact, to wave motion of any sort.   The general term *interference* is applied to the effect produced by two (or more) sets of wave trains which are simultaneously passing through a given region.

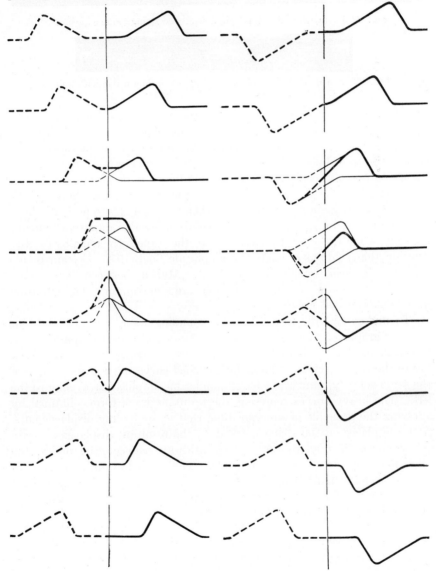

FIG. 22-3.   Reflection at a free end.   FIG. 22-4.   Reflection at a fixed end.

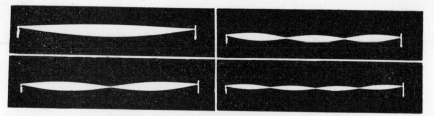

Fig. 22-5.   (a) Standing waves in a stretched string (time exposure).

Fig. 22-5.   (b) Multiflash photograph of a standing wave, with nodes
at the center and at the ends.

The appearance of the string under these circumstances gives no evidence that two waves are traversing it in opposite directions.   If the frequency is sufficiently great so that the eye cannot follow the motion, the string appears subdivided into a number of segments as in the time exposure photograph of Fig. 22-5(a).   A multiflash photograph of the same string, in Fig. 22-5(b), indicates a few of the instantaneous shapes of the string.   At any instant (except those when the string is straight) its shape is a sine curve, but, whereas in a traveling wave the amplitude remains constant while the wave progresses, here the wave form remains fixed in position (longitudinally) while the amplitude fluctuates.   Certain points known as the *nodes* remain always at rest.   Midway between these points, at the *loops* or *antinodes*, the fluctuations are a maximum.   The vibration as a whole is called a *standing wave*.

To understand the formation of a standing wave, consider the four separate graphs of wave form at four instants $\frac{1}{8}$ of a period apart, shown in Fig. 22-6.   The system of short dashed curves represents a wave traveling to the right.   The system of long dashed curves represents a wave of the same velocity, same wave length, and same amplitude traveling to the left.   The heavy curves represent the resultant wave form, obtained by applying the principle of superposition, that is, by adding displacements. At those places on the string marked N, the resultant displacements are always zero.   These are the nodes.   Midway between the nodes, the vibrations have the largest amplitude.   These are the antinodes.   It is evident from the figure that

$$\left.\begin{array}{c}\text{distance between adjacent nodes}\\ \text{or}\\ \text{distance between adjacent antinodes}\end{array}\right\} = \frac{\lambda}{2}.$$

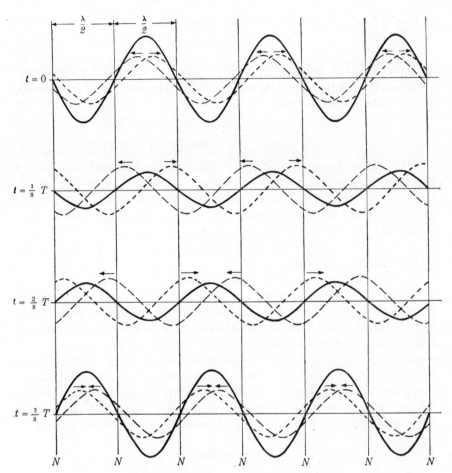

Fɪɢ. 22-6.   The formation of a standing wave.

22-3 Vibration of a string fixed at both ends.   Thus far we have been discussing a long string fixed at one end and have considered the standing waves set up near that end by interference between the incident and reflected waves.   Let us next consider the more usual case, that of a string fixed at both ends.   A continuous train of sine or cosine waves is reflected and re-reflected, and since the string is fixed at both ends, both ends must be nodes.   Since the nodes are one-half a wave length apart, the length of the string may be $\dfrac{\lambda}{2}$, $2\dfrac{\lambda}{2}$, $3\dfrac{\lambda}{2} \cdots$, or, in general, any integral number of half-wave lengths.   Or, to put it differently, if one considers a particular string of length L, standing waves may be set up in the string by vibrations of a number of different frequencies, namely, those which give rise to waves of wave lengths $\dfrac{2L}{1}$, $\dfrac{2L}{2}$, $\dfrac{2L}{3}$, etc.

From the relation $f = u/\lambda$, and since u is the same for all frequencies, the possible frequencies are

$$\frac{u}{2L}, \quad 2\frac{u}{2L}, \quad 3\frac{u}{2L}, \quad \cdots$$

The lowest frequency, $u/2L$, is called the *fundamental* frequency f_1 and the others are the *overtones*. The frequencies of the latter are, therefore, $2f_1$, $3f_1$, $4f_1$, and so on. Overtones whose frequencies are integral multiples of the fundamental are said to form a *harmonic series*. The fundamental is the *first harmonic*. The frequency $2f_1$ is the *first overtone* or the *second harmonic*, the frequency $3f_1$ is the *second overtone* or the *third harmonic*, and so on.

We can now see an important difference between a spring-weight system and a vibrating string. The former has but one natural frequency while the vibrating string has an infinite number of natural frequencies, the fundamental and all of the overtones. If a weight suspended from a spring is pulled down and released, only one frequency of vibration will ensue. If a string is initially distorted so that its shape is the same as *any one* of the possible harmonics, it will vibrate, when released, at the frequency of that particular harmonic. But when a piano string is struck, not only the fundamental, but many of the overtones are present in the resulting vibration. The fundamental frequency of the vibrating string is

$f_1 = \dfrac{u}{2L}$, where $u = \sqrt{\dfrac{F}{\mu}}$. It follows that

$$f_1 = \frac{1}{2L}\sqrt{\frac{F}{\mu}}. \qquad\qquad (22\text{-}1)$$

Stringed instruments afford many examples of the implications of this equation. For example, all such instruments are "tuned" by varying the tension F, an increase of tension increasing the frequency or pitch, and vice versa. The inverse dependence of frequency on length L is illustrated by the long strings of the bass section of the piano or the bass viol compared with the shorter strings of the piano treble or the violin. One reason for winding the bass strings of a piano with wire is to increase the mass per unit length μ, so as to obtain the desired low frequency without resorting to a string which is inconveniently long.

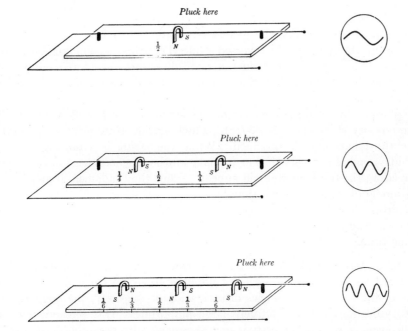

FIG. 22-7.   Demonstration of the harmonics present in the vibration of a plucked string.

22-4 Demonstration of the harmonic series in a vibrating string.

We have seen that a string is capable of vibrating at a number of different frequencies. That it vibrates with many different frequencies *at the same time* may be demonstrated very graphically with the aid of the apparatus depicted in Fig. 22-7. A metal string is stretched between two metal posts which are in turn connected to a "step-up" transformer. The secondary of the transformer is then connected to those plates of a cathode-ray oscilloscope which impart vertical motion to the electron beam. If the string is made to oscillate in a magnetic field, an alternating current will be set up whose variation is exactly the same as the displacement of the string. With proper adjustment of the oscilloscope, this alternating current may be caused to give rise to figures on the screen such as those shown in the circles to the right of Fig. 22-7.

Suppose that one small magnet is placed over the center of the string (Fig. 22-7(a)) and the string is plucked near the center so that this part of the string vibrates perpendicular to the magnetic lines of force. The figure on the oscilloscope shows the fundamental frequency.

Placing one magnet $\frac{1}{4}$ of the way along the string and another magnet *with its polarity reversed* at the $\frac{3}{4}$ mark (Fig. 22-7(b)), and plucking the string near the $\frac{1}{4}$ point, the second harmonic may be obtained. If one of the magnets is quickly reversed while the string is sounding, so as to set the two magnetic fields in the same direction, the fundamental will occur again, showing that the fundamental and second harmonic exist at the same time.

We now place three magnets on the string at the $\frac{1}{6}$, $\frac{1}{2}$, $\frac{5}{6}$ points, with the polarity shown in Fig. 22-7(c). Plucking the string near the $\frac{1}{6}$ point, the third harmonic is obtained. While the string is vibrating, if the middle magnet is reversed so as to make all the magnets point in the same direction, the fundamental will appear. Thus the fundamental and third harmonic exist at the same time.

Proceeding in this manner, we may pick up higher harmonics and demonstrate that a string can vibrate with all of these frequencies at the same time.

22-5 Resonance. In general, whenever a body capable of oscillating is acted on by a periodic series of impulses having a frequency equal to one of the natural frequencies of oscillation of the body, the body is set into vibration with a relatively large amplitude. This phenomenon is called *resonance*, and the body is said to *resonate* with the applied impulses.

A common example of mechanical resonance is provided by pushing a swing. The swing is a pendulum with a single natural frequency depending on its length. If a series of regularly spaced pushes is given to the swing, with a frequency equal to that of the swing, the motion may be made quite large. If the frequency of the pushes differs from the natural frequency of the swing, or if the pushes occur at irregular intervals, the swing will hardly execute a vibration at all.

Unlike a simple pendulum, which has only one natural frequency, a stretched string (and other systems to be discussed later in this chapter) has a large number of natural frequencies. Suppose that one end of a stretched string is fixed while the other is moved back and forth in a transverse direction. If the motion is simple harmonic with a frequency f, standing waves of this frequency are set up in the string. The amplitude of these waves will be relatively large if the frequency f is equal to *any one* of the natural frequencies of the string. If the frequency f is not equal to some one of the natural frequencies, the amplitude of the standing waves will be very much smaller. In Fig. 22-5(a), the right end of the string was fixed and the left end was forced to oscillate vertically with small amplitude. Standing waves of relatively large amplitude resulted when the frequency of oscillation of the left end was equal to the fundamental frequency or to that of the first three overtones.

A bridge or, for that matter, any structure, is capable of vibrating with certain natural frequencies.   If the regular footsteps of a column of soldiers were to have a frequency equal to one of the natural frequencies of a bridge which the soldiers are crossing, a vibration of dangerously large amplitude might result.   Therefore, in crossing a bridge, a column of soldiers is ordered to break step.

Tuning a radio is an example of electrical resonance. By turning a dial, the natural frequency of an alternating current in the receiving circuit is made equal to the frequency of the waves broadcast by the desired station.   Optical resonance may also take place between atoms in a gas at low pressure and light waves from a lamp containing the same atoms. Thus light from a sodium lamp may cause the sodium atoms in a glass bulb to glow with characteristic yellow sodium light.

The phenomenon of resonance may be demonstrated with the aid of the longitudinal waves set up in air by a vibrating plate or tuning fork. If two identical tuning forks are placed some distance apart and one is struck, the other will be heard when the first is suddenly damped.   Should a small piece of wax or modeling clay be put on one of the forks, the frequency of that fork will be altered enough to destroy the resonance.

22-6 Interference of longitudinal waves. The phenomenon of interference between two longitudinal waves in air may be demonstrated with the aid of the apparatus depicted in Fig. 22-8.   A wave emitted by an electrically-driven diaphragm S is sent into a metal tube, where it divides into two waves, one following the constant path SAR, the other the path SBR, which may be varied by sliding the tube B to the right. Suppose the frequency of the source is 1100 vibrations per second.   Then the wave length $\lambda = V/f = 1$ ft.   If both paths are of equal length, the two waves will arrive at R at the same time and the vibrations set up by both waves will be in phase.   The resulting vibration will have an ampli-

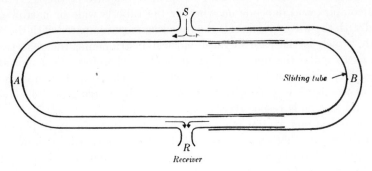

FIG. 22-8.   Apparatus for demonstrating interference of longitudinal waves.

tude equal to the sum of the two individual amplitudes and the phenomenon of *reinforcement* may be detected either with the ear at R or with the aid of a microphone, amplifier, and loudspeaker.

Now suppose the tube B is moved out a distance of three inches, thereby making the path SBR 6 inches longer than the path SAR. The right-hand wave will have traveled a distance $\lambda/2$ greater than the left-hand wave and the vibration set up at R by the right-hand wave will therefore be in opposite phase with that set up by the left-hand wave. The consequent interference is shown by the marked reduction in sound at R.

If the tube B is now pulled out another 3 inches, so that the *path difference*, SBR minus SAR, is one foot (one wave length), the two vibrations at R will again reinforce each other. Thus

$$\left\{\begin{array}{l}\text{Reinforcement takes place}\\ \text{when the path difference}\end{array}\right\} = 0,\ \lambda,\ 2\lambda,\ \text{etc.}$$

$$\left\{\begin{array}{l}\text{Interference takes place}\\ \text{when the path difference}\end{array}\right\} = \frac{\lambda}{2},\ \frac{3\lambda}{2},\ \frac{5\lambda}{2},\ \text{etc.}$$

An acoustical interferometer of this sort is of value only in demonstrating the phenomenon of interference. Optical interferometers, however, whose principles of operation are the same, have many practical uses in physical optics.

22-7 Standing longitudinal waves. Longitudinal waves traveling along a tube of finite length are reflected at the ends of the tube in much the same way that transverse waves in a string are reflected at its ends. Interference between the waves traveling in opposite directions gives rise to standing waves.

If reflection takes place at a closed end, the displacement of the particles at that end must necessarily be always zero. Hence a closed end is a *node*. If the end of the tube is open, the nature of the reflection is more complex and depends on whether the tube is wide or narrow compared with the wave length. If the tube is narrow compared with the wave length, which is the case in most musical instruments, the reflection is such as to make the open end an *antinode*. Therefore the longitudinal waves in a column of fluid are reflected at the closed and open ends of a tube in the same way that transverse waves in a string are reflected at fixed and free ends respectively.

The reflections at the openings where the instrument is blown are found to be such that an antinode is located at or near the opening. The effective length of the air column of a wind instrument is thus less definite than the length of a string fixed at its ends.

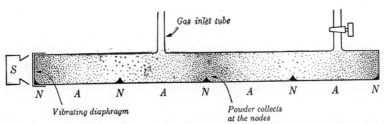

FIG. 22-9.   Kundt's tube for determining the velocity of sound in a gas.   The dots represent the density of the gas molecules at an instant when the pressure at the displacement nodes is a maximum or a minimum.

Standing longitudinal waves in a column of gas may be demonstrated conveniently with the aid of the apparatus shown in Fig. 22-9, known as Kundt's tube.   A glass tube a few feet long is closed at one end with glass and at the other with a flexible diaphragm.   The gas to be studied is admitted to the tube at a known temperature and at atmospheric pressure.   A powerful source of longitudinal waves S, whose frequency may be varied, causes vibration of the flexible diaphragm.   A small amount of light powder or cork dust is sprinkled uniformly along the tube.

When a frequency is found at which the air column is in resonance, the amplitude of the standing waves becomes large enough for the gas particles to sweep the cork dust along the tube, at all points where the gas is in motion.   The powder therefore collects at the displacement nodes where the gas remains at rest.   Sometimes a wire, running along the axis of the tube, is maintained at a dull red heat by an electric current and the nodes show themselves as hot points, compared with the antinodes.

With careful manipulation and with a good variable frequency source, a fair determination of the velocity of the wave may be obtained with Kundt's tube.   Since, in a standing wave, the distance between two adjacent nodes is one-half a wave length, the wave length λ is obtained by measuring the distance between alternate clumps of powder.   Knowing the frequency f, the velocity u is then

$$u = f\lambda.$$

A constant frequency source may be used if the vibrating element is a piston which may be moved along the tube until resonance is obtained.

At a displacement node, the pressure variations above and below the average are a maximum, whereas at an antinode, there are no pressure variations.   This may be understood easily when it is realized that two small masses of gas on opposite sides of a node are vibrating in *opposite phase*.   Thus, when they approach each other, the pressure at the node is a maximum, and when they recede from each other, the pressure at the node is a minimum.   Two small masses of gas, however, on opposite sides

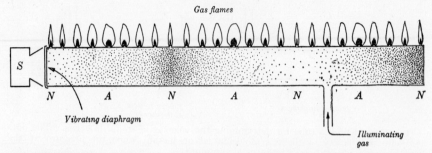

FIG. 22-10. The variations in gas pressure are greatest at the displacement nodes. The dots represent the density of the gas molecules at an instant when the pressure at the displacement nodes is a maximum or a minimum.

of an antinode vibrate *in phase,* and hence give rise to no pressure variations at the antinode.   This may be demonstrated in the case of illuminating gas with the aid of the apparatus shown in Fig. 22-10, where the amplitude of the harmonic variations of gas pressure determines the shape and color of the gas flames.

22-8 Vibrations of organ pipes. If one end of a pipe is open and a stream of air is directed against an edge, vibrations are set up and the tube resonates at its natural frequencies.   As in the case of a plucked string, the fundamental and overtones exist at the same time.   In the case of an open pipe, the fundamental frequency f_1 corresponds to an antinode at each end and a node in the middle, as shown at the top of Fig. 22-11.   Succeeding diagrams of Fig. 22-11 show two of the overtones which are seen to be the second and third harmonics.   *In an open pipe the fundamental frequency is $u/2L$ and all harmonics are present.*

The properties of a closed pipe are shown in the diagrams of Fig. 22-12. The fundamental frequency is seen to be $u/4L$, which is one-half that of

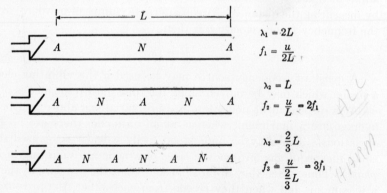

FIG. 22-11. Modes of vibration of an open organ pipe.

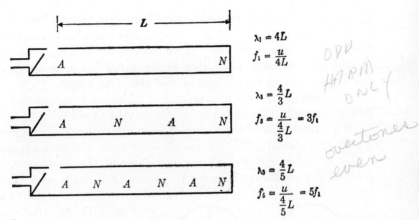

Odd harm only

even overtones

FIG. 22-12. Modes of vibration of a closed organ pipe.

an open pipe of the same length. In the language of music, the pitch of a closed pipe is one octave lower than that of an open pipe of equal length. From the remaining diagrams of Fig. 22-12, it may be seen that the second, fourth, etc., harmonics are missing. Hence, *in a closed pipe, the fundamental frequency is u/4L and only the odd harmonics are present.*

22-9 Vibrations of rods and plates.

A rod may be set in longitudinal vibration by clamping it at some point and stroking it with a chamois skin that has been sprinkled with rosin. In Fig. 22-13(a) the rod is clamped in the middle and consequently, when stroked near the end, a standing wave is set up with a node in the middle and antinodes at each end, exactly

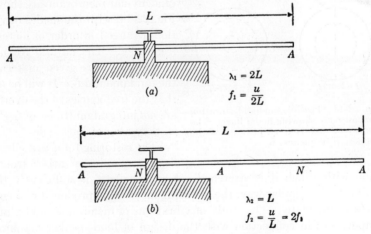

FIG. 22-13. Modes of vibration of a rod.

the same as the fundamental mode of an open organ pipe. The fundamental frequency of the rod is then $V/2L$ where V is the velocity of a longitudinal wave in the rod. Since the velocity of a longitudinal wave in a solid is much larger than that in air, a rod has a higher fundamental frequency than an open organ pipe of the same length.

By clamping the rod at a point $\frac{1}{4}$ of its length from one end, as shown in Fig. 22-13(b), the second harmonic may be produced.

If a stretched flexible membrane, such as a drumhead, is struck a blow, a two-dimensional pulse travels outward from the struck point and is reflected and re-reflected at the boundary of the membrane. If some point of the membrane is forced to vibrate periodically, continuous trains of waves travel along the membrane. Just as with the stretched string, standing waves can be set up in the membrane and each of these waves has a certain natural frequency. The lowest frequency is the fundamental and the others are overtones. In general, when the membrane is vibrating, a number of overtones are present.

The nodes of a vibrating membrane are lines (nodal lines) rather than points. The boundary of the membrane is evidently one such line. Some of the other possible nodal lines of a circular membrane are shown in Fig. 22-14, with the modes of vibration arranged in order of increasing frequency. The natural frequency of each mode is given in terms of the fundamental f_1. It will be noted that the frequencies of the overtones are *not* integral multiples of f_1. That is, they are not harmonics.

The restoring force in a vibrating flexible membrane arises from the tension with which it is stretched. A metal plate, if sufficiently thick, will vibrate in a similar way, the restoring force being produced by bending stresses in the plate. The study of vibrations of membranes and plates is of importance in connection with the design of loud-speaker diaphragms and the diaphragms of telephone receivers and microphones.

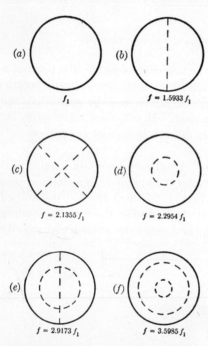

(a) f_1

(b) $f = 1.5933\,f_1$

(c) $f = 2.1355\,f_1$

(d) $f = 2.2954\,f_1$

(e) $f = 2.9173\,f_1$

(f) $f = 3.5985\,f_1$

Fig. 22-14. Possible modes of vibration of a membrane, showing nodal lines. The frequency of each is given in terms of the fundamental frequency, f_1.

Problems — Chapter 22

22-1. A steel wire of length $L = 100$ cm and density $\rho = 8$ gm/cm³ is stretched tightly between two rigid supports. Vibrating in its fundamental mode, the frequency is $f = 200$ cycles per sec. (a) What is the velocity of transverse waves on this wire? (b) What is the longitudinal stress in the wire (in dynes/cm²)? (c) If the maximum acceleration at the mid-point of the wire is 80,000 cm/sec², what is the amplitude at the mid-point?

22-2. A stretched string is observed to vibrate with a frequency of 30 cycles per second in its fundamental mode when the supports are 60 cm apart. The amplitude at the antinode is 3 cm. The string has a mass of 30 gm. (a) What is the velocity of propagation of a transverse wave in the string? (b) Compute the tension in the string. (c) Write the equation representing this wave motion, using the constants given above and computed in (a).

22-3. An aluminum weight is hung from a steel wire. The fundamental frequency for transverse standing waves on the wire is 300 cycles/sec. The weight is then immersed in water so that one-half of its volume is submerged. What is the new fundamental frequency?

22-4. The equation of a transverse wave in a stretched string is

$$y = 4 \sin 2\pi \left(\frac{t}{.02} - \frac{x}{400} \right),$$

where y and x are in centimeters and t is in seconds. (a) Is the wave a traveling wave or a standing wave? (b) What is the amplitude of the wave? (c) What is its wave length? (d) What is its velocity of propagation? (e) What is its frequency?

22-5. Standing waves are set up in a Kundt's tube by the longitudinal vibration of an iron rod one meter long, clamped at the center. If the frequency of the iron rod is 2480 vibrations per second and the powder heaps within the tube are 6.9 cm apart, (a) what is the velocity of the waves in the iron rod, and (b) in the gas?

22-6. A copper rod one meter long, clamped at the $\frac{1}{4}$ point, is set in longitudinal vibration and is used to produce standing waves in a Kundt's tube containing air at 300°K. Heaps of cork dust within the tube are found to be 4.95 cm apart. What is the velocity of longitudinal waves in copper?

22-7. Find the fundamental frequency and the first four overtones of a 6-inch pipe (a) if the pipe is open at both ends, (b) if the pipe is closed at one end. (c) How many overtones may be heard by a person having normal hearing for each of the above cases?

22-8. A long tube contains air at a pressure of 1 atm and temperature 77°C. The tube is open at one end and closed at the other by a movable piston. A tuning fork near the open end is vibrating with a frequency of 500 cycles/sec. Resonance is produced (standing waves are set up in the air column) when the piston is at distances 18.0, 55.5, and 93.0 cm from the open end. (a) From these measurements, what is the velocity of sound in air at 77°C? (b) From the above result, what is the ratio of the specific heats γ for air?

22-9. An organ pipe A of length 2 ft, closed at one end, is vibrating in the first overtone. Another organ pipe B of length 1.35 ft, open at both ends, is vibrating in its fundamental mode. Take the velocity of sound in air as 1120 ft/sec. Neglect end corrections. (a) What is the frequency of the tone from A? (b) What is the frequency of the tone from B?

CHAPTER 23

ACOUSTICAL PHENOMENA

23-1 Pressure variations in a sound wave. We shall limit ourselves in this chapter to the consideration of longitudinal waves only, and in particular to those which, when striking the ear, give rise to the sensation of sound. Such waves, within the frequency range from 20 to 20,000 vibrations per second, are called, for simplicity, *sound waves*.

The reception of a sound wave by the ear gives rise to a vibration of the air particles at the ear drum with a definite frequency and a definite amplitude. This vibration may also be described in terms of the variation of air pressure at the same point. The air pressure rises above atmospheric pressure and then sinks below atmospheric pressure with simple harmonic motion of the same frequency as that of an air particle. The maximum amount by which the pressure differs from atmospheric pressure is called the *pressure amplitude*. It can be proved that the pressure amplitude is proportional to the displacement amplitude and also to the frequency.

Measurements of sound waves show that the maximum pressure variations in the loudest sounds which the ear can tolerate are of the order of magnitude of 280 dynes/cm² (above and below atmospheric pressure of about 1,000,000 dynes/cm²). The corresponding maximum displacement for a frequency of 1000 vibrations per second is about a thousandth of a centimeter. The displacement amplitudes, even in the loudest sounds, are therefore extremely small.

The maximum pressure variations in the *faintest* sound of frequency 1000 vibrations per second are only about 2×10^{-4} dynes/cm². The corresponding displacement amplitude is about 10^{-9} cm. By way of comparison, the wave length of yellow light is 6×10^{-5} cm, and the diameter of a molecule about 10^{-8} cm. It will be appreciated that the ear is an extremely sensitive organ.

23-2 Intensity. From a purely geometrical point of view, that-which-is-propagated by a traveling wave is the *wave form*. From a physical viewpoint, however, something else is propagated by a wave, namely, *energy*. The most outstanding example, of course, is the energy supply of the earth, which reaches us from the sun via electromagnetic waves. The *intensity I* of a traveling wave is defined as *the time average rate at* *which energy is tranported by the wave per unit area* across a surface perpendicular to the direction of propagation. More briefly, the intensity is the average power transported per unit area.

We have seen that the power developed by a force equals the product of force times velocity. Hence the power per unit area in a sound wave equals the product of the excess pressure (force per unit area) times the *particle* velocity. Averaging over one cycle, it can be proved that

$$I = \frac{P^2}{2\rho_0 u}, \tag{23-1}$$

where P is the pressure amplitude, ρ_0 is the average density of the air, and u is the velocity of the sound wave. It will be noted that the *intensity* is proportional to the *square of the amplitude*, a result which is true for any sort of wave motion.

The intensity of a sound wave of pressure amplitude $P = 280$ dynes/cm^2 (roughly, the loudest tolerable sound) is

$$I = \frac{(280)^2}{2 \times 0.00122 \times 3.46 \times 10^4}$$

$$= 940 \text{ ergs per second, per square centimeter}$$

$$= 94 \times 10^{-6} \text{ watts/cm}^2.^{[1]}$$

The pressure amplitude of the faintest sound wave which can be heard is about 0.0002 dynes/cm^2 and the corresponding intensity is about 10^{-16} watts/cm^2.

The total power carried across a surface by a sound wave equals the product of the intensity at the surface times the surface area, if the intensity over the surface is uniform. The average power developed as sound waves by a person speaking in an ordinary conversational tone is about 10^{-5} watts, while a loud shout corresponds to about 3×10^{-2} watts. Since the population of the city of New York is about six million persons, the acoustical power developed if all were to speak at the same time would be about 60 watts, or enough to operate a moderate sized electric light. On the other hand, the power required to fill a large auditorium with loud sound is considerable. Suppose the intensity over the surface of a hemisphere 20 meters in radius is 10^{-4} watts per square centimeter. The area of the surface is about 25×10^6 cm^2. Hence the acoustic power output of a speaker at the center of the sphere would have to be

$$10^{-4} \times 25 \times 10^6 = 2500 \text{ watts}$$

---

[1] The "watt/cm^2" is a hybrid unit, neither cgs nor mks. We shall retain it to conform with general usage in acoustics.

or 2.5 kilowatts.   The electrical power input to the speaker would need to be considerably larger, since the efficiency of such devices is not very high.

23-3 Intensity level and loudness.   Because of the large range of intensities over which the ear is sensitive, a logarithmic rather than an arithmetic intensity scale is more convenient.   Accordingly the *intensity level β* of a sound wave is defined by the equation

$$\beta = 10 \log \frac{I}{I_0}, \tag{23-2}$$

where I_0 is an arbitrary reference intensity which is taken as 10^{-16} watt/cm^2, corresponding roughly to the faintest sound which can be heard.   Intensity levels are expressed in *decibels*, abbreviated db.[1]

If the intensity of a sound wave equals I_0 or 10^{-16} watts/cm^2, its intensity level is zero.   The maximum intensity which the ear can tolerate, about 10^{-4} watt/cm^2, corresponds to an intensity level of 120 db.   Table 23-1 gives the intensity levels in db of a number of familiar noises.   It is taken from a survey made by the N. Y. City Noise Abatement Commission.

TABLE 23-1

Noise Levels Due to Various Sources

(Representative values)

Source or description of noise	Noise level-db
Threshold of pain	120
Riveter	95
Elevated train	90
Busy street traffic	70
Ordinary conversation	65
Quiet automobile	50
Quiet radio in home	40
Average whisper	20
Rustle of leaves	10
Threshold of hearing	0

The intensity of a sound wave is a purely objective or physical attribute of a wave, and can be measured by acoustical apparatus without making use of the hearing sense of a human observer.   However, if we

---

[1] Originally, a scale of intensity levels in *bels* was defined by the relation

$$\text{Intensity level} = \log \frac{I}{I_0}.$$

This unit proved rather large and hence the decibel, one-tenth of a bel, has come into general use.   The unit is named in honor of Alexander Graham Bell.

listen to a sound wave whose intensity is gradually increased, the sensation which we describe as *loudness* increases also. The term loudness is reserved to refer to this sensation, and since it is a sensation or a subjective attribute of a sound wave, loudness can not be measured by physical apparatus. Nevertheless it is possible to establish a numerical scale of loudness sensation. It is found that while an increase of intensity results in an increase of the loudness sensation, loudness is by no means proportional to intensity. That is, a sound of intensity 10^{-6} watt/cm² is not one hundred times as loud as one of intensity 10^{-8} watt/cm². Rather, the loudness sensation is more nearly, although not directly, proportional to the logarithm of the intensity or to the *intensity level*. In other words, the loudness sensation produced by a sound wave of intensity level 60 db exceeds the loudness sensation produced by the same type of wave of intensity level 40 db, by approximately the same amount as the sensation produced by the 40 db wave exceeds that produced by a wave of intensity level 20 db.

The preceding discussion holds only for the comparison of the physiological effects produced by the *same type of wave* at various intensities. It may break down completely when comparing waves of different types. For example, it is possible to create one wave of one frequency only and another wave of many frequencies, so that both waves have exactly the same intensity level. The two waves, however, may give rise to entirely different sensations of loudness.

23-4 The ear and hearing. Fig. 23-1 is a semidiagrammatic section of the right ear. The scale of the inner ear has been exaggerated in order to show details. Sound waves traveling down the ear canal strike the ear drum. A linkage of three small bones, the hammer, anvil, and stirrup, transmits the vibrations to the oval window. The oval window in turn transmits them to the inner ear, which is filled with fluid. The terminals of the auditory nerve, of which there are about 30,000 in each ear, are distributed along the basilar membrane which divides the spiral channel or cochlea into two canals. The 30,000 nerve terminals actually occupy an area only about 30 millimeters long and 1/3 of a millimeter wide, a remarkable feat of engineering.

A great deal of work has been done in recent years, notably by Dr. Harvey Fletcher of the Bell Telephone Laboratories, on the processes by which the sound waves set up in the cochlea are picked up by the nerve endings. To represent the process graphically, the cochlea is drawn as a conventionalized spiral. (Fig. 23-2.) Each division along the spiral refers to a so-called "patch" of 1% of the nerve endings (about 300 terminals).

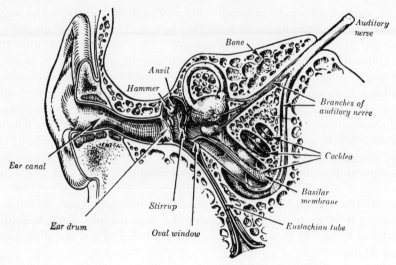

FIG. 23-1. Diagrammatic section of the right ear.

The width of the blackened strip in Fig. 23-3 shows the extent to which the corresponding nerve patches are stimulated by a 200-cycle tone at an intensity level of 90 db. Diagrams of this sort are called *auditory patterns*. Although the response of the ear to a pure tone is not localized at any one point, notes of lower frequency stimulate chiefly those patches near the inner portion of the spiral and vice versa. When listening to a street noise or a symphony orchestra, all portions of the cochlea will be stimulated to a greater or lesser extent.

The range of frequencies and intensities to which the ear is sensitive is conveniently represented by a diagram like that of Fig. 23-4, which is a graph of the *auditory area* of a person of good hearing. The height of the lower curve at any frequency represents the intensity level of the faintest pure tone of that frequency which can be heard. It will be seen from the diagram that the ear is most sensitive to frequencies between 2000 and 3000 cycles/sec where the *threshold of hearing*, as it is called, is about −5 db. The height of the upper curve at any frequency corresponds to the intensity level of the loudest pure tone of that frequency which can be tolerated. At intensities above this curve, which is called the *threshold of feeling*, the sensation changes from one of hearing to discomfort or even pain. The height of the upper curve is approximately constant at a level of about 120 db for all frequencies. Every pure tone which can be heard may be represented by a point lying somewhere in the area between these two curves.

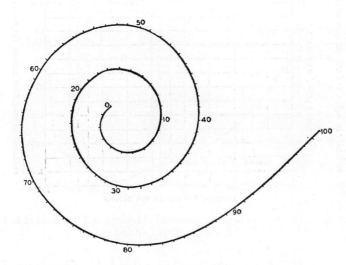

Fig. 23-2.   Conventionalized diagram of the cochlea.
(*Courtesy of Dr. Harvey Fletcher*)

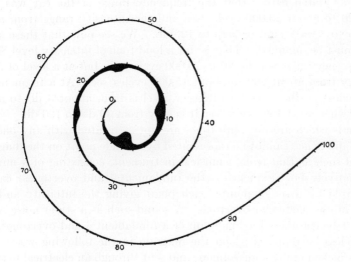

Fig. 23-3.   Auditory pattern of a 200-cycle tone at an intensity level of 90 db
(*Courtesy of Dr. Harvey Fletcher.*)

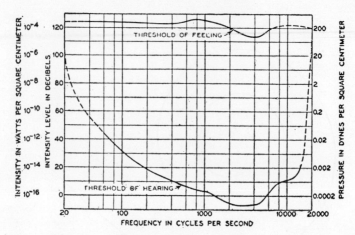

Fig. 23-4. Auditory area between threshold of hearing and threshold of feeling.
(*Courtesy of Dr. Harvey Fletcher*)

Only about 1% of the population has a threshold of hearing as low as the bottom curve in Fig. 23-4. 50% of the population can hear pure tones of a frequency of 2500 cycles when the intensity level is about 8 db, and 90% when the level is 20 db.

It was stated earlier that the frequency range of the ear was from about 20 to about 20,000 cycles/sec and the intensity range from about 10^{-16} to 10^{-4} watt/cm^2, or zero to 120 db. We see now that these statements must be qualified. That is, for a loud tone of intensity level 80 db, the frequency range is from 20 to 20,000 cycles/sec, but at a level of 20 db it is only from about 200 to about 15,000 cycles/sec. At a frequency of 1000 cycles/sec the range of intensity level is from about 3 db to about 120 db, whereas at 100 cycles/sec it is only from 30 db to 120 db.

Sounds which are not pure tones are not associated with any one frequency and hence cannot be represented by a single point on the diagram. A sound such as that from a musical instrument, consisting of a mixture of a relatively few frequencies (the fundamental and overtones) can be represented by a set of points, each point giving the intensity and frequency of one particular overtone. A sound such as a street noise, while it cannot be considered as made up of a fundamental and overtones, can nevertheless be represented on the diagram in the following way. The sound is picked up by a microphone and sent through an electrical network which selects a narrow range of frequencies and measures the average intensity within this range. By repeating the process at a large number of frequencies throughout the audible range, a series of points are obtained which can be plotted. A continuous curve drawn through them is called the *spectrogram* of the sound. A typical spectrogram of street noise is shown in Fig. 23-5.

The term "spectrogram" is borrowed from optics. The process just described is entirely analogous to the optical one of dispersing a beam of light waves into a spectrum by means of a prism and measuring the intensity at a number of points throughout the spectrum. The light emitted by a gas in an electrical discharge is a mixture of waves of a number of definite frequencies and corresponds to the sound emitted by a musical instrument. Most light beams, however, are a mixture of all frequencies and are therefore the optical analogue of noise.

The total intensity level of a noise can be found from its spectrogram by an integration process. There are also instruments known as noise meters which measure the level directly. The level of the street noise in Fig. 23-5 is about 85 db and is shown by the short heavy line.

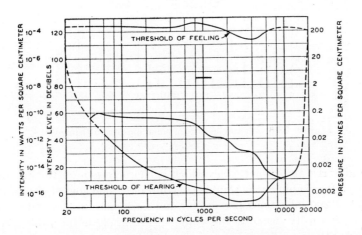

FIG. 23-5. Spectrogram of street noise.
(*Courtesy of Dr. Harvey Fletcher*)

23-5 Quality and pitch. A string that has been plucked or a plate that has been struck, if allowed to vibrate freely, will vibrate with many frequencies at the same time. It is a rare occurrence for a body to vibrate with only one frequency. A carefully made tuning fork struck lightly on a rubber block may vibrate with only one frequency; but, in the case of musical instruments, the fundamental and many harmonics are usually present at the same time. The impulses that are sent from the ear to the

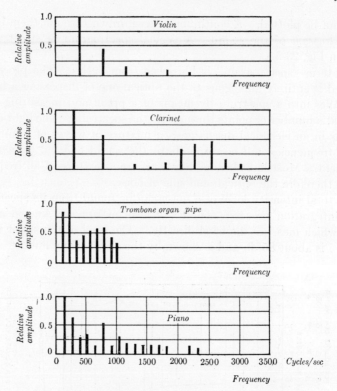

FIG. 23-6.   Sound spectra of some musical instruments.
(*Courtesy of Dr. Harvey Fletcher*)

brain give rise to one net effect which is characteristic of the instrument. Suppose, for example, the sound spectrum of a tone consisted of a fundamental of 200 vibrations per second and harmonics 2, 3, 4, and 5, all of different intensity; whereas the sound spectrum of another tone consisted of exactly the same frequencies but with a different intensity distribution. The two tones would sound different; they are said to differ in *quality*.

Adjectives used to describe the quality of musical tones are purely subjective in character, such as reedy, golden, round, mellow, tinny, etc. *The quality of a sound is determined by the number of overtones present and their respective intensities.* The sound spectra of various musical instruments are shown in Fig. 23-6.

Another subjective attribute of a musical sound that is described with the aid of the adjectives high, medium, low, etc., is called the *pitch*. It is a simple matter to explain the pitch of a sound produced by a wave of only one frequency. If we take a set of tuning forks differing in size and cause each one to sound its fundamental only, then it becomes apparent that the greater the frequency, the higher the pitch. The situation, however, is very much more complicated when the sound is produced by a wave of many frequencies. As we have pointed out, many of the notes played on musical instruments are rich in harmonics, some of which may be more prominent than the fundamental. Presented with an array of frequencies constituting a harmonic series, the ear will still assign a characteristic pitch to the combination, this pitch being that associated with the fundamental frequency of the series. So definite is this pitch sensation that it is possible, by means of filters, to eliminate the fundamental frequency entirely without any observable effect upon the pitch! The ear apparently will supply the fundamental, provided the correct harmonics are present. It is this rather surprising property of the ear that enables a small loudspeaker which does not radiate low frequencies well to nevertheless give the impression of good radiation in the low frequency region. Because the speaker is a fairly efficient radiator for the frequencies of the harmonics, the listener believes he is actually hearing the low frequencies, when instead he is hearing only multiples of these frequencies and his ear is supplying the fundamental. It is possible, by deliberate distortion of the harmonics associated with low musical notes, to make a very small radio set, totally inadequate in the low frequency range, sound somewhat like a larger, acoustically superior console set. Such synthetic bass is, to the critical ear, inferior in sound to true bass reproduction, where the harmonic content is closer to that of the original sound.

When the ear is exposed to a pure note of constant frequency, there is a change in the pitch sensation *as the intensity level is raised.* This change is usually a decrease, the amount of the change being a function of the frequency of the source and the intensity at the ear. Many listeners can detect a drop in apparent frequency when certain loud notes are sounded on the organ, an instrument of great acoustic power. This may be due to actual fluctuations at the source because of large air amplitudes in the pipe, or may be an effect occurring at the ear.

23-6 Beats. Standing waves in an air column have been cited as one example of interference. They arise when two wave trains of the same amplitude and frequency are traveling through the same region in opposite directions. We now wish to consider another type of interference which results when two wave trains of equal amplitude but slightly different frequency travel through the same region. Such a condition exists when two tuning forks of slightly different frequency are sounded simultaneously or when two piano wires struck by the same key are slightly "out of tune."

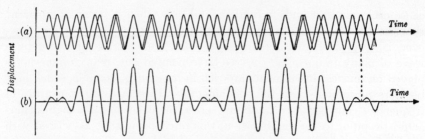

FIG. 23-7. Beats are fluctuations in amplitude produced by two sound waves of slightly different frequency.

If we consider some one point of space through which the waves are simultaneously passing, the displacements due to the two waves separately are plotted as a function of the time on graph (a) of Fig. 23-7. If the total extent of the time axis represents one second, the graphs correspond to frequencies of 16 vibrations per second and of 18 vibrations per second. Applying the principle of superposition to find the resultant vibration, we get graph (b), where it is seen that the amplitude varies with the time. These variations of amplitude give rise to variations of loudness which are called *beats*. It can be seen from Fig. 23-7 that *the number of beats per second is equal to the difference between the two frequencies.* Two strings may be tuned to the same frequency by tightening one of them while sounding both until the beats disappear.

23-7 Combination tones. Beats between two tones can be detected by the ear up to a beat frequency of 6 or 7 per second. At higher frequencies, individual beats can no longer be distinguished and the sensation merges into one of *consonance* or *dissonance* depending on the frequency ratio of the tones. A beat frequency, even though it lies within the frequency range of the ear, is not interpreted by the ear as a tone of that frequency. Nevertheless, a tone can be heard of frequency equal to the frequency difference between two others sounded simultaneously. Such a tone is called a *difference* tone. Although not as easy to recognize, a frequency called a *summation* tone and equal to the sum of the frequencies of the two tones can also be heard. The general term applied to both difference tones and summation tones is *combination* tones.

Combination tones are similar to beats but are due to the nature of the hearing mechanism. The ear is one of a number of devices whose response is said to be *nonlinear*. A vacuum tube operated on the curved portion of its characteristic is another. Fig. 23-8 illustrates the situation schematically. The response to a given stimulus is represented by the

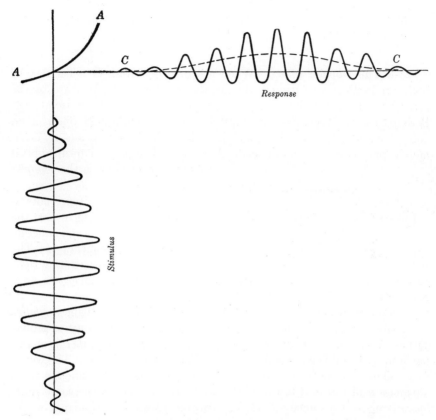

Fɪɢ. 23-8.   Illustrates production of combination tones.

curved line AA.   (In a vacuum tube the "response" would be the plate current and the "stimulus" the grid potential.)   The curve extending vertically downward represents the displacement of the air at a point through which two waves of different frequency are passing simultaneously. The response to this stimulus is obtained by projecting upward from every point of this curve to the curve AA and then projecting across.   It will be seen that because of the curvature (or nonlinearity) of AA, the response curve is not symmetrical but has an "average" upward sweep indicated by the dotted line.   Hence, if the graph represents the motion of the ear drum, it is seen that the latter will vibrate at a frequency equal to the beat frequency or the difference in frequencies of the two tones.   This vibration is superposed on the much higher frequency of the individual waves in the tone.   Note carefully that if the response curve AA were *linear*, the curve CC would be symmetrical and no such motion of the ear drum would ensue.

23-8 The Doppler effect. When a source of sound, or a listener, or both, are in motion relative to the air, the observed pitch as heard by the listener is, in general, not the same as when source and listener are at rest. Perhaps the most common example is the sudden drop in pitch of an automobile horn which takes place just as one meets and passes an automobile proceeding in the opposite direction. The general term applied to this phenomenon is the *Doppler effect*.

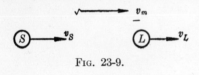

Fig. 23-9.

In Fig. 23-9, S represents a source of sound moving toward the right with a velocity v_S and emitting sound waves of a frequency f_0. The listener, moving toward the right with a velocity v_L, is represented by L. Velocities v_S and v_L are both relative to the earth.

A sound wave emitted by the source S at time $t = 0$ advances *relative to the medium* with a velocity of propagation u. (The velocity of propagation of sound waves in or relative to a medium is a property of the medium only and is independent of the velocity of the source. The waves forget about the source as soon as they leave it.) Hence in time t, a wave advances a distance ut toward the right. The source, in the same time, has advanced a distance $v_S t$ and has emitted $f_0 t$ waves. Hence $f_0 t$ waves occupy the distance between the source and the wave emitted at time $t = 0$, or a distance $ut - v_S t = (u - v_S)t$. The distance between any two consecutive waves, or the wave length, is therefore

$$\lambda = \frac{(u - v_S)\,t}{f_0 t} = \frac{u - v_S}{f_0}. \tag{23-3}$$

Consider next the listener. Sound waves traveling with a velocity u are passing him, but his own velocity is v_L. Hence the velocity of the waves relative to the listener is $u - v_L$. The number of waves that pass the listener per unit time, or the apparent frequency f, is the ratio of the relative velocity to the wave length, or

$$f = \frac{u - v_L}{(u - v_S)/f_0},$$

or

$$\boxed{\frac{f}{f_0} = \frac{u - v_L}{u - v_S},}$$ (23-4)

where $\dfrac{f}{f_0}$ is the ratio of apparent to true frequency.

Careful attention must be paid to the construction of the diagram and to algebraic signs when using this equation. The diagram must be drawn as in Fig. 23-9, with the source at the left of the listener, and all velocities shown by vectors. If, in a given case, any velocity is opposite to that in Fig. 23-9, its sign should be reversed in Eq. (23-4). The velocity of propagation, u, is considered positive always.

Examples. (1) A stationary source in still air emits a sound wave of frequency f_0. What is the apparent frequency heard by a listener approaching the source with a velocity of magnitude v_L?

See Fig. 23-10(a). Since the source is at rest, $v_S = 0$, and since v_L is directed toward the left,

$$f = f_0 \frac{u + v_L}{u}.$$

The apparent frequency is higher than the true frequency, in agreement with common experience.

(2) A listener moves away from a stationary source in still air with a velocity of magnitude v_L. Find the ratio of apparent to true frequency.

See Fig. 23-10(b). Evidently

$$f = f_0 \frac{u - v_L}{u}$$

and the apparent frequency drops when the listener recedes from the source.

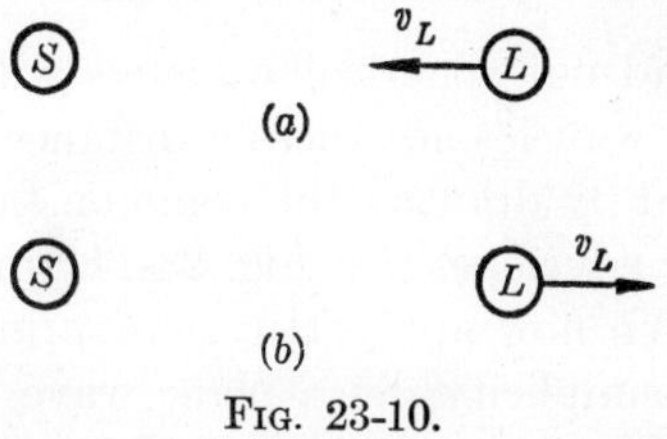

(a)

(b)

Fig. 23-10.

In the preceding analysis the medium was assumed to be at rest with respect to the earth. In the event that the medium is moving with a velocity v_m (positive to the right and negative to the left), it is a simple matter to show that Eq. (23-4) becomes

$$\frac{f}{f_0} = \frac{u + v_m - v_L}{u + v_m - v_S}.$$

The Doppler effect is not confined to sound waves. The light from a star which is approaching the earth is of somewhat higher frequency or shorter wave length than it would be if the two were at relative rest. Much valuable information regarding stellar motions has been obtained in this way.

23-9 Reflection of sound waves. We have already mentioned the reflection of sound waves at the open or closed ends of an organ pipe. The familiar phenomenon of an echo also arises from the reflection of sound. The reflection of a three-dimensional sound wave from a surface which it strikes can be treated with the help of a useful graphical method called Huygens' principle. The same principle is extremely useful in dealing with light waves.

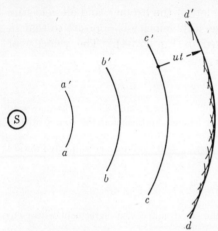

In Fig. 23-11, the point S represents a small source of sound and the circular arcs aa', bb', etc., are traces of sound waves spreading out from the source with velocity u. Suppose we know that at some instant a wave has the shape cc' and we wish to find its shape after a time interval t. Huygens' principle states that every point of the wave cc' may be considered a "secondary" source from which there

FIG. 23-11. Huygens' method for finding the shape of a wave.

spread out spherical wavelets with the velocity u. In a time interval t each wavelet advances a distance ut, and the new position of the wave is found by drawing the common tangent to the wavelets or, as it is called, their envelope. In Fig. 23-11, this is the wave dd'.

We now apply Huygens' principle to the reflection of a sound wave. For simplicity, let a plane wave aa' in Fig. 23-12(a) strike a fixed plane surface AA'. Construct Huygens' wavelets of radius ut from each point of aa'. The envelope of those from the lower part of aa' is the portion of the new wave bO. The wavelets from the upper part of aa', had the surface not been present, would have advanced to the positions of the dotted circles. Actually, since they cannot penetrate the surface, they spread out in the opposite direction and their envelope is the portion of the new wave Ob'.

The angle θ between the incident wave aa' and the surface is called the *angle of incidence;* the angle θ' between the reflected wave Ob' and the surface is the *angle of reflection.* It is easy to see that the right triangles $Ob'a'$ and Oca' are similar and hence $\theta' = \theta$. That is, a plane sound wave

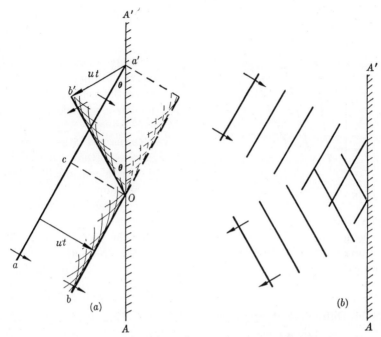

FIG. 23-12.   (a) Two stages in the reflection of a plane wave from a plane surface. (b) Reflection of a train of plane waves from a plane surface.

is reflected from a plane surface with the angle of reflection equal to the angle of incidence.   It will be recognized that this is the same law governing the reflection of light waves from a plane mirror.

Fig. 23-12(b) shows successive stages in the reflection of a plane wave from a plane surface, or it may be considered to represent a "snapshot" of a train of plane waves, incident on and reflected from the surface.

If the surface from which the sound wave is reflected is perfectly rigid, there is no loss of energy in the process of reflection.   No actual surface fulfills this requirement, but yields to some extent under the pressure of the wave.   Furthermore, if the surface is at all porous, the air in the pores or cavities is set into turbulent motion.   Consequently, some heat is always developed when sound waves strike a surface and the reflected energy is less than the incident energy.   The energy lost by the sound wave is said to be *absorbed* by the surface.

23-10 Refraction of sound waves.   We have shown that the velocity of propagation of a sound wave in a gas varies with the temperature.

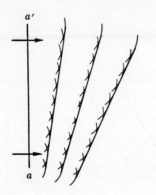

FIG. 23-13.   Refraction of a sound wave.

Consider a plane sound wave in air such as aa' in Fig. 23-13. The plane of the wave is vertical and the wave is advancing from left to right. Suppose the temperature of the air, and hence the velocity of propagation, increases with elevation. The Huygens' wavelets at the top of the wave then have a larger radius than those at the bottom, with the result that the wave continually alters direction as shown. This change in direction, caused by variation in velocity from point to point, is called *refraction*.

In general, the temperature of the air over the earth's surface is not the same at all points and it will be evident that refraction of sound is an important factor in the process of sound ranging, that is, the location of a source of sound such as a distant plane or an exploding shell or bomb.

23-11 Diffraction of sound waves.   The reflecting surface in Fig. 23-12 was purposely taken considerably larger than the breadth of the train of sound waves. We may next inquire what would happen if a train of waves advancing as in Fig. 23-14 were to encounter an obstacle A having the relative dimensions shown. A complete analysis of the situation is beyond the scope of this book. It will suffice to state that if the dimen-

sions of the obstacle are large compared with the wave length of the sound waves, Huygens' principle may be applied, as in Fig. 23-12, to find the shape of the reflected waves. If, however, the dimensions of the obstacle are of the same order of magnitude as the wave length of the sound waves, the process is much more complex. A portion of the incident wave "bends" or "flows" around the obstacle and continues

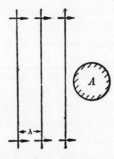

FIG. 23-14

to advance toward the right. Superposed on this wave is another so-called *scattered* wave which spreads out in all directions from the obstacle, but with an intensity which is different in different directions. The general term applied to the phenomenon is *diffraction*.

Diffraction effects are of importance in acoustical engineering since Fig. 23-14 might represent the sound waves from a person speaking and A might be a microphone. The response of a microphone depends on the pressure variations at its surface and these in turn are determined by the precise nature of the diffraction effects. A text on the mathematical theory of sound should be consulted for further details.

Diffraction effects are also exhibited by light waves when they encounter an obstacle. The reason that diffraction of light is a less familiar phenomenon than, say, the regular reflection of light by a mirror, is because the wave lengths of visible light waves (about 5×10^{-5} cm) are so small that most optical instruments are large by comparison. On the other hand, the wave length in air of a 500-cycle sound wave is about 2 ft and evidently the dimensions of much acoustical apparatus, such as microphones and loudspeakers, are of the same order of magnitude. Hence diffraction effects are of relatively greater importance in acoustics than in optics.

The upper frequency limit of audible sound is about 15,000 cycles/sec, corresponding to a wave length in air of about one inch. Shorter wave lengths (higher frequencies) than this are called *ultrasonic* waves. Such waves are, of course, inaudible, but they can be produced and detected by the same type of mechanical or electrical instruments as are used in the audible region. The dimensions of apparatus are readily made much larger than the wave lengths of ultrasonic waves so that diffraction effects are of less importance and ultrasonic waves can readily be reflected, refracted, focused, etc., in the same way as light waves.

23-12 Musical intervals and scales. If certain musical tones are produced in succession, an untrained listener, as well as an accomplished musician, recognizes a relationship among them. Such relations are described in musical language by words such as octave, major third, minor third, etc. The listener recognizes something basic in these intervals, and experimental measurement of the fundamental frequencies of the separate tones discloses that they bear simple whole-number ratios to one another. Thus, the fundamental frequencies of middle C of the piano and its *octave* above, C^1, are to each other as 1 to 2. Another basic set of tones is obtained by playing C, E, G. These constitute what is known as a *major triad*, and the frequencies are found to be proportional to 4, 5, and 6.

Starting at middle C of the piano, and playing only the white notes toward the right, it is possible to find, within only nine notes, three major triads. These are shown in Table 23-2, and enable one to calculate the frequencies of all the notes, once one of them has been chosen arbitrarily. By international agreement, the frequency of the A above middle C is chosen to be 440 vibrations per second.   The frequencies of all the notes, shown in row 5 of Table 23-2, are those that correspond to the *major diatonic scale* of the key of C.   The frequency ratios of adjacent notes are seen to be either 9/8, 10/9, or 16/15.   The interval between two tones whose frequencies bear the ratio 9/8 or 10/9 are called *whole tones*, whereas the interval between two notes of frequency ratio 16/15 is a *half tone*.

TABLE 23-2

FREQUENCY RELATIONS IN THE MAJOR DIATONIC SCALE
AND IN THE EQUALLY TEMPERED SCALE

		Do	Re	Mi	Fa	Sol	La	Ti	Do'	Re'
	Frequency relations	Middle C	D	E	F	G	A	B	C'	D'
1	Octave, key of C.....	1							2	
2	Major triad, key of C..	4		5		6			(8)	
3	Major triad, key of F..				4		5		6	
4	Major triad, key of G..		(3)			4		5		6
5	Diatonic scale, key of C	264	297	330	352	396	440	495	528	594
6			9/8 whole	10/9 whole	16/15 half	9/8 whole	10/9 whole	9/8 whole	16/15 half	9/8 whole
7	Equally tempered scale suitable for all keys..	261.6	293.7	329.6	349.2	392.0	440	493.9	523.3	587.4
8			$\sqrt[6]{2}$	$\sqrt[6]{2}$	$\sqrt[12]{2}$	$\sqrt[6]{2}$	$\sqrt[6]{2}$	$\sqrt[6]{2}$	$\sqrt[12]{2}$	$\sqrt[6]{2}$

If a major diatonic scale were constructed, starting at D instead of at C, four new notes would be needed for a perfect diatonic scale.   If all possible musical keys were to be provided for, seventy-two notes would be needed for each octave.   To avoid this tremendous complication, what is known as the *equally tempered scale* has been devised (used by J. S. Bach and probably earlier musicians).   In this scheme there are 12 half-tone intervals in every range of an octave, adjacent notes a half-tone apart bearing the constant ratio of the twelfth root of 2, i.e., 1.05946. Simple as this scheme is, it results in no one scale being exactly diatonic. Since the ratios of the diatonic scale were originally selected to suit the preferences of the ear (being made up of three sets of major triads, each of which constitutes a harmonious combination), this means that music which makes use of the equally tempered scale is not quite so pleasant to the ear. The difference, however, is apparently slight to any but the most critical.

23-13 Consonance and dissonance. What constitutes a pleasant combination of frequencies and what is an unpleasant combination has long been a subject for discussion among both musicians and physicists. The disagreeable sound of certain combinations was attributed by Helmholtz to beat effects, either between the fundamental frequencies themselves or between some of their harmonics. He believed that for the middle of the audible spectrum the difference frequency or beat rate which produced aural irritation covered the range of about 30 to 130 cycles-sec^{-1}. Two adjacent half-tones in the neighborhood of 440 cycles-sec^{-1} differ by about 25 cycles and when sounded together are on the verge of being disagreeable to the ear. Two adjacent whole tones in this region differ by about 45 cycles and the combination of two such notes is usually considered dissonant. Even though the fundamental frequencies of two sounds with rich harmonic structures are far enough apart to produce consonance, there may be a particular harmonic of one tone which is close to a harmonic of the other, and the result is an over-all effect of dissonance.

There is a strong individual subjective element in the matter of consonance and dissonance that often determines the final impression. There is also no doubt that musical fashions change. Much of the music written in recent years is highly and continuously dissonant to ears accustomed to Haydn and Mozart, yet adherents of this newer musical style welcome each crashing "discord" with great satisfaction. Such sharp cleavages in musical taste make it difficult to draw any very certain conclusions in the matter of consonance and dissonance.

Problems — Chapter 23

23-1. (a) If the pressure amplitude in a sound wave is tripled, by how many times is the intensity of the wave increased? (b) By how many times must the pressure amplitude of a sound wave be increased in order to increase the intensity by a factor of 16 times?

23-2. (a) Two sound waves, one in air and one in water, are equal in intensity. What is the ratio of the pressure amplitude of the wave in water to that of the wave in air? (b) If the pressure amplitudes of the waves are equal, what is the ratio of their intensities?

23-3. Relative to the arbitrary reference intensity of 10^{-16} watt/cm², what is the intensity level in db of a sound wave whose intensity is 10^{-10} watt/cm²? What is the intensity level of a sound wave in air whose pressure amplitude is 2 dynes/cm²?

23-4. (a) Show that if β_1 and β_2 are the intensity levels in db of sounds of intensities I_1 and I_2 respectively, the difference in intensity levels of the sounds is

$$\beta_2 - \beta_1 = 10 \log \frac{I_2}{I_1}.$$

(b) Show that if p_1 and p_2 are the pressure amplitudes of two sound waves, the difference in intensity levels of the waves is

$$\beta_2 - \beta_1 = 20 \log \frac{p_2}{p_1}.$$

(c) Show that if the reference level of intensity is $I_0 = 10^{-16}$ watt/cm², the intensity level of a sound of intensity I is

$$\beta = 160 + 10 \log I.$$

23-5. Two loudspeakers, A and B, radiate sound uniformly in all directions. The output of acoustic power from A is 8×10^{-4} watt, and from B it is 13.5×10^{-4} watt. Both loudspeakers are vibrating in phase at a frequency of 173 cycles/sec.

(a) Determine the difference in phase of the two signals at a point C, 3 m from B and 4 m from A. (b) Determine the intensity at C from speaker A if speaker B is turned off, and the intensity at C from speaker B if speaker A is turned off. (c) With both speakers on, what is the intensity and intensity level at C?

23-6. The intensity due to a number of independent sound sources is the sum of the individual intensities. How many db greater was the intensity level when all five of the quintuplets cried simultaneously than when a single one cried? How many more crying babies would be required to produce a further increase in the intensity level of the same number of db?

23-7. A window whose area is 1 m² opens on a street where the street noises result in an intensity level, at the window, of 60 db. How much "acoustic power" enters the window via the sound waves?

23-8. (a) What are the upper and lower limits of intensity level of a person whose auditory area is represented by the graph of Fig. 23-4? (b) What are the highest and lowest frequencies he can hear when the intensity level is 40 db?

23-9. Two whistles, A and B, each have a frequency of 500 cycles/sec. A is stationary and B is moving toward the right (away from A) at a velocity of 200 ft/sec. An observer is between the two whistles, moving toward the right with a velocity of 100 ft/sec. Take the velocity of sound in air as 1100 ft/sec. (a) What is the frequency from A as heard by the observer? (b) What is the frequency from B as heard by the observer? (c) What is the beat frequency heard by the observer?

23-10. A railroad train is traveling at 100 ft/sec in still air. The frequency of the note emitted by the locomotive whistle is 500 cycles/sec. What is the wave length of the sound waves (a) in front of, (b) behind the locomotive? What would be the frequency of the sound heard by a stationary listener (c) in front of, (d) behind the locomotive? What frequency would be heard by a passenger on a train traveling at 50 ft/sec and (e) approaching the first, (f) receding from the first? (g) How is each of the preceding answers altered if a wind of velocity 30 ft/sec is blowing in the same direction as that in which the locomotive is traveling?

23-11. A source of sound waves S, emitting waves of frequency 1000 cycles/sec, is traveling toward the right in still air with a velocity of 100 ft/sec. At the right of the source is a large smooth reflecting surface moving toward the left with a velocity of 400 ft/sec. (a) How far does an emitted wave travel in 0.01 sec? (b) What is the wave length of the emitted waves in front of (i.e., at the right of) the source? (c) How many waves strike the reflecting surface in 0.01 sec? (d) What is the velocity of the reflected waves? (e) What is the wave length of the reflected waves?

ANSWERS TO PROBLEMS

NOTE: The data given in the problems should be assumed correct to three significant figures (i.e., 2 cm implies 2.00 cm) and, in general, your answers should be carried out to three significant figures or "slide rule accuracy." Only two significant figures are given in the answers to most of the problems. The purpose of the answers is not to give you a figure which should be checked exactly, but to let you know if you are on the right track.

CHAPTER 1

1-3. (a) 18.5 lb.   (b) 9.2 lb.

1-5. 47 lb in the negative Y direction.

1-7. (a) 7 lb, 2.9 lb.
(b) 7.6 lb.
(d) 11 lb.

1-9. $R = 0$.

CHAPTER 2

2-5. (a) 150 lb in A, 180 lb in B, 200 lb in C.
(b) 200 lb in A, 280 lb in B, 200 lb in C.
(c) 550 lb in A, 670 lb in B, 200 lb in C.
(d) 167 lb in A, 58 lb in B, 125 lb in C.

2-7. (a) Parts (b) and (c) can be solved.
(b) In part (a) another side or angle is necessary.

2-9. 630 lb.

2-11. 1400 lb.

2-13. (a) zero.   (d) 4 lb.
(b) 5 lb.   (e) 4 lb.
(c) 8 lb.

2-15. Sliding down 53°, sliding up 37°.

2-17. (b) 10 lb.   (c) 30 lb.

CHAPTER 3

3-1. The resultant of a couple is zero, but zero force does not produce the same effect as a couple.

3-3. (a) −6 lb, 10 lb.
(b) 5/3.
(c) 12 lb.
(d) 2 ft from right end of bar.

3-5. (a) $F_D = 64$ lb, $F_E = 36$ lb.
(b) $V_A = 70$ lb, $V_B = 30$ lb.
(c) At point A, 90 lb to right, 70 lb down.
At point C, 90 lb to left, 34 lb up.
At point E, 36 lb up.

3-7. (a) 12 lb.
(b) 53° with horizontal.

3-9. 1000 lb.

3-11. (a) $R = 460$ lb.   (b) $H = 180$ lb, $V = 24$ lb.

3-13. (b) Each guide exerts 200 lb.

3-15. 67 lb.

3-17. The center of gravity lies at a point on the perpendicular bisector of the line joining the 9- and 12-lb weights, at a distance of 0.6 ft from this line.

3-19. 7.4 inches from large end.

CHAPTER 4

4-1. (a) 0.0037 mi/sec.   (c) 600 cm/sec.
(b) 13 mi/hr.   (d) 20 ft/sec.

4-3. (a) 0, 1, 1.5, 2.5, 2.5, 2.5, 1, 0 ft/sec^2. Acceleration is constant only between $t = 6$ and $t = 12$ sec.
(b) 10 ft, 25 ft, 170 ft, 2.5 ft/sec^2, 1 ft/sec^2, 0.

4-5. 4 ft/sec^2, 620 ft.

4-7. 1500 ft.

4-9. (a) 4.6 ft/sec^2 South.
(b) 4.8 sec.
(c) 210 ft.

4-11. (a) 24 ft/sec.   (c) 0.38 sec.
(b) 0.75 sec.   (d) 6.8 ft.

4-13. (a) 320 ft/sec. (b) 400 ft.

4-15. (a) 36 ft. (b) 0.5 sec.
(c) 32 ft/sec, -32 ft/sec^2, -16 ft/sec, -32 ft/sec^2.

4-17. (a) $x_1 = 10 + 20t + 8t^2 - t^3$.
(b) $x_2 = 10t + 8t^2 - t^3$.

4-19. (a) 4 m/sec^2. (c) 4.5 m.
(b) 6 m/sec.

4-21. 20° E of N, 170 mi/hr.

CHAPTER 5

5-1. (a) 400 lb.   (c) 12,800 newtons.
(b) 12,800 dynes.

5-3. (a) 2 m/sec^2. (c) 20 m/sec.
(b) 100 m.

5-5. Action and reaction do not act on the same body.

5-7. (a) 10 gm.
(b) Yes.
(c) Yes, if g is the acceleration due to gravity on Mars.
(d) No.
(e) Spring balance is really a force-measuring device, it is calibrated in grams for the convenience of Earthlings.

5-9. (a) 40 lb.   (c) zero.
(b) 4 ft/sec^2 down.

5-11. (a) 625 ft.
(b) 1000 lb.

5-13. 90 cars.

5-15. (a) 12 sec after force is applied.
(b) 8 ft/sec^2.

5-17. $W = 2 wa/(g + a)$.

5-19. (a) 37°.   (c) 2.5 sec.
(b) 6.4 ft/sec^2.

5-21. (a) 6 lb. (b) 8 ft/sec^2.

5-23. (a) 400 lb.   (g) 6 ft/sec^2 down.
(b) 1200 lb.   (h) 2100 lb.
(c) 2400 lb.   2700 lb.
(d) 2800 lb.   2100 lb.
(e) 1200 lb.   2900 lb.
(f) 2000 lb.

5-25. 5 sec.

5-27. (a) 200 cm/sec^2.
(b) 314,000 dynes.

5-29. (a) to left.   (c) 43.3 lb.
(b) 2.13 ft/sec^2.

5-31. Acceleration of m_1: $\dfrac{2m_2g}{4m_1 + m_2}$

Acceleration of m_2: $\dfrac{m_2g}{4m_1 + m_2}$

5-33. (a) 16 ft/sec^2. (c) 21 lb.
(b) 27 lb.

5-35. (a) 1 sec.
(b) 1 ft.

5-37. (a) 6.4 ft/sec^2.
(b) $a = 6.4x - 32$.

5-39. 6.2×10^{27} grams.

CHAPTER 6

6-1. 183 ft/sec.

6-3. (a) 20 sec.   (b) 6000 ft.   (c) $v_x = 300$ ft/sec, $v_y = 640$ ft/sec.

6-5. (a) 192 ft, 64 ft.
(b) 415 ft, 223 ft.

6-7. (a) 110 ft from where it is thrown.
(b) 400 ft.

6-9. 1300 ft.

6-11. 17 ft/sec.

6-13. (a) 90 cm.   (b) Horizontally.

6-15. (a) 80 ft/sec.
(b) 128 ft.

6-17. (a) 670 ft/sec.
(b) 2700 ft.
(c) Horizontal component is 530 ft/sec.
Vertical component is 560 ft/sec.

6-19. It is a straight line.

CHAPTER 7

7-1. 63.4×10^6 ft-lb.

7-3. (a) 5 lb, 10 lb, 20 lb.
(b) 1.3 ft-lb, 5 ft-lb, 20 ft-lb.

7-5. (a) 55,000 ft-lb.
(b) 4 times.

7-7. 2×10^6 ft-lb.

7-9. 7.35×10^6 ergs.

7-11. (a) 160 ft-lb. It goes into kinetic energy.
(b) 160 ft-lb.

7-13. 16 lb; 320 ft-lb; it goes into potential energy.

7-15. (a) 8200 joules.   (c) 412 watts.
(b) 8200 joules.

7-17. (a) 50 lb.
(b) 300 ft-lb.

7-19. 42 lb, 105 ft-lb.

7-21. (a) 40 ft/sec.
(b) 20 ft/sec.

7-23. 10 cm.

7-25. 6%.

7-27. (a) 120 ft.
(b) 0.0073 hp.

7-29. (a) 55,000 dynes.   (c) 1.7.
(b) 1.3.   (d) 79%

7-31. 12,000 lb.

7-37. (a) 18×10^{20} ergs.
(b) 18×10^{26} ergs/sec.
(c) 1.2×10^{13} grams (about 3 billion gallons).

CHAPTER 8

8-1. (a) 28,000 slug-ft/sec.
(b) 60 mi/hr.
(c) 43 mi/hr.

8-3. (a) 8×10^5 m/sec².
(b) 4×10^4 newtons.
(c) 5×10^{-4} sec.
(d) 20 newton-sec.

8-5. (a) zero.
(b) 4 m/sec to the left, 1.5 m/sec to the right.
(c) 33 joules.

3-7. (a) 0.19 ft/sec.   (c) 0.25 ft/sec².
(b) 1.3 lb.

8-9. 280 m/sec (note that the initial *KE* of the bullet is *not* equal to the final *PE* of pendulum).

8-11. (a) 0.16.   (c) 0.32 joule.
(b) 240 joules.

8-13. (a) 5×10^6 ergs.
(b) 100 cm/sec.
(c) 10,000 cm/sec.

8-15. (a) 10 ft/sec.   (c) 8 ft/sec.
(b) 11 ft/sec.

8-17. (a) 0.707.
(b) 2 ft-lb.

CHAPTER 9

9-1. (a) 1.5 radians.
(b) 1.6 radians, 90°.
(c) 120 cm, 120 ft.

9-3. (a) 20 ft/sec.
(b) 230 rpm.

9-5. 5 rad/sec², 1000 rad.

9-7. 20 rad/sec².

9-9. (b) $a_T = 0$, $a_R = \omega^2 R$.
(c) Yes, $a_T = R\alpha$; yes, $a_R = R\omega^2$.

9-11. (a) 40π rad/sec.
(b) 130π radians.
(c) 600π inches/sec.
(d) 14,000 inches/sec².

9-13. (a) 28 ft/sec², tangential to path.
(b) 27 ft/sec², 45° from string.

9-15. $\dfrac{mg \pm \mu Mg}{M\omega^2}$.

9-17. $v = \sqrt{gRb/2h}$.

9-19. (a) 11°.
(b) 6.2 times the mass of the plane in slugs.
(c) 32.8 m (using $g = 32.2$ ft/sec²).

9-21. (a) 10 tons downward.
(b) 2 tons upward.
(c) Safety Factor: 2.

9-23. (a) 15 lb.
(b) 5 lb.

CHAPTER 10

10-1. (a) 4400 lb-ft.   (c) 190 ft/sec.
(b) 5900 lb.

10-3. (a) 2.7 kgm-m².
(b) 11 kgm-m².
(c) 1.6×10^{-3} kgm-m².

10-5. (a) Smallest: (A). (b) Largest: (D).
(More mass is farther from the axis).

10-7. (a) 4 rad/sec².
(b) $\omega = 14$ rad/sec.
(c) 32,000 ft-lb.

10-9. 1.1 slug-ft².

10-11. (a) 240 cm/sec, 320 cm/sec.
(b) 5×10^5 gm-cm².
(c) 1600 cm/sec².
(d) 780 cm/sec².
(e) 51,000 dynes tension.

10-13. 1 ft.

10-15. 0.08 revolution/second.

10-17. $\omega = 2\sqrt{g/3R}$.

10-19. (a) 2 m/sec².
(b) 9.8 newtons.

10-21. (a) 1.8 hr.
(b) 130,000 lb-ft.

CHAPTER 11

11-1. 25×10^6 lb/in².

11-3. 1.4×10^7 lb/in².
1.6×10^4 lb/in².

11-5. (a) 1.8 ft.
(b) 30,000 lb/in² in steel,
12,000 lb/in² in copper.
(c) 0.001 in steel, 0.0006 in copper.

11-7. $SP/2$.

11-9. 2000 lb.

11-11. Steel 0.64×10^{-6} atm⁻¹.
Water 50×10^{-6} atm⁻¹.
Water is 78 times more compressible.

11-13. (a) Shearing stress in A is 2400 lb/in²; in B, zero.
(b) 1800 lb/in² tension in A.
(c) 1800 lb/in² compression in B.

CHAPTER 12

12-1. (a) 9470 cm/sec²; 377 cm/sec.
    (b) 5680 cm/sec²; 301 cm/sec.
    (c) 0.0368 sec.

12-3. (a) 2400 π^2 ft/sec².
    (b) 740 lb.
    (c) 43 mi/hr.

12-5. 23 lb.

12-7. $A_1 > A_2$.

12-9. (a) $L_1 = 35$ cm.   (c) 1 second.
       $L_2 = 25$ cm.

12-11. (a) 9 vib/sec.
     (b) 20×10^6 lb/in².

12-13. 979.78 cm/sec².

12-15. (a) 40 rad/sec.
     (b) 34 rad/sec.
     (c) 120 rad/sec² clockwise.

12-17. 67 cm.

CHAPTER 13

13-1. 21 lb/in².

13-3. 120 lb/in², 18,000 lb/ft².

13-5. 270,000 ft³, 9.3 tons lift using helium.

13-7. (a) 100 lb/ft³.
    (b) E will read 5 lb.
       D will read 15 lb.

13-11. (a) 4500 lb.
     (b) 10,000 lb.
     (c) 230 lb.

13-13. (b) 4 lb.
     (c) 1 ft³.

13-17. 13,720 dynes/cm².

13-19. (a) 70.7 cm of Hg.
     (b) 71.2 cm of Hg.
     (c) 11 cm.

13-21. 4.3 cm.

13-23. 40 dynes/cm².

CHAPTER 14

14-1. 36 ft/sec, 0.2 ft³/sec.

14-3. (a) 0.056 ft³/sec.   (b) 3 ft.

14-5. (a) 0.2 ft³/sec.   (c) 3 ft.
    (b) 4.7 ft.

14-7. (a) 2.5 sec.   (c) 4700 lb/ft².
    (b) 43 lb/in².

14-9. 50 hp.

14-11. (a) 0.08 ft³/sec.
     (b) −11 lb/in².

14-13. (a) 580 lb/ft².
     (b) Water will not rise.

14-15. 0.033 cm/sec, 5.5 cm/sec.

CHAPTER 15

15-1. (a) 1800°F. (b) 7.8×10^{-6} per F°.
    (c) 42×10^{-6} per C°. (d) −40°F
    = −40°C.

15-3. 1.6 ft.

15-5. Water, 0° to 4°C.

15-7. 1.3 inches.

15-9. 2×10^{-5} per C°.

15-11. Period decreases 4.6×10^{-4} sec.

15-13. 270,000 lb.

15-15. 480 atm.

15-17. Tension in steel is 72,000 lb/in² assuming the area of the brass bar is so large it is relatively unaffected by the tensile stress.

15-19. 13,700 lb/in².

CHAPTER 16

16-1. 74 ft^3.

16-3. 4.0 Btu.

16-5. 0.1.

16-7. 1.00, 0.827, 0.35.

16-9. 725 cal.

16-11. It melts the ice.

16-13. 24°C.

16-15. 40°C.

16-17. Mass of water 100 gm, change in temperature 20°C, mass of steam 4 gm, calculated heat of vaporization is 445 cal/gm.

16-19. (a) 1.1×10^{-2} ft^3.
(b) 650 ft-lb.
(c) 1800 Btu.
(d) 1.4×10^6 ft-lb (work done by oil is negligible).

CHAPTER 17

17-1. (a) 1.8 cal/sec.
(b) 20 cm.

17-3. (a) 40°C.
(b) 2.4 cal/sec.

17-5. 110°C.

17-7. 0.23¢.

17-9. 816,000 cal.

17-11. 1.7 watts.

CHAPTER 18

18-3. 520 cal.

18-5. 57,000 ft-lb.

18-7. $W = Q_2 - Q_1$.

CHAPTER 19

19-1. 3.6 lb/in^2.

19-3. (a) 0.75 atm.
(b) 2 gm.

19-5. 3.5.

19-7. Adiabatic expansion.

19-9. -16 liter-atmospheres.

19-11. (a) When piston is 3.8 inches from bottom.
(b) 570°K $= 297$°C.

19-13. $\rho = pM/RT$.

19-15. (a) 50 ft/sec.
(b) 36 ft/sec.

19-19. 16%.

19-21. 1.38×10^{-16} ergs/molecule-degree.

19-23. (a) 3.1×10^{-8} cm.
(b) About the same.

19-25. 1860 ft/sec.

CHAPTER 20

20-1. 4.

20-3. 93 C°.

20-5. 15%.

20-7. (a) 2 atm, 5 liters; 1 atm, 5 liters; 1 atm, 3 liters; 2 atm, 3 liters.
(b) 2 liter-atmospheres.

CHAPTER 21

21-1. 320 m/sec.

21-3. 48×10^{-6} atm^{-1}.

21-5. (a) 322 m/sec. (b) 1320 m/sec.

21-7. (a) 132 cycles/sec.
(b) 1320 cycles/sec.
(c) 13,200 cycles/sec.

CHAPTER 22

22-1. (a) 4×10^4 cm/sec.
(b) 1.28×10^{10} dynes/cm^2.
(c) 0.05 cm.

22-3. 270 cycles/sec.

22-5. (a) 5000 m/sec.
(b) 340 m/sec.

22-7. (a) 1100 cycles/sec.
2300 cycles/sec.
3400 cycles/sec.
4500 cycles/sec.
5700 cycles/sec.
(b) 570 cycles/sec.
1700 cycles/sec.
2800 cycles/sec.
4000 cycles/sec.
5100 cycles/sec.
(c) 16, 17.

22-9. (a) 420 cycles/sec.
(b) 415 cycles/sec.

CHAPTER 23

23-1. (a) 9 times.
(b) 4 times.

23-3. 60 db, 77 db.

23-5. (a) π radians.
(b) Due to A: 4×10^{-10} watt/cm^2.
Due to B: 12×10^{-10} watt/cm^2.
(c) 2.1×10^{-10} watt/cm^2, 63 db.

23-7. 10^{-6} watt.

23-9. (a) 454 cycles/sec.
(b) 462 cycles/sec.
(c) 8 cycles/sec.

23-11. (a) 11 ft.
(b) 1 ft.
(c) Almost 15 waves.
(d) 1100 ft/sec.
(e) 0.49 ft.

SUPPLEMENTARY PROBLEMS

*Publisher's Note: These problems have been
reproduced from the plates used in the first
edition*

Problems—Chapter 1

(1) Find graphically the horizontal and vertical components of a 40-lb force the direction of which is 50° above the horizontal to the right. Let $\frac{1}{16}$ in. = 1 lb.

(2) A box is pushed along the floor as in Fig. 1-1 by a force of 20 lb making an angle of 30° with the horizontal. (a) Using a scale of 1 in. = 5 lb, find the horizontal and vertical components of the force by the graphical method. (b) Check your results by calculating the components.

(3) (a) How large a force F must be exerted on a block as in Fig. 1-8 in order that the component parallel to the plane shall be 16 lb? (b) How large will be the component F_y? Let $\alpha = 20°$, $\theta = 20°$, $\phi = 70°$. Solve graphically, letting 1 in. = 8 lb.

(4) Find the X- and Y-components of each of the four forces in Fig. 1-16. Use the graphical method and any convenient scale.

(5) Find graphically the resultant of two 10-lb forces applied at the same point: (a) when the angle between the forces is 30°; (b) when the angle between them is 130°. Use any convenient scale.

(6) Two men pull horizontally on ropes attached to a post, the angle between the ropes being 45°. If man A exerts a force of 150 lb and man B a force of 100 lb, find the magnitude of the resultant force and the angle it makes with A's pull. Solve: (a) graphically, by the parallelogram method; (b) graphically, by the triangle method; (c) analytically, by the method of rectangular resolution. Let 1 in. = 50 lb in (a) and (b).

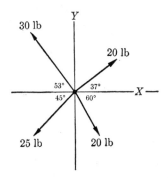

Fig. 1-16.

(7) Find the resultant of the following set of forces by the method of rectangular resolution: 80 lb, vertically down; 100 lb, 53° above horizontal to the right; 60 lb, horizontal to the left. Check by the polygon method.

(8) Use the method of rectangular resolution to find the resultant of the following set of forces and the angle it makes with the horizontal: 200 lb, along the X-axis toward the right; 300 lb, 60° above the X-axis to the right; 100 lb, 45° above the X-axis to the left; 200 lb, vertically down.

(9) Find graphically the resultant of the set of forces in Prob. 8. Use the polygon method.

(10) Vector A is 2 inches long and is 60° above the X-axis in the first quadrant. Vector B is 2 inches long and is 60° below the X-axis in the fourth quadrant. Find graphically (a) the vector sum $A + B$, and (b) the vector differences $A - B$ and $B - A$.

(11) A vector A of length 10 units makes an angle of 30° with a vector B of length 6 units. Find the magnitude of the vector difference $A - B$, and the angle it makes with vector A: (a) by the parallelogram method; (b) by the triangle method; (c) by the method of rectangular resolution.

Problems—Chapter 2

(1) A block rests on a horizontal surface. (a) What two forces act on it? (b) By what bodies are each of these forces exerted? (c) What are the reactions to these forces? (d) On what body is each reaction exerted, and by what body is each exerted?

(2) A block is given a push along a table top, and slides off the edge of the table. (a) What force or forces are exerted on it while it is falling from the table to the floor? (b) What is the reaction to each force, that is, on what body and by what body is the reaction exerted? Neglect air resistance.

(3) A block is at rest on an inclined plane. (a) Show in a diagram all of the forces acting on the block. (b) What is the reaction to each force?

(4) A ball is attached to a string and whirled in a vertical circle. (a) Show in a diagram all of the forces exerted on it when it is at the lowest point of its path. (b) By what body is each of these forces exerted? (c) What is the reaction to each force?

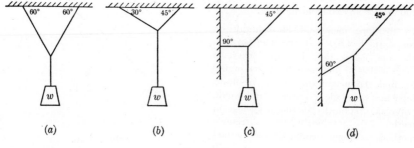

FIG. 2-12.

(5) Find the tension in each cord in Fig. 2-12 if the suspended weight is 200 lb.

(6) Find the tension in the cable and the compression in the strut in Fig. 2-13. Let the suspended weight in each case be 1000 lb. Neglect the weight of the strut.

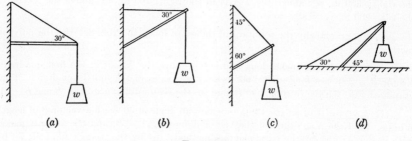

FIG. 2-13.

(7) A horizontal boom 8 ft long is hinged to a vertical wall at one end, and a weight of 500 lb hangs from its outer end. The boom is supported by a guy wire from its outer end to a point on the wall directly above the boom. (a) If the tension in this wire is not to exceed 1000 lb, what is the minimum height above the boom at which it may be fastened to the wall? (b) By how many pounds would the tension be increased if the wire were fastened 1 ft below this point, the boom remaining horizontal? Neglect the weight of the boom.

(8) A block hangs from a cord 10 ft long. A second cord is tied to the midpoint of the first, and a horizontal pull equal to half the weight of the block is exerted on it, the second cord being always kept horizontal. (a) How far will the block be pulled to one side? (b) How far will it be lifted?

(9) A load of building material weighing 300 lb is hoisted from the ground as in Fig. 2-14, where it hangs 20 ft below the pulley. (a) What horizontal force P is needed to pull it a horizontal distance of 6 inches toward the building? (b) What force to pull it a horizontal distance of 6 ft? (c) What will then be the tension in the supporting cord? The length of the cable is kept fixed.

(10) Find the tension in cord A in Fig. 2-15. Neglect the weight of the strut.

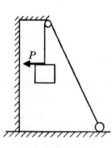

Fig. 2-14.

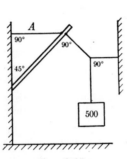

Fig. 2-15.

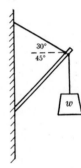

Fig. 2-16.

(11) Find the largest weight which can be supported by the structure in Fig. 2-16 if the maximum tension the upper rope can withstand is 1000 lb and the maximum compression the strut can withstand is 2000 lb. The vertical rope is strong enough to carry any load required.

(12) (a) What force P parallel to the sloping surface of the plane will push a 20-lb block up a frictionless 30° plane at constant speed? (b) What horizontal force will push it up the plane at constant speed? (c) What force at an angle of 20° with the horizontal? (See Fig. 2-17.) (d) What is the normal force exerted on the block by the plane in each instance?

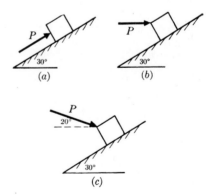

Fig. 2-17.

(13) A 30-lb block is pulled at constant speed up a frictionless inclined plane by a weight of 10 lb hanging from a cord attached to the block and passing over a frictionless pulley at the top of the plane. (See Fig. 2-8.) Find (a) the slope angle of the plane, (b) the tension in the cord, and (c) the normal force exerted on the block by the plane.

(14) A block weighing 20 lb rests on a horizontal surface. The coefficient of static friction between block and surface is 0.40 and the coefficient of sliding friction is 0.20. (a) How large is the friction force exerted on the block? (b) How great will the friction force be if a horizontal force of 5 lb is exerted on the block? (c) What is the minimum force which will start the block in motion? (d) What is the minimum force which will keep the block in motion once it has been started? (e) If the horizontal force is 10 lb, how great is the friction force?

(15) Coefficients of sliding friction are sometimes expressed in "pounds per ton," that is, the number of pounds of horizontal force needed to maintain a load of 1 ton in steady motion on a level surface. If the coefficient of sliding friction between two surfaces is 0.20, express this in "pounds per ton."

(16) Block A, in Fig. 2-18, weighs 4 lb and rests on block B which weighs 8 lb. The blocks are connected by a cord passing around a frictionless pulley. The coefficient of sliding friction between blocks A and B, and between B and the surface, is 0.25. Find the force P required to drag block B toward the left at constant speed.

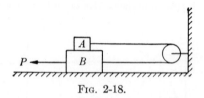

Fig. 2-18.

(17) What force P at an angle ϕ above the horizontal is needed to drag a box weighing w pounds at constant speed along a level floor, if the coefficient of sliding friction between box and floor is μ?

(18) A safe weighing 600 lb is to be lowered at constant speed down skids 8 ft long, from a truck 4 ft high. If the coefficient of sliding friction between safe and skids is 0.30, (a) will the safe need to be pulled down or held back? (b) How great a force parallel to the plane is needed?

(19) If a force of 86 lb parallel to the surface of a 20° inclined plane will push a 120-lb block up the plane at constant speed, (a) what force parallel to the plane will push it down at constant speed? (b) What is the coefficient of sliding friction?

Problems—Chapter 3

(1) The center of gravity of a log 10 ft long and weighing 100 lb is 4 ft from one end of the log. It is to be carried by two men, one at the heavy end. Where should the other man hold the log if each is to carry half the load?

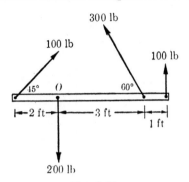

FIG. 3-19.

(2) A rod AB which is 3 ft long and whose own weight can be neglected rests on a knife edge 1 ft from end A. A 10-lb weight hangs from end B. (a) What weight must be hung from A to maintain equilibrium? (b) What is then the force exerted by the knife edge?

(3) The rod in Fig. 3-19 is pivoted about an axis through O. (a) Find the moment of each force, and the resultant torque, about the axis. Consider clockwise moments positive. (b) Find the magnitude and direction of the force which must be exerted at the right end, perpendicular to the rod, to maintain equilibrium.

(4) The member BOA in Fig. 3-20 is pivoted at O. (a) What torque about O is produced by a pull of 20 lb in the direction AC? (b) What force in the direction BD will balance this torque? (c) What will then be the X- and Y-components of the force exerted on the pivot at O?

(5) Find the upward force at each end of the table in Fig. 3-21.

(6) If the strut in Fig. 3-22 weighs 40 lb and its center of gravity is at its center, find the tension in the cable and the H and V components of the force exerted on the strut at the wall.

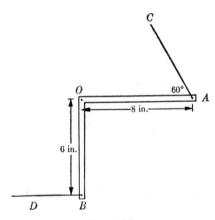

FIG. 3-20.

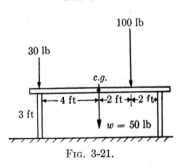

FIG. 3-21.

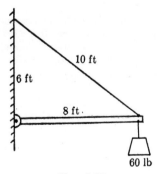

FIG. 3-22.

(7) The boom in Fig. 3-23 is uniform and weighs 500 lb. Find the tension in the guy wire, and the H and V components of the force exerted on the boom at its lower end.

(8) The uniform boom OA in Fig. 3-24 is 20 ft long and supports a weight of 3600 lb at end A. (a) If the weight of the boom is negligible, find the tension in the cable AB and the magnitude and direction of the force exerted on the pin at O. (b) If the boom weighs 2800 lb, find the tension in the cable and the magnitude and direction of the force on the pin at O.

(9) If the weight of the strut in Fig. 3-25 is neglected, (a) what weight w is necessary to produce a tension of 200 lb in the horizontal cable? (b) What will then be the magnitude and direction of the force exerted on the strut at its lower end?

(10) A ladder 13 ft long leans against a vertical frictionless wall with its lower end 5 ft from the wall. The ladder weighs 80 lb and its center of gravity is at its center. Find the magnitude and direction of the force exerted on the lower end of the ladder.

(11) A ladder 25 ft long leans against a vertical frictionless wall with its lower end 15 ft from the wall. The ladder weighs 80 lb and its center of gravity is at its center. The coefficient of static friction between the foot of the ladder and the ground is 0.40. (a) How far up the ladder can a 180-lb man climb before the ladder starts to slip? (b) How far can the foot of the ladder be pulled out from the wall before it starts to slip, with no load on the ladder except its own weight?

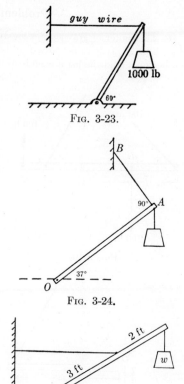

FIG. 3-23.

FIG. 3-24.

FIG. 3-25.

(12) A door 7 ft high and 3 ft wide is hung from hinges 6 ft apart and 6 inches from the top and bottom of the door. If the door weighs 60 lb and its center of gravity is at its center, find the magnitude and direction of the resultant force exerted on the door at each hinge. Assume each hinge carries half the weight of the door.

(13) A table 8 ft long and 3 ft high, weighing 100 lb, has its center of gravity 6 inches below the center of the table top. The table is pushed at constant speed along a horizontal surface by a horizontal force applied at one end of the table top. The coefficient of sliding friction is 0.40. Compute the upward force and the friction force at each table leg.

(14) A bench is 6 ft long, 2 ft high, and weighs 50 lb. Its center of gravity is midway between its ends. (a) What force applied at one end and 30° above the horizontal will drag the bench at constant speed along a horizontal surface? (b) What is the upward force at each end of the bench? The coefficient of sliding friction is 0.20.

(15) The chair in Fig. 3-26 is to be dragged to the right at constant speed along a horizontal surface, the coefficient of sliding friction being 0.30. The chair weighs 50 lb. (a) What horizontal force is needed? (b) What is the upward force at each leg if the force dragging the chair is applied at point A? (c) What is the upward force at each leg if the force is applied at point B? (d) What is the maximum height at which the dragging force can be applied without causing the chair to tip?

(16) The table referred to in Prob. 13 is to be pushed at constant speed up a sloping surface inclined at an angle of 20° with the horizontal, by a horizontal force applied at one end of the table top. The coefficient of sliding friction is 0.40. (a) What force is required? (b) What is the resultant force at each table leg? Fig. 3-27.

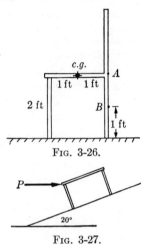

Fig. 3-26.

(17) In Fig. 3-8, let $F_1 = 3$ lb, $F_2 = 6$ lb, $x_1 = 2$ ft, $x_2 = 5$ ft. Find the magnitude and line of action of the resultant.

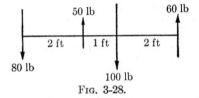

Fig. 3-28.

(18) Find the magnitude and line of action of the resultant of the four forces in Fig. 3-28.

(19) Find the resultant of the three forces in Fig. 3-29.

(20) Weights of 2, 4, 6, and 8 lb are fastened to the corners of a light wire frame 2 ft square. Find the position of the center of gravity of the weights.

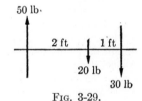

Fig. 3-29.

(21) Find the position of the center of gravity of the L-shaped plate in Fig. 3-30.

(22) Find the position of the center of gravity of the U-shaped plate in Fig. 3-31.

(23) Find the position of the center of gravity of the T-shaped plate in Fig. 3-32.

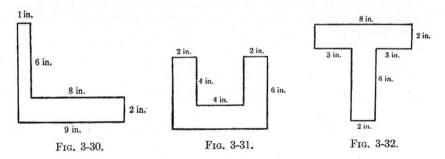

Fig. 3-30.   Fig. 3-31.   Fig. 3-32.

Problems—Chapter 4

(1) A runner on a straight track covers 100 yd in 10 sec. Compute his average velocity in ft /sec, cm /sec, m /sec, and mi /hr.

(2) The 2-mile record on an indoor track is 8 min, 51 3/10 sec. To what average velocity in mi /hr does this correspond?

(3) Refer to the example at the end of Sec. 4-3, in which the motion of a body along the X-axis was described by the equation $x = 10t^2$. Compute the instantaneous velocity of the body at time $t = 3$ sec. Let Δt first equal 0.1 sec, then 0.01 sec, and finally 0.001 sec. What limiting value do the results seem to be approaching?

(4) An automobile is provided with a speedometer calibrated to read ft /sec rather than mi /hr. The following series of speedometer readings was obtained during a start.

Time (sec)......................	0	2	4	6	8	10	12	14	16
Velocity (ft /sec)...............	0	0	2	5	10	15	20	22	22

(a) Compute the average acceleration during each 2-sec interval. Is the acceleration constant? Is it constant during any part of the time? (b) Make a velocity-time graph of the data above, using scales of 1 in = 2 sec horizontally, and 1 in = 5 ft /sec vertically. Draw a smooth curve through the plotted points. What is the acceleration when $t = 8$ sec? When $t = 13$ sec? When $t = 15$ sec?

(5) Each of the following changes in velocity takes place in a 10-sec interval. What is the magnitude, the algebraic sign, and the direction of the average acceleration in each interval?

(a) At the beginning of the interval a body is moving toward the right along the X-axis at 5 ft /sec, and at the end of the interval it is moving toward the right at 20 ft /sec.

(b) At the beginning it is moving toward the right at 20 ft /sec, and at the end it is moving toward the right at 5 ft /sec.

(c) At the beginning it is moving toward the left at 5 ft /sec, and at the end it is moving toward the left at 20 ft /sec.

(d) At the beginning it is moving toward the left at 20 ft /sec, and at the end it is moving toward the left at 5 ft /sec.

(e) At the beginning it is moving toward the right at 20 ft /sec, and at the end it is moving toward the left at 20 ft /sec.

(f) At the beginning it is moving toward the left at 20 ft /sec, and at the end it is moving toward the right at 20 ft /sec.

(g) In which of the above instances is the body decelerated?

(6) An automobile starts from rest and acquires a velocity of 40 mi /hr in 15 sec. (a) Compute the acceleration in miles per hour, per second, and in feet per second, per second, assuming it to be constant. (b) If the automobile continues to gain velocity at the same rate, how many more seconds are needed for it to acquire a velocity of 60 mi /hr? (c) Find the distances covered by the automobile in parts (a) and (b).

(7) An airplane taking off from the landing field has a run of 2000 ft. (a) What is its acceleration, assumed constant, if it leaves the ground in 15 sec from the start? (b) With what velocity, in mi /hr, does it take off?

(8) A body moving with constant acceleration covers the distance between two points 180 ft apart in 6 sec. Its velocity as it passes the second point is 45 ft /sec. (a) What is its acceleration? (b) What is its velocity at the first point?

(9) An automobile accelerates from rest at a constant rate, and passes two points 80 ft apart in 2 sec. Its velocity as it passes the second point is 48 ft/sec. Find (a) its acceleration, (b) its velocity when it passed the first point, and (c) the distance of the first point from the start.

(10) The "reaction time" of the average automobile driver is about 0.7 sec. (The reaction time is the interval between the perception of a signal to stop and the application of the brakes.) If an automobile can decelerate at 16 ft/sec², compute the total distance covered in coming to a stop after a signal is observed: (a) from an initial velocity of 30 mi/hr, (b) from an initial velocity of 60 mi/hr.

(11) At the instant the traffic lights turn green, an automobile that has been waiting at an intersection starts ahead with a constant acceleration of 6 ft/sec². At the same instant a truck, traveling with a constant velocity of 30 ft/sec, overtakes and passes the automobile. (a) How far beyond its starting point will the automobile overtake the truck? (b) How fast will it be traveling?

(12) The engineer of a passenger train traveling at 100 ft/sec sights a freight train whose caboose is 600 ft ahead on the same track. The freight train is traveling in the same direction as the passenger train with a velocity of 30 ft/sec. The engineer of the passenger train immediately applies the brakes, causing a constant deceleration of 4 ft/sec², while the freight train continues with constant speed. (a) Will there be a collision? (b) If so, where will it take place?

(13) A ball is released from rest and rolls down an inclined plane, requiring 4 sec to cover a distance of 100 cm. (a) What was its acceleration, in cm/sec²? (b) How many centimeters would it have fallen vertically in the same time?

(14) (a) With what velocity must a ball be thrown vertically upward in order to rise to a height of 50 ft? (b) How long will it be in the air?

(15) A ball is thrown vertically downward from the top of a building, leaving the thrower's hand with a velocity of 30 ft/sec.
(a) What will be its velocity after falling for 2 sec?
(b) How far will it fall in 2 sec?
(c) What will be its velocity after falling 30 ft?
(d) If it moved a distance of 3 ft while in the thrower's hand, find its acceleration while in his hand.
(e) If the ball was released at a point 120 ft above the ground, in how many seconds will it strike the ground?
(f) What will be its velocity when it strikes?

(16) A balloon, rising vertically with a velocity of 16 ft/sec, releases a sandbag at an instant when the balloon is 64 ft above the ground. (a) Compute the position and velocity of the sandbag at the following times after its release: ¼ sec, ½ sec, 1 sec, 2 sec. (b) How many seconds after its release will the bag strike the ground? (c) With what velocity will it strike?

(17) A stone is dropped from the top of a tall cliff, and 1 sec later a second stone is thrown vertically down with a velocity of 60 ft/sec. How far below the top of the cliff will the second stone overtake the first?

(18) A ball dropped from the cornice of a building takes 0.25 sec to pass a window 9 ft high. How far is the top of the window below the cornice?

(19) "Near the earth's surface a body falls with uniformly increasing acceleration." Is this statement correct? If not, correct it.

(20) A river flows due north with a velocity of 3 mi/hr. A man rows a boat across the river, his velocity relative to the water being 4 mi/hr due east. (a) What is his velocity relative to the earth? (b) If the river is 1 mile wide, how far north of his starting point will he reach the opposite bank? (c) How long a time is required to cross the river?

(21) (a) In what direction should the rowboat in Prob. 20 be headed in order to reach a point on the opposite bank directly east from the start? (b) What will be the velocity of the boat, relative to the earth? (c) How long a time is required to cross the river?

(22) An airplane pilot wishes to fly due north. The wind is blowing from NE to SW at 30 mi/hr, and the speed of the plane relative to the air is 180 mi/hr. (a) In what direction should the pilot set his course? (b) What will be his velocity relative to the ground?

Problems—Chapter 5

(For problem work, use the approximate values of $g = 32$ ft/sec^2 = 9.8 m/sec^2 = 980 cm/sec^2. A force diagram should be constructed for each problem.)

(1) (a) What resultant horizontal force is required to accelerate a 1600-lb automobile on a level road at 8 ft/sec^2? (b) A 1600-gm block rests on a horizontal frictionless surface. What horizontal force is needed to accelerate it at 8 cm/sec^2? (c) A 1600-kgm block rests on a horizontal frictionless surface. What horizontal force is needed to accelerate it at 8 m/sec^2?

(2) The Springfield rifle bullet weighs 150 grains (7000 grains = 1 lb), its muzzle velocity is 2700 ft/sec, and the length of the rifle barrel is 30 in. Compute the resultant force accelerating the bullet, assuming it to be constant.

(3) A body of mass 15 kgm rests on a smooth horizontal plane and is acted on by a horizontal force of 30 newtons. (a) What acceleration is produced? (b) How far will the body travel in 10 sec and what will be its velocity at the end of 10 sec?

(4) A constant horizontal force of 10 lb acts on a body on a smooth horizontal plane. The body starts from rest and is observed to move 250 ft in 5 sec. (a) What is the mass of the body? (b) If the force ceases to act at the end of 5 sec, how far will the body move in the next 5 sec?

(5) A .22 rifle bullet, traveling at 36,000 cm/sec, strikes a block of soft wood which it penetrates to a depth of 10 cm. The mass of the bullet is 1.8 gm. Assume a constant retarding force. (a) How long a time was required for the bullet to stop? (b) What was the decelerating force, in dynes? in lb?

(6) An electron (mass = 9×10^{-28} gm) leaves the cathode of a radio tube with zero initial velocity and travels in a straight line to the anode, which is 1 cm away. It reaches the anode with a velocity of 6×10^8 cm/sec. If the accelerating force was constant, compute (a) the accelerating force, in dynes, (b) the time to reach the anode, (c) the acceleration. The gravitational force on the electron may be neglected.

(7) Fig. 5-12 is a top view of a block whose mass is 5 kgm, resting on a horizontal frictionless surface and acted on by four horizontal forces. Find the magnitude and direction of the acceleration of the block.

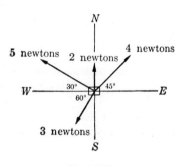

FIG. 5-12.

(8) An elevator weighing 3200 lb rises with an acceleration of 4 ft/sec^2. What is the tension in the supporting cable?

(9) An 8-lb block is accelerated upward by a cord whose breaking strength is 20 lb. Find the maximum acceleration which can be given the block without breaking the cord.

(10) A body hangs from a spring balance supported from the roof of an elevator. (a) If the elevator has an upward acceleration of 4 ft/sec^2 and the balance reads 45 lb, what is the true weight of the body? (b) Under what circumstances will the balance read 35 lb? (c) What will the balance read if the elevator cable breaks?

(11) A 5-kgm block is supported by a cord and pulled upward with an acceleration of 2 m/sec². (a) What is the tension in the cord? (b) After the block has been set in motion the tension in the cord is reduced to 49 newtons. What sort of motion will the block perform? (c) If the cord is now slackened completely, the block is observed to move up 2 meters farther before coming to rest. With what velocity was it traveling?

(12) A body of mass 10 kgm is moving with a constant velocity of 5 m/sec on a horizontal surface. The coefficient of sliding friction between body and surface is 0.20. (a) What horizontal force is required to maintain the motion? (b) If the force is removed, how soon will the body come to rest?

(13) If the coefficient of friction between its tires and the road is 0.80, find the shortest distance in which an automobile traveling at 80 mi/hr can be stopped on a level road.

(14) A hockey puck leaves a player's stick with a velocity of 30 ft/sec and slides 120 ft before coming to rest. Find the coefficient of friction between the puck and the ice.

(15) A 16-lb block rests on a horizontal surface. The coefficient of sliding friction between block and surface is 0.25 and the coefficient of static friction is 0.30. (a) What is the resultant force on the block when an external horizontal force of 8 lb is exerted on it? (b) If the 8-lb force acts for 4 sec and is then removed, find the total distance moved by the block before coming to rest.

(16) A block of mass m slides down a smooth plane inclined at an angle α with the horizontal. (a) What is the magnitude of the force causing the block to slide down the plane? (b) What is the acceleration of the block?

(17) A block of mass m is projected up a smooth inclined plane of slope angle α with an initial velocity v_0. How far up the plane will it slide?

(18) A body of mass 5 kgm starts from rest at the foot of a smooth inclined plane of angle 30° and length 4.9 meters, and reaches the top of the plane in 10 sec. What external force parallel to the plane was exerted on the body?

(19) A body weighing 64 lb slides down an inclined plane of angle 37° and length 16 ft in 2 sec. If the body started from rest at the top of the plane, what was the coefficient of sliding friction?

(20) A block is found to slide down a 45° inclined plane with an acceleration of 8 ft/sec². For what angle of inclination will it slide down the same plane at constant velocity?

(21) A block slides with constant velocity down an inclined plane of slope angle α. With what acceleration will it slide down the same plane when the slope angle is increased to a larger value, θ?

(22) A block slides with constant velocity down an inclined plane of slope angle α. If it is projected up the same plane with an initial velocity v_0, how far up the plane will it move before coming to rest?

(23) A block slides down an inclined plane with constant velocity when the slope angle of the plane is 14°. Compute the acceleration of the same block down the same plane when the slope angle is increased to 37°.

(24) What horizontal force is necessary to push a 10-kgm block up the sloping surface of a 37° inclined plane with an acceleration of 4 m/sec², if the coefficient of sliding friction between block and plane is 0.20?

(25) What horizontal force is necessary to push a 10-lb block up the sloping surface of a 37° inclined plane with an acceleration of 4 ft/sec², if the coefficient of sliding friction between block and plane is 0.20?

(26) What horizontal force P is required to push a block of mass m up a plane of slope angle α with an acceleration a, if the coefficient of sliding friction between block and plane is μ?

(27) A horizontal force of 2 lb will drag a 10-lb block along a certain horizontal surface with constant velocity. If the same surface is inclined at an angle of 37° with the horizontal, what force parallel to the plane will draw the block up the plane with an acceleration of 8 ft/sec²?

(28) Block A rests on a horizontal frictionless surface and is connected by a cord passing over a pulley to a hanging block B. The inertia of cord and pulley can be neglected. The mass of block B is 10 kgm. The system is released from rest and block B is observed to descend 80 cm in 4 sec. (a) Show in a diagram all of the forces acting on block B, and compute the tension in the cord. (b) Show in a second diagram all of the forces exerted on block A, and compute its mass.

(29) A block of mass m_1, on a horizontal frictionless surface, is connected by a cord passing over a pulley to a hanging block of mass m_2. (a) What is the acceleration of the system and the tension in the cord? (b) How are these answers changed if the coefficient of sliding friction between block and plane is μ?

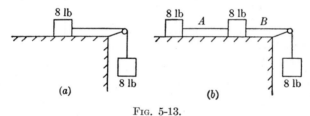

FIG. 5-13.

(30) (a) Find the acceleration of the blocks in Fig. 5-13 (a) and the tension in the cord. The coefficient of sliding friction between the block and the surface is 0.25. (b) If a second 8-lb block is added as in Fig. 5-13 (b), compute the acceleration and the tensions in cords A and B.

(31) A block whose mass is 1 slug rests on a horizontal frictionless surface and is connected by a cord passing over a pulley to a hanging weight. (a) What must be the tension in the cord to produce an acceleration of the 1-slug body of 1 ft/sec²? (b) What hanging weight will produce this acceleration?

(32) Compute the acceleration of the system and the tension in each cord in Fig. 5-14, if the coefficient of sliding friction between the block and the surface is 0.20.

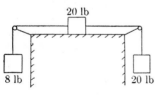

FIG. 5-14.

(33) A body of mass M on a smooth inclined plane of angle α is connected by a cord passing over a frictionless pulley to a second block of mass m hanging from the cord, as in Fig. 5-15. (a) What is the acceleration of each body? (b) What is the tension in the cord?

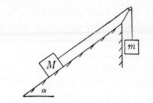

Fig. 5-15.

(34) The car alone in Fig. 5-16 weighs 1 ton and the counterweight weighs 800 lb. If friction is neglected, find (a) the time required for the empty car to move from the bottom to the top of the incline, starting from rest, and (b) the time required for the car to descend, starting from rest, with a load of 600 lb. The length of the incline is 150 ft.

Fig. 5-16.

(35) Two 100-gm blocks hang at the ends of a light flexible cord passing over a small frictionless pulley as in Fig. 5-17. A 40-gm block is placed on the block on the right, and removed after 2 sec. (a) How far will each block move in the first second after the 40-gm block is removed? (b) What was the tension in the cord before the 40-gm block was removed? After it was removed? (c) What was the tension in the cord supporting the pulley before the 40-gm block was removed? Neglect the weight of the pulley.

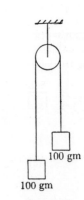

100 gm

100 gm

Fig. 5-17.

(36) Two 10-lb blocks hang at the ends of a cord as in Fig. 5-17. What weight must be added to one of the blocks to cause it to move down a distance of 4 ft in 2 sec?

(37) An 8-kgm and a 16-kgm block are suspended at opposite ends of a cord passing over a pulley. Compute (a) the acceleration of the system, (b) the tension in the cord connecting the blocks, and (c) the tension in the cord supporting the pulley. The weight of the pulley may be neglected.

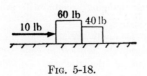

Fig. 5-18.

(38) A force of 10 lb is exerted horizontally against a 60-lb block, which in turn pushes a 40-lb block as in Fig. 5-18. If the blocks are on a frictionless surface, what force does one block exert on the other?

(39) If in Prob. 38 the coefficient of friction between the 60-lb block and the surface is 0.05, and that between the 40-lb block and the surface is 0.10, what is the acceleration and what force does one block exert on the other?

(40) Compute the tensions in cords A and B in Fig. 5-7, if the 8-lb and 16-lb bodies are interchanged.

(41) The mass of the moon is approximately 6.7×10^{22} kgm and its distance from the earth is about 250,000 mi. (a) What is the gravitational force of attraction between the earth and the moon, in tons? (b) If the moon were to be retained in its orbit by a steel cable, instead of by gravity, what should be the diameter of the cable if the stress in it is not to exceed 60,000 lb/in²?

(42) Two spheres, each of mass 625 kgm, are placed with their centers 50 cm apart. Compute the force of gravitational attraction between them.

(43) In round numbers, the distance from the earth to the moon is 250,000 mi, the distance from the earth to the sun is 93 million miles, the mass of the earth is 6×10^{27} gm and the mass of the sun is 2×10^{33} gm. Approximately, what is the ratio of the gravitational pull of the sun on the moon to that of the earth on the moon?

(44) The mass of the moon is one eighty-first, and its radius is one-fourth, that of the earth. What is the acceleration of gravity on the surface of the moon?

Problems—Chapter 6

(1) A ball rolls off the edge of a horizontal table top 30 inches high and strikes the floor at a distance of 5 ft horizontally from the edge of the table.   What was the velocity of the ball at the instant of leaving the table?

(2) A golf ball is driven horizontally from an elevated tee with a velocity of 80 ft/sec. It strikes the fairway 2.5 sec later.   (a) How far has it fallen vertically?   (b) How far has it travelled horizontally?   (c) Find the horizontal and vertical components of its velocity, and the magnitude and direction of its resultant velocity, just before it strikes. Neglect air resistance.

(3) A .22 rifle bullet is fired in a horizontal direction with a muzzle velocity of 900 ft/sec.   In the absence of air resistance, how far will it have dropped in traveling a horizontal distance of (a) 50 yd?   (b) 100 yd?   (c) 150 yd?   (d) How far will it drop in one second?

(4) A bomb is released from an airplane flying horizontally at an elevation of 1600 ft, with a velocity of 200 mi/hr.   (a) How far does the bomb travel horizontally before striking the earth?   (b) What will be the magnitude and direction of its velocity just before striking?   (c) How long is it in the air?   Neglect air resistance.

(5) The table below is taken from the results of recent studies of the ballistics of large (100–2000 lb) aircraft bombs, released from a plane in level flight traveling at 200 mi/hr.   See Fig. 6-7 for the meaning of the symbols.

h(ft)	t(sec)	R(ft)	v(ft/sec)	θ(deg)
1000	7.97	2270	377	40.0
5000	18.1	4950	590	64.5
10000	26.0	6990	754	72.3
25000	42.7	10450	980	80.5

Calculate a few values of t, R, v, and θ, neglecting air resistance, and compare with the observed values.

(6) A level-flight bombing plane, flying at 200 mi/hr at an elevation of 10,000 ft, releases a heavy bomb.   If the plane continues with unchanged course and speed, how far ahead of the target is it when the bomb strikes?   Use the table in Prob. 5.

(7) A bombing plane in level flight releases three bombs at intervals of 1 sec.   What is the vertical distance between the first and second, and between the second and third, (a) at the instant the third is released, (b) after the first has fallen 200 ft?   Neglect air resistance.

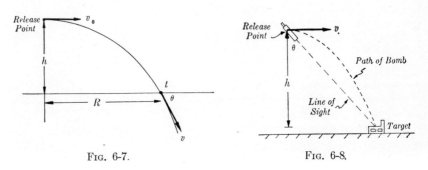

FIG. 6-7.   FIG. 6-8.

(8) Fig. 6-8 illustrates the principle of the bomb sight used in level-flight bombing. The height of the plane h and its velocity v over the ground are known to the bomber. The bombs are released when the line of sight to the target makes an angle θ with the vertical. Find an expression for θ in terms of h and v.

(9) A level-flight bombing plane, flying at an altitude of 1024 ft with a velocity of 240 ft/sec, is overtaking a motor torpedo boat traveling at 80 ft/sec in the same direction as the plane. At what distance astern of the boat should a bomb be released in order to hit the boat, if air resistance is neglected?

(10) A ball is projected with an initial upward velocity component of 80 ft/sec and a horizontal velocity component of 100 ft/sec. (a) Find the position and velocity of the ball after 2 sec; 3 sec; 6 sec. (b) How long a time is required to reach the highest point of the trajectory? (c) How high is this point? (d) How long a time is required for the ball to return to its original level? (e) How far has it travelled horizontally during this time? Show your results in a neat sketch, large enough to show all features clearly.

(11) A batted baseball leaves the bat at an angle of 30° above the horizontal, and is caught by an outfielder 400 ft from the plate. (a) What was the initial velocity of the ball? (b) How high did it rise? (c) How long was it in the air?

(12) A golf ball is driven with a velocity of 200 ft/sec at an angle of 37° above the horizontal. It strikes a green at a horizontal distance of 800 ft from the tee. (a) What was the elevation of the green above the tee? (b) What was the velocity of the ball when it struck the green?

(13) During the first World War, the Germans bombarded Paris with a specially constructed long-range gun. A newspaper report listed the following statistics on this gun:

Length of barrel...........................	118 ft
Diameter of bore...........................	8.26 in
Weight of projectile........................	264 lb
Muzzle energy.............................	46,700 ft-tons
Muzzle velocity	4760 ft/sec
Angle of elevation.........................	55°
Range.....................................	132,000 yd
Weight of gun.............................	318,000 lb

(a) Use the given values of muzzle velocity and angle of elevation to compute the range, in the absence of air resistance, and compare with the actual range. (b) Compute also, neglecting air resistance, the maximum height reached, in miles, and the time of flight. (Note: the rotation of the earth and its curvature, as well as air resistance, are important factors influencing the trajectories of long-range projectiles.)

(14) The projectile of a trench mortar has a muzzle velocity of 300 ft/sec. (a) Find the two angles of elevation to hit a target at the same level as the mortar and 300 yd distant. (b) Compute the maximum height of each trajectory, and the time of flight of each. Make a neat sketch of the trajectories, approximately to scale.

(15) A gun fires a projectile with a muzzle velocity of 1200 ft/sec. It is desired to hit a target distant 1000 yd horizontally from the gun, and at an elevation of 980 ft above it. What is the minimum angle of elevation of the gun?

(16) If a baseball player can throw a ball a maximum distance of 200 ft over the ground, what is the maximum vertical height to which he can throw it? Assume the ball to have the same initial speed in each case.

(17) In the absence of air resistance, what must be the velocity of a projectile fired vertically upward, to reach an altitude of 20,000 ft? (a) What velocity is required to reach the same height if the gun makes an angle of 45° with the vertical? (b) Compute the time required to reach the highest point in both trajectories. (c) How many feet would a plane traveling at 300 mi/hr move in this time?

(18) The angle of elevation of an anti-aircraft gun is 70° and the muzzle velocity is 2700 ft/sec. For what time after firing should the fuse be set, if the shell is to explode at an altitude of 5000 ft? Neglect air resistance.

Problems—Chapter 7

(1) The locomotive of a freight train exerts a constant force of 5 tons on the train while drawing it at 40 mi/hr on a level track. How many foot-pounds of work are done by the locomotive in a distance of 1 mi?

(2) A horse is towing a canal boat, the towrope making an angle of 10° with the towpath. If the tension in the rope is 100 lb, how many foot-pounds of work are done by the horse while moving 100 ft along the towpath?

FIG. 7-13.

(3) A 100-lb block is pushed a distance of 20 ft along a level floor at constant speed by a force at an angle of 30° with the horizontal, as in Fig. 7-13. The coefficient of friction between block and floor is 0.30. How many foot-pounds of work are done?

(4) The force in pounds required to stretch a certain spring a distance of x ft beyond its unstretched length is given by $F = 10x$. (a) What force will stretch the spring 6 in.? 1 ft? 2 ft? (b) How much work is required to stretch the spring 6 in.? 1 ft? 2 ft?

(5) A block is pushed 4 ft along a horizontal surface by a horizontal force of 10 lb. The opposing force of friction is 2 lb. (a) How much work is done by the agent exerting the 10-lb force? (b) How much energy is converted into heat?

(6) (a) Compute the kinetic energy of an 1800-lb automobile traveling at 40 mi/hr. (b) How many times as great is the kinetic energy if the velocity is doubled?

(7) Compute the kinetic energy, in ergs and in joules, of a 2-gm rifle bullet traveling at 500 m/sec.

(8) An electron strikes the screen of a cathode-ray tube with a velocity of 10^9 cm/sec. Compute its kinetic energy in ergs. The mass of an electron is 9×10^{-28} gm.

(9) What is the potential energy of a 1600-lb elevator at the top of the Empire State building, 1248 ft above street level? Assume the potential energy at street level to be zero.

(10) What is the increase in potential energy of a 1-kgm body when lifted from the floor to a table 1 meter high?

(11) A meter stick whose mass is 200 gm is pivoted at one end as in Fig. 7-14 and displaced through an angle of 60°. What is the increase in its potential energy?

(12) The scale of a certain spring balance reads from zero to 200 lb and is 8 in. long. (a) What is the potential energy of the spring when it is stretched 8 in.? 4 in.? (b) When a 50-lb weight hangs from the spring?

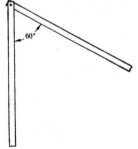

FIG. 7-14.

(13) A block weighing 16 lb is pushed 20 ft along a horizontal frictionless surface by a horizontal force of 8 lb. The block starts from rest. (a) How much work is done? What becomes of this work? (b) Check your answer by computing the acceleration of the block, its final velocity, and its kinetic energy.

(14) In the preceding problem, suppose the block had an initial velocity of 10 ft/sec, other quantities remaining the same. (a) How much work is done? (b) Check by computing the final velocity and the increase in kinetic energy.

(15) A 16-lb block is pushed 20 ft along a horizontal surface by a constant horizontal force of 16 lb. The coefficient of sliding friction is 0.50. (a) How much work is done? What becomes of this work? (b) Check by computing separate terms.

(16) A 16-lb block is lifted vertically at a constant velocity of 10 ft/sec through a height of 20 ft. (a) How great a force is required? (b) How much work is done? (c) What becomes of this work?

(17) A 100-lb block is pushed a distance of 20 ft up the sloping surface of a 37° inclined plane by a force of 100 lb parallel to the sloping surface. The block starts from rest, and the coefficient of friction between block and plane is 0.2. Find (a) the work done by the agent exerting the 100-lb force, (b) the increases in kinetic and potential energy of the block and (c) the energy converted to heat.

(18) The hammer of a pile driver weighs 1 ton. It drops 10 ft onto a pile which it drives in 3 in. Compute the force exerted on the pile, from energy considerations. (Assume the force to be constant.)

(19) A block weighing 2 lb is released from rest at point A on a track which is one quadrant of a circle of radius 4 ft. (Fig. 7-15.) It slides down the track and reaches point B with a velocity of 12 ft/sec. From point B it slides on a level surface a distance of 9 ft to point C, where it comes to rest. (a) What was the coefficient of sliding friction on the horizontal surface? (b) How much work was done against friction as the body slid down the circular arc from A to B?

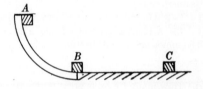

Fig. 7-15.

(20) An elevator, with its load, weighs 2400 lb. The elevator starts from rest at the first floor, and 5 sec later it passes the 5th floor, 60 ft above the first, with a velocity of 30 ft/sec. Find (a) the total work done on the elevator during the 5-sec interval, and (b) the average horsepower developed. Neglect friction.

(21) Compute the horsepower developed by the locomotive in Prob. 1.

(22) What average horsepower is developed by a 180-lb man when climbing in 10 sec a flight of stairs which rises 20 ft vertically? Express this power in watts and kilowatts.

(23) The hammer of a pile driver weighs 1000 lb and must be lifted a vertical distance of 6 ft in 3 sec. What horsepower engine is required?

(24) A ski tow is to be operated on a 37° slope 800 ft long. The rope is to move at 8 mi/hr and power must be provided for 80 riders at one time, each weighing, on an average, 150 lb. Estimate the horsepower required to operate the tow.

(25) (a) If energy costs 5 cents per kwh, how much is one horsepower-hour worth? (b) How many ft-lb can be purchased for one cent?

(26) Compute the monetary value of the kinetic energy of the projectile of a 14-in. naval gun, at the rate of 2 cents per kwh. The projectile weighs 1400 lb and its muzzle velocity is 2800 ft/sec.

(27) At 5 cents per kwh, what does it cost to operate a 10-hp motor for 8 hr?

(28) A horizontal force of 16 lb acts on a body of mass 2 slugs, initially at rest on a horizontal frictionless surface. (a) Find the instantaneous power developed at the end of 1 sec; at the end of 5 sec. (b) Find the average power developed during the first second and during the first 5 sec. (c) Explain why the power is not constant.

(29) The engine of an automobile develops 20 hp when the automobile is traveling at 30 mi/hr. (a) What is the resisting force in pounds? (b) If the resisting force is proportional to the velocity, what horsepower will drive the car at 15 mi/hr? At 60 mi/hr?

(30) The engine of a motorboat delivers 40 hp to the propeller while the boat is making 20 mi/hr. What would be the tension in the towline if the boat were being towed at the same speed?

(31) (a) If 20 hp are required to drive a 2400-lb automobile at 30 mi/hr on a level road, what is the retarding force of friction, windage, etc.? (b) What power is necessary to drive the car at 30 mi/hr up a 10% grade, i.e., one rising 10 ft vertically in 100 ft horizontally? (c) What power is necessary to drive the car at 30 mi/hr *down* a 2% grade? (d) Down what grade would the car coast at 30 mi/hr?

(32) A screw jack moves upward $\frac{1}{4}$ in. when turned through one revolution, that is, the pitch is $\frac{1}{4}$ in. What load could be lifted if a force of 20 lb is applied at the end of a bar 2 ft long, if friction is neglected?

(33) A force of 6 lb is required to raise a weight of 30 lb by means of a pulley system. If the weight is raised 1 ft while the applied force acts through a distance of 8 ft, find (a) the ideal mechanical advantage, (b) the actual mechanical advantage, and (c) the efficiency.

(34) Prove that the ideal mechanical advantage of the inclined plane shown in Fig. 7-9(a) is equal to the length of the plane divided by its height.

(35) Prove that the ideal mechanical advantage of the lever shown in Fig. 7-9(c) is the distance from the fulcrum to the point of application of F divided by the distance from the fulcrum to the point of application of the load.

(36) Prove that the ideal mechanical advantage of the crank and axle shown in Fig. 7-9(d) is equal to the length of the crank divided by the radius of the wheel.

(37) Calculate the ideal mechanical advantage of the device shown in Fig. 7-16.

(38) A body moves a distance of 10 ft under the action of a force which has the constant value of 5.5 lb for the first 6 ft and then decreases to a value of 2 lb as shown by the graph in Fig. 7-17. (a) How much work is done in the first 6 ft of the motion? (b) How much work is done in the last 4 ft?

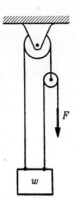

Fig. 7-16.

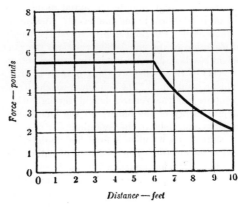

Distance — feet

Fig. 7-17.

Problems—Chapter 8

(1) (a) What is the momentum of a 10-ton truck whose velocity is 30 mi/hr?   At what velocity will a 5-ton truck have (b) the same momentum? (c) the same kinetic energy?

(2) A baseball weighs $5\frac{1}{2}$ oz.   (a) If the velocity of a pitched ball is 80 ft/sec, and after being batted it is 120 ft/sec in the opposite direction, find the change in momentum of the ball and the impulse of the blow.   (b) If the ball remains in contact with the bat for 0.002 sec, find the average force of the blow.

(3) An empty freight car weighing 10 tons rolls at 3 ft/sec along a level track and collides with a loaded car weighing 20 tons, standing at rest with brakes released.   If the two cars couple together, find (a) their velocity after the collision and (b) the decrease in kinetic energy as a result of the collision.

(4) Prove that when a moving body makes a perfectly inelastic collision with a second of equal mass, initially at rest, one-half of the original kinetic energy is "lost."

(5) With what velocity should the loaded car in Prob. 3 be rolling toward the empty one, in order that both shall be brought to rest by the collision?

(6) A bullet weighing 0.02 lb is fired with a muzzle velocity of 2700 ft/sec from a rifle weighing 7.5 lb.   (a) Compute the recoil velocity of the rifle, assuming it free to recoil.   (b) Find the ratio of the kinetic energy of the bullet to that of the rifle.

(7) Find the average recoil force on a machine gun firing 120 shots per minute. The weight of each bullet is 0.025 lb and the muzzle velocity is 2700 ft/sec.   Hint: average force equals average rate of change of momentum.

(8) A rifleman who, together with his rifle, weighs 160 lb, stands on roller skates and fires 10 shots horizontally from an automatic rifle.   Each bullet weighs 0.0257 lb (180 grains) and has a muzzle velocity of 2500 ft/sec.   (a) If the rifleman moves back without friction, what is his velocity at the end of the ten shots?   (b) If the shots were fired in 10 sec, what was the average force exerted on him?   (c) Compare his kinetic energy with that of the ten bullets.

(9) A 75 mm gun fires a projectile weighing 16 lb with a muzzle velocity of 1900 ft/sec.   By how many mi/hr is the velocity of a plane mounting such a gun decreased, when a projectile is fired directly ahead?   The plane weighs 32,000 lb.

(10) The projectile of a 16-in. seacoast gun weighs 2400 lb, travels a distance of 38 ft in the bore of the gun, and has a muzzle velocity of 2250 ft/sec.   The gun weighs 300,000 lb.   (a) Compute the initial recoil velocity.   (b) What is the acceleration of the projectile while in the gun barrel?   Assume it to be constant.   (c) How long a time is required for the projectile to travel the length of the gun barrel?   (d) If the angle of elevation of the gun is 30°, compute the range of the projectile and the maximum height reached, in miles, neglecting air resistance.

(11) A rifle bullet weighing 0.02 lb is fired with a velocity of 2500 ft/sec into a ballistic pendulum.   The pendulum weighs 10 lb and is suspended from a cord 3 ft long. Compute (a) the vertical height through which the pendulum rises, (b) the initial kinetic energy of the bullet, (c) the kinetic energy of bullet and pendulum after the bullet is embedded in the pendulum.

(12) A 5 gm bullet is fired horizontally into a 3-kgm wooden block resting on a horizontal surface.   The coefficient of sliding friction between block and surface is 0.20. The bullet remains embedded in the block, which is observed to slide 25 cm along the surface.   What was the velocity of the bullet?

(13) A bullet of mass 2 gm, traveling at 500 m/sec, is fired into a ballistic pendulum

of mass 1 kgm suspended from a cord 1 meter long. The bullet penetrates the pendulum and emerges with a velocity of 100 m/sec. Through what vertical height will the pendulum rise?

(14) A 10-gm block slides at a velocity of 20 cm/sec on a smooth level surface and makes a head-on collision with a 30-gm block moving in the opposite direction with a velocity of 10 cm/sec. If the collision is perfectly elastic, find the velocity of each block after the collision.

(15) A block of mass 200 gm, sliding with a velocity of 12 cm/sec on a smooth level surface, makes a perfectly elastic head-on collision with a block of mass m gm, initially at rest. After the collision the velocity of the 200-gm block is 4 cm/sec in the same direction as its initial velocity. Find (a) the mass m, and (b) its velocity after the collision.

(16) A freight elevator is rising with a constant velocity of 5 ft/sec. A stationary observer drops a ball from a point which is 21 ft above the platform at the instant the ball is released. The coefficient of restitution between ball and platform is 0.50. How far above (or below) its starting point does the ball rise on its first bounce?

(17) A ball is thrown against a vertical wall, striking it at a point 4 ft above the floor with a horizontal velocity of 20 ft/sec. After rebounding from the wall, the ball strikes the floor at a point 8 ft from the wall. (a) What was the coefficient of restitution? (b) If the ball weighed 0.5 lb, how much kinetic energy was "lost" in the impact with the wall?

(18) A squash ball, dropped from a height of 8 ft, rebounds to a height of 3 ft. With what velocity must it be projected horizontally against a vertical wall, at a height of 6 ft above the floor, in order that it may rebound a horizontal distance of 15 ft?

(19) A golf ball is dropped on a hard surface from a height of 1 meter and rebounds to a height of 64 cm. (a) What is the height of the second bounce? of the nth bounce? After (about) how many bounces is the height reduced to 1 cm? (b) What is the time of the first bounce, i.e., between the first and second contacts with the surface? What is the time of the nth bounce? (c) What is the coefficient of restitution?

Problems—Chapter 9

(1) (a) What angle in radians is subtended by an arc 3 ft in length, on the circumference of a circle whose radius is 2 ft? (b) What angle in radians is subtended by an arc of length 78.54 cm on the circumference of a circle of diameter 100 cm? What is this angle in degrees? (c) The angle between two radii of a circle is 0.60 radians. What length of arc is intercepted on the circumference of a circle of radius 200 cm? of radius 200 ft?

(2) Compute the angular velocity, in rad/sec, of the crankshaft of an automobile engine rotating at 3600 rpm.

(3) (a) A cylinder 3 inches in diameter rotates in a lathe at 1500 rpm. What is the tangential velocity of the surface of the cylinder? (b) The proper tangential velocity for machining cast iron is about 2 ft/sec. At how many rpm should a piece of stock 2 inches in diameter be rotated in a lathe?

(4) The flywheel of the engine in Prob. 2 is 18 inches in diameter. Find (a) the tangential velocity of a point on its rim, and (b) of a point halfway between rim and center.

(5) An electric motor running at 1800 rpm has on its shaft three pulleys, of diameters 2, 4 and 6 in. respectively. Find the linear velocity of the surface of each pulley, in ft/sec. The pulleys may be connected by a belt to a similar set on a countershaft; the 2 in. to the 6 in., the 4 in. to the 4 in., and the 6 in. to the 2 in. Find the three possible angular velocities of the countershaft, in rpm.

(6) A wheel 3 ft in diameter starts from rest and accelerates uniformly to an angular velocity of 100 rad/sec in 20 sec. Find (a) the angular acceleration and (b) the angle turned through.

(7) The angular velocity of a flywheel decreases uniformly from 900 rpm to 800 rpm in 5 sec. Find (a) the angular acceleration and (b) the number of revolutions made by the wheel in the 5 sec interval. (c) How many more seconds are required for the wheel to come to rest?

(8) A flywheel requires 3 sec to rotate through 234 radians. Its angular velocity at the end of this time is 96 rad/sec. Find its constant angular acceleration.

(9) A flywheel whose angular acceleration is constant and equal to 2 rad/sec^2, rotates through an angle of 75 radians in 5 sec. How long had it been in motion at the beginning of the 5 sec interval if it started from rest?

(10) (a) What is the tangential acceleration of a point on the rim of the wheel in Prob. 6? (b) Of a point halfway between rim and center?

(11) (a) Distinguish clearly between tangential and radial acceleration. (b) A flywheel rotates with constant angular velocity. Does a point on its rim have a tangential acceleration? a radial acceleration? (c) A flywheel is rotating with constant angular acceleration. Does a point on its rim have a tangential acceleration? a radial acceleration? Are these accelerations constant in magnitude?

(12) At time $t = 0$ a body is moving East at 10 cm/sec. At time $t = 2$ sec it is moving 20° North of East at 14 cm/sec. Find graphically its change in velocity during this time and its average acceleration.

(13) A racing car is driven with a velocity of 90 ft/sec, constant in magnitude, around a circular track whose circumference is 3600 ft. Find graphically the magnitude and direction of the average acceleration of the car in an interval of (a) 8 sec, (b) 4 sec, (c) 2 sec. (d) Compare the answer to (c) with the magnitude and direction of the instantaneous radial acceleration.

(14) A wheel rotates with a constant angular velocity of 10 rad/sec. (a) Compute the radial acceleration of a point 2 ft from the axis, from the relation $a_R = \omega^2 R$. (b) Find the tangential velocity of the point, and compute its radial acceleration from the relation $a_R = v^2/R$.

(15) Find the required angular velocity of an ultracentrifuge, in rpm, in order that the radial acceleration of a point 1 cm from the axis shall equal 300,000 g (i.e., 300,000 times the acceleration of gravity).

(16) The pilot of a dive bomber who has been diving at a velocity of 400 mi/hr pulls out of the dive by changing his course to a circle in a vertical plane. (a) What is the minimum radius of the circle in order that the acceleration at the lowest point shall not exceed "$7g$". (b) How much does a 180-lb pilot apparently weigh at the lowest point of the pull-out?

(17) A flywheel of radius 30 cm starts from rest and accelerates with a constant angular acceleration of 0.50 rad/sec². Compute the tangential acceleration, the radial acceleration, and the resultant acceleration, of a point on its rim (a) at the start; (b) after it has turned through 120°; (c) after it has turned through 240°.

(18) A wheel starts from rest and accelerates uniformly to an angular velocity of 900 rpm in 20 sec. (a) Find the position, at the end of 1 sec, of a point originally at the top of the wheel. (b) Compute and show in a diagram the magnitude and direction of the tangential and radial components of its acceleration at this instant. The distance of the point from the axis is 6 in.

(19) A small block weighing 2 lb revolves in a horizontal circle on a frictionless table top, at the end of a cord 2 ft long attached to a pin set in the table top. The angular velocity of the block is 3 rad/sec. Compute (a) the radial acceleration of the block and (b) the tension in the cord.

(20) Find the centripetal force exerted on a 4-oz bolt at the rim of the flywheel of an engine, 18 inches in diameter, rotating at (a) 2000 rpm; (b) 4000 rpm.

(21) A block is placed 10 cm from the axis of a horizontal turntable which is gradually accelerated from rest. At an angular velocity of 7 rad/sec the block starts to slip. Find the coefficient of friction between block and turntable.

(22) A small block weighing 2 lb is attached to a cord 2 ft long and set rotating in a vertical circle. Its angular velocity at the top of the circle is 8 rad/sec. Show in a diagram all of the forces acting on the block at this point, and compute the tension in the cord.

(23) Find the tangential velocity of the block in Prob. 22 at the lowest point of the circle, and the tension in the cord at this point.

(24) A bicycle and rider, weighing together 160 lb, loop-the-loop in a circular track of radius 8 ft. The velocity at the lowest point is $32\sqrt{2}$ ft/sec. (a) Find the radial acceleration at the highest point. Assume that the bicycle "coasts" without friction. (b) Show in a diagram all of the forces acting on the bicycle and rider at the highest point, and compute the force with which the track pushes against the bicycle. (c) With what force does the bicycle press against the track? (d) What is the minimum velocity the bicycle can have at the highest point without leaving the track?

(25) A 2400-lb automobile rounds a level curve of radius 400 ft, on an unbanked road, with a velocity of 40 mi/hr. (a) What is the minimum coefficient of friction between tires and road in order that the automobile shall not skid? (b) At what angle should the roadbed be banked for this velocity?

(26) A curve of 600 ft radius on a level road is banked at the correct angle for a velocity of 30 mi/hr. If an automobile rounds this curve at 60 mi/hr, what is the minimum coefficient of friction between tires and road so that the automobile will not skid? Assume all forces to act at the center of gravity.

(27) (a) With what angular velocity must the apparatus in Fig. 9-23 rotate about a vertical axis in order that the cord shall make an angle of 45° with the vertical? (b) What is then the tension in the cord? (Given L = 20 cm, a = 10 cm, m = 200 gm.)

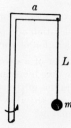

Fig. 9-23.

(28) The apparent weight of a man at the equator is 180 lb. By how many ounces does this differ from his true weight?

(29) (a) With what angular velocity would the earth have to rotate in order that the apparent weight of a body at the equator would be zero? (b) What would then be the length of a day?

(30) (a) Compute the torque developed by an airplane engine whose output is 2000 hp at an angular velocity of 2400 rpm. (b) If a drum 18 inches in diameter were attached to the motor shaft, and the power output of the motor were used to raise a weight hanging from a rope wrapped around the shaft, how large a weight could be lifted? (c) With what velocity would it rise?

Problems—Chapter 10

(1) Small blocks, each of mass m, are clamped at the ends and at the center of a light rigid rod of length L. Compute the moment of inertia and the radius of gyration of the system about an axis perpendicular to the rod and passing through a point one-quarter of the length from one end. Neglect the moment of inertia of the rod.

(2) The radius of the earth is 4000 mi and its mass is 4×10^{21} slugs (approximately). Find (a) its moment of inertia about an axis through its center, and (b) its radius of gyration in miles. Assume the density to be uniform.

(3) The inner radius of a hollow cylinder is 3 inches, the outer radius is 4 inches, and the length is 6 inches. What is the radius of gyration of the cylinder about its axis?

(4) A flywheel consists of a solid disk 1 ft in diameter and 1 inch thick, and two projecting hubs 4 inches in diameter and 3 inches long. If the material of which it is constructed weighs 480 lb/ft³, find (a) its moment of inertia and (b) its radius of gyration about the axis of rotation.

(5) A grinding wheel 6 inches in diameter, weighing 4 lb, is rotating at 3600 rpm. (a) What is its kinetic energy? (b) How far would it have to fall to acquire the same kinetic energy?

(6) The flywheel of a small gasoline engine is required to give up 250 ft-lb of energy while its angular velocity decreases from 600 rpm to 580 rpm. What moment of inertia is required?

(7) The flywheel of a stationary engine has a moment of inertia of 20 slug-ft². (a) What constant torque is required to bring it up to an angular velocity of 900 rpm in 10 sec, starting from rest? (b) What is its final kinetic energy?

(8) A grindstone in the form of a solid cylinder weighs 80 lb and is 2 ft in diameter. What force applied at right angles to the end of a crank 9 inches long will bring it up to an angular velocity of 120 rpm in 5 sec?

(9) A grindstone 3 ft in diameter, weighing 96 lb, is rotating at 900 rpm. A tool is pressed normally against the rim with a force of 45 lb, and the grindstone comes to rest in 10 sec. Find the coefficient of friction between the tool and the grindstone. Neglect friction in the bearings.

(10) A constant torque of 20 newton-meters is exerted on a pivoted wheel for 10 sec, during which time the angular velocity of the wheel increases from zero to 100 rpm. The external torque is then removed and the wheel is brought to rest by friction in its bearings in 100 sec. Compute (a) the moment of inertia of the wheel, (b) the friction torque, (c) the total number of revolutions made by the wheel.

(11) A cord is wrapped around the rim of a flywheel 2 ft in radius and a steady pull of 10 lb is exerted on the cord as in Fig. 10-14(a). The wheel is mounted in fric-

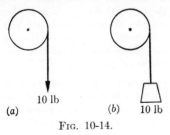

10 lb

(a)

(b)   10 lb

FIG. 10-14.

tionless bearings on a horizontal shaft through its center. The moment of inertia of the wheel is 2 slug-ft². (a) Compute the angular acceleration of the wheel. (b) Show that the work done in unwinding 20 ft of cord equals the gain in kinetic energy of the wheel. (c) If a 10-lb weight hangs from the cord as in Fig. 10-14(b), compute the angular acceleration of the wheel. Why is this not the same as in part (a)?

(12) A solid cylinder of mass 15 kgm, 30 cm in diameter, is pivoted about a horizontal axis through its center, and a rope wrapped around the surface of the cylinder carries at its end a block of mass 8 kgm. (a) How far does the block descend in 5 sec, starting from rest? (b) What is the tension in the rope? (c) What is the force exerted on the cylinder by its bearings?

(13) A bucket of water weighing 64 lb is suspended by a rope wrapped around a windlass in the form of a solid cylinder 1 ft in diameter, also weighing 64 lb. The bucket is released from rest at the top of a well and falls 64 ft to the water. (a) What is the tension in the rope while the bucket is falling? (b) With what velocity does the bucket strike the water? (c) What was the time of fall? Neglect the weight of the rope.

(14) A 16-lb block rests on a horizontal frictionless surface. A cord attached to the block passes over a pulley, whose diameter is 6 inches, to a hanging block which also weighs 16 lb. The system is released from rest, and the blocks are observed to move 16 ft in 2 sec. (a) What was the moment of inertia of the pulley? (b) What was the tension in each part of the cord?

(15) A man sits on a piano stool holding a pair of dumbbells at a distance of 3 ft from the axis of rotation of the stool. He is given an angular velocity of 2 rad/sec, after which he pulls the dumbbells in until they are but 1 ft distant from the axis. The moment of inertia of the man about the axis of rotation is 3 slug-ft^2 and may be considered constant. The dumbbells weigh 16 lb each and may be considered point masses. Neglect friction. (a) What is the initial angular momentum of the system? (b) What is the angular velocity of the system after the dumbbells are pulled in toward the axis? (c) Compute the kinetic energy of the system, before and after the dumbbells are pulled in. Account for the difference, if any.

(16) A block of mass 50 gm is attached to a cord passing through a hole in a horizontal frictionless surface as in Fig. 10-15. The block is originally revolving at a distance of 20 cm from the hole with an angular velocity of 3 rad/sec. The cord is then

FIG. 10-15.

pulled from below, shortening the radius of the circle in which the block revolves to 10 cm. The block may be considered a point mass. (a) What is the new angular velocity? (b) Find the change in kinetic energy of the block.

(17) A uniform rod of mass 30 gm and 20 cm long, rotates in a horizontal plane about a fixed vertical axis through its center. Two small bodies, each of mass 20 gm, are mounted so that they can slide along the rod. They are initially held by catches at positions 5 cm on either side of the center of the rod, and the system is rotating at 15 rpm. Without otherwise changing the system, the catches are released and the masses slide outward along the rod and fly off at the ends. (a) What is the angular velocity of the system at the instant when the small masses reach the ends of the rod? (b) What is the angular velocity of the rod after the small masses leave it?

(18) A turntable rotates about a fixed vertical axis, making one revolution in 10 sec. The moment of inertia of the turntable about this axis is 720 slug-ft^2. A man weighing 160 lb, initially standing at the center of the turntable, runs out along a radius. What is the angular velocity of the turntable when the man is 6 ft from the center?

(19) A man weighing 160 lb stands at the rim of a turntable of radius 10 ft and moment of inertia 2500 slug-ft^2, mounted on a vertical frictionless shaft at its center. The whole system is initially at rest. The man now walks along the outer edge of the turntable with a velocity of 2 ft/sec, relative to the earth. (a) With what angular velocity and in what direction does the turntable rotate? (b) Through what angle will it have rotated when the man reaches his initial position on the turntable? (c) Through what angle will it have rotated when he reaches his initial position relative to the earth?

(20) A man weighing 160 lb runs around the edge of a horizontal turntable mounted on a vertical frictionless axis through its center. The velocity of the man, relative to the earth, is 4 ft/sec. The turntable is rotating in the opposite direction with an angular velocity of 0.2 rad/sec. The radius of the turntable is 8 ft and its moment of inertia about the axis of rotation is 320 slug-ft^2. Find the final angular velocity of the system if the man comes to rest, relative to the turntable.

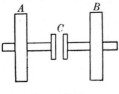

FIG. 10-16.

(21) Two flywheels, A and B, are mounted on shafts which can be connected or disengaged by a friction clutch C. (Fig. 10-16.) The moment of inertia of wheel A is 4 slug-ft^2. With the clutch disengaged, wheel A is brought up to an angular velocity of 600 rpm. Wheel B is initially at rest. The clutch is now engaged, accelerating B and decelerating A until both wheels have the same angular velocity. The final angular velocity of the system is 400 rpm. (a) What was the moment of inertia of wheel B? (b) How much energy was lost in the process? Neglect all bearing friction.

(22) The stabilizing gyroscope of a ship weighs 50 tons, its radius of gyration is 5 ft, and it rotates about a vertical axis with an angular velocity of 900 rpm. (a) How long a time is required to bring it up to speed, starting from rest, with a constant power input of 100 hp? (b) Find the righting moment exerted on the ship, in lb-ft, when the axis is forced to precess in a vertical fore-and-aft plane at the rate of 1 degree/sec.

(23) The mass of the rotor of a toy gyroscope is 150 gm and its moment of inertia about its axis is 1500 gm-cm^2. The mass of the frame is 30 gm. The gyroscope is supported on a single pivot as in Fig. 10-17 with its center of gravity distant 4 cm horizontally from the pivot, and is precessing in a horizontal plane at the rate of 1 revolution in 6 sec. (a) Find the upward force exerted by the pivot. (b) Find the angular velocity with which the rotor is spinning about its axis, ex-

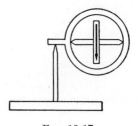

FIG. 10-17.

pressed in rpm. (c) Copy the diagram, and show by vectors the angular velocity of the rotor and the angular velocity of precession.

(24) If the projection that rests on the pivot in Fig. 10-17 were extended to the left, at what horizontal distance from the pivot should a 200-gm body be hung to cause an angular velocity of precession of 1 revolution in 10 sec, in a direction opposite to that in Fig. 10-17?

Problems—Chapter 11

(1) (a) Compute the stress and strain in a steel cable 0.5 inch in diameter when supporting a load of 4 tons.   (b) What is the elongation of the cable if its unstressed length was 100 ft?   (c) Find the maximum upward acceleration that can be given the 4-ton load, if the stress in the cable is not to exceed 60,000 lb/in^2.

(2) (a) What is the maximum load that can be supported by an aluminum wire 0.05 inch in diameter without exceeding the elastic limit of 14,000 lb/in^2?   (b) If the wire was originally 20 ft long, how much will it elongate under this load?

(3) A copper wire 12 ft long and 0.036 inch in diameter was given the test below. A load of 4.5 lb was originally hung from the wire to keep it taut.   The position of the lower end of the wire was read on a scale.

Added load (lb)	Scale reading (in.)
0	3.02
2	3.04
4	3.06
6	3.08
8	3.10
10	3.12
12	3.14
14	3.65

(a) Make a graph of these values, plotting the increase in length horizontally and the added load vertically.   (b) Calculate the value of Young's modulus.   (c) What was the stress at the elastic limit?

(4) A 10-lb weight hangs on a vertical steel wire 2 ft long and 0.001 in^2 in cross section.   Hanging from the bottom of this weight is a similar steel wire which supports a 5-lb weight.   Compute (a) the longitudinal strain and (b) the elongation of each wire.

(5) A bar of copper 2 ft long is welded end-to-end with a bar of steel 15 inches long. The cross section of each bar is 0.5 in^2.   The compound bar is compressed by forces of 1000 lb applied at its ends.   Compute (a) the longitudinal stress and (b) the decrease in length of each bar.

(6) A copper wire 320 inches long and a steel wire 160 inches long, each of cross section 0.1 in^2, are fastened end-to-end and stretched with a tension of 100 lb.   (a) What is the change in length of each wire?   (b) What is the elastic potential energy of the system?

(7) A rigid horizontal bar 4 ft long, of uniform cross section and weighing 100 lb, is supported by two vertical wires, one of steel and one of copper.   Each wire is 5 ft long and 0.005 in^2 in cross section.   The copper wire is attached to one end of the bar and the steel wire at such a distance x from this end that both wires stretch by the same amount.   Find (a) the tension in each wire and (b) the distance x.

(8) A 32-lb weight, fastened to the end of a steel wire of unstretched length 2 ft, is whirled in a vertical circle with an angular velocity at the bottom of the circle of 2 rps.   The cross section of the wire is 0.01 in^2.   Calculate the elongation of the wire when the weight is at the lowest point of its path.

(9) Two strips of metal are riveted together at their ends by four rivets, each of diameter of 0.25 inch.   What is the maximum tension that can be exerted by the riveted strip if the shearing stress on the rivets is not to exceed 10,000 lb/in^2?   Assume each rivet to carry one-quarter of the load.

(10) Refer to Fig. 11-4(b). The initial volume of the block is 500 cm³ and the pressure is 2000 lb/in². Find the decrease in volume of the block (a) if of steel, (b) if of lead. (c) The compressibility of the liquid in the cylinder is 25×10^{-6} atm⁻¹ and its initial volume is 1 ft³. Find its decrease in volume.

(11) Find the weight-density of ocean water at a depth where the pressure is 4700 lb/in². The weight-density at the surface is 64 lb/ft³.

(12) (a) Compute the compressibility of steel, in reciprocal atmospheres, and compare with that of water. (b) Which material is the more readily compressed?

Problems—Chapter 12

(1) A body is vibrating with simple harmonic motion of amplitude 15 cm and frequency 4 vibr/sec. Compute (a) the maximum values of the acceleration and velocity, (b) the acceleration and velocity when the displacement is 9 cm, (c) the time required to move from the equilibrium position to a point 12 cm distant from it.

(2) A body of mass 10 gm moves with simple harmonic motion of amplitude 24 cm and period 4 sec. The displacement is +24 cm when $t = 0$. Compute (a) the position of the body when $t = 0.5$ sec, (b) the magnitude and direction of the force acting on the body when $t = 0.5$ sec, (c) the minimum time required for the body to move from its initial position to the point where $x = -12$ cm, (d) the velocity of the body when $x = -12$ cm.

(3) The motion of the piston of an automobile engine is approximately simple harmonic. (a) If the stroke of an engine (twice the amplitude) is 4 inches and the angular velocity is 3600 rpm, compute the acceleration of the piston at the end of its stroke. (b) If the piston weighs 1 lb, what resultant force must be exerted on it at this point? (c) What is the velocity of the piston, in mi/hr, at the midpoint of its stroke?

(4) A 4-lb weight hung from a spring is found to stretch the spring 8 inches. (a) What is the force constant of the spring? (b) What would be the period of vibration of the 4-lb weight, if suspended from this spring? (c) What would be the period of an 8-lb weight hanging from the same spring?

(5) The scale of a spring balance reading from zero to 32 lb is 6 inches long. A body suspended from the balance is observed to oscillate vertically at 1.5 vibr/sec. What is the weight of the body?

(6) A body whose mass is 4.9 kgm hangs from a spring and oscillates with a period of 0.5 sec. How much will the spring shorten when the body is removed?

(7) Four passengers whose combined weight is 600 lb are observed to compress the springs of an automobile by 2 inches when they enter the automobile. If the total load supported by the springs is 1800 lb, find the period of vibration of the loaded automobile.

(8) Find the length of a simple pendulum whose period is exactly 1 sec at a point where $g = 32.2$ ft/sec².

(9) A simple pendulum 8 ft long swings with an amplitude of 1 ft. (a) Compute the velocity of the pendulum at its lowest point. (b) Compute its acceleration at the ends of its path.

(10) A pendulum clock which keeps correct time at a point where $g = 980.0$ cm/sec² is found to lose 10 sec per day at a higher altitude. Find the value of g at the new location.

(11) The balance wheel of a watch vibrates with an angular amplitude of π radians and with a period of 0.5 sec. (a) Find its maximum angular velocity. (b) Find its angular velocity when its displacement is one-half its amplitude. (c) Find its angular acceleration when its displacement is 45°.

Problems—Chapter 13

(1) The piston of a hydraulic automobile lift is 12 inches in diameter. What pressure, in lb/in², is required to lift a car weighing 2400 lb?

(2) The expansion tank of a household hot-water heating system is open to the atmosphere and is 30 ft above a pressure gauge attached to the furnace. What is the gauge pressure, in lb/in²?

(3) The submarine Squalus sank at a depth of 240 ft. Compute the absolute pressure at this depth in lb/in² and lb/ft². The specific gravity of sea water is 1.025.

(4) A stone which weighs 120 lb in air appears to weigh only 70 lb when under water. Compute (a) the volume and (b) the weight-density of the stone.

(5) The densities of air, helium, and hydrogen (at standard conditions) are respectively 0.00129 gm/cm³, 0.000178 gm/cm³, and 0.0000899 gm/cm³. (a) What is the volume in cubic feet displaced by a hydrogen-filled dirigible which has a total "lift" of 10 tons? (b) What would be the "lift" if helium were used instead of hydrogen?

(6) What is the area of the smallest block of ice 1 ft thick that will just support a man weighing 180 lb? The specific gravity of the ice is 0.917, and it is floating in fresh water.

(7) A cubical block of wood 10 cm on a side floats at the interface between oil and water as in Fig. 13-9, with its lower surface 2 cm below the interface. The density of the oil is 0.6 gm/cm³. (a) What is the mass of the block? (b) What is the gauge pressure at the lower face of the block?

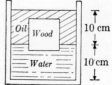

Fig. 13-9.

(8) A cubical block of wood 10 cm on a side and of density 0.5 gm/cm³ floats in a jar of water. Oil of density 0.8 gm/cm³ is poured on the water until the top of the oil layer is 4 cm below the top of the block. (a) How deep is the oil layer? (b) What is the gauge pressure at the lower face of the block?

(9) A cubical block of steel (density = 7.8 gm/cm³) floats on mercury (density = 13.6 gm/cm³). (a) What fraction of the block is above the mercury surface? (b) If water is poured on the mercury surface, how deep must the water layer be so that the water surface just rises to the top of the steel block?

(10) A hollow cylindrical can 20 cm in diameter floats in water with 10 cm of its height above the water line when a 10 kgm iron block hangs from its bottom. If the block is now placed inside the can, how much of the cylinder's height will be above the water line? The density of iron is 7.8 gm/cm³.

(11) A block of balsa wood placed in one scale pan of an equal arm balance is found to be exactly balanced by a 100-gm brass "weight" in the other scale pan. Find the true mass of the balsa wood, if its specific gravity is 0.15.

(12) A hydrometer consists of a spherical bulb and a cylindrical stem of cross section 0.4 cm². The total volume of bulb and stem is 13.2 cm³. When immersed in water the hydrometer floats with 8 cm of the stem above the water surface. In alcohol, 1 cm of the stem is above the surface. Find the density of the alcohol.

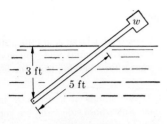

FIG. 13-10.

(13) A 12-lb uniform rod 6 ft long, whose specific gravity is 0.50, is hinged at one end 3 ft below a water surface as in Fig. 13-10. (a) What weight w must be attached to the other end of the rod so that 5 ft of the rod are submerged? (b) Find the magnitude and direction of the force exerted by the hinge on the rod.

(14) A cubical block of wood 1 ft on a side is weighted so that its center of gravity is at the point shown in Fig. 13-11(a), and it floats in water with one-half its volume submerged. Compute (a) the righting moment and (b) the metacentric height when the block is "heeled" at an angle of 45° as in Fig. 13-11(b).

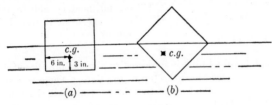

FIG. 13-11.

Problems—Chapter 14

(1) A circular hole 1 inch in diameter is cut in the side of a large standpipe, 20 ft below the water level in the standpipe. Find (a) the velocity of efflux and (b) the discharge rate. Neglect the contraction of the stream lines after emerging from the hole.

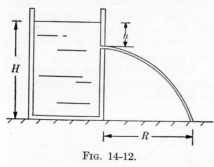

Fig. 14-12.

(2) Water stands at a depth H in a large open tank whose side walls are vertical. (Fig. 14-12) A hole is made in one of the walls at a depth h below the water surface. (a) At what distance R from the foot of the wall does the emerging stream of water strike the floor? (b) At what height above the bottom of the tank could a second hole be cut so that the stream emerging from it would have the same range?

(3) Water in an enclosed tank is subjected to a gauge pressure of 4 lb/in² applied by compressed air introduced into the top of the tank. There is a small hole in the side of the tank 16 ft below the level of the water. Calculate the velocity with which water escapes from this hole.

(4) What gauge pressure is required in the city mains in order that a stream from a fire hose connected to the mains may reach a vertical height of 60 ft? Neglect friction effects.

(5) A pipe line 6 inches in diameter, flowing full of water, has a constriction of diameter 3 in. If the velocity in the 6-inch portion is 4 ft/sec, find (a) the velocity in the constriction and (b) the discharge rate in ft³/sec.

(6) A horizontal pipe of 6 in² cross section tapers to a cross section of 2 in². If sea water of density 2 slugs/ft³ is flowing with a velocity of 180 ft/min in the large pipe where a pressure gauge reads 10.5 lb/in², what is the gauge pressure in the adjoining part of the small pipe? The barometer reads 30 inches of mercury.

(7) At a certain point in a horizontal pipe line the gauge pressure is 6.24 lb/in². At another point the gauge pressure is 4.37 lb/in². If the areas of the pipe at these two points are 3 in² and 1.5 in² respectively, compute the number of cubic feet of water which flow across any cross section of the pipe per minute.

(8) Water flowing in a horizontal pipe discharges at the rate of 0.12 ft³/sec. At a point in the pipe where the cross section is 0.01 ft² the absolute pressure is 18 lb/in². What must be the cross section of a constriction in the pipe such that the pressure there is reduced to 15 lb/in²?

(9) The pressure difference between the main pipe line and the throat of a Venturi meter is 15 lb/in². The areas of the pipe and the constriction are 1 ft² and 0.5 ft². How many cubic feet per second are flowing through the pipe? The liquid in the pipe is water.

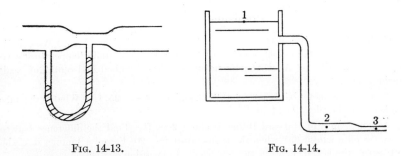

Fig. 14-13. Fig. 14-14.

(10) The section of pipe shown in Fig. 14-13 has a cross section of 0.04 ft² at the wider portions and 0.01 ft² at the constriction. One cubic foot of water is discharged from the pipe in 5 sec. (a) Find the velocities at the wide and the narrow portions. (b) Find the pressure difference between these portions. (c) Find the difference in height between the mercury columns in the U-tube.

(11) Water flows steadily from a reservoir shown in Fig. 14-14. The elevation of point 1 is 40 ft; of points 2 and 3 it is 4 ft. The cross section at point 2 is 0.5 ft² and at point 3 it is 0.25 ft². The area of the reservoir is very large compared with the cross sections of the pipe. (a) Compute the absolute pressure at point 2. (b) Compute the discharge rate in ft³/sec.

(12) Sea water of density 2 slugs/ft³ flows steadily in a pipe line of constant cross section leading out of an elevated tank. At a point 4.5 ft below the water level in the tank the gauge pressure in the flowing stream is 1 lb/in². (a) What is the velocity of the water at this point? (b) If the pipe rises to a point 9 ft above the level of the water in the tank, what are the velocity and the pressure at the latter point?

(13) At a certain point in a pipe line the velocity is 2 ft/sec and the gauge pressure is 35 lb/in². Find the gauge pressure at a second point in the line 50 ft lower than the first, if the cross section at the second point is one-half that at the first. The liquid in the pipe is water.

(14) The water surface in a large standpipe is at an elevation of 64 ft above the outlet of a pipe line of uniform cross section of 0.10 ft². (a) What is the discharge rate, in ft³/sec? (b) What are the absolute and the gauge pressures at a point in the line 20 ft above the outlet?

(15) Modern airplane design calls for a "lift" of about 20 lb/ft² of wing area. Assume that air flows past the wing of an airplane with streamline flow. The specific gravity of air may be assumed constant and equal to 1.29×10^{-3}. If the velocity of flow past the lower wing surface is 300 ft/sec, what is the required velocity over the upper surface to give a "lift" of 20 lb/ft²?

(16) A fire engine pumps 10,000 lb of water per minute from a lake, and ejects it from a nozzle 17 ft above the lake surface with a velocity of 32 ft/sec. What horsepower output must the engine have, if friction losses are neglected?

Problems—Chapter 15

(1) The temperature of the surface of the sun is about 6500° C. (a) What is this temperature on the fahrenheit scale? (b) What is the centigrade temperature corresponding to 68° F? (c) At what temperature do the fahrenheit and centigrade scales coincide?

(2) One steel meter bar is correct at 0° C, and another at 25° C. What is the difference between their lengths at 20° C?

(3) The length of Harvard Bridge is about 2000 ft. Find the difference between its lengths on a winter day when the temperature is −20° F, and a summer day when the temperature is 100° F. Use the coefficient of expansion of steel.

(4) A surveyor's 100-ft steel tape is correct at a temperature of 65° F. The distance between two points, as measured by this tape on a day when the temperature is 95° F, is 86.57 ft. What is the true distance between the points?

(5) To ensure a tight fit, the aluminum rivets used in airplane construction are made slightly larger than the rivet holes and cooled by "dry ice" (solid CO_2) before being driven. If the diameter of a hole is 0.2500 inch, what should be the diameter of a rivet at 20° C if its diameter is to be equal to that of the hole when the rivet is cooled to −78° C, the temperature of dry ice?

(6) A steel ring of 3.000 inches inside diameter at 20° C is to be heated and slipped over a brass shaft measuring 3.002 inches in diameter at 20° C. (a) To what temperature should the ring be heated? (b) If the ring and shaft together are cooled by some means such as liquid air, at what temperature will the ring just slip off the shaft?

(7) At a temperature of 20° C, the volume of a certain glass flask, up to a reference mark on the stem of the flask, is exactly 100 cm³. The flask is filled to this point with a liquid whose cubical coefficient of expansion is 120×10^{-5} per C°, with both flask and liquid at 20° C. The linear coefficient of expansion of the glass is 8×10^{-6} per C°. The cross section of the stem is 1 mm² and can be considered constant. How far will the liquid rise or fall in the stem when the temperature is raised to 40° C?

(8) A glass flask, when filled at a temperature of 20° C, holds 680 gm of mercury. How much mercury overflows when the whole is heated to 100° C? The linear coefficient of expansion of the glass is 8×10^{-6} per C°.

(9) A clock whose pendulum makes one vibration in 2 sec is correct at 25° C. The pendulum shaft is of steel and its moment of inertia may be neglected compared with that of the bob. (a) What is the fractional change in length of the shaft when it is cooled to 15° C? (b) How many seconds per day will the clock gain or lose at 15° C?

(10) A slender steel rod oscillates as a physical pendulum about a horizontal axis through one end. If the rod is 2 ft long at 20° C, compute the change in its period when the temperature is increased to 30° C.

(11) A steel rod 2 cm² in cross section is 30 cm long at 20° C. If it is heated to 520° C and then cooled to 20° C without being allowed to contract, compute the stress in the rod.

(12) The cross section of a steel rod is 0.5 in². What is the least force that will prevent it from contracting while cooling from 520° C to 20° C?

(13) A steel wire 0.01 inch in diameter is fastened between clamps at the ends of a large brass bar. The tension in the wire is zero at 0° C. Find the tension when bar and wire are at 20° C.

(14) What hydrostatic pressure is necessary to prevent a steel block from expanding when its temperature is increased from 20° C to 30° C?

(15) A steel bomb is filled with water at 10° C. If the whole is heated to 75° C and no water is allowed to escape, compute the increase in pressure in the bomb. Assume the bomb to be sufficiently strong so that it is not stretched by the increased pressure.

Problems—Chapter 16

(1) (a) What quantity of heat, in Btu, is required to raise the temperature of the water in a 40-gallon hot-water tank from 60° F to 140° F? (There are 7.5 gallons in a cubic foot.) (b) If the water is heated by the combustion of gas, how many cubic feet of gas must be burned if stack losses amount to 20%? (c) If the water is heated by an electric heater, how many kwh are required? The efficiency of the electric heater may be assumed 100%.

(2) (a) A certain house burns 10 tons of coal in a heating season. If stack losses are 15%, how many Btu were actually used to heat the house? (b) In some localities large tanks of water are heated by solar radiation during the summer and the stored energy is used for heating during the winter. Find the required dimensions of the storage tank, assuming it to be a cube, to store a quantity of energy equal to that computed in part (a). Assume that the water is heated to 120° F in the summer and cooled to 80° F in the winter.

(3) An automobile engine whose output is 40 hp uses 4.5 gallons of gasoline per hour. The heat of combustion of gasoline is 3×10^7 calories per gallon. What is the efficiency of the engine?

(4) The electric power input to a certain electric motor is 0.50 kw, and the mechanical power output is 0.54 hp. (a) What is the efficiency of the motor? (b) How may Btu are developed in the motor in one hour of operation?

(5) 400 gm of water are contained in a copper vessel of mass 200 gm. The water is heated by a friction device which dissipates mechanical energy, and it is observed that the temperature of the system rises at the rate of 3 C° per minute. Neglect heat losses to the surroundings. What power in watts is dissipated in the water?

(6) How long could a 2000 hp motor be operated on the heat energy liberated by one cubic mile of ocean water when the temperature of the water is lowered by 1 C°, if all of this heat were converted to mechanical energy? Why do we not utilize this tremendous reservoir of energy?

(7) A lead bullet, traveling at 350 m/sec, strikes a target and is brought to rest. What would be the rise in temperature of the bullet if none of the heat developed were lost to the surroundings?

(8) Compute from Table 16-1 the heat capacities of one gramatomic weight of Al, Cu, Pb, Hg, and Ag, and compare with the values predicted by the Dulong and Petit law.

(9) Compare the heat capacities of equal *volumes* of water, copper, and lead.

(10) A copper calorimeter whose mass is 300 gm contains 500 gm of water at a temperature of 15° C. A 560-gm block of copper, at a temperature of 100° C, is dropped into the calorimeter and the temperature is observed to increase to 22.5° C. Neglect heat losses to the surroundings. (a) Find the specific heat of copper. (b) What is the water equivalent of the calorimeter?

(11) A billet of iron weighing 30 lb is taken from an annealing furnace and quenched in a tank containing 100 lb of oil at a temperature of 72° F. The temperature of the oil increases to 116° F. The specific heat of the oil is 0.45 Btu per lb–F°. Neglect the heat capacity of the tank and heat losses to the surroundings. Find the temperature of the annealing furnace.

(12) A 50-gm sample of a material, at a temperature of 100° C, is dropped into a calorimeter containing 200 gm of water initially at 20° C. The calorimeter is of copper and its mass is 100 gm. The final temperature of the calorimeter is 22° C. Compute the specific heat of the sample.

(13) An open vessel contains 500 gm of ice at $-20°$ C. The heat capacity of the container can be neglected. Heat is supplied to the vessel at the constant rate of 1000 cal/min for 100 min. Plot a curve showing the elapsed time as abscissa and the temperature as ordinate.

(14) A copper calorimeter of mass 100 gm contains 150 gm of water and 8 gm of ice in thermal equilibrium at atmospheric pressure. 100 gm of lead at a temperature of $200°$ C are dropped into the calorimeter. Find the final temperature, if no heat is lost to the surroundings.

(15) 500 gm of ice at $-16°$ C are dropped into a calorimeter containing 1000 gm of water at $20°$ C. The calorimeter can is of copper and has a mass of 278 gm. Compute the final temperature of the system, assuming no heat losses.

(16) A tube leads from a flask in which water is boiling under atmospheric pressure to a calorimeter. The mass of the calorimeter is 150 gm, its water equivalent is 15 gm and it contains originally 340 gm of water at $15°$ C. Steam is allowed to condense in the calorimeter until its temperature increases to $71°$C, after which the total mass of calorimeter and contents is found to be 525 gm. Compute the heat of condensation of steam from these data.

(17) A 2-kgm iron block is taken from a furnace where its temperature was $650°$ C and placed on a large block of ice at $0°$ C. Assuming that all of the heat given up by the iron is used to melt the ice, how much ice is melted?

(18) In a household hot-water heating system, water is delivered to the radiators at $140°$ F and leaves at $100°$ F. The system is to be replaced by a steam system in which steam at atmospheric pressure condenses in the radiators, the condensed steam leaving the radiators at $180°$ F. How many pounds of steam will supply the same heat as was supplied by 1 lb of hot water in the first installation?

(19) A piece of ice falls from rest into a lake at $0°$ C, and one-half of one percent of the ice melts. Compute the minimum height from which the ice falls.

(20) What must be the initial velocity of a lead bullet at a temperature of $25°$ C, so that the heat developed when it is brought to rest shall be just sufficient to melt it?

Problems—Chapter 17

(1) A slab of a thermal insulator is 100 cm² in cross section and 2 cm thick. Its thermal conductivity is 2×10^{-4} cal/sec-cm-C°. If the temperature difference between opposite faces is 100 C°, how many calories flow through the slab in one day?

(2) One end of a copper bar 18 cm long and 4 cm² in cross section, is in a steam bath and the other in a mixture of melting ice and water. Heat loss across the curved surface can be neglected. (a) What is the heat current in the bar? (b) What is the temperature at a point 4 cm from the cooler end?

(3) A compound bar 2 meters long is constructed of a solid steel core 1 cm in diameter surrounded by a copper casing whose outside diameter is 2 cm. The outer surface of the bar is thermally insulated and one end is maintained at 100° C, the other at 0° C. (a) Find the total heat current in the bar. (b) What fraction is carried by each material?

(4) (a) What would be the ratio of the heights of the columns in the U-tube in Fig. 17-4, if the liquid is water and one arm is at 4° C while the other is at 75° C? (b) What is the difference between the pressures at the foot of two columns of water each 10 meters high, if the temperature of one is 4° C and that of the other is 75° C?

(5) A furnace wall is constructed of two layers, the inner of thickness 10 cm and thermal conductivity 0.0004 cal/sec-cm-C°, the outer of thickness 20 cm and thermal conductivity 0.002 cal/sec-cm-C°. The cross section of the wall is 1 m². The inner surface is maintained at a temperature of 600° C and the outer surface at a temperature of 460° C. Compute (a) the steady-state heat current through the wall, (b) the temperature at the interface.

(6) Three slabs each 10 cm² in cross section and 1 cm thick are piled one on top of the other. The thermal conductivities are 0.1, 0.2, and 0.4 cal/cm-sec-C°. Find the thermal conductivity of a single slab 5 cm² in cross section and 3 cm thick which transmits the same heat current with the same temperature difference between its faces.

(7) One experimental method of measuring the thermal conductivity of an insulating material is to construct a box of the material and measure the power input to an electric heater, inside the box, which maintains the interior at a measured temperature above the outside surface. Suppose that in such an apparatus a power input of 120 watts is required to keep the interior of the box 120 F° above the outside temperature. The total area of the box is 25 ft² and the wall thickness is 1.5 inches. Find the thermal conductivity of the material in the commercial system of units.

(8) The operating temperature of a tungsten filament in an incandescent lamp is 2450° K and its emissivity is 0.30. Find the surface area of the filament of a 25-watt lamp.

(9) A blackened solid copper sphere of radius 2 cm is placed in an evacuated enclosure whose walls are kept at 100° C. At what rate must energy be supplied to the sphere to keep its temperature constant at 127° C?

Problems—Chapter 18

(1) A gas contained in a cylinder surrounded by a thick layer of felt is quickly compressed, the temperature rising several degrees.

     (a) Has there been a transfer of heat?

     (b) Has work been done?

(2) A resistor, immersed in running water, carries an electric current. Regarding the resistor as the system under consideration,

     (a) Is there a flow of heat into the resistor?

     (b) Is there a flow of heat into the water?

     (c) Is work done on the resistor?

     (d) Assuming the state of the resistor to remain unchanged, apply the first law to this process.

(3) In a certain process, 500 cal of heat are supplied to a system and at the same time 100 joules of work are done on the system. What is the increase in its internal energy?

(4) 200 Btu are supplied to a system in a certain process, and at the same time the system expands against a constant external pressure of 100 lb/in². The internal energy of the system is the same at the beginning and end of the process. Find the increase in volume of the system.

(5) 1 lb of water, when boiled at 212° F and atmospheric pressure, becomes 26.8 ft³ of steam.

     (a) Compute the external work, in ft-lb.

     (b) Compute the increase in internal energy, in Btu.

(6) A substance undergoes a series of processes which bring it back to its initial state. In this cycle, heat Q_2 is absorbed by the substance and heat Q_1 is rejected. What is the net amount of work done?

Problems—Chapter 19

(1) (a) 2 gm of nitrogen at 27° C occupy a volume of 2 liters. What is the pressure? (b) If the pressure is doubled and the temperature raised to 127° C, calculate the final volume.

(2) A liter of helium under a pressure of 2 atm and at a temperature of 27° C is heated until both pressure and volume are doubled. (a) What is the final temperature? (b) How many grams of helium are there?

(3) A flask contains 1 gm of oxygen at an absolute pressure of 10 atm and at a temperature of 47° C. At a later time it is found that because of a leak the pressure has dropped to $\frac{5}{8}$ of its original value and the temperature has decreased to 27° C. (a) What is the volume of the flask? (b) How many grams of oxygen leaked out between the two observations?

(4) A bubble of air of radius 5 cm rises from the bottom of a lake 20.4 m deep. The temperature at the bottom of the lake is 7° C and the temperature at the surface is 27° C. What is the radius of the bubble when it reaches the surface?

(5) The submarine Squalus sank at a point where the depth of water was 240 ft. The temperature at the surface is 27° C and at the bottom it is 7° C. The density of sea water may be taken as 2 slugs/ft³. (a) If a diving bell in a form of a circular cylinder 8 ft high, open at the bottom and closed at the top, is lowered to this depth, to what height will the water rise within it when it reaches the bottom? (b) At what gauge pressure must compressed air be supplied to the bell while on the bottom to expel all the water from it?

(6) A bicycle pump is full of air at an absolute pressure of 15 lb/in². The length of stroke of the pump is 18 inches. At what part of the stroke does air begin to enter a tire in which the gauge pressure is 40 lb/in²? Assume the compression to be isothermal.

(7) A vertical cylindrical tank 1 m high has its top end closed by a tightly-fitting frictionless piston of negligible weight. The air inside the cylinder is at an absolute pressure of 1 atm. The piston is depressed by pouring mercury on it slowly. How far will the piston descend before mercury spills over the top of the cylinder? The temperature of the air is maintained constant.

(8) 10 liters of air at atmospheric pressure is compressed isothermally to a volume of 2 liters and is then allowed to expand adiabatically to a volume of 10 liters. Show the process in a p-V diagram.

(9) An ideal gas is contained in a cylinder closed with a movable piston. The initial pressure is 1 atm and the initial volume is 1 liter. The gas is heated at constant pressure until the volume is doubled, then heated at constant volume until the pressure is doubled, and finally expanded adiabatically until the temperature drops to its initial value. Show the process in a p-V diagram.

(10) An ideal gas at a pressure of 1 atm is heated at constant pressure until its volume is doubled, then heated at constant volume until its pressure is doubled, and finally allowed to expand isothermally until its pressure drops to 1 atm. Show the process in a p-V diagram.

(11) Sketch three isotherms of a real gas, one below the critical temperature, one at the critical temperature, and one above the critical temperature.

(12) (a) What is the relative humidity on a day when the temperature is 68° F and the dew point is 41° F? (b) What is the partial pressure of water vapor in the atmosphere? (c) What is the absolute humidity, in gm/m³?

(13) (a) What is the dew point temperature on a day when the air temperature is 20° C and the relative humidity is 60%? (b) What is the absolute humidity, in gm/m³?

(14) The volume of a closed room, kept at a constant temperature of 20° C, is 60 m³. The relative humidity in the room is 10%. If a pan of water is brought into the room, how many grams will evaporate?

(15) An air conditioning system is required to increase the relative humidity of 10 ft³ of air per second from 30% to 65%. The air temperature is 68° F. How many pounds of water are needed per hour?

Problems—Chapter 20

(1) What is the efficiency of an Otto cycle in which the compression ratio is 8 and $\gamma = 1.50$?

(2) A Carnot engine whose high temperature reservoir is at 127° C, takes in 100 cal of heat at this temperature in each cycle, and gives up 80 cal to the low temperature reservoir. Find the temperature of the latter reservoir.

(3) A Carnot engine whose low temperature reservoir is at 7° C, has an efficiency of 40%. It is desired to increase the efficiency to 50%. By how many degrees must the temperature of the high temperature reservoir be increased?

(4) (a) What is the coefficient of performance of a Carnot refrigerator which removes heat from a reservoir at $-10°$ C and delivers heat to a reservoir at 30° C? (b) How many kwh of energy would have to be supplied to the refrigerator to remove from the low temperature reservoir an amount of heat equal to that required to melt 100 lb of ice? (c) What would be the cost of this energy, at 5 cents/kwh?

Problems—Chapter 21

(1) A steel wire 2 m long has a mass of 20 gm and is stretched with a tension of 1000 newtons. What is the velocity of propagation of a transverse wave in the wire?

(2) What must be the stress (F/A) in a stretched wire of a material whose Young's modulus is Y, in order that the velocity of longitudinal waves shall equal 100 times the velocity of transverse waves?

(3) The velocity of longitudinal waves in water is approximately 1450 m/sec at 20° C. Compute the adiabatic compressibility $(1/B_{ad})$ of water and compare with the isothermal compressibility listed in Table 11-2 on page 197.

(4) Provided the amplitude is sufficiently great, the human ear can respond to longitudinal waves over a range of frequencies from about 20 vibrations per second to about 20,000 vibrations per second. Compute the wave lengths corresponding to these frequencies (a) for waves in air, (b) for waves in water. (See Problem 3.)

(5) At a temperature of 27° C, what is the velocity of longitudinal waves in (a) helium, (b) hydrogen? Compare with the velocity in air at the same temperature.

(6) What is the difference between the velocities of longitudinal waves in air at $-3°$ C and at 27° C?

(7) The sound waves from a loud speaker spread out nearly uniformly in all directions when their wave length is large compared with the diameter of the speaker. When the wave length is small compared with the diameter of the speaker, much of the sound energy is concentrated in the forward direction. For a speaker of diameter 12 inches, compute the frequency for which the wave length of the sound waves, in air, is (a) 10 times the diameter of the speaker, (b) equal to the diameter of the speaker, (c) 1/10 the diameter of the speaker.

(8) A traveling transverse wave on a stretched string is represented by the equation

$$y = A \cos \frac{2\pi}{\lambda} (x - Vt).$$

Let $A = 1$ in, $\lambda = 2$ in, and $V = \frac{1}{4}$ in/sec. (a) At time $t = 0$, compute the transverse displacement y at $\frac{1}{4}$ inch intervals of x (i.e. at $x = 0$, $x = \frac{1}{4}$ in, $x = \frac{1}{2}$ in, etc.) from $x = 0$ to $x = 4$ inches. Show the results in a graph. This is the shape of the string at time $t = 0$. (b) Repeat the calculations, for the same values of x, at times $t = 1$ sec, $t = 2$ sec, $t = 3$ sec, and $t = 4$ sec. Show on the same graph the shape of the string at these instants. In what direction is the wave traveling?

(9) Show that the equation in Problem 8 may be written

$$y = A \cos 2\pi \left(\frac{t}{T} - \frac{x}{\lambda} \right).$$

Problems—Chapter 22

(1) A steel piano wire 50 cm long, of mass 5 gm, is stretched with a tension of 400 newtons. (a) What is the frequency of its fundamental mode of vibration? (b) What is the number of the highest overtone that could be heard by a person who can hear frequencies up to 10,000 cycles/sec?

(2) Suppose the piano wire in Problem 1 is set vibrating at twice its fundamental frequency. (a) Sketch the shape of the wire at a few instants. (b) What is the wave length of transverse waves in the wire? (c) What is the wave length, in air, of the sound waves emitted by the wire?

(3) A standing wave of frequency 1100 vibrations per second in a column of methane at 20° C produces nodes that are 20 cm apart. What is the ratio of the heat capacity at constant pressure to that at constant volume?

(4) Standing waves are set up in a Kundt's tube by the longitudinal vibration of an iron rod one meter long, clamped at the center. If the frequency of the iron rod is 2480 vibrations per second and the powder heaps within the tube are 6.9 cm apart, (a) what is the velocity of the waves in the iron rod, and (b) in the gas?

(5) A copper rod one meter long, clamped at the $\frac{1}{4}$ point, is set in longitudinal vibration and is used to produce standing waves in a Kundt's tube containing air at 300° K. Heaps of cork dust within the tube are found to be 4.95 cm apart. What is the velocity of longitudinal waves in copper?

(6) Find the frequencies of the fundamental and the first four overtones of an organ pipe 4 ft long, (a) if the pipe is open, (b) if the pipe is closed. End corrections may be neglected.

(7) Compare the fundamental frequencies of an open organ pipe one meter long, (a) when the pipe is filled with air, (b) when it is filled with hydrogen.

(8) A plate cut from a quartz crystal is often used to control the frequency of an oscillating electrical circuit. Longitudinal standing waves are set up in the plate with displacement antinodes at opposite faces. The fundamental frequency of vibration is given by the equation

$$f_1 = \frac{2.87 \times 10^5}{s},$$

where f_1 is in cycles/sec and s is the thickness of the plate in cm. (a) Compute Young's modulus for the quartz plate. (b) Compute the thickness of plate required for a frequency of 1200 kilocycles/sec. (1 kilocycle = 1000 cycles.) The density of quartz is 2.66 gm/cm³.

Problems — Chapter 23

(1) (a) If the pressure amplitude in a sound wave is doubled, by how many times is the intensity of the wave increased? (b) By how many times must the pressure amplitude of a sound wave be increased in order to increase the intensity by a factor of 10 times?

(2) (a) Two sound waves, one in air and one in water, are equal in intensity. What is the ratio of the pressure amplitude of the wave in water to that of the wave in air? (b) If the pressure amplitudes of the waves are equal, what is the ratio of their intensities?

(3) (a) Relative to the arbitrary reference intensity of 10^{-16} watt/cm², what is the intensity level in db of a sound wave whose intensity is 10^{-8} watt/cm²? (b) What is the intensity level of a sound wave in air whose pressure amplitude is 2 dynes/cm²?

(4) (a) Show that if β_1 and β_2 are the intensity levels in db of sounds of intensities I_1 and I_2 respectively, the difference in intensity levels of the sounds is

$$\beta_2 - \beta_1 = 10 \log \frac{I_2}{I_1}.$$

(b) Show that if P_1 and P_2 are the pressure amplitudes of two sound waves, the difference in intensity levels of the waves is

$$\beta_2 - \beta_1 = 20 \log \frac{P_2}{P_1}.$$

(c) Show that if the reference level of intensity is $I_0 = 10^{-16}$ watt/cm², the intensity level of a sound of intensity I is

$$\beta = 160 + 10 \log I.$$

(5) What is the ratio of the intensities of two sound waves whose intensity levels differ by (a) 10 db? (b) 20 db? What is the difference between the intensity levels of two sound waves if (c) the intensity of one wave is twice that of the other? (d) the pressure amplitude of one is twice that of the other?

(6) The intensity due to a number of independent sound sources is the sum of the intensities of the separate sources. (a) What is the increase in intensity level, over that produced by a single violin, when two violins play in unison? (b) If a single violin produces a sound of intensity level of 40 db, how many are needed to increase the level to 60 db? (c) To 80 db?

(7) A window whose area is 1 m² opens on a street where the street noises result in an intensity level, at the window, of 80 db. How much "acoustic power" enters the window via the sound waves?

(8) (a) What are the upper and lower limits of intensity level, at a frequency of 200 cycles/sec, for a person whose auditory area is represented by the graph of Fig. 23-7? (b) What are the highest and lowest frequencies he can hear when the intensity level is 40 db?

(9) Compare the frequencies heard by a listener under the following circumstances: (a) A listener in still air moves with a velocity of 100 ft/sec directly toward a stationary source emitting sound waves of a frequency 1000 cycles/sec. (b) The listener remains at rest while the source moves directly toward him at 100 ft/sec.

(10) A railroad train is traveling at 100 ft/sec in still air. The frequency of the note emitted by the locomotive whistle is 500 cycles/sec. What is the wave length of the sound waves (a) in front of, (b) behind the locomotive? What would be the frequency of the sound heard by a stationary listener (c) in front of, (d) behind the locomotive? What frequency would be heard by a passenger on a train traveling at 50 ft/sec and (e) approaching the first, (f) receding from the first? (g) How is each of the preceding answers altered if a wind of velocity 30 ft/sec is blowing in the same direction as that in which the locomotive is traveling?

(11) A man stands at rest in front of a large smooth wall. Directly in front of him, between him and the wall, he holds a vibrating tuning fork of frequency f_0 cycles/sec. He now moves the fork toward the wall with a velocity v. How many beats per sec will he hear between the sound waves reaching him directly from the fork, and those reaching him after being reflected from the wall? Represent the velocity of sound in air by V. For a numerical example, let $f_0 = 400$ cycles/sec and $v = 4$ ft/sec.

(12) The floor of a room measures 5 m by 10 m, and the room is 3 m high. (a) What is the reverberation time if the average absorption coefficient of all surfaces is 0.05? (b) To what value would the reverberation time be reduced if the ceiling were covered with Celotex?

ANSWERS TO SUPPLEMENTARY PROBLEMS

CHAPTER 1

1. 25.7 lb to right, horizontal; 30.6 lb upward, vertical.

3. 17.0 lb; 5.8 lb.

5. (a) 19.32 lb in a direction midway between the 10 lb forces.

(b) 8.46 lb in a direction midway between the 10 lb forces.

7. $R = 0$.

9. 308 lb at 25° above horizontal to right.

11. 5.65 units at 32° to direction of A.

CHAPTER 2

5. (a) 115.4 lb in A and B; 200 lb in C.

(b) 147 lb in A; 180 lb in B.

(c) 200 lb in A; 283 lb in B.

(d) 547 lb in A; 670 lb in B.

7. 4.62 ft; 220 lb.

9. 7.5 lb; 90 lb; 313 lb.

11. 1370 lb.

13. 19.3°; 10 lb; 28.3 lb.

15. 400 lb per ton.

17. $\dfrac{\mu W}{\cos \phi + \mu \sin \phi}$

19. 4 lb; 0.398.

CHAPTER 3

1. 2 ft from light end.

3. 283 lb-ft; 0; −780 lb-ft; −400 lb-ft; −897 lb-ft or 897 lb-ft counterclockwise; 224 lb vertically downward.

5. 100 lb; 80 lb.

7. 722 lb; 722 lb; 1500 lb.

9. 212 lb; 19° above horizontal.

11. (a) 13.7 ft.
(b) 15.6 ft.

13. 32.5 lb and 13 lb on each front leg; 17.5 lb and 7 lb on each rear leg.

15. (a) 15 lb.

(b) 5 lb on each front leg; 20 lb on each rear leg.

(c) 8.75 lb on each front leg; 16.25 lb on each rear leg.

(d) 3.33 ft above floor.

17. 4 ft from axis.

19. $R = 0$.

21. $\bar{x} = 3.5$ in., $\bar{y} = 2.0$ in. (Origin at lower left-hand corner.)

23. $\bar{x} = 0$, $\bar{y} = 5.3$ in. (Origin at midpoint of bottom edge.)

CHAPTER 4

1. 30 ft/sec, 900 cm/sec, 9 m/sec, 21 mi/hr.

3. 61 cm/sec, 60.1 cm/sec, 60.01 cm/sec 60 cm/sec.

CHAPTER 4 (continued)

5. (a) $+1.5$ ft/sec², right.
(b) -1.5 ft/sec², left.
(c) -1.5 ft/sec², left.
(d) $+1.5$ ft/sec², right.
(e) -4 ft/sec², left.
(f) $+4$ ft/sec², right.

7. (a) 17.7 ft/sec²,
(b) 182 mi/hr.

9. (a) 8 ft/sec².
(b) 32 ft/sec.
(c) 64 ft.

11. (a) 300 ft.
(b) 60 ft/sec.

13. (a) 12.5 cm/sec².
(b) 7840 cm.

15. (a) 94 ft/sec.
(b) 124 ft.
(c) 53 ft/sec.
(d) 150 ft/sec².
(e) 1.96 sec.
(f) 93 ft/sec.

17. 39.4 ft.

19. No. The acceleration is constant.

21. (a) 48.5° S of E.
(b) 2.65 mi/hr.
(c) 0.38 hr.

CHAPTER 5

1. (a) 400 lb.
(b) 12,800 dynes.
(c) 12,800 newtons.

3. (a) 2 m/sec².
(b) 100 m; 20 m/sec.

5. (a) 0.000555 sec.
(b) 117×10^6 dynes; 263 lb.

7. 32.5° W. of N.; 1.12 m/sec².

9. 48 ft/sec².

11. (a) 59.0 newtons.
(b) constant velocity.
(c) 6.25 m/sec.

13. 268 ft.

15. (a) 4 lb.
(b) 128 ft.

17. $v_0^2/2g \sin \alpha$.

19. 0.438.

21. $a = g (\sin \theta - \tan \alpha \cos \theta)$.

23. 12.8 ft/sec².

25. 13 lb.

27. 10.1 lb.

29. (a) $a = \dfrac{m_2}{m_1 + m_2} \cdot g$,

$T = \dfrac{m_1 m_2 g}{m_1 + m_2}$.

(b) $a = \dfrac{m_2 - \mu m_1}{m_1 + m_2} \cdot g$,

$T = \dfrac{m_1 m_2 (1 + \mu) g}{m_1 + m_2}$.

31. (a) 1 lb.
(b) 1.03 lb.

33. $a = \dfrac{m - M \sin \alpha}{M + m} \cdot g$,

$T = \dfrac{mMg(1 + \sin \alpha)}{M + m}$.

35. (a) 327 cm.
(b) 1.14×10^5 dynes,
9.8×10^4 dynes.
(c) 2.28×10^5 dynes.

37. (a) 3.27 m/sec².
(b) 105 newtons.
(c) 210 newtons.

39. (a) 0.96 ft/sec².
(b) 5.2 lb.

41. (a) 1.88×10^{16} tons.
(b) 2,356,000 ft = 445 mi.

43. 2.4.

CHAPTER 6

1. 12.7 ft/sec.

3. 0.44 ft; 1.8 ft; 4 ft; 16 ft.

5. For $h = 5000$ ft: $t = 17.7$ sec; $R = 5200$ ft; $v = 642$ ft/sec; $\theta = 63°$.

7. (a) 48 ft; 16 ft.
(b) 98 ft; 65 ft.

9. 1280 ft.

11. 121 ft/sec; 57.2 ft; 3.8 sec.

13. 222,000 yd; 45 mi; 243 sec.

15. 22°.

17. (a) 1130 ft/sec.
(b) 1600 ft/sec; 35 sec; 15,500 ft.

CHAPTER 7

1. 52.8×10^6 ft-lb.

3. 350 joules.

5. 40 ft-lb; 32 ft-lb.

7. 25×10^8 ergs; 250 joules.

9. 1,998,000 ft-lb.

11. 4.9×10^6 ergs.

13. (a) 160 ft-lb.   It goes into kinetic energy.
(b) 160 ft-lb.

15. (a) 320 ft-lb.   It goes into heat and kinetic energy.
(b) 160 ft-lb of kinetic energy; 160 ft-lb of heat developed.

17. 2000 ft-lb; 480 ft-lb; 1200 ft-lb; 320 ft-lb.

19. (a) 0.25.
(b) 3.5 ft-lb.

21. 1070 horsepower.

23. 3.6 horsepower.

25. (a) 3.7 cents.
(b) 5.4×10^5 ft-lb.

27. $2.98.

29. (a) 250 lb.
(b) 5 horsepower.
(c) 80 horsepower.

31. (a) 250 lb.
(b) 39 horsepower.
(c) 16 horsepower.
(d) 10.5% grade.

33. (a) 8.
(b) 5.
(c) 63%.

37. 3.

CHAPTER 8

1. (a) 27,500 slug-ft/sec.
(b) 60 mi/hr.
(c) 42.5 mi/hr.

3. 1 ft/sec; 1872 ft-lb.

5. 1.5 ft/sec toward empty car.

7. 4.22 lb.

9. 0.65 mi/hr.

11. (a) 0.39 ft.
(b) 1950 ft-lb.
(c) 3.9 ft-lb.

13. 3.3 cm.

15. (a) 100 gm.
(b) 16 cm/sec.

17. (a) 0.80.
(b) 1.13 ft-lb.

19. (a) 41 cm; $100 \,(0.64)^n$; 10.
(b) 0.71 sec; $0.9 \times (.8)^n$ sec.
(c) 0.8.

CHAPTER 9

1. (a) 1.5 rad.
  (b) 1.57 rad.
  (c) 120 cm; 120 ft.

3. (a) 19.6 ft/sec.
  (b) 230 rpm.

5. 15.7 ft/sec; 31.4 ft/sec; 47.1 ft/sec; 600 rpm; 1800 rpm; 5400 rpm.

7. -2.09 rad/sec^2; 71 rev; 40 sec.

9. 5 sec.

11. (b) $A_T = 0$; $A_R = \omega^2 R$.
  (c) Yes; $A_T = R\alpha$; yes; $A_R = \omega^2 R$.

13. (a) 13.2 ft/sec at 54° to original direction.
  (b) 13.9 ft/sec at 72° to original direction.
  (c) 14 ft/sec at 81° to original direction.

(d) 14.1 ft/sec at 90° to original direction.

15. 2730 rev/sec.

17. Resultant accelerations:
  (a) 15 cm/sec^2.
  (b) 65 cm/sec^2.
  (c) 126 cm/sec^2.

19. (a) 18 ft/sec^2.
  (b) $1\frac{1}{8}$ lb.

21. 0.5.

23. (a) $16\sqrt{2}$ ft/sec.
  (b) 18 lb.

25. (a) 0.27.
  (b) 15°.

27. 6.4 rad/sec.

29. 1.22×10^{-3} rad/sec; 1.41 hr.

CHAPTER 10

1. $\frac{11}{16} mL^2$; $0.478L$.

3. 3.55 in.

5. (a) 278 ft-lb.
  (b) 70 ft.

7. (a) 60π ft-lb.
  (b) $9000\pi^2$ ft-lb.

9. 0.47.

11. (a) 10 rad/sec^2.
  (b) 200 ft-lb.
  (c) 6.15 rad/sec^2.

13. (a) 21.3 lb.
  (b) 52.3 ft/sec.
  (c) 2.45 sec.

15. (a) 24 slug-ft^2/sec.
  (b) 6 rad/sec.
  (c) 24 ft-lb, 72 ft-lb.

17. (a) 6 rpm.
  (b) 6 rpm.

19. (a) -0.04 rad/sec.
  (b) 60 degrees.
  (c) 72 degrees.

21. (a) 2 slug-ft^2.
  (b) 2620 ft-lb.

23. (a) 176,600 dynes.
  (b) 4300 rev/min.

CHAPTER 11

1. (a) 40,800 lb/in^2; 0.00136
  (b) 0.136 ft.
  (c) 15.2 ft/sec^2.

3. 1.41×10^7 lb/in^2; 1.62×10^4 lb/in^2.

5. 2000 lb/in^2; 0.0032 inch; 0.0010 inch.

7. 34.8 lb; 65.2 lb; 3.07 ft.

9. 1960 lb.

11. 64.0071 lb/ft^3.

CHAPTER 12

1. (a) ∓ 7560 cm/sec^2; ± 301 cm/sec.
   (b) -3830 cm/sec^2; 261 cm/sec.
   (c) 0.029 sec.

3. (a) $2400\pi^2$ ft/sec^2.
   (b) 740 lb.
   (c) 43 mi/hr.

5. 24 lb.

7. 0.79 sec.

9. (a) 2 ft/sec.
   (b) 4 ft/sec^2.

11. (a) 39.5 rad/sec.
    (b) 34.2 rad/sec.
    (c) 124 rad/sec^2 clockwise.

CHAPTER 13

1. 21.2 lb/in^2.

3. 121 lb; 17,400 lb/ft^2.

5. 267,000 ft^3; 9.25 tons.

7. (a) 680 gm.
   (b) 7,840 dynes/cm^2.

9. (a) $0.426 = 42.6\%$.
   (b) 46% of the height of the block.

11. 100.87 gm.

13. (a) 2.33 lb.
    (b) 5.67 lb downward.

CHAPTER 14

1. 35.8 ft/sec; 0.195 ft^3/sec.

3. 39.6 ft/sec.

5. (a) 16 ft/sec.
   (b) 0.79 ft^3/sec.

7. 12 ft^3/min.

9. 27 ft^3/sec.

11. (a) 12 lb/in^2 above atmospheric pressure.
    (b) 12 ft^3/sec.

13. 56.7 lb/in^2.

15. 325 ft/sec.

CHAPTER 15

1. (a) $12,000°$F.
   (b) $20°$C.
   (c) $-40°$F $= -40°$C.

3. 1.6 ft.

5. 0.2506 inch.

7. 235 cm.

9. (a) 1.2×10^{-4}.
   (b) 5.18 sec per day.

11. 180,000 lb/in^2 or 12×10^9 dynes/cm^2.

13. 0.378 lb.

15. 480 atm.

CHAPTER 16

1. (a) 26,700 Btu.
   (b) 55 ft^3.
   (c) 7.84 kwh.

3. 19%.

5. 87.6 watts.

7. 470 C°.

9. 1.00; 0.827; 0.35.

11. 700°F.

15. 0°C; 200 gm of ice melted.

17. 0.92 gm of ice per gm of iron.

19. 17,100 cm.

ANSWERS TO SUPPLEMENTARY PROBLEMS

CHAPTER 17

1. 86,400 cal/day.

3. 1.13 cal/sec; 4% through steel, 96% through copper.

5. (a) 40 cal/sec.
(b) 500°C.

7. 52 Btu-in/hr-ft^2-F°.

9. 1.74 watts.

CHAPTER 18

3. 524 cal.

5. 56,900 ft-lb; 897 Btu.

CHAPTER 19

1. (a) 0.88 atm.
(b) 1.33 liters.

3. (a) 82 cm^3.
(b) 0.33 gm.

5. (a) 7.06 ft.
(b) 106 lb/in^2.

7. 24 cm.

13. (a) 11.4°C.
(b) 10.3 gm/m^3.

15. 13.4 lb/hr.

CHAPTER 20

1. 64.6%.

3. 93 C°.

CHAPTER 21

1. 316 m/sec.

3. 48 × 10^{-6} atm^{-1}.

5. 1020 m/sec; 1320 m/sec; 347 m/sec.

7. (a) 113 cycles/sec.
(b) 1130 cycles/sec.
(c) 11,300 cycles/sec.

CHAPTER 22

1. (a) 200 cycles/sec.
(b) 49*th* overtone.

3. 1.28.

5. 2 × 10^5 m/sec.

7. (a) 174 cycles/sec.
(b) 660 cycles/sec.

CHAPTER 23

1. (a) 4 times.
(b) 3.16 times.

3. (a) 80 db.
(b) 76.5 db.

5. (a) 10.
(b) 100.
(c) 3 db.
(d) 6 db.

7. 10^{-4} watts.

9. (a) 1090 vibr/sec.
(b) 1100 vibr/sec.

11. 2.9 beats/sec.

INDEX

Common Logarithms

N	0	1	2	3	4	5	6	7	8	9
0	. .	0000	3010	4771	6021	6990	7782	8451	9031	9542
1	0000	0414	0792	1139	1461	1761	2041	2304	2553	2788
2	3010	3222	3424	3617	3802	3979	4150	4314	4472	4624
3	4771	4914	5051	5185	5315	5441	5563	5682	5798	5911
4	6021	6128	6232	6335	6435	6532	6628	6721	6812	6902
5	6990	7076	7160	7243	7324	7404	7482	7559	7634	7709
6	7782	7853	7924	7993	8062	8129	8195	8261	8325	8388
7	8451	8513	8573	8633	8692	8751	8808	8865	8921	8976
8	9031	9085	9138	9191	9243	9294	9345	9395	9445	9494
9	9542	9590	9638	9685	9731	9777	9823	9868	9912	9956
10	0000	0043	0086	0128	0170	0212	0253	0294	0334	0374
11	0414	0453	0492	0531	0569	0607	0645	0682	0719	0755
12	0792	0828	0864	0899	0934	0969	1004	1038	1072	1106
13	1139	1173	1206	1239	1271	1303	1335	1367	1399	1430
14	1461	1492	1523	1553	1584	1614	1644	1673	1703	1732
15	1761	1790	1818	1847	1875	1903	1931	1959	1987	2014
16	2041	2068	2095	2122	2148	2175	2201	2227	2253	2279
17	2304	2330	2355	2380	2405	2430	2455	2480	2504	2529
18	2553	2577	2601	2625	2648	2672	2695	2718	2742	2765
19	2788	2810	2833	2856	2878	2900	2923	2945	2967	2989
20	3010	3032	3054	3075	3096	3118	3139	3160	3181	3201
21	3222	3243	3263	3284	3304	3324	3345	3365	3385	3404
22	3424	3444	3464	3483	3502	3522	3541	3560	3579	3598
23	3617	3636	3655	3674	3692	3711	3729	3747	3766	3784
24	3802	3820	3838	3856	3874	3892	3909	3927	3945	3962
25	3979	3997	4014	4031	4048	4065	4082	4099	4116	4133
26	4150	4166	4183	4200	4216	4232	4249	4265	4281	4298
27	4314	4330	4346	4362	4378	4393	4409	4425	4440	4456
28	4472	4487	4502	4518	4533	4548	4564	4579	4594	4609
29	4624	4639	4654	4669	4683	4698	4713	4728	4742	4757
30	4771	4786	4800	4814	4829	4843	4857	4871	4886	4900
31	4914	4928	4942	4955	4969	4983	4997	5011	5024	5038
32	5051	5065	5079	5092	5105	5119	5132	5145	5159	5172
33	5185	5198	5211	5224	5237	5250	5263	5276	5289	5302
34	5315	5328	5340	5353	5366	5378	5391	5403	5416	5428
35	5441	5453	5465	5478	5490	5502	5514	5527	5539	5551
36	5563	5575	5587	5599	5611	5623	5635	5647	5658	5670
37	5682	5694	5705	5717	5729	5740	5752	5763	5775	5786
38	5798	5809	5821	5832	5843	5855	5866	5877	5888	5899
39	5911	5922	5933	5944	5955	5966	5977	5988	5999	6010
40	6021	6031	6042	6053	6064	6075	6085	6096	6107	6117
41	6128	6138	6149	6160	6170	6180	6191	6201	6212	6222
42	6232	6243	6253	6263	6274	6284	6294	6304	6314	6325
43	6335	6345	6355	6365	6375	6385	6395	6405	6415	6425
44	6435	6444	6454	6464	6474	6484	6493	6503	6513	6522
45	6532	6542	6551	6561	6571	6580	6590	6599	6609	6618
46	6628	6637	6646	6656	6665	6675	6684	6693	6702	6712
47	6721	6730	6739	6749	6758	6767	6776	6785	6794	6803
48	6812	6821	6830	6839	6848	6857	6866	6875	6884	6893
49	6901	6911	6920	6928	6937	6946	6955	6964	6972	6981
50	6990	6998	7007	7016	7024	7033	7042	7050	7059	7067
N	0	1	2	3	4	5	6	7	8	9

N	0	1	2	3	4	5	6	7	8	9
50	6990	6998	7007	7016	7024	7033	7042	7050	7059	7067
51	7076	7084	7093	7101	7110	7118	7126	7135	7143	7152
52	7160	7168	7177	7185	7193	7202	7210	7218	7226	7235
53	7243	7251	7259	7267	7275	7284	7292	7300	7308	7316
54	7324	7332	7340	7348	7356	7364	7372	7380	7388	7396
55	7404	7412	7419	7427	7435	7443	7451	7459	7466	7474
56	7482	7490	7497	7505	7513	7520	7528	7536	7543	7551
57	7559	7566	7574	7582	7589	7597	7604	7612	7619	7627
58	7634	7642	7649	7657	7664	7672	7679	7686	7694	7701
59	7709	7716	7723	7731	7738	7745	7752	7760	7767	7774
60	7782	7789	7796	7803	7810	7818	7825	7832	7839	7846
61	7853	7860	7868	7875	7882	7889	7896	7903	7910	7917
62	7924	7931	7938	7945	7952	7959	7966	7973	7980	7987
63	7993	8000	8007	8014	8021	8028	8035	8041	8048	8055
64	8062	8069	8075	8082	8089	8096	8102	8109	8116	8122
65	8129	8136	8142	8149	8156	8162	8169	8176	8182	8189
66	8195	8202	8209	8215	8222	8228	8235	8241	8248	8254
67	8261	8267	8274	8280	8287	8293	8299	8306	8312	8319
68	8325	8331	8338	8344	8351	8357	8363	8370	8376	8382
69	8388	8395	8401	8407	8414	8420	8426	8432	8439	8445
70	8451	8457	8463	8470	8476	8482	8488	8494	8500	8506
71	8513	8519	8525	8531	8537	8543	8549	8555	8561	8567
72	8573	8579	8585	8591	8597	8603	8609	8615	8621	8627
73	8633	8639	8645	8651	8657	8663	8669	8675	8681	8686
74	8692	8698	8704	8710	8716	8722	8727	8733	8739	8745
75	8751	8756	8762	8768	8774	8779	8785	8791	8797	8802
76	8808	8814	8820	8825	8831	8837	8842	8848	8854	8859
77	8865	8871	8876	8882	8887	8893	8899	8904	8910	8915
78	8921	8927	8932	8938	8943	8949	8954	8960	8965	8971
79	8976	8982	8987	8993	8998	9004	9009	9015	9020	9025
80	9031	9036	9042	9047	9053	9058	9063	9069	9074	9079
81	9085	9090	9096	9101	9106	9112	9117	9122	9128	9133
82	9138	9143	9149	9154	9159	9165	9170	9175	9180	9186
83	9191	9196	9201	9206	9212	9217	9222	9227	9232	9238
84	9243	9248	9253	9258	9263	9269	9274	9279	9284	9289
85	9294	9299	9304	9309	9315	9320	9325	9330	9335	9340
86	9345	9350	9355	9360	9365	9370	9375	9380	9385	9390
87	9395	9400	9405	9410	9415	9420	9425	9430	9435	9440
88	9445	9450	9455	9460	9465	9469	9474	9479	9484	9489
89	9494	9499	9504	9509	9513	9518	9523	9528	9533	9538
90	9542	9547	9552	9557	9562	9566	9571	9576	9581	9586
91	9590	9595	9600	9605	9609	9614	9619	9624	9628	9633
92	9638	9643	9647	9652	9657	9661	9666	9671	9675	9680
93	9685	9689	9694	9699	9703	9708	9713	9717	9722	9727
94	9731	9736	9741	9745	9750	9754	9759	9763	9768	9773
95	9777	9782	9786	9791	9795	9800	9805	9809	9814	9818
96	9823	9827	9832	9836	9841	9845	9850	9854	9859	9863
97	9868	9872	9877	9881	9886	9890	9894	9899	9903	9908
98	9912	9917	9921	9926	9930	9934	9939	9943	9948	9952
99	9956	9961	9965	9969	9974	9978	9983	9987	9991	9996
100	0000	0004	0009	0013	0017	0022	0026	0030	0035	0039
N	0	1	2	3	4	5	6	7	8	9

NATURAL TRIGONOMETRIC FUNCTIONS

Angle	Sine	Cosine	Tangent	Angle	Sine	Cosine	Tangent
0°	0.000	1.000	0.000				
1°	.018	1.000	.018	46°	.719	.695	1.036
2°	.035	0.999	.035	47°	.731	.682	1.072
3°	.052	.999	.052	48°	.743	.669	1.111
4°	.070	.998	.070	49°	.755	.656	1.150
5°	.087	.996	.088	50°	.766	.643	1.192
6°	.105	.995	.105	51°	.777	.629	1.235
7°	.122	.993	.123	52°	.788	.616	1.280
8°	.139	.990	.141	53°	.799	.602	1.327
9°	.156	.988	.158	54°	.809	.588	1.376
10°	.174	.985	.176	55°	.819	.574	1.428
11°	.191	.982	.194	56°	.829	.559	1.483
12°	.208	.978	.213	57°	.839	.545	1.540
13°	.225	.974	.231	58°	.848	.530	1.600
14°	.242	.970	.249	59°	.857	.515	1.664
15°	.259	.966	.268	60°	.866	.500	1.732
16°	.276	.961	.287	61°	.875	.485	1.804
17°	.292	.956	.306	62°	.883	.470	1.881
18°	.309	.951	.325	63°	.891	.454	1.963
19°	.326	.946	.344	64°	.899	.438	2.050
20°	.342	.940	.364	65°	.906	.423	2.145
21°	.358	.934	.384	66°	.914	.407	2.246
22°	.375	.927	.404	67°	.921	.391	2.356
23°	.391	.921	.425	68°	.927	.375	2.475
24°	.407	.914	.445	69°	.934	.358	2.605
25°	.423	.906	.466	70°	.940	.342	2.747
26°	.438	.899	.488	71°	.946	.326	2.904
27°	.454	.891	.510	72°	.951	.309	3.078
28°	.470	.883	.532	73°	.956	.292	3.271
29°	.485	.875	.554	74°	.961	.276	3.487
30°	.500	.866	.577	75°	.966	.259	3.732
31°	.515	.857	.601	76°	.970	.242	4.011
32°	.530	.848	.625	77°	.974	.225	4.331
33°	.545	.839	.649	78°	.978	.208	4.705
34°	.559	.829	.675	79°	.982	.191	5.145
35°	.574	.819	.700	80°	.985	.174	5.671
36°	.588	.809	.727	81°	.988	.156	6.314
37°	.602	.799	.754	82°	.990	.139	7.115
38°	.616	.788	.781	83°	.993	.122	8.144
39°	.629	.777	.810	84°	.995	.105	9.514
40°	.643	.766	.839	85°	.996	.087	11.43
41°	.656	.755	.869	86°	.998	.070	14.30
42°	.669	.743	.900	87°	.999	.052	19.08
43°	.682	.731	.933	88°	.999	.035	28.64
44°	.695	.719	.966	89°	1.000	.018	57.29
45°	.707	.707	.000	90°	1.000	.000	∞

$$\pi = 3.1416$$
$$\epsilon = 2.7183$$
$$\log_e 10 = 2.3026$$

1 Angström unit $= A = 10^{-8}$ cm
1 micron $= 0.001$ mm
1 centimeter $= 0.39370$ in
1 inch $= 2.5400$ cm
1 foot $= 30.480$ cm
1 radian $= 57.2958$ degrees

1 gram $= 15.432$ grains
1 ounce $= 28.350$ gm
1 newton $= 0.224$ lb $= 10^5$ dynes
1 pound (wt.) $= 445,000$ dynes

1 atmosphere $= 14.697$ lb per sq in
1 joule $= 10,000,000$ ergs
1 calorie $= 4.186$ joules
1 sq inch $= 6.4516$ sq cm
1 sq foot $= 929.03$ sq cm
1 cu inch $= 16.387$ cu cm
1 liter $= 1000$ cu cm
1 gallon $= 3.785$ liters
1 gallon $= 231$ cu in

1 pound $= 453.59$ gm
1 kilogram $= 2.2046$ lb
1 slug $= 14.6$ kgm

1 foot-pound $= 1.3549$ joules
1 B.t.u. $= 252.00$ cal
1 B.t.u. $= 778$ ft-lb
1 horsepower $= 746$ watts

Greek Alphabet

A	α	Alpha
B	β	Beta
Γ	γ	Gamma
Δ	δ	Delta
E	ϵ	Epsilon
Z	ζ	Zeta
H	η	Eta
Θ	θ	Theta
I	ι	Iota
K	κ	Kappa
Λ	λ	Lambda
M	μ	Mu
N	ν	Nu
Ξ	ξ	Xi
O	o	Omicron
Π	π	Pi
P	ρ	Rho
Σ	σ	Sigma
T	τ	Tau
Υ	υ	Upsilon
Φ	ϕ	Phi
X	χ	Chi
Ψ	ψ	Psi
Ω	ω	Omega

PERIODIC TABLE

The italic number at the right of the symbol is the Atomic Number of the element and the number below is the Atomic Weight.

Periods	Group O	Group I		Group II		Group III		Group IV		Group V		Group VI		Group VII		Group VIII
Type of Oxide		R_2O		RO		R_2O_3		RO_2		R_2O_5		$R_2O_6(RO_3)$		R_2O_7		RO_4
Type of Hydride		RH		RH_2		RH_3		RH_4		RH_3		RH_2		RH		......
		A	B	A	B	A	B	A	B	A	B	A	B	A	B	
First short period	He 2 / 4.002	H 1 / 1.0078	Li 3 / 6.940		Be 4 / 9.02		B 5 / 10.82		C 6 / 12.00		N 7 / 14.008		O 8 / 16.00		F 9 / 19.00	
Second short period	Ne 10 / 20.183	Na 11 / 22.997		Mg 12 / 24.32		Al 13 / 26.97		Si 14 / 28.06		P 15 / 31.02		S 16 / 32.06		Cl 17 / 35.457		
First long period — Even Series	A 18 / 39.944	K 19 / 39.10		Ca 20 / 40.08		Sc 21 / 45.10		Ti 22 / 47.90		V 23 / 50.95		Cr 24 / 52.01		Mn 25 / 54.93		Fe 26 / 55.84, Co 27 / 58.94, Ni 28 / 58.69
First long period — Odd Series			Cu 29 / 63.57		Zn 30 / 65.38		Ga 31 / 69.72		Ge 32 / 72.60		As 33 / 74.93		Se 34 / 79.2		Br 35 / 79.916	
Second long period — Even Series	Kr 36 / 82.9	Rb 37 / 85.44		Sr 38 / 87.63		Y 39 / 88.92		Zr 40 / 91.22		Cb 41 / 93.3		Mo 42 / 96.0		Tc 43		Ru 44 / 101.7, Rn 45 / 102.91, Pd 46 / 106.7
Second long period — Odd Series			Ag 47 / 107.880		Cd 48 / 112.41		In 49 / 114.8		Sn 50 / 118.70		Sb 51 / 121.76		Te 52 / 127.5		I 53 / 126.932	
Third long period — Even Series	Xe 54 / 130.2	Cs 55 / 132.81		Ba 56 / 137.36		La 57 / 138.90		Ce 58 / 140.13									
Third long period — Odd Series																
Fourth long period — Even Series								Hf 72 / 178.6		Ta 73 / 181.4		W 74 / 184.0		Re 75 / 186.31		Os 76 / 190.8, Ir 77 / 193.1, Pt 78 / 195.23
Fourth long period — Odd Series			Au 79 / 197.2		Hg 80 / 200.61		Tl 81 / 204.39		Pb 82 / 207.22		Bi 83 / 209.0		Po 84		At 85	
Fifth period	Rn 86 / 222	Fr 87		Ra 88 / 225.97		Ac 89 / 227		Th 90 / 232.12		UX$_2$ 91		U 92 / 238.14		Np 93		Pu 94, Am 95, Cm 96

The Rare Earth Elements — Atomic Numbers 59–71